135

Doré

ADAM AND EVE DRIVEN FROM THE GARDEN

BIBLE STORY BOOK

A Complete Narration
from Genesis to Revelation
for
Young and Old

By Elsie E. Egermeier

NEW AND REVISED EDITION

Fifteenth Printing

THE WARNER PRESS
Anderson, Indiana

PREFACE

Behind every task attempted there lies a purpose. In the writing of the Bible-Story Book the author has endeavored to familiarize herself with the viewpoint of children and to adapt her language accordingly. With vivid recollections of the capacity of the child-mind to grasp and retain Scripture truths, she has labored prayerfully and conscientiously to present these stories in such a simple, direct manner that her youthful readers will have no difficulty in comprehending their teaching.

The thought-life that is early trained to respect and reverence God's Word becomes a powerful factor in the formation of Christian character. Hence the importance of arresting the attention of children with stories from the Sacred Book. From these stories they may glean their first knowledge of the relationship which exists between God and man, broken by sin but reestablished by faith in the sacrificial offering of Jesus Christ.

The author acknowledges her indebtedness especially to Blaikie's *Manual of Bible History* for helpful suggestions as to chronological outlines and historical information.

With a prayer that He who said, "Suffer the children to come unto me," may in this book find a medium to draw them to Himself, I am,

A servant of the Lord,

ELSIE E. EGERMEIER

TABLE OF SIGNS USED IN THE BIBLE STORY BOOK

The signs used in this list are intended to be as few and simple as possible, and to indicate in such a way as can most easily be understood the ordinary pronunciation.

The words of which the pronunciation is marked are divided into syllables by short hyphens (-). The syllable on which most stress is to be laid in reading is marked ('). In compound names two accents are often introduced.

ä	*as in*	ah, arm, father.
ă	"	abet, hat, dilemma.
ā	"	tame.
â	"	fare.
ạ	"	call.
ĕ	"	met, her, second.
ē	"	mete.
ë	=	a *in* tame.
ī	*as in*	fine.
ĭ	"	him, fir, plentiful.
î	"	machine
ị	"	peculiar.
ō	"	alone.
ŏ	"	on, protect.
ô	"	nor.
ọ	"	son.
ū	"	tune.
û	"	rude.

ŭ	*as in*	us.
ụ	"	turner.
ȳ	"	lyre.
y̆	"	typical, fully.
āa	=	a *of* am.
æ	*as in*	mediæval.
âi	"	aisle.
āo	=	o *in* alone.
âu	*as in*	maul.
êe	"	heed.
Eu	"	Euphrates
ôi	"	oil.
œ	"	Phœnicia
ç	"	celestial.
ch	"	character.
ġ	"	giant.
ṡ	"	his.
s̄i	"	adhesion.

CONTENTS

—————◆—————

PART FIRST

STORIES ABOUT THE PATRIARCHS
GENESIS; JOB

Story 1—How the World Was Made.. 23
    Gen. 1:1—2:7
Story 2—The Story of the First Earth-Home.................................... 24
    Gen. 2:8—3:24
Story 3—The Story of the First Children.. 27
    Genesis 4
Story 4—The First Great Ship and Why It Was Built.................... 31
    Gen. 5:1—9:17
Story 5—The Tower of Babel, and Why It Was Never Finished.... 35
    Gen. 9:18—11:9
Story 6—A Man Who Heard and Obeyed God's Call...................... 36
    Gen. 11:27—12:20
Story 7—How Abram Ended a Quarrel.. 39
    Genesis 13
Story 8—How Lot's Choice Brought Trouble.................................... 40
    Genesis 14
Story 9—Things that Happened Inside and Outside Abram's Tent-Home.... 43
    Genesis 15-17
Story 10—Strange Visitors at Abraham's Tent-Home...................... 44
    Genesis 18
Story 11—What Happened to Sodom.. 46
    Genesis 19
Story 12—The Little Boy Who Became a Great Hunter.................. 48
    Gen. 20:1—21:21
Story 13—How Abraham Gave Isaac Back to God.......................... 50
    Gen. 22:1-20
Story 14—How Abraham Found a Wife for Isaac............................ 52
    Gen. 23:1—25:18
Story 15—What Two Boys Thought About Their Father's Blessing.... 56
    Gen. 25:19—27:41
Story 16—Jacob's Lonely Journey and His Wonderful Dream........ 59
    Gen. 27:42—29:12
Story 17—How Jacob Was Deceived by Laban................................ 61
    Gen. 29:13—31:55
Story 18—Why Jacob's Name Was Changed to Israel.................... 64
    Genesis 32—35
Story 19—How Jacob's Favorite Son Became a Slave.................... 67
    Genesis 37
Story 20—Joseph a Prisoner in Egypt.. 71
    Gen. 37:36—40:23
Story 21—Joseph a Ruler in Egypt.. 73
    Genesis 41

Story 22—How Joseph's Dreams Came True... 76
    Genesis 42
Story 23—Joseph Makes Himself Known to His Brothers............................. 79
    Gen. 43:1—45:24
Story 24—Joseph's Father and Brothers Come to Live in Egypt............... 84
    Gen. 45:25—50:26
Story 25—The Story of Job.. 88
    Job 1:1—42:17

PART SECOND

STORIES ABOUT MOSES

EXODUS; LEVITICUS; NUMBERS; DEUTERONOMY

Story 1—How the Child Moses Came to Live in the King's Palace............. 93
    Exod. 1:1—2:10
Story 2—Why Moses Lived in the Wilderness... 96
    Exod. 2:11-25
Story 3—How God Spoke to Moses From a Burning Bush........................ 98
    Exodus 3, 4
Story 4—Moses and Aaron Talk With a Stubborn King............................ 101
    Exod. 5:1—7:24
Story 5—Pharaoh Sees God's Mighty Signs and Miracles........................ 105
    Exod. 7:25—10:29
Story 6—When the Death-Angel Visited Pharaoh's Palace........................ 108
    Exodus 11—13
Story 7—How God Showed His Power at the Red Sea............................. 112
    Exod. 14:1—15:21
Story 8—What Happened in the Wilderness of Shur................................ 116
    Exod. 15:22-27
Story 9—How God Fed the Hungry People in the Wilderness.................... 117
    Exodus 16
Story 10—How God Showed His Power at Rephidim................................ 120
    Exodus 17, 18
Story 11—The Voice from a Smoking Mountain..................................... 121
    Exodus 19—24
Story 12—The Story of a Golden Calf.. 124
    Exodus 32
Story 13—How God Planned to Live Among His People.......................... 127
    Exodus 34—39; Numbers 1—5
Story 14—The Tabernacle, Where the Israelites Worshiped God............... 129
    Exodus 40
Story 15—How the People Worshiped God at the Tabernacle.................... 131
    Leviticus 1—10:7
Story 16—The Israelites Journey from Sinai to the Border of Canaan........ 133
    Numbers 9—12
Story 17—How Ten Men Spoiled God's Plan.. 135
    Numbers 13, 14
Story 18—Why God Caused the Earth to Swallow Some Israelites............ 139
    Numbers 16, 17
Story 19—Things That Happened to the Israelites During the Forty Years They
    Lived in the Wilderness.. 142
    Numbers 20; Deut. 2:1-15
Story 20—Why the Brass Serpent Hung on a Pole in the Israelites' Camp.... 144
    Num. 21:4-9

Story 21—How God Helped the Israelites When They Trusted in Him...................... 145
    Num. 21:12—22:2
Story 22—What Happened to a Wise Man who Tried to Disobey God...................... 146
    Num. 22:1-35
Story 23—How Balaam Tried to Please the King............................... 149
    Num. 22:36—32:9
Story 24—The Last Journey of Moses............................ 150
    Num. 27:12-23; Deuteronomy 34

———————◆———————

PART THIRD

STORIES ABOUT JOSHUA AND THE JUDGES OF ISRAEL

JOSHUA; JUDGES; RUTH; 1 SAMUEL 1—8

Story 1—How a Woman Spoiled the Plan of a Wicked King............................ 153
    Joshua 1, 2
Story 2—How the Israelites Crossed Over a Dangerous River........................ 155
    Josh. 3:1—5:1
Story 3—What Happened to the Stone Walls of Jericho...................... 157
    Josh. 5:13—6:27
Story 4—The Story About a Buried Sin........................ 161
    Joshua 7, 8
Story 5—The Altar Where God's Law Was Written upon Stone................... 163
    Deuteronomy 27, 28; Josh. 8:30-35
Story 6—The People Who Fooled Joshua...................... 164
    Josh. 9:3-27
Story 7—Why Joshua Spoke to the Sun and to the Moon...................... 165
    Joshua 10—12
Story 8—How the Land of Canaan Became the Land of Israel................... 167
    Joshua 13—19
Story 9—How God Planned to Use Some Cities in the Land of Israel............... 169
    Joshua 20, 21
Story 10—The Story of the Altar Beside the Jordan River.................... 170
    Joshua 22
Story 11—Joshua's Last Meeting with the Israelites........................ 173
    Joshua 23, 24
Story 12—How God Helped the Israelites Out of Their Troubles................... 174
    Judg. 1:1—3:14
Story 13—The Left-Handed Man Who Judged Israel........................ 176
    Judg. 3:15-31
Story 14—Two Brave Women Who Helped the Israelites Out of Trouble.............. 178
    Judges 4, 5
Story 15—How a Brave Man Tore Down an Altar of Baal...................... 180
    Judges 6
Story 16—How the Midianites Were Surprized at Midnight................... 184
    Judg. 7:1—8:28
Story 17—The Man Who Made Himself King over Israel...................... 186
    Judg. 8:32—10:5
Story 18—How a Girl Suffered for Her Father's Rash Promise................ 188
    Judg. 10:6—12:7
Story 19—The Story of a Strong Man Who Judged Israel...................... 191
    Judges 13—16
Story 20—How Samson Came to His Death........................ 194
    Judg. 16:4-31

Story 21—The Young Woman Who Forsook Idols to Serve God................................198
            Ruth 1—4
Story 22—The Little Boy Whose Mother Lent Him to the Lord................................ 202
            1 Sam. 1:1—3:18
Story 23—The Story of the Stolen Ark.. 205
            1 Sam. 3:19—4:22
Story 24—How the Ark of God Troubled Dagon and His Worshipers.................... 207
            1 Sam. 5:1—7:2
Story 25—How Samuel Judged the Israelites.. 209
            1 Samuel 7, 8

———————◆———————

PART FOURTH

STORIES ABOUT THE THREE KINGS OF UNITED ISRAEL

1 AND 2 SAMUEL; 1 KINGS 1—12; 1 AND 2 CHRONICLES 1—11

Story 1—The Tall Man Whom God Chose to Become Israel's First King................. 213
            1 Samuel 9, 10
Story 2—How the Eyes of Some of Saul's People Were Saved............................... 216
            1 Samuel 11, 12
Story 3—King Saul and His People in Trouble.. 218
            1 Samuel 13
Story 4—How the Faith of a Brave Young Prince Brought a Great Victory............. 220
            1 Sam. 14:1-46
Story 5—How Sin Robbed Saul of His Kingdom.. 222
            1 Sam. 14:47—15:35
Story 6—Why God Sent Samuel to Bethlehem... 224
            1 Sam. 16:1-13
Story 7—Why Jesse Sent David to Visit King Saul... 227
            1 Sam. 16:14-23
Story 8—How David Killed the Giant Goliath... 228
            1 Sam. 17:1-54
Story 9—How Saul Became David's Enemy.. 234
            1 Sam. 17:55—18:30
Story 10—How Jonathan and Michal Saved David's Life... 236
            1 Sam. 19:1—20:2
Story 11—Why a Little Boy Picked Up Arrows for a Prince.................................... 238
            1 Samuel 20
Story 12—Things That Happened While David Had no Home................................... 240
            1 Sam. 21:1—22:5
Story 13—How a Wicked Servant Obeyed a Wicked King....................................... 242
            1 Sam. 22:6-23
Story 14—How David Spared Saul's Life... 244
            1 Samuel 23—27
Story 15—The Unhappy Ending of Saul's Life... 248
            1 Sam. 28:3—31:13
Story 16—What Happened to David's Home at Ziklag... 250
            1 Sam. 29:1—2 Sam. 2:3
Story 17—When the Shepherd-Boy Became the King of Israel................................. 252
            2 Sam. 2:4—6:18
Story 18—What Happened to a Little Lame Prince When He Grew Up.................... 254
            2 Sam. 4:4—9:13
Story 19—David's Sin and His Punishment.. 255
            2 Sam. 11:1—12:26

Story 20—The Wicked Prince Who Tried to Steal His Father's Kingdom..................... 257
　　　2 Samuel 15—17
Story 21—How the Wicked Prince Was Hung in the Boughs of a Great Oak-Tree....... 259
　　　2 Samuel 18, 19
Story 22—Why the Death-Angel Visited Jerusalem.................... 261
　　　2 Samuel 24; 1 Chronicles 21
Story 23—Why Solomon Rode Upon the King's Mule.................... 263
　　　1 Kings 1:1—2:12
Story 24—How God Spoke in a Dream to Solomon.................... 265
　　　1 Kings 3:3-15; 4:29-34; 10:1-13
Story 25—The Temple of the Lord, Which Solomon Built on Mount Moriah.................. 268
　　　1 Kings 5:1—9:9
Story 26—The Last Days of King Solomon.................... 270
　　　1 Kings 11

PART FIFTH

STORIES ABOUT THE DIVIDED KINGDOM

1 AND 2 KINGS; 1 AND 2 CHRONICLES; JONAH; JEREMIAH

Story　1—The Foolish Young Prince Who Lost His Father's Kingdom.................. 273
　　　1 Kings 12:1-24
Story　2—The Story About Two Golden Calves.................... 275
　　　1 Kings 12:25—13:6
Story　3—Why a Prophet Was Killed by a Lion.................... 278
　　　1 Kings 13:7-32
Story　4—What the Blind Prophet Told the Queen of Israel.................... 280
　　　1 Kings 14:1-20
Story　5—The Story of a King Who Tried to Destroy Idol-Worship.................. 281
　　　1 Kings 15:8-24; 2 Chron. 14:1—16:14
Story　6—Why Birds Fed a Prophet by a Brook Near Jordan.................... 283
　　　1 Kings 16:29—17:24
Story　7—How God Showed His Great Power on Mount Carmel.................... 287
　　　1 Kings 18:1-40
Story　8—The Little Cloud That Brought a Great Rain.................... 290
　　　1 Kings 18:40—19:3
Story　9—What an Angel Found Under a Juniper-Tree in the Wilderness.................... 292
　　　1 Kings 19:3-21
Story 10—Ahab and the Beggar King.................... 295
　　　1 Kings 20
Story 11—How a King's Pout Cost a Man's Life.................... 297
　　　1 Kings 21
Story 12—When Fire Fell from the Sky and Burned Up Some Wicked Men.................... 300
　　　2 Kings 1
Story 13—The Story of a Great Whirlwind.................... 302
　　　2 Kings 2:1-18
Story 14—Why Two Hungry Bears Killed Some Children from Bethel.................... 304
　　　2 Kings 2:19-25
Story 15—Elisha's Miracle That Saved Two Boys from Becoming Slaves.................... 306
　　　2 Kings 4:1-7
Story 16—The Story About a Little Boy Who Died and Became Alive Again.................. 308
　　　2 Kings 4:8-37
Story 17—Elisha's Kindness to the Poor.................... 311
　　　2 Kings 4:38-44; 6:1-7

Story 18—How a Little Slave-Girl Helped a Heathen Man to Find the True God........ 312
    2 Kings 5:1-27
Story 19—A Little Boy Who Became King, and How He Ruled in Judah...................... 317
    2 Chron. 22:11—24:27
Story 20—How Elisha Led His Enemies Into a Trap.. 319
    2 Kings 6:8-23
Story 21—Where Four Lepers Found Food for a Starving City........................... 321
    2 Kings 6:24—7:20
Story 22—The Prophet Who Tried to Run Away from God.... 323
    Jonah 1—4
Story 23—The Sad Ending of the Kingdom of Israel.................................... 327
    2 Kings 17
Story 24—The Good King Hezekiah... 328
    2 Kings 18—20; 2 Chronicles 29—32
Story 25—The Story About a Forgotten Book.. 332
    2 Chronicles 34, 35
Story 26—The Weeping Prophet, and His Great Work................................... 334
    Jeremiah 1—52

PART SIXTH

STORIES ABOUT THE JEWS

DANIEL; NEHEMIAH; HAGGAI; EZRA; ESTHER; MALACHI

Story 1—How the People of Judah Lived in a Strange Land.......................... 339
    2 Chron. 36:14-21
Story 2—Four Brave Boys Who Stood Before a Great King.......................... 340
    Daniel 1
Story 3—How Daniel Became a Great Man in Babylon............................... 342
    Daniel 2
Story 4—What the King Saw in the Fiery Furnace.................................. 345
    Daniel 3
Story 5—How God Humbled the Proud Heart of Nebuchadnezzar.................. 347
    Daniel 4
Story 6—The Strange Handwriting on the Wall of the Palace..................... 350
    Daniel 5
Story 7—Daniel in the Lions' Den.. 353
    Daniel 6
Story 8—Daniel's Angel Visitor.. 356
    Daniel 8—12
Story 9—The Home-Coming of the Jews... 358
    Ezra 1:1—3:7
Story 10—How the New Temple Was Built in Jerusalem........................... 359
    Ezra 3:7—6:22; Haggai 1, 2
Story 11—The Beautiful Girl Who Became a Queen............................... 362
    Esther 1, 2
Story 12—Why a Proud Man Planned to Destroy All the Jews................... 364
    Esther 3:1—4:3
Story 13—How Queen Esther Saved the Lives of Her People...................... 366
    Esther 4:4—10:3
Story 14—Ezra, the Good Man Who Taught God's Law to the Jews............... 371
    Ezra 7—10; Nehemiah 8
Story 15—The King's Cupbearer and His Story................................... 373
    Neh. 1:1—2:18
Story 16—How the Walls of Jerusalem Were Rebuilt.............................. 375
    Neh. 2:19—13:31; Malachi 1—4

STORIES OF THE NEW TESTAMENT

PART FIRST

STORIES ABOUT JESUS

MATTHEW; MARK; LUKE; JOHN
Acts 1:1-14

What Happened Between the Old and the New Testament................ 379

Story 1—An Angel Visitor in the Temple................ 383
    Luke 1:1-23

Story 2—The Heavenly Messenger in Galilee................ 385
    Matt. 1:18-25; Luke 1:26-56

Story 3—How the Dumb Priest and His Wife Named Their Child................ 388
    Luke 1:57-80

Story 4—The Story of a Wonderful Baby's Birth................ 390
    Luke 2:1-39

Story 5—The Wise Men Who Followed a Star................ 394
    Matthew 2

Story 6—When Jesus Was a Boy Twelve Years Old................ 397
    Luke 2:40-52

Story 7—The Strange Preacher in the Wilderness................ 401
    Matthew 3; Mark 1:2-11; Luke 3:1-23; John 1:15-34

Story 8—The Temptations of Jesus................ 403
    Matt. 4:1-11; Mark 1:12, 13; Luke 4:1-14

Story 9—How Five Men Became Acquainted with Jesus................ 405
    John 1:35-51

Story 10—The Wedding-Feast Where Jesus Showed His Power................ 408
    John 2:1-11

Story 11—The Great Teacher in Jerusalem................ 411
    John 2:13—3:21

Story 12—The Tired Stranger Who Rested by a Well................ 414
    John 4:1-43

Story 13—The Story of a Man Who Had Great Faith in Jesus' Power................ 416
    John 4:45-54

Story 14—The Angry Mob on the Hill-Top of Nazareth................ 418
    Luke 4:16-32

Story 15—Four Fishermen Who Left Their Nets to Follow Jesus................ 420
    Matt. 4:18-22; Mark 1:16-34; Luke 4:33—5:11

Story 16—How Matthew the Publican Became a Disciple of Jesus................ 424
    Matt. 9:9-13; Mark 2:14-17; Luke 5:27-32

Story 17—How Jesus Healed a Cripple and a Man Whose Hand Was Withered................ 427
    Matt. 12:1-15; Mark 2:23—3:6; Luke 6:1-12; John 5:1-18

Story 18—The Twelve Men Who Were Called Apostles................ 430
    Matt. 10:2-4; Mark 3:13-19; Luke 6:12-16

Story 19—The Sermon on the Mountain-Side................ 431
    Matthew 5—7; Luke 6:17-49

Story 20—How Jesus Healed a Man Who Was a Leper................ 433
    Matt. 8:1-4; Mark 1:40-45; Luke 5:12-16

Story 21—How a Roman Captain Showed His Great Faith in Jesus................ 434
    Matt. 8:5-13; Luke 7:1-10

Story 22—Why Four Men Tore Up the Roof of a Crowded House................ 436
    Matt. 9:2-8; Mark 2:1-12; Luke 5:18-26

Story 23—When a Widow's Sorrow Was Changed into Joy................ 438
    Luke 7:11-17

Story 24—A Pharisee, a Sinful Woman, and the Savior................ 440
    Luke 7:36-50

Story 25—Story-Sermons by the Sea.. 442
            Matt. 13:1-53; Mark 4:1-34
Story 26—The Flooded Ship That Did Not Sink, and the Wild Man Made Well........ 445
            Matt. 8:23-34; Mark 4:35—5:20; Luke 8:22-40
Story 27—The Little Girl Who Died and Became Alive Again............................. 448
            Matt. 9:18—10:42; Mark 5:22-43; Luke 8:41—9:6
Story 28—A Boy's Lunch-Basket, and a Great Miracle..................................... 450
            Matt. 14:13-23; Mark 6:31-46; Luke 9:7-17; John 6:1-15
Story 29—The Man Who Walked on the Water and Became Afraid..................... 452
            Matt. 14:23-36; Mark 6:46-56; John 6:16-29
Story 30—How Jesus Answered a Mother's Prayer... 454
            Matt. 15:21-29; Mark 7:24-30
Story 31—What a Multitude Learned About Jesus... 455
            Matt. 15:29-39; Mark 7:31—8:10
Story 32—The Blind Man of Bethsaida; How Peter Answered a Great Question........ 457
            Matt. 16:13-28; Mark 8:22—9:1; Luke 9:18-27
Story 33—The Glorified Master on the Mountain-Side..................................... 458
            Matt. 17:1-13; Mark 9:2-13; Luke 9:28-36
Story 34—A Suffering Child, an Anxious Father, and Jesus............................. 460
            Matt. 17:14-21; Mark 9:14-29; Luke 9:37-45
Story 35—Jesus and His Disciples in Capernaum... 461
            Matt. 17:22—18:14; Mark 9:30-43; Luke 9:43-50
Story 36—Jesus Teaches Peter a Lesson on Forgiveness................................ 462
            Matt. 18:21-35
Story 37—The Unfriendly Samaritans; The Ten Lepers.................................... 464
            Luke 9:51-62; 17:11-19
Story 38—Jesus at the Great Feast in Jerusalem... 465
            John 7:2-53
Story 39—How Jesus Answered His Enemies' Question................................... 467
            John 8
Story 40—What Happened to the Blind Man Whom Jesus Healed..................... 469
            John 9
Story 41—Little Children Are Brought to Jesus; A Young Man Goes Away Sad........ 472
            Matt. 19:13-30; Mark 10:13-31
Story 42—Seventy Other Disciples Sent Out; The Good Samaritan.................... 473
            Luke 10:1-37
Story 43—Lazarus, the Dead Man Whom Jesus Called Out of the Grave........... 476
            John 11:1-54
Story 44—Jesus Heals the Sick, and Teaches in a Pharisee's House................ 478
            Luke 14:1-24
Story 45—A Crooked Woman Healed; The Pharisees Try to Frighten Jesus; Parables
            by the Way 480
            Luke 13:11—15:32
Story 46—Four Short Story-Sermons Which Jesus Preached............................ 483
            Luke 16; 18:1-14
Story 47—Happenings on the Way to Jerusalem.. 486
            Matt. 20:17-34; Mark 10:32-52; Luke 18:31-43
Story 48—The Little Man Who Climbed into a Tree to See Jesus.................... 488
            Luke 19:1-28
Story 49—How Mary Showed Her Love for Jesus... 490
            Matt. 26:6-16; Mark 14:3-11; John 12:1-11
Story 50—How Jesus Rode into Jerusalem as a King..................................... 493
            Matt. 21:1-11; Mark 11:1-11; Luke 19:29-40; John 12:12-19
Story 51—The Teachings of Jesus in the Temple... 496
            Matt. 21:12-46; Mark 11:12—12:12; Luke 19:41—20:19
Story 52—Jesus' Last Days in the Temple.. 498
            Matt. 22:1—24:1; Mark 12:13—13:1; Luke 20:20—21:4; John 12:20-36
Story 53—Jesus' Teaching on the Mount of Olives... 502
            Matt. 23:37—25:46; Mark 13; Luke 21:5-38
Story 54—The Last Supper Jesus Ate with the Twelve................................... 504
            Matt. 26:17-30; Mark 14:12-26; Luke 22:3-39; John 13

Story 55—How an Untrue Disciple Sold His Lord................................ 507
    Matt. 26:36-75; Mark 14:32-72; Luke 22:39-71; John 18:1-27
Story 56—The Darkest Day in All the World................................ 511
    Matt. 27:1-54; Mark 15:1-39; Luke 23:1-47; John 18:28—19:31
Story 57—The Watchers at the Tomb of Jesus................................ 515
    Matt. 27:55—28:1; Mark 15:42—16:5
    Luke 23:50—24:3; John 19:31—20:1
Story 58—When Jesus, the Crucified Savior, Arose from the Dead................ 518
    Matt. 28:2-16; Mark 16:5-14; Luke 24:4-12; John 20:2-18
Story 59—The Stranger on the Road to Emmaus; Doubting Thomas................ 520
    Luke 24:13-48; John 20:19-31
Story 60—Jesus' Last Meeting with His Disciples by the Seashore and on the Mount
    of Olives 524
    Mark 16:15-19; Luke 24:50-53; John 21; Acts 1:1-14

PART SECOND

STORIES ABOUT THE APOSTLES

THE BOOK OF ACTS; THE EPISTLES; THE BOOK OF REVELATION

Story   1—The Sound as of a Rushing Wind, and What It Brought.......... 529
    Acts 1:15—2:47
Story   2—The Crippled Beggar Who Received a Wonderful Gift.......... 532
    Acts 3:1—4:31
Story   3—The Story About Two Hypocrites in the Early Church.......... 535
    Acts 4:32—5:11
Story   4—When Prison Doors Swung Open by an Angel's Touch.......... 538
    Acts 5:12-42
Story   5—The Preacher Who Was Stoned to Death.......... 540
    Acts 6:1—8:2
Story   6—A Man Who Tried to Buy the Holy Spirit with Money.......... 543
    Acts 8:1-25
Story   7—Philip Preaches to a Stranger on a Lonely Road.......... 545
    Acts 8:26-40
Story   8—The Wicked Plan that Was Spoiled by a Vision of Jesus.......... 547
    Acts 9:1-20
Story   9—How a Basket Was Used to Save a Man's Life.......... 551
    Acts 9:21-31; 22:17-21; Gal. 1:17-24
Story 10—A Sick Man Healed, and a Dead Woman Brought Back to Life.......... 554
    Acts 9:32-43
Story 11—The Great Sheet Let Down from Heaven, and What It Taught.......... 555
    Acts 10:1—11:18
Story 12—How Peter's Coming Broke Up a Midnight Prayer-Meeting.......... 559
    Acts 12
Story 13—Where Believers in Jesus were First Called Christians.......... 561
    Acts 11:19-30
Story 14—The First Missionaries in the Early Church.......... 563
    Acts 13:1—14:7
Story 15—How Idol-Worshipers in Lystra Treated Barnabas and Paul.......... 565
    Acts 14:8-28
Story 16—A Puzzling Question, and How It Was Answered.......... 567
    Acts 16:1-34
Story 17—A Call for Help From a Far-Off Land.......... 569
    Acts 15:36—16:15

Story 18—The Prayer-Meeting in Prison, and Its Happy Ending.................................... 571
　　　Acts 16:16-40
Story 19—How the Gospel Was First Preached in Other Cities of Macedonia............. 574
　　　Acts 17:1-15
Story 20—Paul Tells the Wise Men of Greece about the Unknown God....................... 576
　　　Acts 17:16—18:23
Story 21—How a Great Heathen City Received the Gospel.. 578
　　　Acts 18:24—19:20
Story 22—The Uproar a Covetous Man Caused in a Great City.................................... 580
　　　Acts 19:21—20:4
Story 23—The Faithful Missionary, and His Last Farewell.. 583
　　　Acts 20:5—21:17
Story 24—How the Prophet's Words Came True.. 587
　　　Acts 21:18—23:10
Story 25—How a Young Man Saved His Uncle's Life... 589
　　　Acts 23:11—24:27
Story 26—A King Listens to Paul's Story.. 592
　　　Acts 25, 26
Story 27—The Story of a Shipwreck.. 595
　　　Acts 27
Story 28—How a Chained Prisoner Brought Joy to Islanders....................................... 598
　　　Acts 28:1-10
Story 29—The Last of Paul's Journey, and His Life in Rome... 600
　　　Acts 28:11-31; Philemon; Colossians; 2 Timothy
Story 30—Things We Learn from the Epistles.. 604
　　　The Epistles
Story 31—What God's Faithful Servant Saw While He Was on a Lonely Island......... 606
　　　Revelation 1:1—22:21

LIST OF PICTURES

Page

Adam and Eve driven from the garden (frontispiece).. 2
The beautiful garden of Eden (full page).. 26
Cain and Abel bring their offering.. 29
The dove returning to the ark.. 30
The animals going into the big ark (full page)... 32
The tower of Babel... 36
Abram listening to God... 38
Adam giving Lot his choice of the land (full page, colored).........................opposite 40
Abram rescuing Lot (full page)... 42
Lot and his daughters fleeing from Sodom... 47
Abraham and Isaac on the mountain.. 52
Eliezer meeting Rebekah at the well.. 54
Isaac blessing Jacob (full page, colored)...opposite 57
Jacob meeting Laban.. 61
The angel telling Jacob to let him go.. 65
Hebron as it is today.. 66
Joseph dreaming of the sheaves... 67
Joseph sold by his brothers into Egypt... 70
Joseph interpreting the dream of the butler and baker (full page, colored).........opposite 73
Joseph telling the meaning of Pharaoh's dreams... 74
Joseph's brothers bowing before him in Egypt... 77
Judah pleads for Benjamin.. 78
Joseph kissing his young brother, Benjamin... 83
Joseph's father talking to the king (full page).. 86
Joseph, ruler of Egypt (full page, colored)...opposite 88
Job and his three comforters... 90
Moses breaking the tablets of stone upon the rocks... 92
The Israelites as slaves in Egypt.. 94
Moses and the fire in the bush... 98
Aaron's rod swallowing the rods of the magicians.. 102
Moses and Aaron before Pharaoh (full page).. 104
Israelites sprinkling blood on the door-frame... 109
The death-angel visited the house of Pharaoh.. 110
The pillar of fire going before the hosts of Israel (full page)............................. 113
The Israelites safe, and the Egyptians being drowned (full page)............................ 114
God sending quails into the camp of Israel.. 118
Journey of Israel to Canaan (animated map).. 119
Moses on the Mount.. 122
The tabernacle; plan of tabernacle and court.. 132
Moses, leader and lawgiver (full page, colored).....................................opposite 136
The spies returning from Canaan... 136
Korah and his friends being swallowed by the earth.. 140
Aaron's rod was the only one that grew.. 141
Moses' farewell 151
Joshua, the new leader (full page, colored)...opposite 153
The River Jordan.. 154
Israelites crossing through the Jordan River.. 156
Joshua and his army... 158
The fall of Jericho... 159
Achan confessing before Joshua.. 162
Safely reaching a city of refuge.. 170
Joshua's farewell address... 174
Call of Gideon.. 183
Gideon's army blowing their trumpets.. 185
Samson killing a lion... 192
Samson killing the Philistines with a dry bone.. 193
Samson pulling down the Philistine temple... 197
Ruth and Naomi.. 200
Ruth (full page, colored)...opposite 200
Ruth gleaning in the fields of Boaz (full page)... 201

Page

The infant Samuel 203
Telling Eli the ark has been stolen... 206
Samuel's farewell address... 211
Saul anointed by Samuel (full page).. 212
Saul rejected by the Lord (full page, colored)..........................opposite 217
Samuel anointing David king (full page, colored)......................opposite 224
David playing before Saul (full page)... 226
David kills a lion... 230
David and his sling (full page)... 232
David slays the giant.. 233
King Saul throwing his spear at David... 235
David and Jonathan... 239
King Saul in David's cave... 245
David spares Saul's life.. 247
A recent picture of Endor, the place where Saul found the witch 249
The prophet speaking to King David.. 256
David telling Solomon to build the temple (full page, colored)......opposite 264
Solomon's dream 267
Dedication of Solomon's temple.. 269
Jerusalem from the Mount of Olives as it is today................... 272
Rehoboam taking the young men's counsel................................. 274
Period of the Divided Kingdom (animated map)......................... 277
Offering sacrifices of thanksgiving in Asa's good reign (full page, colored)........opposite 281
Elijah being fed by the ravens (full page)................................... 284
Elijah restores the widow's son.. 286
Mount Carmel, where the priests and prophets met (full page)....... 291
The angel finding Elijah... 293
Naboth refusing to sell his vineyard... 298
Elijah meeting wicked Ahab... 299
Ruins of the beautiful palace at Samaria.. 300
Elijah going to heaven in the whirlwind... 303
The miracle of the widow's oil.. 307
Elisha restores a boy to life... 310
The captive maid telling about the prophet (full page)............ 314
Naaman in the River Jordan.. 316
Crowning the boy Joash... 318
Jonah preaching in Nineveh... 325
Jonah under the gourd vine.. 326
Hezekiah spreading the letter before the Lord (full page)....... 331
Jeremiah being cast into the dungeon... 336
King Nebuchadnezzar bowing before Daniel (full page)........... 338
Daniel refusing the king's food... 341
The three who refused to worship the image............................... 345
Nebuchadnezzar in the fields... 349
The handwriting on the palace wall (full page)......................... 351
The men watching Daniel pray (full page)................................... 354
Daniel among the hungry lions... 355
Building the new temple.. 360
Esther, the beautiful queen... 363
Esther touches the king's scepter.. 369
Nehemiah before King Artaxerxes... 374
Building the walls of Jerusalem... 376
Ezra teaching the law... 378
The boy Christ (full page) 382
Angel appearing to Zacharias (full page)..................................... 384
The annunciation (full page)... 386
The angel talking to the shepherds in a field near Bethlehem (full page)........... 389
Arrival of the shepherds.. 391
Adoration of the shepherds (full page, colored)..........................opposite 393
The shepherds' visit.. 393
Simeon holding Mary's baby, Jesus.. 394

Page

Jesus in the carpenter shop (full page).. 398
The boy Jesus in the temple with the doctors (full page)................... 400
Jesus on the Mount of Temptation... 404
Christ and the fishermen.. 406
The ministry of Jesus (animated map)... 409
Philip and Nathanael (full page, colored)......................opposite 408
Jesus making wine out of water.. 410
Jesus talking to Nicodemus.. 412
Jesus and the woman of Samaria.. 415
Jesus preaching in the synagog at Nazareth............................... 418
Miraculous draught of fishes (full page)...................................... 421
Jesus calling Matthew (full page).. 426
Jesus healing the withered hand... 429
Jesus and the twelve 430
Jesus bringing to life the widow's son (full page)...................... 439
Jesus stilling the storm... 445
Jesus telling Peter to come... 453
Jesus feeding the five thousand (full page, colored)......opposite 456
Jesus and the little child... 461
Jesus healing a blind man... 470
The rich young ruler (full page, colored).....................opposite 473
The good Samaritan and the wounded man.................................... 475
Jesus healing the woman.. 481
Lazarus at the rich man's gate... 484
Jesus and Zacchaeus (full page, colored)....................opposite 489
Jesus calling to Zacchaeus.. 489
Mary anointing Jesus (full page)... 491
Jesus entering Jerusalem 494
Driving out the money changers... 497
Jesus and his disciples at the Last Supper (full page, colored)........opposite 504
The Garden of Gethsemane as seen from Jerusalem (full page)......... 508
Christ in Gethsemane... 509
Pilate with Jesus before the angry Jews.. 512
Jesus crucified (full page, colored)...............................opposite 512
Judas throwing down the money... 513
The descent from the cross (full page).. 516
Angels on the way to Jesus' tomb.. 519
Jesus and Mary 520
Recognizing Jesus (full page).. 521
Jesus appearing on the shores of Galilee...................................... 525
Jesus ascending to heaven.. 527
The work of the apostles (animated map)....................................... 528
The coming of the Holy Spirit.. 530
Peter and John healing the lame man... 533
Helping one another.. 536
The sad death of Ananias.. 537
Stephen making his defense.. 542
Philip teaching the man from Ethiopia... 546
The north gate of Jerusalem, through which Saul no doubt passed. It is called the
    Damascus Gate (full page)... 548
Saul struck down.. 550
Saul escaping in a basket.. 552
Peter's vision on the housetop.. 556
Peter telling Cornelius about Jesus.. 558
Peter being delivered from prison (full page, colored).....opposite 560
Paul and Barnabas... 562
The jailer with Paul and Silas after the earthquake..................... 573
Paul preaching on Mars Hill... 576
Burning the books at Ephesus.. 581
A theater of Paul's time.. 582
Ephesians bidding Paul good-by... 584

Page

Tyre, where Paul met with brethren.. 586
Paul being bound... 588
Paul speaking before Agrippa.. 593
Cast ashore on the Island of Melita.. 597
Paul preaching in Rome.. 601
The ruins of Rome's ancient forum, where justice was administered..................... 603

STORIES OF THE OLD TESTAMENT
SIX PARTS

Part First
STORIES ABOUT THE PATRIARCHS

Part Second
STORIES ABOUT MOSES

Part Third
STORIES ABOUT JOSHUA AND THE JUDGES OF ISRAEL

Part Fourth
STORIES ABOUT THE THREE KINGS OF UNITED ISRAEL

Part Fifth
STORIES ABOUT THE DIVIDED KINGDOM

Part Sixth
STORIES ABOUT THE JEWS

STORIES OF THE NEW TESTAMENT
TWO PARTS

Part First
STORIES ABOUT JESUS

Part Second
STORIES ABOUT THE APOSTLES

Stories of the Old Testament
In Six Parts

PART FIRST
STORIES ABOUT THE PATRIARCHS
Genesis; Job

STORY 1

HOW THE WORLD WAS MADE
Gen. 1: 1—2: 7

THIS great world in which we live did not always exist. The broad expanse of sky, which smiles upon us when days are fair, and frowns and weeps when days are foul, did not always form an arch above our earth-home. Long, long ago there was no world at all. There was no sun to shine, there were no stars to twinkle, nor moonbeams to play through the night shadows. But even then there was God; for he ever has been and always shall be the same unchanging Divine Being.

Then, away back in that long ago, at the very beginning of time, God made the world. Not as we see it today, for at first water covered everything, and all was darkness everywhere. What a strange, unfriendly world this must have been, for no living creature could dwell in it! But God planned to make it beautiful, so he caused the light to shine. This light he called Day and the darkness he called Night. And then the evening and morning of the first day of time passed by.

On the second day God made the beautiful blue sky, and placed above the water-covered earth clouds to carry the sky-moisture. He called the sky Heaven. On the third day he caused the waters to flow together in wide, deep places, and he called them Seas. Dry land then rose up, and this he called Earth. But as yet there were no grasses, flowers, nor trees—the whole earth was barren and desolate. So God caused a carpet of grass to grow upon the bare ground and beautiful flowers to spring up from the earth. The trees and herbs also he made to grow at his will. When God beheld all these things he saw that they were good.

On the fourth day appeared the great lights which we see in the sky—the sun, the moon, and the stars. These he made to divide the day from the night.

After these things were made, God began to create living creatures. He made fishes of all kinds and sizes to swim about in the seas and birds of every description to fly about above the water and land, just as we see them doing today. Thus the world continued to become more de lightful, and the fifth day of the first week of time passed by.

On the sixth day God made all the animals, great and small, and every creeping thing. Then there was life abounding in the woods and on the plains, as well as in the air and in the sea. What a beautiful world! Still what a strange world, for there were no people in it! Not a home anywhere—not a man, woman, nor little child to be seen. What a very strange world indeed!

But God had not yet finished his work of creation, for he wished to have people live in the wonderful world he had made. They could enjoy its beauties and take care of it as no other living creature could do. And more, they could know who had made all these great things, and knowing God they could love and worship him. So it was that God made the first man. Out of the dust of the ground he made the man's body, then he breathed into that body with the breath of life and man became a living soul.

This first man God called Adam, and to Adam he gave the power to rule over all the other living creatures. These animals and birds he brought to Adam, and Adam gave each of them a name. But not one of them did Adam find suitable for a helper, and because he needed a helper very much God made for him a woman. This woman became Adam's wife, and he loved her very much. He called her name Eve.

When the sixth day ended God had made the world and had placed everything in it just as he wished, therefore on the seventh day he rested from his work.

STORY 2

THE STORY OF THE FIRST EARTH-HOME
Gen. 2: 8—3: 24

God himself made for Adam and Eve their first earth-home. And a beautiful home it was. We shall call it a garden-home. God chose a place from which four rivers flowed and there he planted a large garden. We do not know the many kinds of trees and flowers and vegetables and grasses that he caused to grow in this garden. But we are sure that no park which man has made could be so lovely as was the Garden of

Eden. In the midst of this garden God planted a wonderful tree, called the tree of life. Whoever might eat of the fruit of this tree would live on and on forever.

Adam and Eve were very happy. God had given them good things to enjoy, and they knew nothing about evil and wrong-doing. They often talked with God and listened to his voice as he walked and talked with them in the cool of evening time.

God wanted Adam and Eve to prove their love for him, and for this reason he planted in the beautiful garden one test-tree, called the tree of knowledge of good and evil. "Of the fruit of every other tree in this garden you may eat," God had told them, "but the fruit of this test-tree you must not taste. If you do, you shall surely die."

We do not know how long Adam and Eve enjoyed their beautiful garden-home, but we do know that one day a sad thing happened. Sin crept slyly into this lovely place. It came first to Eve. She heard a voice and saw a serpent talking to her. She was not afraid, because she had never known fear. So she listened. "Has God said that you must not eat the fruit of every tree in this garden?" the serpent asked.

"We may eat of every tree except one," Eve answered. "God has told us that we must not eat of the tree of knowledge of good and evil, lest we die."

"That is a mistake; you will not surely die," the serpent replied. "God knows that if you eat fruit from this tree you will become wise to know good and evil, as he is wise, therefore he has forbidden you to eat of it."

Until this time Eve had not touched the forbidden tree; but now she looked at its fruit and thought that if it really would make her wise, like God, she wanted to taste it. Soon she yielded to the temptation and plucked the fruit, and then she gave some to Adam, and he too ate of it.

At once Adam and Eve knew what a dreadful thing sin is. They knew they had disobeyed God. A strange something stole into their hearts; it was fear. How afraid they were to meet God! They had never been afraid before, but now they tried to find a hiding-place among the beautiful trees in the garden. Their hearts had become wicked.

Soon a voice called, "Adam, where are you?" and the frightened man answered, "Lord, I heard your voice and I was afraid, therefore I hid myself." "Why should you be afraid to meet me?" God asked. "Have you eaten of the forbidden fruit?" Then Adam told God that Eve had given him some of the fruit and he had eaten it.

"What is this you have done?" God questioned Eve. **And she**

THE BEAUTIFUL GARDEN OF EDEN

told him what the serpent had said. "I listened to the tempter and then ate of the fruit and gave it to my husband," was her sorrowful confession.

God was grieved because Adam and Eve had failed to obey him. Now he knew they could no longer enjoy his presence with them, because sin had spoiled their lives. They were no longer fit to live in the beautiful garden-home he had made for them. So he sent them away out into the world to make a home for themselves. And he placed an angel at the gate of the garden to prevent them from coming back to eat of the fruit that grew on the wonderful tree of life.

To Eve, God said, "Because you listened to the tempter's voice and disobeyed me, you shall have pain and trouble all the days of your life."

Adam also received a sentence of punishment from God. No longer should the ground yield freely of the fruits and vegetables which Adam and Eve ate for food; now Adam must work hard to keep these things growing. And he would find that weeds and thorns and thistles would grow in his fields to make his work even harder. Then by and by he should grow old and feeble, and then he should die and his body would again become dust as it was before God created him. All these sorrows came because of sin.

But while God drove Adam and Eve out of the beautiful garden, he at the same time gave them the promise that he would send a Savior to make all men free from sin and death.

STORY 3

THE STORY OF THE FIRST CHILDREN

Genesis 4

After sin caused God to shut Adam and Eve out of the beautiful home that he had made for them, they built a home for themselves somewhere outside the garden gate. Here they began to feel more and more the punishment which their sin had brought upon them. Adam had to toil hard and long to secure food for himself and for Eve. No doubt his hands and feet were sometimes bruised and torn by thistles and thorns. Eve too learned the sad meaning of pain and sorrow. Her home was not so happy as it had been before she listened to the tempter's voice, and chose to disobey God.

But all the while God loved Adam and Eve. We can not know how great was his grief when they sinned. No longer could he walk and talk with them as he had done before. Now sin, like a great, black monster, had stepped in and spoiled their friendship, and where sin dwells God will not go. No doubt Adam and Eve were sorry, too. No longer could they have God's presence in their home because sin had fastened itself in their hearts.

But because God loved them still, he gave Adam and Eve a promise of a Savior. And because they believed the promise, hope came into their hearts again. Although they could not talk to God as they had done in their garden-home, now they confessed their sins to him, and it appears certain that they brought gifts which they offered upon altars. These altars they built by piling up either stones or earth, making a flat top, and placing on the top some wood, all cut and ready to be burned. Next they laid their offering upon the wood, then set fire to the wood, and that burned up the offering.

We are sure that Adam and Eve must have felt lonely, with no friends in all the big, wide world. But God planned that there should be more people, and so one day he gave Adam and Eve a little child—a baby boy. This baby they named Cain. How they must have loved him! After a while God gave them another little boy, and they named him Abel.

When Cain and his little brother Abel grew old enough to understand, Adam and Eve told them about the great God, and how they themselves had disobeyed him before Cain and Abel were born. They wanted their sons to love this God and try to please him. But alas! sin, like a tiny seed, was already buried in the hearts of these little boys, causing them to think naughty thoughts, or say unkind words, or do wrong deeds, just as little boys and girls are tempted to do today. Abel wanted to please God and he was sorry because he sinned; but Cain allowed the tiny sin-seed to grow and grow until his heart became very wicked.

By and by Cain and Abel became men, like Adam, and Cain worked in the fields raising grain and fruits, while Abel took care of a flock of sheep. These brothers built altars, upon which they offered their gifts to God, as their parents did. Cain brought for his offering fruit from the field where he had labored, and Abel brought a fat lamb. But Cain's offering did not please God. When he saw that God was displeased, he became very angry. God talked to him. He warned him of the harm that might come if he should continue to be angry instead of becoming sorry for his sins. But Cain was not willing to listen; he was not sorry for his sins.

Abel believed the promise which God had given to his parents, and when he offered his gift he prayed and asked God to forgive his sins. God was pleased with Abel's offering.

One day while the brothers were together in the field, Cain quarreled with Abel. Now, we are sure that nothing good can come of quarrels, because they are so wrong. This quarrel ended dreadfully. Cain grew so angry with Abel that he killed him. What an awful deed!

CAIN AND ABEL BRING THEIR OFFERING

God spoke again to Cain, and asked, "Where is Abel, your brother?"

Cain replied, "I know not. Am I my brother's keeper?"

Wicked Cain did not know that God had seen all he did. And now for a punishment God told Cain that he must go farther away out into the wide world. Never again should he know the blessing of his old home, for hereafter he should wander about from place to place like a frightened, hunted animal. He should have a terrible fear in his heart always that some one would kill him as he had killed his brother.

Now at last Cain felt sorry, but he was sorry only because he was to be punished for his sin. He thought God was punishing him more than he could bear. Then God placed a mark upon him that all could see, and by that mark they would know that God did not want them to kill Cain.

After this Cain wandered far away into a land called Nod. There he lived for many long years.

Adam and Eve lived a long time, and God gave them other children besides Cain and Abel. Then the time came at last when their bodies

THE DOVE RETURNING TO THE ARK

grew feeble with age and they died, as God had said they should when they ate the forbidden fruit.

STORY 4

THE FIRST GREAT SHIP AND WHY IT WAS BUILT

Gen. 5:1—9:17

The children of Adam and Eve lived to be very old. Their children also lived for several hundreds of years. And so it was that grandsons became grandfathers before their own grandfathers died. Thus several generations lived and worked together. After a while there were many people living in the world.

We do not know very much about those people of long ago except the fact that many of them were very wicked. Among them was one man, however, who, like Abel, tried to please God. This man's name was Ē'-nŏ͟ch. The Bible tells us that Ē'-nŏ͟ch walked with God. We understand that he loved God better than he loved anything else, and talked to God and listened when God talked to him. Finally Ē'-nŏ͟ch became an old man. At last, when he was three hundred and sixty-five years old, one day God took him away from earth to heaven, and he did not die. Ē'-nŏ͟ch had a son whom he named Mĕ-thū'-sĕ-lăh. This man lived for nine hundred and sixty-nine years, until he was older than any other man had ever been. Then he died, like all other people had done except his father Ē'-nŏ͟ch.

By this time there were many, many people living in the world. And their hearts were so full of sin that their thoughts and words and deeds were all very wicked. They did not try to please God at all. They did not love him. They did not thank him for the blessings of food and shelter and sunshine which he gave to them. They did not teach their children to love good, pure things, but allowed them to grow up and become evil men and women like themselves. What a sad world this was! for sin was everywhere.

Finally God planned to destroy all the people because they were no longer fit to live. He felt sorry that he ever had made man. He thought he would destroy everything—people, animals, and every other creature that lived on the earth. He would cause a great flood of water to cover the earth.

Then God remembered Noah. Here was a man who had tried to do right regardless of all his wicked surroundings. And he had taught his sons to do right also. God was pleased with Noah and with his sons. Sometimes he talked to Noah. Now he told him about his plan to destroy the world. But because Noah and his family had been trying

THE ANIMALS GOING INTO THE BIG ARK

to do right and trust in the Lord, God promised that they should not be destroyed with the wicked people.

"Get ready to build an ark," God told Noah, "and then when it is finished you and your wife, your sons and their wives may go into this ark and live there until the flood is ended."

Now that God decided to save a few people he also arranged to save a pair of each kind of animal and of bird and of every living thing on the earth that breathed. These creatures were to be housed in the ark, too, while the flood should last.

Noah believed God and made ready to build the ark. God had told him how it should be built. For a long time, while others went their wicked way, he and his sons worked, sawing boards and hammering nails, and making every part of the ark just exactly as God had said it should be made. Then by and by every nail was driven securely into its place, the inside walls were finished, and every part was ready for the purpose it should serve. What a queer-looking building now stood before them—a very large boat-like house three stories high, away out on dry land! Doubtless the people laughed much at faithful old Noah and his three sons. Perhaps they thought that only feeble-minded folk could believe that there ever would be such a thing as a flood. Still Noah continued to warn them that they should repent of their sins lest God destroy them.

One day, when the ark was completed and everything else was in readiness, God called Noah and told him to bring his wife, his three sons and their wives, and come into the ark. And the animals and birds and creeping things God caused to come also, two and two of every kind; and of those animals which man should need after the flood, and birds, seven pairs of each kind came. When they were all inside the ark, God himself shut the door.

After a few days the rain began to fall. And such a rain! Great sheets of water poured down from the clouds as if windows in the sky had been opened and water was flowing through them. Soon the tiny streamlets were raging torrents and the rivers were overflowing their banks. People began to forsake their homes and rush to the hills for safety. Animals, too, ran pell-mell everywhere, trying to find a place of refuge and shelter from the storm. But still it rained, and higher and higher the waters rose until every one believed at last that Noah had told the truth. But now it was too late to repent and seek refuge in the ark, for God had shut the door. And so when the waters crept up to the tops of the hills and mountains and finally buried them out of sight, every living creature on the face of the earth was drowned. Those in the ark were the only ones left alive.

For forty days and nights the downpour of rain continued; but Noah and his family were safe. When the waters rose high enough they lifted the ark off the ground, and it began to float about like a great ship on the top of the flood. For six months and more it floated high above the water-covered earth. Then one day it came to a standstill. God had caused a wind to blow over the waters to dry them up, and as the flood-tide became gradually lower, the ark had found a lodging-place on the top of a mountain. Here it rested for two months, and all the while the water-mark continued to drop lower down the mountain-sides.

After waiting for some time, Noah opened a window, which must have been very high up, near the roof. He allowed a bird called a raven to fly out of the window. Now, the raven has strong wings, and this bird flew to and fro until the waters had gone down. After some days, Noah sent out a dove; but this bird could not find a place to build her nest, so she soon returned again to the ark. Another week of waiting passed, and Noah sent the dove out once more. She stayed longer this time; and when evening came she flew back to Noah, bringing a green olive-leaf in her mouth. At this Noah and his family knew that the waters were returning to the rivers and the seas, and that the land again was becoming green and beautiful. One more week they waited, and now when Noah sent out the dove she flew away and never returned.

Now Noah believed that the time had come when he might uncover the roof and look out upon the earth. How glad he must have been to see dry land again; for more than a year had passed since God had shut them inside the ark. And God said to him, ''Come out of the ark, with your wife and your sons and their wives, and every living thing that is with you in the ark.'' So Noah opened the great door, and he and his family stepped out upon the dry ground. All the animals and the birds and the creeping things came out also, and began to live upon the earth as they had done before the flood.

Noah was thankful to God because his life and the lives of his family had been saved when all other people had perished from off the earth. He built an altar as soon as he came out of the ark, and brought his offering to God. Because Noah had been obedient, God accepted his offering and was pleased with his household.

God then promised that never again would he send another flood to destroy every living creature, and that as long as the earth should remain there would be summer and winter, springtime and autumn.

and day and night. And because God wanted mankind to remember always the promise that he would never again destroy the earth with a flood, he placed in the sky a sign of his promise. That sign was a beautiful rainbow. Have you ever seen that rainbow-sign? It is God's promise to all mankind—to you and to me as well as to Noah and his children.

•

STORY 5

THE TOWER OF BABEL, AND WHY IT WAS NEVER FINISHED
Gen. 9: 18—11: 9

A clean, new world lay before Noah and his three sons when they stepped out of the ark. Now there were no wicked neighbors to mock at them when they built altars to worship God. Even the wicked works of those wicked people had been swept away out of sight. Everything was ready for a new beginning.

Noah and his sons set to work and made new homes. Noah's sons were named Shem, Ham, and Jā'-phĕth. After a while God gave them children. These children grew up and made homes for themselves. Then there were other children; and so it came about that the number of people grew and grew until the earth became as full of people as it was before the flood.

From the mountain of Ăr'-ă-răt, where the ark lodged when the waters went down, the human family went into the south country. Later they moved east, into the valley of Mĕs-ŏ-pŏ-tā'-mĭ-ă, and there they lived on a plain in the land of Shī'-när.

"Let us build for ourselves a city," said the people some time after they reached Shī'när, "and let us make a tower so great and high that its top will reach up to the sky. Then we shall not be scattered over the face of the earth, and separated from one another." And so the people set to work.

In this land of Shī'-när the soil is such that bricks can be made of it, and soon many bricks were made and ready for use. What a busy people! Some were making brick, others were mixing mortar, and still others were carrying brick and mortar to the workmen who were building the city and the tower. Everything was moving fast and everybody was thinking that some day their city and their wonderful tower would be finished.

Then something happened that the people had not expected to happen at all. God came to see the city and the tower. He did not talk to the builders, and very likely they did not know he had been there to look upon their work. But God was not pleased with what he saw. He knew that men would become more sinful if they should finish that great tower. Already they were thinking more and more about their own work and less and less about the God who gave them

THE TOWER OF BABEL

strength with which to labor. Soon they might forget God entirely and worship the work their own hands had made. So God planned to stop their building.

Until this time all the people in the world spoke one language. Now God caused them to speak different languages. The people of one family could not understand what their neighbors were talking about. Neither could their neighbors understand what they were saying. Such a great change caused the people to become restless, and all those who spoke one language moved into neighborhoods by themselves. They could no longer go on with their great building, either, because the workmen could not understand one another's language; and so at last they quit trying to finish the tower whose top they had planned should reach the sky. And the name of the city was called Babel.

Soon the people of one language gathered together their possessions and moved away from Babel. Others did the same. Across the plains they journeyed and over the mountains into strange lands where men's feet had never walked before. They built cities and planted fields and vineyards, and their numbers grew until they became strong nations.

STORY 6

A MAN WHO HEARD AND OBEYED GOD'S CALL

Gen. 11: 27—12: 20

The people who moved away from Babel into different parts of the world did not pray to God. Their hearts were sinful, and they shrank away from the purity of God, like Adam and Eve did when they tried to hide from God's presence in the Garden of Eden. But we find that the people prayed to something. In every country where they went they had some kind of worship. Many of them worshiped things that God had made, such as the sun, the moon, and the stars. Afterward they also worshiped rivers and mountains and hills. They made images of wood and of stone to these things which they worshiped, and called the images gods. And so there was the sun-god, which they called Shä'-mäsh, and the moon-god, which they called Ur, besides many others.

Not far from the city of Babel, where the tower was left unfinished, another city was built. This city was called Ur of the Chăl'-dêeś, because it was built in the home country of the Chăl-de'-ăn people. These people worshiped the moon-god, Ur, and when they built their great city they named it in honor of their god. And so the moon-god became famous and was worshiped by the Chăl-de'-ăns everywhere.

On the plains near Ur lived an old man who was a shepherd-farmer, that is, he tilled the soil and also raised large flocks of sheep and herds of cattle. His name was Tē'-räh. He had three grown sons, and their names were Abram, Nahor, and Hâr-ăn. They were also shepherd-farmers. Hâr-ăn did not live to be very old. When he died he left a son named Lot.

Now, Abram the son of Tē'-räh was a good man. He did not worship the moon-god as did his neighbors and friends and kinsfolk. He believed in the true God. He built altars and brought offerings to sacrifice to God just as Abel and Noah had done long years before. And his offerings pleased God, and his prayers were heard.

One day Abraham heard the voice of God calling to him. He listened. God told him to gather together his family and his flocks and herds, bid farewell to his neighbors and friends, and start out on a long journey. God promised to lead him to a land far away, where he would bless him and make his name great. His children and their children in the generations to come God promised to bless, and to make into a great nation. And through them God promised to give a blessing to all families in the world.

Perhaps Abram did not understand the meaning of all God's promise. He did not know that in the years to come a Savior should be born among the people of his own family, who would then be called the Jews. This Savior, we know, is the blessing which God promised to give to all families in the world, if Abram would obey his voice.

Although Abram did not know these things, nor even the country to which God wished to lead him, he was not afraid to go. So he took all his family—his wife, whose name was Sâr′-ā-ī, his aged father, Tĕ′räh, his brother Nahor and his wife, and the young son of his dead brother Hâr′-ăn. They and their servants Abram urged to start out with

ABRAM LISTENING TO GOD

him on his journey. And they took all their possessions too—the tents in which they lived, and the large flocks of sheep and herds of cattle.

Day after day they journeyed up the great River Ēu-phrā′-tēs until they came to a place called Hâr′-ăn. Here they stopped to rest, and here Abram's aged father died and was buried. Even before that God spoke to Abram and urged him to continue his journey. But Nahor, Abram's brother, was unwilling to go farther, so he remained at Hâr′-ăn and made his home at that place.

After this Abram made a second start. Now he took only his wife, Sâr′-ā-ī, his nephew Lot, and their servants. Driving their flocks and herds before them, they turned away from the great river and journeyed southwest, toward the land of Canaan. On one side of them the mountains rose wild and high, while on the other side, as far as they could see, the barren desert stretched away toward the south. On and on they traveled—across rivers, through valleys, over hills—each day farther from their homeland and nearer to the land which God had promised. We do not know how many days and weeks and months passed by before they came to the plain of Mō′-rēh, where God spoke again to Abram. "This is the land," God told him, "that I will give to you and to your children." And Abram built an altar there and worshiped God.

Now, this land of promise was called Canaan, because the Canaanite people lived in it. These people had been there for a long time and had built some towns and cities. Abram did not live among the Canaanite people, but pitched his tents out on the hills or plains, wherever he could find grass for his cattle and sheep to eat and water for them to drink. All the while his flocks and herds grew larger, until finally Abram became very rich.

Then there came a famine in the land. The grass failed and the waters of the brooks dried up. Nowhere could Abram find pasture, so he moved away from Canaan into the country called Egypt. Here he saw the great River Nile, and possibly even the pyramids and the sphinx. But he did not remain long in Egypt, because God did not want him to dwell there. When the famine ended in Canaan, he returned again to that country.

———◆———

STORY 7

HOW ABRAM ENDED A QUARREL

Genesis 13

After Abram returned from Egypt, he and Lot journeyed to the place where they had first pitched their tents in Canaan. There Abram had built an altar to worship God. At the very same place he now sacrificed another offering, and again talked to God.

Abram was now a very rich man. Not only did he possess many servants, flocks, and herds, but he also possessed much silver and gold. And we find that his nephew Lot owned many servants and sheep and cattle too. Wherever these men and their servants pitched their tents, the place looked like a tent-town. And the country all around them would be dotted with cattle and sheep.

After some time trouble arose between the servants of Abram and Lot. Some of Abram's servants were caretakers of his cattle and sheep. They and the servants who cared for Lot's flocks quarreled. Abram's servants wanted the best pasture-land for Abram's flocks, and Lot's servants wanted that same land for their master's flocks. And so the trouble grew. By and by news of the quarrel reached the ears of Abram. He looked out over the crowded country and saw how hard it must be for the servants. How could they always find places near by where tender grasses grew and where water was plentiful! He saw, too, the villages of the Canaanites not far away, and he knew there was not room enough in that part of the country for all to dwell together peaceably.

So Abram called Lot and said, "Let there be no quarrel between us, or between our servants. There is not room enough for both of us to dwell together with our flocks and herds. But see, the whole land lies before us. Let us separate. If you choose to go to the west country, then I shall journey east; but if you desire the east country, then I shall go west."

From the height upon which Abram and Lot stood to view the country they could see far to the east and to the west. Because Abram was the one to whom God had promised all this land he could have chosen the better part, or he could have sent Lot and his servants away out of the land altogether. But Abram was not selfish. He kindly offered Lot the first choice. And Lot, forgetting the kindness of his uncle, thought only of his own interests and chose the east country, through which the Jordan River flowed. "I can always find plenty of grass and water there," he reasoned, "and my flocks and herds will grow in number until soon I shall become very rich, too."

After Lot departed with his possessions, God spoke again to Abram. Perhaps God saw that Abram felt lonely. So he comforted him by reminding him of the promise that the whole of Canaan's land should belong to him and to his children. As yet Abram and Sâr'-ā-ī had no children, but God said that some day the children of their grandsons and great-grandsons should be many. And Abram believed God. God also told Abram to journey through the length and breadth of Canaan's land to see how large a country is was. So Abram moved away from the place where he and Lot had lived together for the last time, and came to a plain called Măm'-rē. Here he pitched his tents under the oak-trees near the city of Hē'-brŏn, and then built another altar to worship God.

STORY 8

HOW LOT'S CHOICE BROUGHT TROUBLE

Genesis 14

When Lot selected the fertile plains of Jordan for his share of Canaan's land, he thought he was making a wise choice. He saw in the distance the large cities of the plain, called Sodom and Gō-mŏr'-răh. He knew that in those cities he could sell sheep and cattle from his flocks and herds, and soon have much silver and gold. So he moved toward Sodom. After a while he pitched his tents still nearer the city walls, and finally he moved his family inside the gate.

Now, Sodom was not a nice place for good people to live. The people of Sodom cared nothing about God. Some of them were very rich, and perhaps they had beautiful homes. But they had unlovely hearts.

ABRAM GIVING LOT HIS CHOICE OF THE LAND

SIDON, ANCIENT CITY OF THE CANAANITES

The crowded old world city of Sidon, its white, flat-topped roofs, and its alabaster minarets, gleaming against the blue of the Mediterranean, ever fascinates the traveler. The trades of dyer, weaver, sweetmeat maker, iron monger, rope-spinner, baker, and shipbuilder, are still pursued as in the days of Abraham. Sidon is described in Gen. 10:15-19 as the western boundary of the land to which Abraham was called.

The Bible tells us that the men of Sodom were wicked and great sinners in God's sight. But in Lot's sight they were rich men, and clever, and so he brought his family to dwell among them. This was a sad mistake.

One day trouble came upon Sodom. There had been war in the land and the kings of Sodom, Gō-mŏr'-răh, and three other cities had gone out to battle. The army against which they fought defeated them. Then the conquering soldiers entered the gates of Sodom and of Gō-mŏr'-răh, crowded through the streets, and pushed their way into rich men's houses, taking everything that they could find to carry away. They even took people and led them away to become slaves. And Lot with his wife and children were taken with the others.

One of the captured men escaped and fled across the country to the place near Hē'-brŏn where Abram lived. He told about the battle and what had happened to Lot. When Abram heard of Lot's trouble, he took three hundred and eighteen of his men servants and, with some friends, hurried in pursuit of the captives. After a long, hard march across the country they came upon the enemy's camp at a place in the north of Canaan, called Dan. It was night, and the unsuspecting enemies lay asleep. Abram and his men rushed upon them and frightened them. They thought a great army had come to fight against them, and they were not prepared for a battle. So they rose up in haste and ran away, leaving behind their tents and all the goods and the people which they had taken away from Sodom and Gō-mŏr'-răh.

This was a great victory for Abram. The people of Canaan honored him for his courage, and the king of Sodom went out to meet him. He offered Abram all the gold and silver and food and clothing that he had taken away from the enemy's camp, and asked only that the people be returned again to Sodom. But Abram would not accept any reward from the king, because he had promised God that he would not keep anything for himself. And so all the people and their possessions were again returned to their homes.

Another king also came out to meet Abram. His name was Mĕl-chĭz'-ĕd-ĕk, and he was king of Sā'-lĕm, a place which was later called Jerusalem. Mĕl-chĭz'-ĕd-ĕk was different from the other people of Canaan because he loved the true God and worshiped him. He was a priest of God. When this king met Abram he brought food for him, and then he asked God to bless Abram. He also thanked God for giving Abram such a great victory.

Because Mĕl-chĭz'-ĕd-ĕk was a priest of the true God, Abram gave him a tenth of all the goods he had taken from the enemy's camp.

ABRAM RESCUING LOT

After this experience, Lot took his wife and children and went back again to live in wicked Sodom; but Abram returned to his quiet tent-home under the oak-trees near Hḗ'-brŏn.

———— • ————

STORY 9

THINGS THAT HAPPENED INSIDE AND OUTSIDE ABRAM'S TENT-HOME

Genesis 15—17

Abram was now growing old. Although he had great riches and many servants, yet he had no children. One night while he lay asleep in his tent-home, God appeared to him in a vision. "Do not be afraid," God told him, "for I will protect you, and will give you a great reward because you are faithful."

"What will you give me for a reward?" Abram asked. And God answered that some day Abram should have a son. Then, at God's bidding, Abram rose up and went outside his tent door and looked up at the starlit heavens. "The children of your family," God told Abram, "shall some day be as many as the stars—so many that no one can count them." Abram understood by this that God was speaking of the people who should some day possess Canaan's land, for they should be Abram's descendants. And he believed in the Lord, although he could not see even the beginning of that great family of promise.

God also caused Abram to understand that there would be a time when the children of his family should become slaves in a strange land, and should dwell there for four hundred years. After that they should again return to Canaan, and possess the land for their own. We shall see in later stories how this came to pass.

We remember that at one time Abram and his household jour neyed into Egypt, during a famine in the land of Canaan. When they returned to Canaan they brought with them an Egyptian servant-girl named Hā'-gär. They taught Hā'-gär to know about the true God and to listen if he should speak to her. And they expected her to work faithfully for them, as good servants should.

One day Hā'-gär did not please her mistress, Sâr'-ā-ī. This was wrong, and Sâr'-ā-ī punished her severely. Hā'-gär became very unhappy, until finally she decided to run away.

Now, running away is never an easy thing to do, and as Hā'-gär hastened along the sandy, desert road she grew very tired. So she stopped to rest by a fountain of water along the roadside. In this lonely place, in the deep wilderness, some one found her. It was an angel of the Lord.

"Hā'-gär, Sâr'-ā-ī's maid, where did you come from? and where are you going?" the angel inquired.

"I am fleeing from my mistress," Hā'-gär replied, "because I am unhappy."

"Return again," the angel said, "and try to please Sâr'-ā-ī. After a while God will give you a little son. He shall grow up to be a strong man, and he shall be called Ĭsh'-mā-ĕl."

Hā'-gär knew it was a messenger from God who spoke to her. And she knew now that she could never run away from God, because he had seen her all the while. So she obeyed the angel's word and returned again to her mistress. Afterward that fountain of water in the wilderness where the angel found her was called Beêr-lā'-hâi-rôi, a word which means, "A well of the Living One who sees me."

So after Hā'-gär returned to Sâr'-ā-ī's tent-home, God gave her the child he had promised. Abram named him Ish'-mā-ĕl, which means, "God hears." And Hā'-gär remembered that this was the name by which the angel had said the child should be called. Abram loved Ĭsh'-mā-ĕl; but Ĭsh'-mā-ĕl was not the child that God had promised to give to him. We shall learn more about Hā'-gär and Ĭsh'-mā-ĕl by and by.

The years passed on until Abram was nearly one hundred years old. Then God spoke to him again. Abram fell on his face and listened. God said, "I will make a covenant with you." Now, a covenant is a promise between two persons, each one agreeing to do something for the other. In this covenant God promised to give Abram a son and Abram promised to serve God faithfully. Then God said, "Your name shall no more be called Abram, but Abraham, which means, 'The father of many,' and your wife, Sâr'-ā-ī, shall be called 'Sarah,' which means, 'Princess.'"

STORY 10

STRANGE VISITORS AT ABRAHAM'S TENT-HOME

Genesis 18

It was noonday, and everywhere the sun shone hot upon the plains. But Abraham sat in the cool shade of his tent door, beneath a tree. Presently three strange men drew near. They did not look like other men, and Abraham knew they were from a far country. He hurried out to meet them, and, bowing low toward the ground just as he always did when greeting a friend or a visitor, he urged them to rest for a while in the cool shade. This they were quite ready to do.

Now we shall see how Abraham entertained his guests. First he sent for water to wash their feet. This was not unusual because people wore sandals in that long-ago time and is was customary for them to remove their sandals and wash their feet whenever they sat down to rest and visit. Next, Abraham told his wife to make ready and bake some barley cakes upon the hearth, while he should prepare some meat, for his guests. Then he ran out to his herd and selected a young calf, which he gave to a servant to dress and cook. When all was ready, he brought the food to his guests, and they ate while he stood under a tree near by. Abraham was glad to serve these strangers because he was kind to every one.

When the meal was ended, the men arose to continue their journey. Abraham walked with them for a little way. By this time he knew they were not like other men, but they were heavenly beings. Two of them were angels. The other one was the Lord. And Abraham felt that he was unworthy to entertain such wonderful visitors. But because he was a good man the Lord loved him.

"Shall I hide from Abraham this thing which I do?" the Lord asked his companions. "I know that he will teach his children to keep my ways and to do right."

Then, turning toward Abraham the Lord said, "I am going to visit Sodom and Gō-mŏr'-răh to see if these cities are as wicked as they seem, for the cry of their sins has reached me."

The two men hurried on; but Abraham detained the Lord a while longer, because he wanted to talk to him. He knew the Lord would destroy the cities if he found them to be as wicked as they seemed, and he thought of Lot. Now, we remember that Lot had gone back to live again in Sodom after Abraham and his servants had rescued him and his family from the enemy's camp. Abraham knew that Lot too might perish if the cities should be destroyed. And he loved Lot. He wished once more to try to save him, so he said, "Will you destroy the righteous persons in the city, will you not spare the lives of all for their sake?" And the Lord promised to spare Sodom if he could find fifty righteous persons in it.

Abraham feared that there might be less than fifty. And he was troubled for Lot's safety. So he spoke again. "I know that I am but a common man, made of dust," said he, "yet I speak to the Lord. If there should be only forty-five righteous persons living in Sodom, will you spare the city?'' And the Lord said he would spare Sodom for the sake of only forty-five righteous persons.

Still Abraham felt troubled. He feared there might not be even forty-five. So he asked if the city might be spared for the sake of forty. The Lord knew it was Abraham's love for the people which caused him to plead so earnestly for Sodom, and he promised to spare the city for the sake of forty.

"What," thought poor, distressed Abraham, "if there should not be even forty righteous persons found in Sodom?'' And once more he spoke. "O Lord, be not angry with me," he said, "but if there are only thirty righteous persons, will you spare the city for their sakes?'' And the Lord promised to spare the entire city if only thirty righteous people could be found in it. Abraham continued to plead until he had asked the Lord if he would spare the city if only ten righteous persons were found, and the Lord promised to spare Sodom if he could find only ten. Then the Lord passed on, and Abraham returned to his tent.

———————

STORY 11

WHAT HAPPENED TO SODOM

Genesis 19

The long shadows of evening-time were stealing over the hills and through the valleys, and everywhere people were hurrying toward home. Soon the city gates would be closed, and the wise men who sat there during the daytime to judge the people would be turning homeward, too.

Among the wise men who sat in Sodom's gate was Lot. On this evening he saw two strangers approaching, and he greeted them with a low bow, just as Abraham had greeted these same men earlier in the day. For they were no other than the angels who had dined with the Lord at Abraham's tent. Lot invited them to his home to spend the night, but they said they would stay out in the streets. Now, Lot knew the wicked men of Sodom would try to harm them if they remained in the streets, so he urged them to come with him. Finally they consented.

Here again the angels were entertained with hospitality, which may have reminded them of Abraham's kindness, for Lot brought water to wash their dusty feet and prepared good things for them to eat. Possibly Lot did not yet know that they were heavenly beings;

but he thought they were strangers unlike the wicked men who lived in
that city.

Soon the news spread all over Sodom that Lot had two strange-
looking visitors at his home, and men came hurrying from every part
of the city to see them. They planned to hurt them. But when Lot refused to let them see his guests, they pushed him aside and tried to

LOT AND HIS DAUGHTERS FLEEING FROM SODOM

break open the door. At this the angels drew Lot quickly inside, and
then smote the men with blindness.

Now Lot knew that his visitors were angels, and that they had
come to destroy Sodom because it was such a wicked place. He went
out to the homes of his sons-in-law, two men of Sodom, and told them
that the Lord was going to destroy their city. But they would not believe his words. And they would not listen when he told them to hurry
and escape for their lives. So the night passed by.

When the early morning came, before the sun lightened the earth,
the angels urged Lot and his wife and their two daughters to make

haste and flee out of the city lest they also be destroyed. How hard it seemed for Lot to leave his home and his riches to be destroyed! But God was merciful to him, and the angels seized him and his family and dragged them outside the city. Then they bade them flee to the mountains for their lives, and not even pause long enough to take a backward glance toward their old home, because God would soon destroy the cities of that rich valley, and unless they hurried away they too should perish. But Lot's wife did not obey the angel's words. She looked back, and her body became changed into a pillar of salt.

Poor, unhappy Lot! fear now tormented him from every direction. He thought his life would not be safe even in the mountains, for wild animals might devour him there. So he prayed to God to spare a small city near by and allow him and his daughters to enter that place. God heard his prayer and granted his request, so they fled into that city. That place was called Zō'-är, which means little.

Just as the sun rose, Lot and his daughters entered the gate of Zō'-är, and at that time God sent a great rain of fire and brimstone upon Sodom and Gō-mŏr'-räh and all the neighboring cities. So terrible was the fire that it completely destroyed the cities and all the wicked people near by. Lot and his daughters feared that their lives were not safe in Zō'-är, so they hurried to the mountains, where God had first told them to go. There they lived in a cave-home, far away from other people. After this time we hear no more about Lot, the man whose home and riches were destroyed because he chose to live among wicked people who hated God.

STORY 12

THE LITTLE BOY WHO BECAME A GREAT HUNTER
Gen. 20—21:21

After the destruction of Sodom and the other cities of the plain, Abraham moved away from Hē'-brŏn. He journeyed south and west, into the land of the Philistines, near the Great Sea, and made his home in a place called Gē'-rär. Here he lived only a short time when God gave to him and Sarah the child of promise. Abraham named the child Isaac (a word meaning, in his language, ''laughing'') because both he and Sarah had laughed when God told them that they should have a son in their old age.

When the baby Isaac grew old enough to toddle about his tent-home, and to lisp words, his father Abraham made a great feast for him. Perhaps many friends were invited, and every one knew that Isaac's parents thought he was a very wonderful little boy indeed. Before the day passed, however, something happened which brought sadness to the kind heart of Abraham.

You remember that Ĭsh'-mā-ĕl, the son of Hā'-gär, Sarah's maid, also lived in Abraham's tent. These two boys, Ĭsh'-mā-ĕl and Isaac, may have played together sometimes, although Ĭsh'-mā-ĕl was much older than Abraham's little son. On this feast-day, when everybody else was happy, Ĭsh'-mā-ĕl was unkind to Isaac. Perhaps he felt jealous of the honor that Isaac was receiving from so many people.

When Sarah heard how unkindly Ĭsh'-mā-ĕl had treated her little boy she became angry, and called Abraham. ''You must send Ĭsh'-mā-ĕl and his mother away,'' she told him, ''for I do not want our little boy to grow up with such a rude companion.'' Now, Abraham loved Ĭsh'-mā-ĕl too, and he felt sad to hear that the boy had mistreated his son. He thought that Ĭsh'-mā-ĕl might learn to be kind; but God told him to send the boy and his mother away, just as Sarah had said.

So the next morning Abraham called Hā'-gär and told her that she must take Ĭsh'-mā-ĕl and go away. He gave her food for the journey and placed upon her shoulder a bottle filled with water. This bottle was not made of glass, but of the skin of an animal; for people used skin-bottles in that long-ago time. Then Abraham bade them good-by, and perhaps he watched them as they started toward the land of Egypt, where Hā'-gär used to live when she was a little girl.

The road to Egypt led through the same desert where the angel spoke to Hā'-gär when she had run away from Sarah's tent. On this second journey Hā'-gär missed the road and wandered off into the trackless wilderness. She did not know which way to take; and after a while there was no more food in her basket nor water in the bottle which Abraham had given. And the hot sun beamed down upon the dry, burning sand all day, until Hā'-gär and Ĭsh'-mā-ĕl grew so thirsty, faint, and weak that they could go no farther. Then Hā'-gär laid her suffering boy beneath the shade of a little bush, and went away. ''I can not bear to see him suffer and die,'' she said, and then she wept.

But God had not forgotten about Hā'-gär and her boy. Just as he had seen her on her first journey into the wilderness, so he could see her now as she sat weeping all alone. And soon she heard a voice calling to her out of heaven, ''What is the cause of your sorrow, Hā'-gär? Do not be afraid, for God has heard Ĭsh'-mā-ĕl's cry of pain, and he will save his life and make of him a great nation. Go, now, and lift him up.'' Then Hā'-gär saw a spring of water which God caused to bubble out of the dry ground near by, and she quickly filled her empty bottle and gave Ĭsh'-mā-ĕl a drink.

After this Hā'-gär and Ĭsh'-mā-ĕl did not journey on to Egypt, but made their home in the wilderness, far from other people. God cared for them, and Ĭsh'-mā-ĕl grew to be a strong, wild man. He became a hunter, and used a bow and arrow. His children also grew up in the wilderness, and were wild and strong like their father. They finally were called Arabians, and even today their descendants live in the desert and wander about wherever they please, just as Ĭsh'-mā-ĕl, their forefather, did so long ago.

STORY 13

HOW ABRAHAM GAVE ISAAC BACK TO GOD
Gen. 22: 1-20

It is God's will that people show their love for him by what they do. You remember how God wished to have the first man and woman show their love for him. He planted in their garden-home a test-tree, the fruit of which he commanded them not to eat. And you remember also how they failed to obey his command, and so failed to show their love.

Abraham always listened to God's voice and obeyed. He left his own people and his homeland to journey into a country that he did not know, because God called him. And in our last story he sent Ĭsh'-mā-ĕl and Hā'-gär away because God told him to do as Sarah had said. Even when it did not seem easy to obey, Abraham was always ready to do God's bidding.

After the baby Isaac came into Abraham's life, God saw that Abraham's love for the little boy was very strong. And the passing years increased this love, because Abraham knew that Isaac was the child God had promised, and he loved Isaac as a gift from God. He looked forward to the time when Isaac should become a man and should have children also, and he knew that these children should grow up and become the fathers of more people, because God had told him these things. And so whenever he looked upon Isaac and thought about these things, he knew that in this child were bound up all the promises of God for the coming years.

By and by the time came when Isaac grew far away from babyhood into youth. Abraham had taught him to know about God and to worship him. Perhaps he had taken Isaac with him when he offered gifts upon the altar, and he had told Isaac that God would accept the gifts and hear his prayers if he would try to do right. And Isaac loved his father Abraham, and was obedient to him.

When God saw how dearly Abraham loved his son, and how obedient and loving Isaac was toward his father, he thought, "I must prove Abraham this once more, and see whether he loves me better than he loves the gift-child I have given." So he called to Abraham one day, and Abraham answered, "Behold, here am I." Then God said, "Take your son, your only son, Isaac, whom you love so much, and go into the land of Mō-rī'-ăh. There give him back to me as an offering upon an altar, which you must build at the place I will show."

Abraham did not know the reason why God should ask him ᴜᴜ give Isaac back as an offering. He could not understand how the promises concerning Isaac would be fulfilled if now he must offer Isaac upon an altar, just like the lambs which he had given to God at other times. But Abraham believed that God understood why, and so he was not afraid to obey.

The land of Mō-rī'-ăh was some distance from Abraham's tent, and the journey there would require a few days' time. Abraham knew this, and he prepared to start at once. He called two young men servants and Isaac, then saddled his donkey, and they started away. They took wood and fire with which to burn the offering, and traveled on and on for two days, sleeping at night under the trees. On the third day Abraham saw the mountain where God wanted him to build the altar and offer his gift. He left the servants with the donkey to wait by the road-side, while he and Isaac should go on alone. Isaac carried the wood upon his shoulder, and Abraham took the vessel containing the fire.

As they climbed the mountain-side together, Isaac began to wonder why his father had forgotten to bring a lamb for an offering. He did not know what God had asked Abraham to give. He did not understand why they were going so far from home to build the altar. So he said, "My father, see, here is wood and fire for the altar, but where is the lamb for an offering?" Abraham replied, "God will provide himself a lamb."

When they reached the place God had appointed, Abraham built an altar, laid the wood upon it, and then bound Isaac's hands and feet and placed him upon the wood. Next he took his knife, and was about to kill Isaac when a loud voice called to him out of the sky, "Abraham! Abraham!" The old man stopped to listen, and the angel of God said to him, "Do not harm Isaac. Now I know that you love God even better than you love your child. Untie his hands and his feet, and let him go." At this Abraham saw a ram caught by its horns in a thicket near by. He took this animal and offered it as a gift to God instead of offering his son Isaac.

Afterward the angel called to Abraham from the sky again, and said, "Because you have not withheld your dearly loved child from

ABRAHAM AND ISAAC ON THE MOUNTAIN

me, I will surely bless you and will cause your descendants to be as many as the stars in the heavens and as the sands upon the seashore. And I will bless all the nations of the earth through your descendants, because you have obeyed my voice."

No doubt it was a happy father and son who walked down the mountain-side together; for now Abraham knew that

he had surely pleased God, and Isaac knew that his life was precious in God's sight. Abraham called the name of the place where he built the altar, Jĕ-hō'-văh-jī'-rēh, which means in his language, "The Lord will provide." Then they returned to the young men servants who were waiting by the roadside, and then journeyed on to their home at Beer-shē'-bă, where Abraham had planted trees and digged a well some time before this story. Here Abraham lived for many years.

———————•———————

STORY 14

HOW ABRAHAM FOUND A WIFE FOR ISAAC
Gen. 23 : 1—25 : 18

When Sarah, Isaac's mother, was one hundred and twenty-seven years old, she died. Abraham had no place to bury her, so he bought a field from a Hittite who was named Ē'-phrŏn. The field contained a cave such as the people of Canaan used for burial-places, and Abraham buried Sarah in this cave. The field and the cave were called by the name of Măch-pē'-läh.

After Sarah's death, Abraham and Isaac felt lonely. Isaac was now grown to manhood, and Abraham thought he was old enough to be married. The parents usually choose wives for their sons, and husbands for their daughters, in those countries, and Abraham wished to choose a good wife for Isaac. He knew that the women who lived in Canaan were idol-worshipers, and that they would not teach their children to love and to worship the true God. Because he wanted Isaac's children to serve God, he would not choose a young woman of Canaan to be Isaac's wife.

Then Abraham remembered the news that had come to him from his brother Nahor, who lived at Hâr'-ăn, the place in the country of Měs-ŏ-pŏ-tā'-mĭ-ă where he had stopped on his journey to Canaan, and where his aged father had died. Nahor, he had been told, was now the father of twelve sons, some of whom had married and become fathers also. "Perhaps I can send back to my own people at Hâr'-ăn," thought Abraham, "and find among them a wife for Isaac." So he called his trusted servant, Ĕl-ĭ-ē'-zĕr, told him about his desire, and asked him to journey back to Hâr'-ăn and try to find a God-fearing wife for Isaac.

Ĕl-ĭ-ē'-zĕr knew that such a journey would require many days' time and would be attended by many dangers along the way. He knew, too, that Abraham's people might not be willing to send a daughter so far from home to become the wife of a man whom they had never met. But because he was a faithful servant and loved his master, Abraham, Ĕl-ĭ-ē'-zĕr said, "I will go."

Then the long journey began. Ĕl-ĭ-ē'-zĕr took with him ten camels, several attendant servants, and many valuable presents. For days and days they traveled, crossing valleys, hills, and rivers, and edging alongside the great, lonely desert. By and by they came to the land of Měs-ŏ-pŏ-tā'-mĭ-ă, to the northern part, called Pā'-dăn-âr'-ăm, and then at last their tired camels stopped outside the city of Hâr'-ăn and knelt down near a well.

It was evening time, and the women of the city were coming to this well to fill their pitchers with water. Ĕl-ĭ-ē'-zĕr had learned to trust in Abraham's God, and now he lifted up his heart and prayed that God would send out to this well the young woman who would be suitable for Isaac's wife. "Let it come to pass, O Lord," he prayed, "that the young woman of whom I shall ask a drink may offer to draw water for my camels also. By this sign I shall know that she is the one whom you have chosen, for Abraham's sake, to be the wife of Isaac.''

While Ĕl-ĭ-ē′-zĕr was praying, a beautiful young woman approached, with an earthen pitcher upon her shoulder. Ĕl-ĭ-ē′-zĕr waited until she had filled the pitcher with water, then he asked for a drink. Although he was a stranger, she spoke kindly to him and said she would draw water for his camels also.

Again and again she filled her pitcher and poured its contents into the trough that the thirsty animals might drink. When she had done this, Ĕl-ĭ-ē′-zĕr gave her some of the beautiful presents that he had brought, and asked whose d a u g h t e r she was and whether her people could supply lodging for him and for his camels. At her reply that she was the granddaughter of Nahor, Abraham's brother, Ĕl-ĭ-ē′-zĕr knew that his prayer had been answered, and he bowed his h e a d and worshiped God. Then Rebekah—for this was the young woman's name — told Ĕl-ĭ-ē′-zĕr that there

ELIEZER MEETING REBEKAH AT THE WELL

was plenty of room in her father's house to lodge them all, and she hurried to tell what had happened at the well and to show the beautiful presents that Ĕl-ĭ-ē′-zĕr had given her.

When her brother Laban heard her story and saw the costly ornaments which Ĕl-ĭ-ē′-zĕr had given to Rebekah, he ran eagerly to meet the strangers at the well and to invite them to come in. ''We have room for you and for your camels,'' he told them, and they went with him into the city. Laban now showed the same kindness to his guests that Abraham and Lot had shown to their angel visitors. He first brought water to wash their feet and then set food before them.

But Ĕl-ĭ-ē′-zĕr could not eat. ''First let me tell why I have come,'' he said. "I am Abraham's servant, and God has blessed my master greatly, giving him flocks and herds, silver and gold, and many servants, besides camels and asses. God also gave to him and Sarah a son in their old age, and now Abraham has given all his great riches to his son. But as yet this son, Isaac, has no wife, and Abraham will not take a wife for him from the daughters of Canaan, because they worship idols. He has sent me, therefore, to you, his kinsfolk, to find a wife for Isaac." Ĕl-ĭ-ē'-zĕr told also how Rebekah had come to the well and how in answer to his prayer she had offered drink to him and to his thirsty animals.

Rebekah's father and brother Laban were willing to let her go back with Ĕl-ĭ-ē'-zĕr because they believed that God had sent him. And Rebekah, too, was willing to go. Ĕl-ĭ-ē'-zĕr was grateful to know of their willingness, and he bowed his head once more to worship the great God who had helped him on his journey. Afterward he enjoyed the feast which Rebekah's people had prepared for them. That same night he gave other presents of silver and gold and beautiful clothing to Rebekah, and to her mother and brother.

The next morning Ĕl-ĭ-ē'-zĕr said, "Now let me return to my master." Laban and his mother did not want to let Rebekah leave them so soon. "Can you not stay for a few more days?" they asked. But when Ĕl-ĭ-ē'-zĕr insisted that he must go at once, they called Rebekah, and she said, "I will go." So they bade her good-by and sent her away with her nurse and other attending maids.

On the homeward journey Rebekah and her maids rode the camels, and Ĕl-ĭ-ē'-zĕr led the way to Canaan. Very likely they traveled the same road that Abraham had traveled many years before, when he went with Sarah and Lot to the land that God had promised. At last they drew near to the place where Abraham and Isaac now lived. The evening shadows were stealing through the trees, and Isaac was out in the fields alone, thinking about God, when he saw the camels coming. He hurried to meet them, and Rebekah, seeing him, asked who he was. "This is my master, Isaac," Ĕl-ĭ-ē'-zĕr replied, and Rebekah alighted from her camel and covered her face with a veil.

When Isaac met them, Ĕl-ĭ-ē'-zĕr told how God had answered his prayers and had sent Rebekah to him. Isaac took her to his mother's tent, and she became his wife. He loved her, and did not grieve any more because of his mother's death.

The time passed on, and finally Abraham died, too. He had reached the age of one hundred and seventy-five. Ĭsh'-mā-ĕl heard of his death and came to help Isaac bury his father. They placed his body in the cave where Sarah had been buried. After that time Isaac became the possessor of all his father's wealth.

WHAT TWO BOYS THOUGHT ABOUT THEIR FATHER'S BLESSING

Gen. 25:19—27:41

After some years, a change took place in Isaac's home-life. Two children now played about his tent door—two little boys. They were his sons. One of them, the older, was named Esau. His hair was red and it grew all over his body. Although he was a queer-looking child, yet Esau was loved dearly by his father, Isaac. The younger boy was named Jacob. He was not at all like his brother, and it may have been because of his thoughtful actions that he was loved the better by his mother, Rebekah.

When Esau and Jacob grew older, their playtime hours grew less and they were taught to work. They learned to take care of their father's cattle and sheep. Esau was fond of hunting, and would often take his bow and arrow and go out to the woods in search of deer. Not only did he know how to kill the deer, but he knew also how to dress and cook the meat that he brought home from his hunting-trips. This pleased Isaac very much, and because he liked to eat the venison that Esau prepared he loved Esau better than he loved Jacob.

There is a custom among the people of those lands to give the eldest son twice as much of the property upon the death of the father as the other children receive. This is called the "birthright." And Esau, being Isaac's eldest son, was entitled to the birthright.

But the boy Esau cared little about his birthright. He even despised it. His younger brother, Jacob, thought much about the birthright and wished that it might be given to him instead of to Esau. He knew that he should be glad to receive his father's blessing and the double portion of all his wealth, and even the tents in which they lived, and the servants who belonged to his father's household.

One day when Esau came home from his work in the field he saw that Jacob had just prepared a dish of tempting food. And he was very hungry, so he asked Jacob to give him at once some of the food to eat. Jacob answered, "I will give it all to you if you will sell me your birthright today." Esau grew hungrier than ever when he smelled

SUNSET ON THE RIVER NILE

It is flood season on the Nile. The bright evening sun of Egypt is painting with red gold its broad expanse of water and setting off in relief the towers and palm trees of the city of Cairo. Here is the traditional spot where the infant Moses, having been placed for safety in a tiny ark among the reeds by the river's bank, was found by the daughter of Pharaoh. The children of Israel (Jacob) were slaves in this land, and Moses became their deliverer.

ISAAC BLESSING JACOB

the good food in Jacob's dish, and he cared more for his appetite than he did for his birthright. "What can this birthright profit me, anyhow," he questioned, "seeing that I am certain to die anyway?" So he sold his birthright for something to eat. Now, it was very wrong for Esau to despise the good things that Isaac had planned to give to him. And after it was too late to buy back the lost birthright, Esau became very sorry for what he had done.

The years passed by, and Isaac moved into another part of the country. Here he planted fields of grain, and God caused them to yield an abundant harvest. God also blessed him more by increasing his riches until he became so great that his neighbors envied him. They thought he was a mighty prince among them, and they did not care to have him live in their country because he was so much greater than they. Isaac chose rather to go away than to have trouble with his neighbors, so he gathered together all his wealth and all his servants, and moved once more to another part of Canaan. Here he built an altar and worshiped God. Afterward his servants dug a well and found good water. Then Isaac called the name of the place Bēer-shē'-bă.

Isaac lived at Bēer-shē'-bă for a long time, and finally his eyes grew dim with age. No longer could he look out upon the good things that God had given him, and he thought that soon he must die. He wished to give the birthright and his blessing to Esau. Perhaps he did not remember that God had promised the birthright to Jacob, or he may have forgotten about the incident because he was now old and feeble. He called Esau, and said, "My son, take your bow and arrow and go into the woods and hunt one more deer and bring to me the delicious food that you can prepare. After I have eaten of it I shall give you my blessing, for I am soon to die."

Esau hurried away at his father's bidding. He was older now and wished that he had not sold his birthright. But he had done other things that were not right, for he had married two wives who were Canaanitish women, and this had grieved Isaac and Rebekah very much.

Rebekah did not think that Esau was worthy to receive his father's blessing. She wanted her younger son, Jacob, to become heir to God's promises, and when she heard Isaac's instructions to Esau she thought of a plan by which she might secure the promised blessing for Jacob. "My husband can not see," she reasoned, "and I will send Jacob to him instead of Esau. I will cook the tender meat of two young kids, and season the food just as Esau prepares it. Then I will clothe Jacob in Esau's raiment and thus cause my blind husband to think that Esau has come."

At first Jacob feared to try to deceive his dear old father lest his deception be found out and he should receive a curse instead of a blessing. But Rebekah urged him to obey her orders. "Let the sin be upon my own head," she declared, "for you must receive your father's blessing." And Jacob obeyed. But, although he secured the blessing, we shall see later how the sin of his deception fell upon his own head, because sin always reacts upon the evil-doer himself and brings trouble and sorrow.

Isaac was surprized when Jacob approached with the dish of food which Rebekah had prepared. He knew that Esau had not been absent long enough to hunt and kill a deer and then prepare the meat so soon. "How is it that you have come so soon?" he asked, and Jacob replied, "Your God helped me to find the deer at once." Still Isaac wondered how it could be that Esau had returned so much sooner than usual, and because the voice sounded like Jacob's he said, "Come near to me, that I may know whether you are indeed my very son Esau." Now Rebekah had fastened the skin of a hairy animal upon Jacob's hands and neck lest Isaac feel of them and discover the deception, and when the blind old man touched the hairy hands he said, "These are Esau's hands." Finally he ate of the delicious meat and then blessed Jacob with the blessing of his grandfather Abraham.

Esau came with his dish after Jacob had gone away. "Rise up, my father, and eat of my venison," he said, "then give me your blessing." "Who are you?" exclaimed Isaac in dismay; and when Esau replied, "I am your very son Esau," the old man trembled with fear. "Some one has come in your stead," he told Esau, "and to him I have given the blessing."

Esau knew at once that Jacob had secured the blessing which he craved. "Alas!" cried the poor man, "my brother has taken away both my birthright and my blessing." And Esau wept bitterly. "Have you not one blessing for me also?" he entreated. Isaac was deeply troubled. "How can I bless you, seeing that I have given the best of everything to your brother?" Still Esau pleaded for a blessing, and finally Isaac blessed him too, with a lesser promise of greatness.

After this time Esau's heart was filled with hatred toward his brother. "Soon our father will die," he thought, "and then I shall kill Jacob and take all the possessions and all the power which has been given to him." And with these wicked thoughts he consoled himself in his disappointment and grief.

STORY 16

JACOB'S LONELY JOURNEY AND HIS WONDERFUL DREAM

Gen. 27:42—29:12

When Rebekah heard of Esau's intention to kill his brother Jacob as soon as their father, Isaac, should die, she sent for Jacob at once. "You must prepare to go far away," she told him, "because Esau is angry and plans to kill you when your father dies. Let me send you to my brother, Laban, who lives at Hâr'-ăn. Remain there with him for a while, and possibly Esau will forget his anger and wicked plans. Then you can come back again to me; for why should I lose both you and your father?"

Rebekah did not tell Isaac about Esau's anger and about her fears for Jacob's safety. But now that she wanted to send Jacob back to her girlhood home in order to escape from Esau's anger she planned another reason for wishing to send him away. She came to her blind husband and said, "I am very unhappy because our son Esau has taken heathen women to become his wives. If Jacob should marry a daughter of our heathen neighbors, I should wish to die. Send him back to my brother's house, that he may take a wife from among my own people."

Isaac also had been grieved when Esau married women who were idol-worshipers. Now he thought, "God's promise which was first given to my father Abraham, then to me, will be given next to my son Jacob and to his children. If he should marry a heathen woman, then his children would not be taught to worship the true God. He must not marry a heathen woman!" So he called Jacob, and said, "Do not take a wife of the daughters of Canaan, but go back to Pā'-dăn-âr'-ăm and take there a wife from your mother's relatives. And God's blessing shall be upon you, and he shall give you the blessings of your grandfather Abraham."

Jacob then bade his mother and his blind old father good-by, and started out on his long journey. He took no camel to ride upon and no servant for a companion, but journeyed all alone. He feared his brother's wrath, and did not know whether he ever could return again to his home and feel safe. His birthright now could do him no good because the double portion of his father's wealth would not become his own until after his father's death, and if he should remain until that time he believed that his brother would surely kill him. Poor, discouraged Jacob! He must have felt unhappy indeed as he climbed the rocky hillslopes of Canaan and hurried away from the only home he had ever known. We do not know what his thoughts were as he traveled alone all the day, but perhaps he thought that Esau might try to overtake him and kill him before he should get far away. Perhaps he felt sorry because he had deceived his dear, old father, whom he might never see again. Perhaps he repented because he had bought Esau's birthright. Whatever may have been his thoughts as he walked along the dusty road, some One was listening to each and all of them. That One was God.

By and by the sun went down, and Jacob may have felt lonelier than ever with only the dark sky above him. But as he was now very tired, he chose a stone for his pillow, and, wrapping his cloak about him, lay down on the ground to sleep. While he slept he saw in a dream a wonderful ladder the top of which reached to heaven. He saw beautiful angels climbing up and down upon the ladder. And standing at the top he saw God. He dreamed that God spoke to him and said, "I am the God of your grandfather Abraham, and the God of your father Isaac. The land upon which you are lying I will give to you and to your descendants. And your descendants shall be many, as many as the particles of dust upon the earth. Through your family I will bless all the people of the earth. Now, I am with you, and will be with you wherever you go, and will protect you and bring you again to this land. I will never leave you until I have fulfilled this promise."

Jacob awoke from his dream and looked about. Although he saw no one, he felt sure that he was not alone, because the God of his father had promised to be with him. He arose early in the morning and took the stone that he had used for a pillow and set it upright. Then he poured some oil upon it, to consecrate it to God. He called the name of the place Bethel, which means, "The house of God." Then he made a vow and promised to give back to God a tenth of all that God should give him if indeed God would go with him and bless him as he had promised.

After this wonderful dream Jacob's heart must have felt lighter as he hurried on his way. And every day he drew nearer the end of his long, tiresome journey. Then one evening, after he had left the lonely desert far behind, he saw some men, in a field, near a well. Round about them three flocks of sheep were lying down and waiting to be watered. This sight may have reminded him of his father's flocks at home, which he had often cared for. He came nearer and spoke to the men. "Where are you from?" he asked; and when they replied that they were men of Hâr'-ăn he knew that at last he was near his uncle

Laban's home. "Do you know a man of Hâr'-ăn named Laban?" he asked eagerly, and they answered, "Yes, we know him; and, see, here comes his daughter Rachel with his sheep." Jacob saw a beautiful young shepherdess approaching and he hurried to meet her. He rolled the stone away from the well and watered her sheep, then told her that he was her cousin, the son of her father's sister, Rebekah. His joy upon seeing one of his relatives after such a long, lonely journey brought tears to Jacob's eyes and he wept as he kissed the beautiful girl.

No doubt Laban had told Rachel about the strange men who had come from his granduncle Abraham a long time ago and who had taken his sister to become the wife of Abraham's son, Isaac. And so

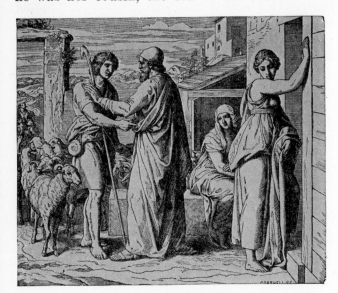

JACOB MEETING LABAN

Rachel hurried home to tell her father that his sister's son had arrived from Canaan and was now taking charge of his flock of sheep at the well.

STORY 17

HOW JACOB WAS DECEIVED BY LABAN
Gen. 29:13—31:55

When Rachel told her father, Laban, that Jacob had arrived, he hurried out to meet his nephew and to welcome him to his home. He was glad to hear tidings from his sister, Rebekah, and to speak face to face with her favorite son. At first he showed much kindness to Jacob.

As the days passed by Jacob willingly assisted his uncle at his work. Then at the end of the first month Laban said, "Let me pay you for your services. What do you ask for wages?" Jacob replied, "I will serve you faithfully for seven years if at the end of that time you will give me your beautiful daughter, Rachel, to be my wife." This may seem a strange request, but Jacob loved Rachel and wished to marry her. He loved her so much that to him the seven years of hard toil seemed only a few days.

At the end of the period of service Jacob reminded his uncle that the time for pay-day had arrived. Laban then arranged a marriage feast. He invited many friends to attend the wedding. In the evening he brought the bride to Jacob. A large veil was thrown about her that no one might look upon her face. This was the usual custom of those people, and even Jacob could not see the face of the woman he was taking to become his wife. Among some people this strange custom is still practised.

After the ceremony had ended and Jacob was permitted to see his wife's face he saw—not the beautiful Rachel, whom he loved so dearly and for whom he had toiled seven years, but her elder sister, Leah. Now Leah did not look beautiful to Jacob, and he had not loved her. He had not wanted to marry her. How unhappy he felt when he realized that his uncle had deceived him! Perhaps he remembered how he had deceived his blind father, and how he had cheated his brother out of the blessing. Now he was suffering from the same kind of sins that he himself had committed against others. And now he understood how painful it is to be deceived or cheated.

When Jacob demanded an explanation of the deception, Laban said that it was not customary in their country to allow the younger daughter to marry first. "If you will serve me for seven years longer, you may have Rachel also for your wife," Laban added; and because Jacob loved Rachel he decided to remain with his uncle for seven more years. We see that those people did not think it a sinful thing for one man to have several wives. Nowadays only very wicked men and heathen people allow such customs.

When the fourteen years had passed by, Jacob desired to return again to Canaan. But Laban was unwilling to let him go. "While you have been with me," he told Jacob, "the Lord has blessed me for your sake." When Jacob insisted that he needed to provide for his own family, Laban agreed to let him have a part of the cattle and sheep and goats. These Jacob separated from Laban's flocks and herds and placed in charge of his sons. He continued to have charge of

Laban's flocks, but kept his own at a distance of three days' journey from Laban's home. And God blessed Jacob and increased his possessions until soon he became rich. He bought camels and asses, and owned many servants. And God gave him eleven sons and one daughter.

When Jacob's riches increased, Laban's sons became envious of him. They said that he had gotten his riches dishonestly. Laban, too, began to feel unkindly toward him. Then the angel of God spoke to Jacob in a dream and comforted him. "I am the God of Bethel," the angel said, "where you anointed the stone, and where you made a vow to me. The time has come for you to return again to your people in Canaan. I will be with you."

Jacob remembered that Laban had been unwilling before to let him go when he expressed a desire to return to his father. Now he feared that Laban would not allow him to take his daughters, Leah and Rachel, to far-off Canaan, so he decided to go away secretly. He waited until Laban went to shear his sheep. Then he called Leah and Rachel out into the field and told them that their father no longer felt kindly toward him. He told them also that God had talked to him and had charged him to return again to Canaan. And they replied, "We are ready to go with you, for our father has sold us." They believed that God was with Jacob.

Busy days followed, in which Jacob prepared to start out on the long road over which he had traveled twenty years before. The sheep and the goats and the cattle and the camels and the asses were all collected from the fields where they had been grazing on the tender grass. The servants drove the animals, while Jacob's wives and children rode on camels. Across the fields they went, and onto the road which wound along the lonely wilderness, where wild mountains rose on the one side and dreary desert sand stretched far away on the other side. Finally they came to a camping-place in mount Gilead where they stopped to rest.

But we must not forget that things were happening back at Hâr′-ăn. Some one told Laban that Jacob had gone away and had taken all his possessions. Laban was angry because Jacob had departed, and still more vexed with him because he had stolen away in secret. "I shall overtake him," thought the angry man, and possibly he planned to compel Jacob to return again to Hâr′-ăn. He took with him several men and hurried in pursuit of Jacob's company. For seven days they followed fast, and at last they saw the tents which Jacob had pitched in mount Gilead. But before they reached the place God spoke to Laban and warned him not to harm Jacob.

This warning from God caused Laban to feel less angry toward Jacob, and soon their quarrel was ended. Afterward Jacob set up a stone for a pillar and the other men gathered stones together in a heap. Laban called this heap of stones Mizpah, which means, "A watch-tower." And he said to Jacob, "May God watch over us while we are absent from each other." Then, bidding his daughters and their children an affectionate farewell, he turned back toward his home at Hâr'-ăn, leaving Jacob and his family to continue their journey toward Canaan.

STORY 18

WHY JACOB'S NAME WAS CHANGED TO ISRAEL

Genesis 32—35

Although twenty years had passed since Jacob's flight from Canaan he had never forgotten the fear that had driven him to Hâr'-ăn. And the memory of that fear still troubled him—what if Esau should never forgive him?

God knew about Jacob's fear, and he sent a company of angels to meet him. After this Jacob felt more courageous and sent some messengers to his brother to announce his coming. He felt that unless Esau should welcome him home he could not be happy in Canaan.

But Esau no longer lived in Canaan. He had moved with his family to the country of E'-dom, which lies south and east of the Dead Sea. There the messengers found him and told him that Jacob was returning to Canaan. He sent word back with the messengers that he would come to meet Jacob. Four hundred men were coming with him.

This news from Esau troubled Jacob greatly. He thought that Esau was intending to kill him and his wives and children. He quickly divided his company into two bands and sent one before the other. But first he sent a valuable present of sheep and oxen, camels and asses to his brother, hoping thereby to arouse a kindly feeling in Esau's heart. After nightfall he moved his camp across the brook, and then returned alone. Then in the darkness a strange man took hold of him and wrestled all the night. Jacob wrestled earnestly, and neither of them gained advantage of the other. When the morning began to dawn Jacob saw that he had been wrestling with the angel of God. The angel said, "Let me go, for the day is breaking." But Jacob answered, "I will not let you go until you bless me." Then the angel asked, "What is your name?" and he said, "My name is Jacob."

Abram's Journey
to Canaan

ABRAM'S JOURNEY TO CANAAN

Abram lived in Ur of the Chaldees near the River Euphrates. His wife's name was Sarah. The people of Ur worshiped the Moon-God, but Abram worshiped the true God. God spoke to Abram and his father, Terah, and told them to go to a land he would show them. Lot, Abram's nephew, went with them. They journeyed up the Euphrates to Haran, where they lived for many years. Here Terah died.

God spoke to Abram again and told him he would be the father of a great nation. Abram left Haran and went to the Land of Canaan, Lot journeying with him. In this land, on the Plain of Moreh, they built an altar and worshiped God. Later they moved to Bethel, where another altar was built. There was strife between the herdsmen of Abram and Lot. Abram said to Lot, "Let there be no strife between us. Is not the whole land before you? Take what you choose and I will take the rest." Lot chose the plain of the Jordan near Sodom. Abram went farther south in Canaan to Hebron. One day three celestial visitors came to Abraham's tent at Hebron and told him Sodom would be burned. Because of the wickedness of this city, the Lord destroyed it.

Abraham lived at Hebron until his death at the age of 175 years.

The angel told him that his name should thereafter be Israel, because he had wrestled with God. Israel means, "A prince of God." When the angel departed, Jacob was crippled in his thigh, for the angel had struck his thigh. Jacob called the name of the place Pĕn'-ĭ-ĕl, which means, "The face of God," because there he saw God face to face and received the blessing that he sought.

THE ANGEL TELLING JACOB TO LET HIM GO

When the sun arose, Jacob crossed the brook and joined the company of his family again. And soon he saw his brother Esau coming to meet him. No doubt his heart beat fast as he arranged his wives and children in separate groups and then hurried forward to be the first to greet Esau. According to the custom of those people he bowed himself to the ground in a very humble manner as he approached his brother. Seven times he bowed thus, as those people do when they meet some great person. Then Esau rushed forward and embraced

Jacob very affectionately and kissed him. The two brothers wept for joy, and all the bitterness of the past seemed to be forgotten.

Afterward Jacob presented his wives and their children to his brother, and told him how God had blessed him while he lived at Hâr'-ăn.

Esau inquired about the animals that he had met, and Jacob told him that they were his present. Esau at first refused to accept them

HEBRON AS IT IS TODAY

because he, too, had much wealth; but finally he consented to take them as a gift from his brother.

After their short visit together, Esau returned again to his home in the land of E'-dom, and Jacob journeyed on to Ca-naan. At Shē'-chĕm he bought a field, where he built an altar and worshiped God. He felt very grateful because God had given him a safe journey from Hâr'-ăn. Later he moved to Bethel, at God's command, and built another altar in memory of the promise that God had given to him when he slept at that place while fleeing from his brother. God appeared to him again, and once more told him that he should be called Jacob no longer, but Israel. God also enlarged the promise that he had made concerning Jacob's descendants, and told him that kings should be born among them in the coming years.

From Bethel, Jacob and his family moved southward toward his old home at Hē'-brŏn, where his father, Isaac, still lived. Many years had passed since he had traveled that same road, alone and afraid; now he was returning to his father's house bringing with him enough servants to form two companies, besides his own family. Surely God had blessed him; and his heart was glad.

But before they arrived at Hē'-brŏn a sad thing happened. Rachel died, leaving a tiny baby boy, whom she had named Benjamin. Jacob buried her at Bethlehem, and set a pillar upon her grave. Afterwards he came to Hē'-brŏn.

Isaac was now a very old man, and for many years he had been expecting to die. No doubt he rejoiced when Jacob returned safely from his long sojourn at Hâ'-răn, bringing with him twelve sons and a daughter. But Isaac did not live much longer after this time, and when he died—at the age of one hundred and eighty years—Esau came and helped Jacob bury him.

STORY 19

HOW JACOB'S FAVORITE SON BECAME A SLAVE
Genesis 37

Among Jacob's twelve sons was one whom he loved better than the others. That one was Joseph—the eleventh son born in his household and the eldest son of Rachel, his beloved wife. Joseph was a good boy indeed, just the kind of boy that a father can trust to do right. Sad to say, his elder brothers were not so careful always to do right, and their wrongdoing brought much pain to Jacob's heart.

Because Jacob loved Joseph so tenderly his brothers became envious of him. And when Jacob made a wonderful coat of many colors and gave it to Joseph, the older sons allowed a bitter feeling of hatred to creep into their wicked hearts. They hated Joseph. One day while he was in the field with four of them he saw their evil conduct and on his return home he told his father how wrongly they had behaved. By doing this he increased the bitter

JOSEPH DREAMING OF THE SHEAVES

feeling that was growing against him in his brothers' hearts, for wicked people are always angered when some one exposes their wickedness. Joseph's brothers would no longer speak kindly to him.

Joseph was now about seventeen years old. One night he had a strange dream. He told his brothers about it. "We were together in the field binding sheaves," he said, "and my sheaf stood upright while yours bowed down around it."

"Do you think you are some day going to rule over us?" the brothers asked in angry voices; and they hated him even more than before.

Soon Joseph dreamed again, a dream more strange than the other one had been. This time he saw the sun, the moon, and eleven stars bowing down before him. If such a dream had any meaning at all, how could it mean anything else than that he should some day become a ruler before whom his relatives should bow themselves? Joseph wondered about the dream and he told it to his father and brothers. His father was displeased, because he thought it would be wrong for a man to bow down before his son. That would seem to make Joseph greater, better, and wiser than he. Still he wondered what such a dream could mean, and he thought much about the matter.

Now Jacob and his family were living at Hē'-brŏn, where Abraham had lived so long ago with his many servants and flocks and herds. Jacob's flocks were so large that they could not find enough pasture near by at all seasons, and sometimes they had to be taken far from home to find grass and water. The time came again when it was necessary to find pasture elsewhere, so Jacob sent his ten eldest sons to Shē'-chĕm with the cattle and sheep. After they had been away from home for some weeks, Jacob sent Joseph on an errand to learn whether or not the young men were getting on well with their work.

Joseph started out alone on his long journey of fifty miles to Shē'-chĕm. When he came to the place, he could not find his brothers, nor their flocks. He did not know where to go in search of them. Soon a man who lived in a town near by met him and told him that his brothers had gone to Dō'-thăn, to find better pasture. Joseph then journeyed on, over the hills and across the valleys, to Dō'-thăn, which was fifteen miles farther from Hē'-brŏn, and there he saw the flocks feeding on the green grass long before he arrived at the place.

When the brothers saw a young man coming across the fields clad in a beautifully colored coat they said at once to each other, "Here comes the Dreamer. Let us kill him, and we shall see what will become of his dreams." The eldest brother, Reuben, felt more kindly toward Joseph and wished to save his life. But he feared the others would not listen if he should tell them not to harm Joseph, so he said, "Let us not kill him; only throw him down into this pit and leave him alone to die." The others quickly agreed to do as Reuben said, and when Joseph approached they seized him, tore off his beautiful coat, and roughly put him into the deep pit.   Then they sat down on the ground and ate their lunch, paying no heed to his pitiful cries.

Now Reuben did not intend to leave Joseph alone to die.   He planned to come back as soon as the others should go away, and rescue his young brother from such a sad death.   But it was not going to be Reuben, after all, who should draw Joseph from the pit.

While the brothers were eating their lunch, Reuben went to another part of the field, and during his absence a company of traveling merchants came riding by on camels.   Some of these travelers were called Ĭsh'-mēē-lītes, because they were descendants of Ĭsh'-mā-ĕl, and they were going to Egypt to sell rich spices and perfumed gum, which had been gathered from trees in other countries.   "Now!" thought Judah, another of Joseph's elder brothers, "here is an opportunity to make some money, and to get rid of our brother without letting him die."   So, calling his brothers, he said, "It would be better to sell Joseph to these merchants than to leave him to die in the pit; for even though we despise him, he is our brother."   The others were quite willing to sell Joseph; so they drew him out of the pit, and soon he saw himself being exchanged to the Ĭsh'-mēē-lītes for twenty pieces of silver.

Poor Joseph! this was a sad time for him.   Now he knew that he should be taken far away by rough strangers who had become his masters.   Now he was sold!   All his pleading and all his tears did not soften the hearts of his wicked brothers, who greedily divided the money among themselves and supposed that they were forever rid of him.   Perhaps they did not even watch the caravan as it moved slowly away toward the south, and disappeared from view behind the green-clad hills.

After the Ĭsh'-mēē-lītes passed on and the brothers too went away to different parts of the field, Reuben came hurrying back to the pit.   Stooping down, he called to Joseph; but no answer came from the dark hole.   Again and again he called, thinking perhaps that Joseph had fallen asleep, but still the silence was unbroken—Joseph did not reply.   Then, after a while, Reuben knew that his brother was not there.   What should he do?   Now he forgot he had been afraid to let his brothers know that he had intended all the while to rescue Joseph from their hands.   He forgot everything except the fact that Joseph had disappeared.   He believed some dreadful thing had happened to the poor boy.   Perhaps a wild beast had devoured him.   Tearing his clothes as people did when they were in deep trouble, he returned to his brothers and said, "The child is gone, and what shall I do?"   Being the eldest son, he felt that he should have taken care of his brother.

Next came the question of how they should account to their father for the disappearance of his favorite son. Finally they decided to dip Joseph's coat in blood, killing a young kid for this purpose, and take the blood-stained garment back to their father, telling him that they

JOSEPH SOLD BY HIS BROTHERS INTO EGYPT

had found it in that condition. We see that they were planning to use a wicked lie to cover up their wicked deed.

Jacob was alarmed when his sons returned without Joseph. When he saw the blood-dyed coat he knew it was the very one that he had made for the lost boy, and he believed at once that wild animals had torn Joseph in pieces. Tearing his own garments apart and dressing himself in rough cloth called sackcloth, he sat down and mourned bitterly for many days, refusing to be comforted.

STORY 20

JOSEPH A PRISONER IN EGYPT

Gen. 37 : 36—40 : 23

At the end of their long, dusty journey the Ĭsh'-mẽe-lītes arrived with Joseph in Egypt. Here Joseph found himself surrounded by a dark-skinned people who spoke a different language from his own. And here he saw large cities, wonderful temples for idol-worship, mighty pyramids, and the great River Nile. How strange all these things must have seemed to this boy, who had always lived in tents!

The Ĭsh'-mẽe-lītes took Joseph to the city where the king of Egypt lived, and there they sold him to an officer in the king's army. Joseph could never forget how terror-stricken he had felt when his own brothers sold him as a slave. But he was a sensible lad, and when he realized that he was indeed a slave he tried to be obedient to his master. And God did not forget him, nor the wonderful dreams he had given to Joseph when he was yet at home. God was now preparing Joseph for the time when those dreams should come true. Although Joseph could not understand God's plan, yet he trusted in God to help him do right.

The Egyptian officer who bought Joseph was named Pŏt'-ĭ-phär. He was a very rich man and had many other servants. Joseph soon learned the speech of the Egyptians, and because he showed a cheerful, obedient spirit, Pŏt'-ĭ-phär took special notice of him. He saw that Joseph was always honest and that he had a good understanding of business affairs. After a while he gave all the oversight of his household and his riches into Joseph's care, and for Joseph's sake God blessed the Egyptian officer with greater riches. For several years Joseph remained in Pŏt'-ĭ-phär's house—a slave in name only, for in reality he was the ruler over his fellow slaves and the caretaker of his master's wealth.

Then there came a sudden change. Pŏt'-ĭ-phär's wife was not a good woman, and she often tried to persuade Joseph to do wickedly. Because he would not, she finally became angry with him and accused him falsely to her husband. Pŏt'-ĭ-phär believed the lie that she told, and to punish Joseph he thrust the noble young man into the king's prison. How cruel this was! Perhaps Joseph wondered why he must suffer so often because of the sins of other people. To be a slave had seemed bad enough; to be thrust into prison while trying to do right was even worse. No doubt Joseph suffered much because of this unjust act.

But Joseph was not the kind of person to fret and pout because of trouble. He showed a cheerful spirit even in the prison, and his manly face soon attracted the attention of the prison-keeper. Day after day the keeper watched him, and finally he decided that Joseph was the very one he needed to help care for the other prisoners. After a while he gave Joseph full charge of all the prisoners, and doubtless Joseph was once more as busy as he had been in Pŏt'-ĭ-phär's house.

About that time Phâr'-āoh, the king of Egypt, became much displeased with two of his special servants—the chief butler, who served him with wines, and the chief baker, who served him with bread. Because of his displeasure he put both of them into prison, and Joseph cared for them there.

One morning Joseph found these men looking unusually sad. "Why are you so troubled?" he asked. And they replied, "We have had strange dreams, and there is no one here to tell us the meaning of them. In the king's court there are wise men who often tell the meaning of dreams, but we can not send for them to come to us in prison."

"Surely God knows the meaning of your dreams," Joseph told them, "and I am his servant. Tell me, therefore, what you have dreamed. He may reveal to me the true meaning."

The chief butler was first to tell his dream. "I saw a grape-vine with three branches," he said, "and while I looked upon it the buds shot forth and became blossoms, and the blossoms became clusters of grapes. Then I squeezed the juice of the grapes into Phâr'-āoh's cup, which I held in my hand. This I gave to the king as I used to do when I stood by his table."

God made Joseph to know the meaning of the dream, and Joseph said, "The three branches that you saw are three days; after that time you will be restored to your former position in the king's palace. But I beg you to remember me when it shall be well with you again, and make mention of me to Phâr' āoh; for I have been stolen from my father's house and sold a captive among these people. And for no wrong-doing of mine I have been thrust into this prison."

The chief baker now told what his dream had been, and wished Joseph to tell its meaning. "There were three baskets upon my head," he said, "and in the topmost one there were bakemeats for the king's table. While I held them, the birds flew down and ate the contents of the topmost basket."

Through the wisdom of God, Joseph knew the meaning of this dream, too. He felt sorry to tell its meaning, though, because he knew that his words would bring more grief to the chief baker's heart. But

THE GREAT SPHINX OF GIZEH

In the drifting sands of Egypt, on the edge of the Libyan Desert, near the pyramids of Gizeh, is this huge image in the form of a recumbent lion with a man's head. Between the forepaws appears an old altar, while at its breast is a memorial plate to Thutmosis II. The entire height from the crown of the head to the pavement on which the forepaws of the lion rest is 66 feet. From the forepaws to the root of the tail it is 187 feet. The ears are 4½ feet high; nose 5 feet 7 inches; mouth 7 feet 8 inches wide; and face 13 feet 8 inches wide. The nose was disfigured by the gunners of the barbarous Mameluke dynasty.

JOSEPH INTERPRETING THE DREAM OF THE
BUTLER AND BAKER

the chief baker expected him to tell, so he said, "In your dream the three baskets mean three days. At that time the king will take you from the prison and hang your body upon a tree, and the birds will eat your flesh."

Three days later Phâr'-āōh held a great feast for his servants in honor of his birthday. During the feast he removed both the chief butler and the chief baker from the prison and disposed of them just as Joseph had said he would. But the chief butler soon forgot about Joseph, and two years passed by before he remembered to speak to the king about the one who had been kind to him while he was in prison.

———•———

STORY 21

JOSEPH A RULER IN EGYPT

Genesis 41

One morning Phâr'-āōh wakened from sleep wondering about the meaning of two strange dreams that he had dreamed during the night. He called the wise men of Egypt to tell him what the dreams meant, but they could not. Then he felt greatly troubled.

When the chief butler heard about the king's distress, he thought at once of his own experiences when he was in prison. And he remembered Joseph's kindness. How long he had forgotten that noble young man! Now he told Phâr'-āōh about Joseph, and immediately the king sent for him.

Joseph was busy caring for the prisoners and thinking perhaps that the chief butler had forever forgotten him when the messenger came from the king's palace. "Phâr'-āōh wishes to see you: come at once," the messenger said.

Joseph shaved his face and changed his prison clothes for clean, fresh garments. Then he hurried to the royal palace, wondering as he went why Phâr'-āōh had sent for him. "If only he would grant me liberty," he thought, "how happy I should be!"

At the palace Phâr'-āōh was anxiously waiting to see him. Others, too, were waiting, and all were feeling deeply troubled. "If this strange young man can not help, what shall we do?" they were wondering. Then there came a sound of footsteps outside the door, and Joseph was brought into their midst. Fair-skinned and handsome, he at once attracted the attention of all, and they thought, "Here indeed is some one different from us, and perhaps he can help." Then Phâr'-āōh spoke:

"I have heard of you," he said, "that you can tell the true meaning of dreams. And I have dreamed two dreams which trouble me greatly; therefore I have sent for you because none of the wise men of Egypt can tell me what these dreams mean."

Joseph replied, "This wisdom does not belong to me, but to the God whom I serve. Tell me what your dreams were, and he will give the meaning of them."

And Phâr'-āoh answered: "In my dream I was standing by the River Nile, and presently I saw seven fat cattle come up out of the river and feed in the green meadow. Later I saw seven other cattle come up out of the river and stand upon the bank. These seven were very lean, and I saw them approach the seven fat cattle and eat them up. Still they were as thin as they had been at the first. Then I awoke.

JOSEPH TELLING THE MEANING OF PHARAOH'S DREAMS

"Afterwards I fell asleep and dreamed again, and saw seven ears of corn grow up out of a stalk. Full, good ears they were, and while I was looking at them seven other ears sprang up after them— withered, thin, and blasted with the east wind. These thin ears devoured the good ones, and once more I awoke."

"Your dreams are indeed wonderful," Joseph told the king, "and both of them have the same meaning. By them God is making known to you what he is about to do.

"The seven fat cattle are seven years, and so also are the seven good, full ears of corn. And in like manner the seven lean cattle and the seven thin, withered ears are seven years which shall follow the first seven. God is making known to you by these dreams that there shall be seven years of plenty throughout all the land of Egypt, and afterwards there shall be seven years of famine. These years of famine shall be so severe that the seven years of plenty shall be forgotten, and everything shall be eaten up throughout the land.

"God has given you these two dreams to show you that these things will surely come to pass soon. He has warned you in this manner to prepare for the time of famine, lest it come upon you and destroy every living creature in your kingdom. It will be well for you to appoint a wise man to look after the food supply. Let him, during the seven plentiful years, lay aside enough each year to make sure of enough for all your people during the years when nothing shall grow.''

Phâr'-aōh and the attendants who stood near his throne listened attentively to Joseph's words, and when he had finished speaking the king said, ''Surely the Spirit of God is in this man and his words are good. Can we find another who could more wisely manage the affairs of this kingdom than he?'' And so it came about that Phâr'-aōh made Joseph ruler over all the land of Egypt.

And Phâr'-aōh clothed Joseph in royal robes and put a gold chain about his neck. He took his signet ring from off his hand and placed it upon Joseph's, and said, ''You shall be overseer of my house, and your word shall govern my people in all the land of Egypt. Only in the throne will I be greater than you.'' And Phâr'-aōh gave Joseph the second chariot that he had. In this Joseph rode through the streets of the city and the people bowed themselves before him. Phâr'-aōh called Joseph, Zăph'-năth-pā-ă-nē'-ăh, which means, ''The man to whom secrets are revealed.'' He also gave Joseph an Egyptian princess for his wife.

All this prosperity did not change the heart of Joseph, for he remained kind and just to all. Day after day he rode through the land and gathered up the food which grew everywhere in abundance. This excess food he stored into buildings for future needs, until finally he had an enormous quantity laid aside for the years of famine.

During this time God blessed Joseph with two sons, whom he named Mă-năs'-seh and Ē'-phră-ĭm. And Joseph was grateful to God for all his blessings. He realized that all his troubles had brought about the great honor that he now enjoyed.

When the seven years of plenty had passed by, the years of trouble began. Nowhere in all the land of Egypt would the fields yield any growth, and people began to have need of food. Then they came to Joseph, and he opened the storehouses, which had been filled during the years of plenty, and sold food to the Egyptians.

Not only in Egypt did the terrible famine rage, but also in the countries round about. From far and near people came to Joseph, imploring him to sell corn to them lest they die of hunger.

HOW JOSEPH'S DREAMS CAME TRUE

Genesis 42

In the land of Canaan the deadly famine was making itself felt. Food was becoming scarce, and people were wondering what they should do. Then good news came that there was plenty of food in Egypt.

Jacob and his eleven sons were rich in silver and gold and cattle. But without grain their riches could not keep them alive. So Jacob sent his ten eldest sons to Egypt to buy corn. He kept his youngest son, Benjamin, at home, because he loved Benjamin the best of all after Joseph was taken away from him. He would never allow Benjamin to go far away from home lest some dreadful thing should happen to him also.

More than twenty years had now passed by since the ten brothers tore Joseph away from his father's loving care. During those years the brothers had grown more thoughtful of each other, and they did not envy Benjamin because he was loved the best. They were kind to him. No doubt they often thought about the terrible wrong they had done by selling Joseph.

Now, as they journeyed to Egypt, perhaps they remembered that the merchants who bought Joseph were going to that same country. And they may have passed along the very same road. But unpleasant thoughts are never cheerful traveling companions, and the brothers may have tried to think about other things. They saw new stretches of country before them and eagerly watched for the first glimpse of Egypt.

When they arrived in Egypt, things looked different from what they had expected. The fields were just as barren as those of Canaan. But they soon learned that although the famine was raging in Egypt, plenty of food was to be had there, for the great storehouses were filled with an abundance of corn. As every one who wished to buy food came to Joseph, they also came.

But the brothers did not know Joseph. More than twenty years had changed him from a mere lad into a full-grown man. Now he sat upon a throne, dressed like a prince, and every one who approached him with a request bowed humbly before him just as if he were the king. His ten brothers also bowed down before him, as the other people did.

Joseph knew his brothers at once, and when they bowed before him he remembered his dreams. Now he knew those dreams had come true, and he understood why God had permitted him to be sold into Egypt. He wished to know if his brothers had changed during the years that had passed. So he pretended that he did not know them. He spoke to them in the language of the Egyptian people and pretended to be stern and harsh.

"Who are you?" he demanded roughly.

They replied, "We are men of Canaan, and we are brothers."

"You are spies," he told them, "and I know you have come to see the stricken condition of our country. You wish to bring an army against us."

"Indeed we are not spies," they answered, "for we are true men, and we have come to buy food for ourselves and our families."

Joseph insisted that they were surely spies, and they told him again that they were brothers, the sons of one man.

"Is your father yet alive?" he asked, "and have you another brother?" What strange questions! they thought, and they told him about their aged father and about his tender love for Benjamin.

Now Joseph wondered whether they were kind to Benjamin. He also

JOSEPH'S BROTHERS BOWING
BEFORE HIM IN EGYPT

wondered if they cared more for their father's happiness than they did when they sold his son Joseph to the Ish'-mee-lites. He thought, "I must find out these things before I let them know that I am Joseph." So he said, "You must prove to me that you are not spies. I will put nine of you into prison and the other one I will send back to Canaan. If he will return with the youngest brother of whom you told me, then I will believe that you are true men."

Into prison, where he had spent several long years, Joseph now placed his ten brothers; not because he hated them, but because he wished to know surely if they were now better men than they used to be. After three days he sent for them again, and said, "I fear God, and I want to do the right thing. If you are indeed true men you can prove it in this manner: I will send nine of you back to your aged father with food, and keep one of you in prison; you must return again and bring that younger brother of whom you spoke, or else I will know surely that you are spies.

The brothers felt at once that this great trouble had come upon them because they had been so unkind and cruel to their young brother Joseph. They did not know this man was Joseph, and that he could understand their language, so they said to each other, "We are suffering now because of our sin. Now we know how terrified Joseph felt when we sold him and when he pleaded with us, but we would not listen." Reuben, the eldest brother and the one who had wished to save Joseph's life, now spoke. "I told you then that you should not sin against the boy, and you would not hear me. Now his blood is being required at our hands."

JUDAH PLEADS FOR BENJAMIN

Joseph pretended not to know what they were saying, but he heard it all and his heart was touched. Now he knew they were sorry for their sin, and he turned his face away and wept for joy. Then he dried his tears and spoke to them again in the language of the Egyptians. He took Simeon, who was the second eldest, and bound him before their eyes, and put him back into the prison. The others he sent away to Canaan, after their sacks had been filled with corn. He had commanded his servants to return their money in each sack with the corn.

On the homeward journey the brothers were sad at heart. What would their dear old father say, they wondered. Joseph was lost to him, and now Simeon was a prisoner, and Benjamin's presence was demanded in Egypt or else Simeon would be killed! No wonder they were sad. At the end of the first day they stopped to feed their asses, and one brother opened his sack and found his bag of money in it. More trouble seemed to be coming upon them; for they feared now that the stern ruler would believe they had stolen the money.

At last they reached home, tired and discouraged. They told their father about the sorrows that had befallen them and explained why

Simeon was left in Egypt. "We can not return again except we take Benjamin," they said.

"I can never let you take my youngest son," Jacob replied, "for Joseph is not, and Simeon is not, and now you will let some misfortune overtake Benjamin also."

Then the brothers emptied their sacks of food in the presence of their father, and found that each one's money had been replaced in his sack. Things seemed to be growing worse for them instead of better, and they were very much afraid.

***

STORY 23

JOSEPH MAKES HIMSELF KNOWN TO HIS BROTHERS
Gen. 43:1—45:24

The famine continued to rage in Canaan; not a cloud appeared in the sky, and not a drop of dew sparkled on the parched grass. The waters of the brooks dried up, and the wells were becoming more shallow every day. After a while the food that Jacob's sons had brought from Egypt was nearly all eaten up. "You must go again," said Jacob, "and buy more corn."

But Judah answered, "We can not go unless we take Benjamin; for the ruler told us we surely should not get any more corn if we failed to bring him."

"Why did you tell him that you had a younger brother?" Jacob asked.

Judah replied, "The man asked us whether we had yet another brother, and we only answered his questions. How could we tell that he would require us to bring him to Egypt?"

Still Jacob shook his head and refused to let Benjamin go; and the days dragged on and the food-supply grew less and less. The brothers looked at each other sorrowfully and wondered what they should do. Although they were grown men, yet they did not dare leave their father on such an errand without his permission; for among those people the father ruled his household as long as he lived. And they could not go without Benjamin. Finally Judah said, "If you do not send us soon, both we and our children shall die of hunger; for, see, only a little food remains. I will certainly take care of Benjamin, and if any harm should befall him I will bear the blame forever." And

Reuben, the eldest, had brought two of his own boys to Jacob, saying, "You may kill my sons if I do not bring Benjamin back safely."

At last, in the face of hunger and starvation, poor old Jacob was persuaded to send Benjamin with his brothers. "If my children must all be taken away from me, then I must bear the loss of them," he said.

Preparations began at once for this second journey. Jacob urged his sons to take for a present to the ruler some of the best things that grew in Canaan, and they selected some rich spices and perfumes, wild honey, and nuts. Then they took back twice as much money as on the first journey; for their father said that perhaps their money had been restored in their sacks by mistake.

When the brothers came into Joseph's presence the second time, and he saw that Benjamin had come with them, he sent them to his own house at once and gave orders to his servants to prepare a feast. "The men from Canaan are going to dine with me," he said to his steward, who was ruler of his house.

The brothers did not understand Joseph's orders to his servants, and they were frightened because they were brought to his own house. "He thinks we stole the money," they told each other, "and now although we are innocent he will accuse us of this wrong-doing and put us all into prison with Simeon. What shall we do?" They decided to tell the steward about their troubles.

"Do not be afraid," the steward said, when he heard their story, "because I had your money, and it must have been your father's God who gave you the treasure in your sacks." Then he gave them food for their asses and water to wash their feet. Afterwards he brought Simeon out to them and told them that they were all invited to eat dinner with his master.

At noon Joseph came home to meet them. He spoke kindly to them and asked at once whether their father were still alive. How deeply interested he seemed to be in the dear old man they had left in Canaan! Next he turned to Benjamin and asked, "Is this the younger brother of whom you spoke?" When he knew that Benjamin was indeed his own brother, he said, "The Lord be gracious to you, my son." He longed to kiss Benjamin and embrace him at once, but he wished to learn more about his ten older brothers before he should let them know that he was Joseph. So he hurried out of the room to hide his tears, and then washed his face lest they should see that he had been weeping.

The brothers were beginning to feel more comfortable. They were glad to find Simeon well, and they hoped to be soon returning again to Canaan with food and with pleasant tidings for their anxious father.

He would be glad to know the stern ruler had been kind to them this time. And he would be happy to see both Benjamin and Simeon return safe.

After the tables had been arranged, Joseph and his brothers entered the dining-hall. Other guests were present—possibly Egyptian officers. The brothers saw that three tables had been arranged—one where Joseph sat alone because he was the ruler, another where the Egyptians sat, and around the third table the brothers were assigned places according to their ages, beginning with Reuben. "How strange!" they thought, "for how can this man know which of us is older than his brother?" Joseph then sent food to them from his table, to each man a portion and to Benjamin five times as much as to the others. Perhaps he wished to see if they were as jealous of Benjamin as they had once been of their brother Joseph.

The meal ended pleasantly, and the brothers thought again of returning to their home. "Fill their sacks with corn as you did before," Joseph instructed the steward, "and put their money back into the sacks again. But in Benjamin's sack put my silver cup also." And the steward did as he was bidden.

On the following morning the brothers started for home. But they had not gone far when the steward came hurrying after them. Joseph had sent him to recover the silver cup. "Why have you rewarded my master evil for good?" he asked when he told them that Joseph's cup was missing from the house.

"God forbid that we should be guilty of stealing the cup," they answered, "for we are honest men. Did we not return the money that we found in our sacks? Why then should your master think us guilty of this offense?"

So sure were they that none of them had done the wicked deed of which they were accused that they said, "Search us and see for yourself: if the cup is found, let that one die in whose sack it is discovered, and the others of us will become your servants."

The steward was unwilling to render such severe punishment. "If I find the cup," said he, "I will take him for my servant in whose sack it is found, and the others may go free."

Then the search began. Every man lowered his sack to the ground and opened it for the steward's examination. And one by one the men rejoiced when the missing cup was not found in their possession. The steward began the search with Reuben's sack, and ended with Benjamin's. And in Benjamin's sack he found the missing cup, where he had placed it.

How astonished the brothers were at this discovery! What could
they do now? Surely some one was trying to bring back the ill will
of the ruler upon them. They could not part with Benjamin, and yet
they had promised the steward he might take that one of them for
a servant who should be guilty of such an offense. Tearing their clothes
as an expression of grief, they replaced the sacks upon their asses and
turned back to the capital city with Joseph's steward and Benjamin.

Joseph was waiting at his house for their coming. "What is this
you have done?" he demanded, sternly, as they fell on their faces before him.

"Alas, God is punishing us for our sins. We are all your servants," exclaimed Judah.

"God forbid that I should keep all of you," answered Joseph, more
kindly now; "only he who took the missing cup will I punish, and the
others may return home." Joseph wished to see if the others were
selfish and willing to let Benjamin suffer if they could escape.

Then Judah, who had promised Jacob to bring Benjamin safely
back to Canaan or else bear the blame forever, fell on his face at
Joseph's feet.

"Please do not be angry with me, but listen to my words," he said,
"for I know you are even as Phâr'-aōh. When we came at the first you
asked whether we had a father or a younger brother and we told you
that we had. We told you about our father's tender love for Benjamin
after his favorite son had been lost. Then you demanded us to bring
Benjamin with us when we should return again to prove that we are
not spies. We replied that our father would not be willing to let him
come because he feared some terrible harm might befall him, too. Still
you insisted that unless we bring him we should never see your face
again.

"When we returned home we told our father about your words,
and he was grieved. He said he would not allow Benjamin to leave
him. But when the food-supply grew low, he wished to send us again,
and we answered that we could not come and see you except Benjamin
be with us. Then after some days of delaying he sent us again, saying, 'If trouble happen to Benjamin, I shall die of grief.' Now, if
we return without the lad our father will die, for he is old and feeble
and his life is bound up in his love for Benjamin. Let him return, I
beg of you, and let me remain in his stead, for I promised our father
that if ill should befall the lad I would bear the blame forever."

Judah's earnest words touched Joseph's heart deeply. How different they sounded from the words he spoke so long ago when he sug-

gested to his brother that they sell Joseph to the Ĭsh'-mē̄e-lītes! Now he was offering himself to become a lifetime slave in place of his younger brother; now he was pleading for the relief of his father's anxiety. A changed Judah, indeed. And Joseph knew that Judah's words were sincere; he believed his brothers were better men; and he longed to embrace them all. So he quickly commanded his Egyptian servants to

JOSEPH KISSING HIS YOUNG BROTHER, BENJAMIN

leave the room, and then, turning to his brothers, he said in their language, "I am your brother Joseph; does my father yet live?"

Surprize and fear overcame the brothers and they could not answer a word. Joseph saw they were afraid, and he wept aloud and called them to come nearer. "I am the same Joseph you sold into Egypt," he told them, "but do not be afraid, nor angry with yourselves, because it was God who sent me here before you to save your lives. This terrible famine will continue for five more years, and you must bring your families and all your possessions into Egypt, or else you may die. I will take care of you here; for God has made me a father even to Phâr'-āoh and the ruler of all his people.'' Then Joseph kissed Benjamin and embraced him fondly, and each of the brothers he kissed with the same forgiving tenderness.

The Egyptian servants heard Joseph weeping, and they hurried to tell Phâr'-āoh that Joseph's brothers had come, and every one was glad, because every one loved Joseph. Phâr'-āoh sent a message to Joseph, urging him to bring his father to Egypt at once.

The homeward journey was begun the second time, and now the men were taking Egyptian wagons loaded with good things to eat. Joseph sent as a present to his father twenty asses loaded with food and other stuff, and to each of his brothers he gave Egyptian clothing. To Benjamin he gave five times as much as he gave to the other ten, and also three hundred pieces of silver.

———•———

STORY 24

JOSEPH'S FATHER AND BROTHERS COME TO LIVE IN EGYPT

Gen. 45: 25—50: 26

The days of anxious waiting seemed long to Jacob as he watched for the home-coming of his sons from Egypt. At last they came with their treasures from Egypt—wagon-loads of good things.

Jacob's joy was greatest when he saw Benjamin and Simeon among the stalwart men who came to give him an affectionate greeting. They told him at once of the good fortune that had overtaken them in Egypt. "We found Joseph!" they exclaimed excitedly, "and he is alive and well. More than that, he is the ruler of all Egypt, and he has sent us to bring you and our wives and sons and daughters to live in Egypt."

At first Jacob could not believe their words, for it seemed impossible that the son whom he had mourned as dead for more than twenty years should be alive in a strange land. But when he saw the wagons Joseph had sent and the twenty asses loaded with provisions as a special present to him, he said, "It is enough; Joseph my son is yet alive, and I will go and see him before I die."

The third journey to Egypt was a happy one. Jacob and his sons' wives and their little children rode in the wagons Joseph had sent, while the grown men drove the herds of cattle and sheep and goats and asses. One night they made camp at Bēer-shē'-bă, where Abraham and Isaac had lived long before this time. Here Jacob offered sacrifices to God as his father and grandfather had done. And God spoke to him once more in a night vision. "Do not be afraid to go to Egypt," God told him, "for I will go with you and will increase your family until they become a great nation. Then I will bring them again into the land which I promised to your grandfather Abraham and to your father Isaac. And you shall indeed see Joseph, and he will place his hand upon your eyes."

After this time Jacob was called Israel, the name which God gave him when he wrestled all night with the angel. And his children were called Israelites. But sometimes they were called Hebrews, a word which means, "From beyond the river," and it referred back to the long-ago time when their forefather Abraham had obeyed God's voice and had crossed the River Eu-phrā'-tēs to journey to Canaan. When the Israelites came into Egypt they numbered sixty-seven people, and when Joseph and his two sons were counted among them they numbered seventy.

At the border-land of Egypt the Israelites camped again, and waited until Judah should go to Joseph to tell of their coming. Joseph prepared his royal chariot and rode into Gō'-shĕn to meet his father and his relatives.

What a happy meeting when Father and son were clasped in each others' arms again! Both wept for joy and spoke many tender words to each other. Then Joseph brought five of his brothers and his aged father to see Phâr'-āoh, the king.

Phâr'-āoh was glad to see them. When he learned that they were shepherds, he told them they might live in the land of Gō'-shĕn. Gō'-shĕn lay between Egypt and the desert, and was in ordinary times a very fertile country because its soil was well watered by the broad River Nile. Joseph provided food for his relatives and for their herds during the remaining years of the famine.

After a while the Egyptian people spent all their money for food. Then they came to Joseph for more corn, and he said, "I will give you corn if you will sell your cattle to Phâr'-āoh." This they did. Then when their cattle were sold and their money was spent their food-supply again grew low. "What must we do now?" they asked Joseph, and he told them to sell their fields and their pastures to the king. And so after a while Phâr'-āoh owned all the land in Egypt except the land which belonged to the priests. By and by the people became hungry again, and they had nothing left to sell except themselves. So they came to Joseph and said, "We would rather sell ourselves to become servants of Phâr'-āoh than die of hunger." And they became servants of the king.

JOSEPH'S FATHER TALKING TO THE KING

When the seven years of awful famine had passed by, Joseph sent the Egyptian farmers back to the fields with seed to plant again. He told them to plant their crops and care for them just as they had done before. Then when the harvest-time should come they should bring one-fifth of the yield of their fields to Phâr'-aōh, and four-fifths they could keep for food and for seed for the coming year. "All the land belongs to Phâr'-aōh," he said, "and hereafter one-fifth of all that grows on the land shall be kept for his portion." And these words of Joseph's became a law throughout all Egypt.

After the famine ended, Joseph's people continued to live in Gō'-shĕn. Israel was one hundred and thirty years old when he left Canaan, and he lived seventeen years in Gō'shĕn. Before he died he called his sons and requested them to take his body to Canaan and bury it in the cave of Măch-pē'-läh, where Abraham and Isaac were buried. Then he gave each of his sons a parting blessing.

Joseph brought his two children, Mă-năs'-sēh and Ē'-phră-ĭm, to see their aged grandfather and to receive his blessing also. And Israel said, "Surely God has been good to me, for I thought I should never see your face again and now I am permitted to see both you and your children." He then placed his trembling, wrinkled hands upon the boys' heads to bless them. Joseph saw he had placed his right hand upon the head of Ē'-phră-ĭm, the younger, and his left hand upon the head of Mă-năs'-sēh. "Not so, my father," he said gently, trying to lift his father's hands and change them so that the right hand should rest upon Mă-năs'-sēh's head. But Israel would not allow the change. "I know what I am doing," he answered, "although I am feeble and my eyes are dim; your younger son shall become greater than the elder, and to him the greater blessing belongs." Israel also gave each of the boys a portion among the inheritance of his own children.

After Israel died, Joseph commanded the Egyptian physicians to embalm his father's body for burial. This required forty days' time. In all, the people spent seventy days mourning the death of this aged man. Then Joseph asked permission of Phâr'-aōh to go with his brothers to place Israel's body in the burial-cave in Canaan.

When they returned again to Gō'-shĕn, the brothers thought, "Perhaps Joseph has been kind to us only for our father's sake, and now he may treat us cruelly because we sinned against him so long ago." So they sent a messenger to Joseph, saying, "Your father before he died asked that you forgive the wrong-doing of your brothers, and now we beg that you do forgive us, for we are servants of the God of your father." The messenger delivered the request of the brothers to Joseph.

Joseph wept when he heard this message. He knew his brothers feared that he might harm them, now that their father had died. So he called them to him and said, "Do not be afraid of me. Am I in the place of God that I should attempt to punish you because of your sin? No; I will care for you and for your children as long as I live." His kind words comforted their hearts, and they believed that he had indeed freely forgiven them.

As the years passed by, Joseph's relatives increased in number until they became a strong nation. And Joseph cared for them as long as he lived. When he reached the age of one hundred and ten years he knew his time had come to die. He called the old men of Israel to his bedside and said, "I am going to die. But God will watch over you, and by and by he will lead you back to the land of your fathers. Do not bury me here in Egypt, but place my body in a coffin and take it back with you when you return to Canaan." And the men of Israel wept as they promised to show this kindness to the one who had been so good to them. Afterwards whenever they looked at Joseph's coffin they remembered his words, and they knew they should not always live in Egypt.

———•———

STORY 25

THE STORY OF JOB

Job 1:1—42:17

Once upon a time—how very long ago we do not know—there lived a good man named Job. His home was in the country called Uz, which lay far east from Egypt and toward the place where the Garden of Eden had once been.

Now Job was a very rich man. His camels and asses and his cattle and sheep were numbered by thousands. His servants, too, were very many. And Job had seven sons and three daughters.

Not only was Job good, and rich, he was also godly—he thought often about God and tried always to do those things which he believed would please God. Although many of his neighbors worshiped the sun and the moon, Job believed that the God who had made these great lights was the only true object of worship. He built altars of earth or of stone as Noah had done many long years before, and placed oxen and sheep upon those altars and gave them to God. Then he prayed and asked God to forgive his sins and to bless him.

And Job was the greatest man in all that country. Everybody

JOSEPH, RULER OF EGYPT

SAND WAVES OF THE EGYPTIAN DESERT

FELLAH PLOWING IN EGYPT

AN EGYPTIAN LANDSCAPE NEAR CAIRO, ON THE NILE

knew about him and everybody honored him. When he passed by, even the children stopped their play to notice him. The poor people loved him because he helped them when they were in trouble.

After Job's sons grew up to manhood and had homes of their own, often they made great feasts. They often invited their brothers and sisters to these feasts. And while they ate and drank together, Job thought about them and wondered whether they were behaving rightly. He wanted them to love God as he did. And he offered sacrifices to God for their sins, and prayed for their forgiveness just as he prayed for himself.

And God took much notice of Job. He blessed him with health and with happiness. He gave him many friends and great honors. He loved him because he knew that Job was a true man.

But one day an enemy spoke against Job. This enemy was Satan. He said, "Job serves God just because God blesses him. If troubles should come—if all his riches and all his blessings should be taken from him—then Job would turn away from God."

This was not true. Satan is called "the father of lies" because he tells wrong things and tries to make others believe his words. God would not believe his words because he knew Job better.

But Satan wanted to trouble Job. So he sent bad men from other countries to steal away his oxen and camels and asses. They even killed his servants. And then a great storm came and tore down the house where Job's sons and daughters were feasting, and killed them every one.

When Job heard about these troubles he tore his clothes as a sign of grief and fell down upon his face. But he did not turn away from God. Instead, he blessed God just as he had always done before.

Then Satan planned to send greater trouble upon Job. He thought, "I will make life so miserable for Job that he will blame God for his suffering. Then he will want to die." In those days many people believed their troubles were always sent from God to punish them for their sins. Because Satan thought Job, too, would believe this, he caused great, ugly sores to break out all over Job's body. These sores were very painful. Everybody looked upon Job with horror and even his wife wished that he might die. Poor Job!

Then three rich men who for a long time had been friends of Job came to see him. They had heard about his troubles and they wanted to comfort him. But when they came near, at first they did not know him. His face looked so changed by the ugly sores that they could hardly believe he was Job. Then finally they sat down on the ground

near him. But they would not speak to him for several days. They
saw how greatly he was suffering and they believed God was surely
punishing him for some awful sins. And when they spoke to him they
did not speak comforting words. They told Job that he was covering

JOB AND HIS THREE "COMFORTERS"

his sins, that he was trying to hide his wrong-doing from God. All
these words only added to Job's sufferings and made him very unhappy
indeed.

Then God spoke to Job out of a whirlwind, and Job bowed down
low on the ground and worshiped. He did not think himself great nor
wise nor good in the sight of God. And God told Job that he was
pleased with him, but that he was not pleased with his three friends.
He told those men to bring offerings for their sins and to ask Job to
pray for them.

After this God caused the ugly sores to become dry, and soon Job's
body was well again. Then God sent many blessings to Job. Every

year he grew richer, until after a while he had twice as many riches as he had before he was troubled by Satan. And God gave him seven sons and three daughters again. These daughters were the most beautiful women in all that country. And so health and happiness and riches and honor came again to Job—this man who would not let any kind of trouble or sorrow turn him away from God. And Job lived to be a very, very old man.

MOSES BREAKING THE TABLETS OF STONE UPON THE ROCKS

PART SECOND
STORIES ABOUT MOSES

Exodus; Leviticus; Numbers; Deuteronomy

STORY 1

HOW THE CHILD MOSES CAME TO LIVE IN THE KING'S PALACE

Exod. 1:1—2:10

Our stories about the Bible Patriarchs, such as were Abraham, Isaac, and Jacob, are now ended, and we are beginning the good stories about one of the most interesting persons in the Old Testament. This person is Moses.

You remember that Jacob, the last of the patriarchs, was called Israel, and that his children were called Israelites. These Israelites lived in the land of Gō'-shĕn for a long time after their fathers who brought them from Canaan had died. And they grew in numbers until they became a strong nation.

During this time Phâr'-aōh, the king who had been kind to Joseph and to his kinsmen, died too, and another ruler called Phâr'-aōh took his place upon the Egyptian throne. This new Pharaoh did not look kindly upon the fast-growing Israelitish nation. He thought, "Soon these people will number more than my own Egyptian people, and they may join themselves to our enemies who come to fight against us. Then they will go away from our country and we can no longer have them for our servants. I can not let them go away from Gō'-shĕn; I must keep them for slaves."

Phâr'-aōh called his people together and told them of his fears concerning the Israelites. "We must do something," he said, "to hinder them from becoming stronger and more powerful than we are." Finally he and his officers decided to make the Israelites work harder than they had ever worked before. Phâr'-aōh wished to have new cities built, where he could store his rich treasures, and he commanded the Israelites to build those cities. Then the officers placed taskmasters over the workmen to compel them to work very hard and very fast. But the harder they worked the stronger they grew, and Phâr'-aōh saw that his plan was not a success. "This will never do," he reasoned, "for the Israelites are growing stronger all the while I afflict them. I must make life even more miserable for them." And he did.

The hard-working Israelites were horror-stricken when one morning this message came to them from the king's house: "Every baby boy that is born among your people must be thrown into the River Nile." Because this was the king's command it had to be obeyed.

After this cruel command had been put into practise, one day the

THE ISRAELITES AS SLAVES IN EGYPT

baby Moses was born. Now, his mother feared God, and she believed it was very wicked to throw a child into the river. Like all true mothers, she loved her baby; and for three months she hid him. When she could hide him no longer she thought of a wise plan, and then she worked carefully to carry it out. First she gathered some bulrushes —plants which grew along the River's bank—then she wove a little ark-like basket, and plastered it well with lime and pitch so that no water could leak through. When this was finished, she made a soft bed

in the ark and placed her baby in it. Now the very hardest part remained to be done; but she was a brave woman and she believed God
would help her save the baby's life. So she carried the basket to the
river, and there among the tall reeds which grew near the water's edge
she placed her precious burden, and went away. Her little daughter
Miriam, who had come along, lingered near the bank to play and to
watch what should happen to the tiny ark. She had not long to wait,
for soon a company of richly dressed women came to the river's bank.
One of them was the Egyptian princess, Phâr'-āoh's daughter. They
had come to bathe in the river.

When the princess saw the strange-looking ark floating among the
reeds, she sent her maid to bring it ashore. "What can be inside this
queer basket?" the women wondered as they gathered round to see it
opened. And how surprized they were when a sweet-faced Israelitish
baby looked up at them and cried.

The princess knew about the cruel command her father had given,
and she said at once, "This is one of the Israelite's children." She
was more kind-hearted than her wicked father, and she wished to spare
this baby's life. So she decided to take him for her own son. Just
then a little Israelite girl came running along the bank. She heard the
princess say about the little baby, "I shall keep him for my own son."
This little girl was Miriam, and her heart was glad because she knew
her baby brother could live. Bravely she stepped up to the princess
and said, "Shall I go and call an Israelite woman to nurse this baby
for you?" Of course there would need to be a nurse, and the princess
was quite willing to hire an Israelite woman, so Miriam hurried home
and quickly brought her own mother. And they carried the baby back
once more to their own home, where they should no longer need to fear
that its cries might attract the attention of their enemies, for every one
learned that this baby had been adopted by the King's daughter.

When the baby grew old enough to leave his mother, he was taken
to Phâr'-āoh's palace and given to the Princess. She called his name
Moses, which means "drawn out," because she had drawn him out
of the water. And she placed him in the best schools of Egypt, that
he might learn all the wisdom of her own people and be ready some
day to occupy the Egyptian throne.

STORY 2

WHY MOSES LIVED IN THE WILDERNESS

Exod. 2: 11-25

When the boy Moses grew to manhood he did not forget his own people—the Israelites. Sometimes he left the beautiful palace and its gardens, where he lived among the princes of Egypt, and went out to the fields and cities where his people were toiling. His heart felt sad when he saw the cruel taskmasters oppress his people. He believed that God had spared his life when a baby in order that he might some day help his own people. How he longed for that time to come! He even despised the riches of Egypt when he saw the hardships and poverty of the Israelites. He despised the idolatry of Egypt when he saw the princes and rulers bow down to worship oxen, and cats, and snakes.

One day Moses, when he had left the king's palace to visit the Israelites, acted very unwisely. He saw an Egyptian beating an Israelite, and this made him very angry. He looked about quickly to see that no one was watching, and then he killed the Egyptian and buried him in the sand. He thought the Israelite would understand that he was trying to help him. The next day he saw two Israelites quarreling between themselves and beginning to fight. "Why are you so unkind to each other?" he asked, and the one who had done the wrong replied crossly, "Who made you a ruler and a judge over us? Do you intend to kill me as you killed the Egyptian yesterday?"

When Moses heard these words he understood at once that his people did not expect him to help them. They did not know how much he loved them and how greatly he desired to relieve their burdens. They were not keeping the secret of his act the day before, and soon Phâr'-aōh would hear of the Egyptian's death. Then Phâr'-aōh would be angry with Moses and would seek to kill him. Knowing this, Moses hurried away from his people with a sad heart, and sought a hiding-place in the wilderness.

After a long, tiresome journey across the desert, Moses one day came to a well. Here he sat down to rest. Presently seven young women came to the well to draw water. They were sisters, and they kept their father's flocks. While they were drawing water for the sheep some wicked shepherds came by and tried to drive them away. Many times before those wicked shepherds had annoyed the young women. But this time Moses defended the women and compelled the wicked shepherds to go away.

When the sisters returned home with the flocks, their father, Jĕth'-rō, who was a priest of Mĭd'-ĭ-ăn, asked, "How is it that you have come home so early today?" "We met a stranger at the well," they replied, "who helped us when the wicked men tried to drive our sheep away." Jĕth'rō then sent for Moses and invited him to live among his people, and to care for his flocks. Later he gave one of his daughters to become Moses' wife, and for many years Moses worked as a shepherd in the land of Mĭd'-ĭ-ăn. Because he was a stranger among the people of Mĭd'-ĭ-ăn, Moses named his eldest son Gĕr'-shŏm, which means, "A stranger here."

During this time a change had taken place in Egypt. The Phâr'-āōh whom Moses feared had died, and a new Phâr'-āōh had come to the Egyptian throne. This ruler was just as cruel as the one whose place he took. Daily he oppressed the Israelites and added miseries to their unhappy lives. As they worked and toiled their hearts grew very sad. They groaned beneath their heavy burdens, and they wept and prayed for relief. And God heard their prayers.

You remember that long before this time God promised to give the land of Canaan to the children of Abraham, Isaac, and Jacob. You remember, too, that Jacob's name was changed to Israel, and that his children and their children after them were called Israelites. And so it was these Israelites to whom God had promised the land of Canaan. Now when God heard their cries of distress in Egypt he remembered his promise to Abraham, Isaac, and Israel. And he planned to deliver them from Phâr'-āōh's cruel bondage and bring them to their own land.

Although forty years had passed since Moses fled out of Egypt, still one of the Israelites remembered that Moses had believed God would some day use him to help his people. This Israelite was Moses' brother, Aaron. Now Aaron, too, had believed that God spared the life of Moses when a baby in order to use him some day as a deliverer for his oppressed kinsmen. But Moses was gone far away now, and Aaron thought he might have forgotten about the suffering of his people.

One day Aaron decided to go out into the great wilderness to search for his lost brother. "If I find him," he thought, "I shall tell him that the king whom he knew and feared is dead, and that the new Phâr'-āōh has been equally as cruel to our people as the one whose place he took. When Moses hears about the suffering of our people, surely he will try to help us." But Aaron did not realize what a changed Moses he should find.

STORY 3

HOW GOD SPOKE TO MOSES FROM A BURNING BUSH

Exodus 3, 4

When Aaron started out from Gŏ'-shĕn to search in the wilderness for his lost brother, Moses was leading his flock to a green pasture near the foot of Mount Hôr'-ĕb. How different Moses looked now from the young man who had once lived in Phâr'-āoh's palace! No longer he wore the princely robes of Egypt. Now his dress was the coarse mantle of a shepherd, and he carried a long shepherd's staff, or rod, in his hand. Day after day and year after year he had cared for his father-in-law's sheep, leading them to fresh pasture-lands and to abundant water-supplies. The sun and the wind had tanned his face and hands, while the years had whitened his flowing hair.

MOSES AND THE FIRE IN
THE BUSH

Although when a young man Moses had learned in all the wisdom of the Egyptians until he became one of the greatest persons the world has ever known, yet he did not think himself great, nor wise. He was contented to fill the humble place of a shepherd. He was glad to live in the great wilderness, far away from the large cities and beautiful grounds of Phâr'-āoh's palace. Here he could see all around him the wonderful things that God had made. He learned much about that country—its pasture-lands and watering-places. He often studied the trees and bushes and flowers. Because he was interested in these things, God spoke to him one day from a bush.

The sheep were feeding on the rich pasture and Moses was looking about at the beauties and wonders of nature when presently he saw a flame of fire burst forth from a bush on the mountain-side. He watched, expecting to see the bush destroyed by the fire; but the flame kept burning, and no harm came to the bush. "What a strange sight!" thought Moses; "I must take a closer look at this unusual bush, which fire can not harm." As he started forward, he heard a voice speak to him from the flame. "Moses! Moses!" the voice called; and Moses replied, "Here am I."

"Do not come near the bush," the voice said. "Put off the shoes from your feet, for you are standing on holy ground."

Moses understood at once that God was speaking to him; for the people in those lands always remove their shoes when they approach a sacred place, and perhaps Moses had done likewise when he stood before an altar to worship God. So he stooped down quickly to loosen and remove his sandals. Then he hid his face, for he was afraid to look upon the flame again.

"I am the God of Abraham, of Isaac, and of Jacob," the voice began once more, "and I have seen the afflictions of my people, the Israelites, in Egypt. I have heard their cries, and I know their sorrows. Now I am come to deliver them from the Egyptians and to bring them into the land that I promised to their fathers."

No doubt Moses was glad to hear this good news, for he still loved his own people. He had thought of them many times as he led his flock to and fro across the desert plains. How like a flock were they, in the hands of a cruel shepherd!

But the voice continued to speak: "Come now, and I will send you to Phâr'-aōh, that you may bring my people out of Egypt."

Although when a young man Moses had expected some day to rescue his people from Phâr'-aōh's cruel oppression, now he did not feel himself great enough to undertake such a task. "Who am I," he asked the Lord, "that I should bring my people out of Egypt? This is too great a work for me to do."

"I will surely go with you and help do the great work," answered the voice from the flame. "And when you bring the Israelites to this mountain, where they shall serve me, then you shall know that certainly I have been with you."

Moses feared that his people would not believe God had sent him to be their deliverer. He said, "When I go to the Israelites and tell them you have sent me, it may be they will have forgotten you. If they ask, 'Who is this God?' what shall I say?"

And God said, "Tell them that my name is I AM, the One who is always living. And tell them that I AM has sent you to help them. Do not be afraid, for they will believe you. Then call together the elders of your families, who are the leaders of your people, and go with them to Phâr'-aōh and tell him, 'Our God, the God of the Hebrews, the Israelites, has met us, and now let us go three days' journey into the wilderness to worship him.' At first the king will refuse to let you go; but after I have shown my power in Egypt he will send you out of the land."

Still Moses was fearful that his people would not believe God had
sent him except he could show them some sign, for a proof. So he
asked God to give him such a sign, and God said to him, ''What is that
in your hand?''

''It is a rod,'' answered Moses.

God told him to throw the rod on the ground, and Moses obeyed.
Instantly the rod was turned into a snake, and when Moses saw it he
was afraid, and ran from it.

But God said, ''Do not be afraid; but take hold of its tail.''

Moses obeyed again, and the snake became once more a rod in his
hand.

Then God told Moses to put his hand into his bosom, under his
mantle, and take it out again. When Moses did so his hand was changed
until it became like the hand of a leper, white as snow and covered
with a scaly crust. Moses was frightened, because leprosy is a dreadful disease. But God said, ''Put your hand into your bosom once
more,'' and when Moses obeyed his hand became like the other, with
a healthy skin. God intended that Moses could use this sign for a second proof to his people and to the Egyptians that God had sent him.
God further told Moses that if they should refuse to believe both these
signs he was to take water from the river and pour it upon the ground
before them. This water God would cause to turn into blood, and this
would be the third sign.

Moses still felt unwilling to go. He told God that he could not
speak well, and asked God to choose some one else for the work. But
God had chosen Moses for the work, and he said to Moses, ''Am I not
the Lord, who made man's mouth? Go, and I will teach you what to
say.''

When Moses continued to ask that some one else should go in his
stead, God said, ''I will send your brother, Aaron, with you, and he
will speak the words you tell him to speak. Even now he is coming into
the wilderness to meet you.''

At last Moses was ready to obey God. He led his flock back to
Jĕth'-rō, his father-in-law, and said, ''Let me return to my people in
Egypt, and see if they are yet alive.'' And Jĕth'-rō said, ''Go in peace.''

God spoke again to Moses in the land of Midian, and told him that
those who had sought his life in Egypt were now dead. Then Moses
took his wife and sons and started toward the land of Gō'-shĕn, carrying in his hand the rod through which God had performed a miracle.
On his way he met Aaron, and together the two brothers returned to
Egypt.

Moses told Aaron all the words God had spoken to him and the signs God had given. Then they called the elders of Israel and told them that God had sent Moses to be their deliverer. When the people heard the words of the Lord and saw the signs God had given, they believed and were glad. Then they bowed their heads and worshiped God because he had heard their prayers.

———•———

STORY 4

MOSES AND AARON TALK WITH A STUBBORN KING
Exod. 5:1—7:24

One day a messenger came to Phâr'-aōh saying, "Two men, who are Israelites, stand outside wishing to speak with you."

"Bring them in," said the King; and the messenger soon returned with Moses and Aaron.

Moses had not forgotten how to behave himself in the king's house even though he had spent long years in the wilderness among common people. He and Aaron spoke to Phâr'-aōh and told him that the Lord God of the Israelites had said, "Let my people go, that they may worship me in the wilderness."

But Phâr'-aōh answered, "Who is the Lord, that I should obey his voice?" Because he was ruler of the great land of Egypt, Phâr'-aōh was too proud to believe there was a higher Power, who could give orders for him to obey. "I do not know the Lord," he said, "and I shall not let Israel go out of my country to worship him."

Moses and Aaron then told Phâr'-aōh that the God of the Hebrews had met with them, and that unless his people were given freedom to go on a three days' journey into the wilderness to serve him there with sacrifices, he would send terrible diseases upon them and kill them.

These words did not move Phâr'-aōh's hard heart in the least. He only frowned, and replied crossly, "Why are you trying to take the people away from their work? I know they are idle, or they would not be asking to go away to sacrifice to their God. Return now, both of you, to your tasks, and let the Israelites alone." And with these words he sent Moses and Aaron out of his court.

On that same day Phâr'-aōh called the taskmasters and commanded that they should make the Israelites work harder than they had ever worked before. At this time they were making bricks and building houses for the rulers of Egypt. In mixing the clay for the bricks they were using straw, chopped up fine, to hold the clay together. Every day the Egyptians brought straw for their work. Now Phâr'-aōh commanded that no straw should be brought to them. "Send them out into the fields to gather straw for themselves," said he, "and see that they make just as many bricks as on other days when straw was brought to them."

Now, instead of getting freedom from Phâr'-aōh's cruel bondage, the Israelites were having greater trouble than ever. Of course they

AARON'S ROD SWALLOWING THE RODS OF THE MAGICIANS

could not gather straw from the fields and still make as many bricks as before; and when their work fell short they were beaten by the task-masters. At once they blamed Moses and Aaron for their trouble. "You promised to bring us out of Egypt, and you are only bringing more sorrow upon us," they said.

Moses loved his people and he pitied them. He cried to the Lord, and said, "Why is it that you sent me to Phâr'-aōh? He will not let the people go, and he is making life more miserable for them."

God spoke comforting words to Moses and sent him to encourage the Israelites; but they were in such deep sorrow that they would not listen to Moses. Then God said, "Go in and speak to Phâr'-āoh again, and show him the signs I have given you." But Moses answered, "How can I go when the Israelites no longer believe you have sent me? Neither will Phâr'-āoh hear my words."

Moses was ready to give up because Phâr'-āoh would not let the people go at once. He did not understand how God was planning to work mighty signs and wonders in Egypt until all the Egyptians should fear Israel's God. Then the Lord told him to return again and again to Phâr'-āoh and perform great miracles before him. "I have made you as a god to Phâr'-āoh," the Lord said, "and Aaron shall be your prophet. Because of this Phâr'-āoh will hear your words, even though he refuses to obey me."

After this Moses took Aaron and went the second time to talk with Phâr'-āoh. And Phâr'-āoh asked them to show him a sign, or miracle, that he might know the God of the Hebrews had surely sent them.

Now Aaron had in his hand the rod that Moses brought from the wilderness. Moses told him to cast this rod down before Phâr'-āoh and before his servants. Aaron did so, and the rod became a snake. Phâr'-āoh knew this was a miracle. But he had in his court some wise men called sorcerers, or magicians, and they also claimed to work miracles. Phâr'-āoh sent for them, and when they came they too threw their rods before him. And their rods became snakes. But Aaron's rod swallowed up their rods and afterwards became a harmless cane in Aaron's hand again.

Even when Phâr'-āoh knew that his magicians could not work so great a miracle as could Moses and Aaron, still he would not listen to them nor believe their sign, and they went away the second time from his presence.

On the next morning God sent Moses and Aaron to speak to Phâr'-āoh again. This time they met him on the bank of the River Nile. Perhaps the king was surprized to see these aged men approach him. Perhaps he felt angry because they were disturbing him so often. But Moses and Aaron were not afraid. They knew God had sent them and they spoke boldly to the king. "Because you refuse to let the Israelites go," they began, "the Lord our God has sent us to you once more. Now he has commanded us to show you another sign." Then Moses spoke to Aaron, and he waved his rod over the waters of the great river. At that very moment the water became blood. Then all the fishes died, and soon a dreadful odor filled the air. Aaron stretched his rod toward the waters of the rivers and streams and lakes and ponds.

MOSES AND AARON BEFORE PHARAOH

and everywhere throughout the land of Egypt the water became blood.

Phâr'-aōh's magicians brought to him water in a vessel and changed it into blood. Then the king turned away and went back to his palace. But the Egyptian people grew alarmed, because they had no water to drink. Nowhere in all the land could they find a drop of water.

———•———

STORY 5

PHARAOH SEES GOD'S MIGHTY SIGNS AND MIRACLES
Exod. 7:25—10:29

A full week passed by before God lifted the terrible plague of blood from the waters of Egypt. Then he sent Moses and Aaron to tell Phâr'-aōh that another terrible plague was coming. This time when Aaron, at God's command, stretched his rod over the rivers and lakes and ponds, frogs came hopping up out of the water in great numbers and covered all the land. They went into the people's houses, and even into Phâr'-aōh's palace, and hopped onto the beds and into the cooking-vessels. The magicians tried, and they, too, brought frogs up out of the water.

Phâr'-aōh was greatly troubled. He had been too stubborn to let any one know how much the plague of blood had annoyed him. But now the frogs worried him very much. When he could endure them no longer he called for Moses and Aaron and begged them to ask God to take the frogs away. "I will let your people go to sacrifice to the Lord," he promised; and Moses asked, "When do you want God to destroy the frogs out of your houses?" Phâr'-aōh answered, "To-morrow."

Moses prayed, and on the next day frogs died everywhere, except in the river. The Egyptians gathered them out of the houses and from the fields and piled them up in great heaps.

But when the frogs were gone Phâr'-aōh did not keep his promise. He grew stubborn again, and refused to let the people go. Then God sent another plague. This time Aaron struck his rod upon the dust of the ground, and the dust became lice and fleas. The magicians tried, but they could not perform this miracle. They told Phâr'-aōh that God's power was greater than theirs. Still Phâr'-aōh would not listen. How hard his heart was growing!

Then God sent Moses and Aaron to the king again as he walked along the river's bank early one morning. "Because you will not let Israel go," they told him, "tomorrow God will send another plague upon your land. Great swarms of flies will fill your palace and the houses of your servants. Everywhere—indoors and out-of-doors, the flies will trouble you. But no flies will enter the houses of the Israelites in Gō'-shĕn."

When the swarms of flies came upon the Egyptians, Phâr'-aōh called for Moses and Aaron again. "Tell your people to sacrifice to their God in Gō'-shĕn," he said.

But Moses replied, "They must go away out of the land, for the Egyptians would stone them if they should see their sacrifices." The Egyptians worshiped oxen, and the Israelites killed oxen and sacrificed them on the altars that they built to worship God. The Egyptians would be very angry if they should see the Israelites kill oxen to sacrifice, because they believed oxen were sacred, or holy animals.

When Moses refused Phâr'-aōh's offer to let the Israelites worship in Gō'-shĕn, the King said, "I will let them go to the wilderness, only do not take them very far away."

Moses answered, "We must go three days' journey; and you must not break your promise to God, for he is a terrible God when once he is angry and he will surely punish you for your wickedness."

But just as soon as God removed the plague of flies in answer to Moses' prayer, Phâr'-aōh grew stubborn again and refused to let the Israelites go.

The next great plague that God sent upon the land of Egypt affected the cattle, and horses, and camels, and oxen, and sheep. Many of the cattle in Egypt died of this great plague, and Phâr'-aōh became alarmed. But when he sent a messenger down to Gō'-shĕn he learned that the Israelites' cattle were all alive and well. Even after this Phâr'-aōh remained stubborn.

God kept telling Moses what to do next, and so the sixth plague came when Moses sprinkled a handful of dust in the air before Phâr'-aōh. Boils now broke out upon the people of Egypt. Dreadful boils they were, and painful. Because of them the magicians could not stand before Phâr'-aōh. Still the king remained stubborn, and unwilling to obey God. Then Moses warned him that the greatest trouble he had ever seen in Egypt should come the next day if he still refused to let the people go. The people were warned to seek shelter for themselves and for their beasts lest they should be killed by this terrible plague. Some of the Egyptians had learned to believe Moses and Aaron, and they hurried to their homes. But others, like Phâr'-aōh were not willing to listen to the warning, and they remained in their fields.

When the sky grew black with storm-clouds and the thunder began to peal, the people became afraid. It seldom rains in Egypt, and they had never heard thunder nor seen lightning before. Soon the hail-stones began to fall as fast as rain-drops, and the lightning ran like fire along the ground. All living things that had remained in the fields were killed by the lightning and hail.

Now Phâr′-aōh was terribly frightened. He called loudly for Moses and Aaron to come at once. And he cried out, "I have sinned this time; I and my people are wicked." He promised that the Israelites might go at once if God would only cause the awful thunder and light-ning and hail-storm to cease. Moses answered, "I will spread out my hands toward heaven as soon as I am outside the city, and the storm will cease, that you may know the earth belongs to God. But I know that you and your people do not yet fear the Lord God as you should fear him."

When the storm-clouds rolled away, Phâr′-aōh looked out upon the bright sunlight again and his heart grew as hard as before. He was not at all willing to obey God.

Moses may have grown tired of going so often to the king. But God told him that more plagues should yet come upon Egypt before Phâr′-aōh would really let the Israelites get out of the land of Gō′-shĕn. The hail-storm had destroyed all the growing crops in the land, but the wheat and rye were not damaged because they had not grown up. The next plague, God told Moses, would be locusts, and they would eat up every green thing which appeared above the ground. When the Egyptians heard that another plague was coming upon the land they hurried to Phâr′-aōh and said, "How long are you going to let these men bother our country? The land is spoiled already by the hail, and if the locusts come they will destroy everything."

So Phâr′-aōh called Moses and Aaron and asked, "Whom do you intend to take with you when you go to worship your God?"

Moses replied, "We will take all of our people, and we will also take our flocks ãnd herds."

"Take only your men and let them sacrifice," Phâr′-aōh said, and, refusing to hear Moses' reply, he drove them from his presence.

When Moses went out from Phâr′-aōh's palace, the Lord said, "Stretch out your hand over the land of Egypt for the locusts to come," and Moses obeyed. Then an east wind began to blow. All that day and all the next night the east wind blew, and when morning came again a great cloud of locusts appeared in the sky. They covered the whole land of Egypt, and were so many that they darkened the land.

Fear came into Phâr'-āōh's heart again, and he sent in haste for Moses and Aaron. "I have sinned against the Lord your God, and against you," he said. "Now forgive me this time, and pray that God will take these locusts away, or I and my people shall die." And Moses prayed again, and the Lord sent a strong west wind, which carried the locusts away and drowned them in the Red Sea.

When Phâr'-āōh hardened his heart again, God told Moses to stretch his hand out toward heaven once more, and this time a great darkness would come upon the land of Egypt. Moses did so, and a thick darkness covered the land. For three days there was no light at all in Egypt—not even moonlight nor starlight.

Phâr'-āōh sent the last time for Moses and Aaron, and said, "I will let all the people go as you have asked; only they must not take their flocks and herds."

But Moses answered boldly, "We shall take with us everything that we have when we go to serve our God."

Now Phâr'-āōh became very angry, and he said, "Get out of my sight. And if I ever see your face again I shall kill you."

Moses answered bravely, "It shall be just as you say; for you shall never see my face again. But know this: God will send one more terrible plague upon you and your people, after which the Israelites will go away out of your land." And so saying he walked out of the Egyptian court.

———————•———————

STORY 6

WHEN THE DEATH-ANGEL VISITED PHARAOH'S PALACE
Exodus 11—13

Evening shadows were beginning to creep over the land of Goshen and across the barren fields of Egypt. Everything had grown quiet around the walls and buildings where the Israelites had toiled. Never again would the men return to pick up their tools and work for Phâr'-āōh. The time had come when they were going to leave Gō'-shĕn.

Before this God had told Moses that one more plague was coming upon Phâr'-āōh and upon Egypt. So terrible should it be that Phâr'-āōh would want to drive the Israelites out of the land. "Tell the people to get ready to leave quickly," the Lord had said; "for they must start at once when Phâr'-āōh's messenger comes."

And the Israelites believed now that God had sent Moses to help them. They honored him as a great man, indeed, and were ready to obey him because they saw the wonders that God brought upon Egypt through Moses' words. Many of the Egyptians, too, honored Moses as a great man, and became friendly toward the Israelites. They even seemed eager to please the people whom they once hated and scorned as slaves. They had seen how God protected his people from the troubles that came upon Egypt.

ISRAELITES SPRINKLING BLOOD ON THE DOOR-FRAME

On this evening every household in Gō'-shĕn was very busy. Instead of preparing for a restful night of sleep, every man, woman, and child was wide awake and very much excited about something. They were obeying the command that Moses had given them from God. Every father was killing a lamb and sprinkling blood upon the door-frame of his dwelling. Every mother was preparing vegetables to cook with the roasted lamb. Every boy and girl was helping to gather the flocks and herds from the scattered pasture-lands of Gō'-shĕn, or to run errands for his parents.

"Tonight at midnight," Moses had said, "God will send an angel through the land, and every house where blood is not sprinkled upon the door-frame this angel will enter. And he will bring death to the eldest child in that home." Moses told the Israelites to kill a lamb for each family, and sprinkle their door-frames with blood. "Then," said Moses, "roast the lamb and with it cook vegetables, and prepare for a midnight supper. For when the death-angel passes over the land you must be dressed and ready to start on a journey. You must eat your

THE DEATH-ANGEL VISITED THE HOUSE OF PHARAOH

supper standing around the table. Neither shall any of you go out into the darkness, lest the angel meet you there and you die."

This midnight supper was called the "Pass-over" supper, because the angel passed over the houses of the Israelites when he saw their blood-sprinkled door-frames. And God commanded that the Israelites should eat such a supper once each year, at the same time, in memory of the night when he kept them from death in Egypt.

Now, the Egyptians did not sprinkle blood on their door-frames, nor prepare a midnight meal. Every one of them had gone to bed as usual, expecting to sleep soundly until the next daydawn. But at midnight they were awakened. Even Phâr'-aōh was aroused. He hurried to the bedside of his eldest son—and found him dead. What a terrible plague! Phâr'-aōh knew God had done this, and he cried aloud. In every home in Egypt the same sad cry arose, "Our eldest child is dead!" What a bitter time!

Not waiting until morning should come, Phâr'-āoh sent a swift messenger to Gō'-shĕn in search of Moses and Aaron. There he found every one wide awake, all of them ready to start on their journey. "Phâr'-āoh has sent word that you and all your people must leave Gō'-shĕn at once," the messenger said. "And he demands that you take everything with you just as you have requested. Do not leave anything behind." The Egyptians, too, sent messengers to Gō'-shĕn and urged the Israelites to hurry out of the land. "We shall all die if you stay here longer," they said.

For many years the Israelites had been slaves. They had no money and they had nothing that could be used as money. Now, at God's command, Moses told the people to ask their Egyptian neighbors for jewels of silver and of gold. And the Egyptians opened their treasure-boxes and gave freely to the Israelites. So eager were they for the Israelites to go away that they were willing to give them anything for which they asked.

And very early in the morning, without waiting to eat breakfast, the Israelites began to leave Gō'-shĕn. Like a great army, six hundred thousand men with their wives and children marched out of Egypt. They took also their flocks of sheep and herds of cattle. The women had mixed dough in their pans for bread but had not put leaven, or yeast, in it to make it rise. They carried the pans on their heads, as people carry loads in that country. When they stopped to eat, they baked the dough in cakes over coals of fire, and this was called unleavened bread. And a rule was made that for one week in every year the Israelites should eat bread without leaven, or yeast, in it. This week was afterwards celebrated as a feast, and was called the Feast of the Unleavened Bread.

Moses and Aaron led the people out of Egypt just as shepherds lead their sheep to fresh pasture-lands. But they did not choose the way to go; for God went with them, and he chose the way. In the daytime he concealed his presence in a great cloud, which moved slowly before the people, and at night, when they rested, he watched over them through a pillar of fire. By day or by night the Israelites could look upon the cloud or the pillar and say, "Our God is going with us, and he is leading the way."

Among the things that the Israelites carried out of Egypt was a coffin. In this coffin the body of Joseph had rested for hundreds of years. You remember that before Joseph died he commanded the

Israelites not to bury him in Egypt, but to place his body in a coffin and carry it back to Canaan when they should return some day to live again in that land. He asked to be buried in the cave where Abraham, and Isaac, and Jacob, his father, had been buried. And now, though long years had passed, the men who were the great, great-grandsons of this mighty prince in Egypt were now carrying his bones back to be buried in the land God had promised to his people.

STORY 7

HOW GOD SHOWED HIS POWER AT THE RED SEA
Exod. 14:1—15:21

When the Israelites came into Gō'-shĕn, they numbered only seventy people. Now when they were returning again to Canaan they numbered many thousands.

This great army was divided into twelve companies, or tribes, and these tribes were called after the names of Israel's sons. There was the tribe of Reuben, Israel's eldest son, in which every one was a descendant of Reuben; and the tribe of Simeon, Israel's second son, in which every one was a descendant of Simeon. And so it was in each of the twelve tribes, which bore the names of Israel's sons.

After this great company left Gō'-shĕn, with their flocks and herds, God led them by the cloud to the shore of the Red Sea. Here they camped. Then they planned to rest from their march.

But suddenly a cry rose in the camp, "Phâr'-aōh's army is coming upon us! We shall be taken as prisoners or else be killed!" The people looked, and sure enough, Phâr'-aōh's army was coming behind them and shutting them away from the only road to safety. They could not swim across the sea. Neither could they fight against Phâr'-aōh's skilful soldiers, for they had never been trained for battle. How frightened they were!

At first the people blamed Moses for bringing greater trouble upon them than they had ever known before. But Moses was not to blame. He had only followed the cloud in which God's presence dwelt, and the cloud had led them here. God wished to show his great power once more to the proud king who refused to obey him.

When Moses cried to God for help, the Lord told him to speak to the people and quiet them. They were all crying out in fear. He commanded them to stand still and see the wonderful path God was mak-

THE PILLAR OF FIRE GOING BEFORE THE HOSTS OF ISRAEL

THE ISRAELITES SAFE, AND THE EGYPTIANS BEING DROWNED

ing for their escape. Then the cloud moved backward and stopped between their camp and Phâr'-aōh's army. To the Israelites the cloud became a pillar of fire and lightened their camp all the night, but to the Egyptians the cloud became all darkness.

God told Moses to stretch his rod over the water of the Red Sea and divide it into two seas. Moses obeyed, and God sent a strong wind, which swept a wide path through the waters and dried the ground. On each side of this path the waters rose like a high wall, and stood still until every one of the Israelites and their flocks and herds had crossed in safety to the other side.

Now Phâr'-aōh's heart had hardened again after he sent the Israelites out of Gō'-shĕn. And Phâr'-aōh said, "I have made a great mistake by letting all my slaves go free. I must send my army after them and bring them back." So he had followed the Israelites. When the cloud lifted and he and his army saw the Israelites walking through the sea upon a dry path between two walls of water, they rushed after them. For a while all went well, but when Phâr'-aōh's army was far out from the shore, trouble came upon him and his soldiers. The horses became tangled in the harness and their feet began to sink in the sand. The chariot-wheels came off. "Let us go back!" the soldiers cried. "Israel's God is fighting against us!" But it was too late; they could not go back, for the walls of water on each side fell down and the whole army was drowned.

This was a great deliverance to the Israelites. They saw that God had saved them from their enemies, and that he had even destroyed the ones who troubled them so many years. Now they were free from slavery.

Moses wrote a beautiful song about this deliverance, and all the people sang and rejoiced together. The women played musical instruments called timbrels, and followed Miriam, the sister of Moses and Aaron, through the camp, singing praises to God.

STORY 8

WHAT HAPPENED IN THE WILDERNESS OF SHUR

Exod. 15: 22-27

After the Israelites celebrated their great deliverance from the Egyptian army, they began their march across the Wilderness of Shur. This was a country very unlike the land of Gō'-shĕn. No waving fields of grain could they see, no grassy pasture-lands could they find for their flocks and herds. On every side the country looked barren and dreary. By and by they came to a camping-place called Mâr'-ăh, and here they found more trouble.

The Israelites began to learn that trouble came in other countries besides Egypt, and from other causes besides wicked taskmasters and proud, hard-hearted, selfish kings. In this wilderness they were suffering because they could find no water to drink. The cattle and sheep were thirsty, too, and every one was tired from the long march across the barren country. At Mâr'-ăh they found a spring of water, and with a glad cry they ran forward to get a drink. But the water was so bitter they could not swallow it. How unhappy they felt! They looked unkindly at Moses and were ready to blame him again for their troubles.

Moses, too, was thirsty, and he felt sorry for the people. But instead of growing impatient and ugly, he cried to God for help. And God told him what to do.

Near the spring where the bitter water was found grew a tree. God told Moses to cut this tree down and throw it into the spring. Moses did so, and the waters became sweet. Then the people drank deeply and were satisfied. The cattle and sheep, too, had an abundance to drink.

God wished to teach the people to trust him for their helper when troubles came. He probably wished to show them by this miracle how he could heal their bodies when sickness should come upon them. He also promised that if the people would obey his voice and do right, he would not let them suffer from any of the diseases that he had sent upon the Egyptians.

From the camp at Mâr'-ăh the Israelites moved forward again, and came to another stopping-place. Here they found a beautiful grove of palm-trees and twelve wells of water. The name of this place was Ē'-lĭm. The people pitched their tents beneath the trees and drank from the wells. They were glad to find such a pleasant place to camp in the wilderness.

STORY 9

HOW GOD FED THE HUNGRY PEOPLE IN THE WILDERNESS
Exodus 16

The Israelites enjoyed their rest at Ē'-lĭm; but after some days the cloud in which God's presence dwelt lifted and began to move slowly away. By this sign the people understood that God wished to lead them farther on their journey. So they took down their tents and prepared to start forward again.

Now they entered a great desert country which lay between Ē'-lĭm and the mountain where God spoke to Moses from the burning bush. This country was called the Wilderness of Sin.

Like fretful children, the Israelites began to find fault with Moses and Aaron. First one thing, then another, displeased them. They could find so little food to eat in the great wilderness, and they grew hungry. Then they forgot how much they had suffered in Egypt. They forgot how many times God had helped them out of trouble. They thought only of their hunger, and of their unhappy state. They said, "We wish we had never left Egypt, for there we always had plenty to eat. We would rather have died there than die in this dreary country."

Moses heard the people complain and he was grieved. God, too, heard them. He spoke to Moses and said, "The people are sinning against me when they find fault with you because you led them out of Egypt. I shall not let them die of hunger, but I have brought them to this place so that they may know that I am the giver of all their blessings. In the evening I shall send meat to them, and in the morning I shall give them bread from heaven."

Then Moses called the people together to hear the words of the Lord. While Aaron spoke to them they looked toward the wilderness and saw in the cloud a glorious light. They knew God had heard their complaints.

In the evening a great many quails flew into the camp, and the people killed them for meat. The next morning a heavy dew lay on the ground. When the sun beamed down warm and bright the dew disappeared, and left the ground covered with something which looked white, like frost. "What is this?" the people asked each other when they looked out of their tents and saw the strange food lying on the ground. In their language "what is this?" are the words "man hu," and so the people said to each other, "Man hu? man hu?" Afterwards the food was called măn'-nă.

Moses told the people that God had sent this food to be their bread. "Go and gather it," said he, "and bring as much as you will need for today. Do not keep any in your vessels for tomorrow, because God will send a fresh supply. Each morning he will cause this bread to fall, except on the morning of the seventh day. On the sixth day you must gather twice as much as usual, and what is left after you have

eaten of that gathering you may keep for the seventh day. It will not spoil on the seventh day, because God wishes you to keep that day as a holy Sabbath and do no work."

At Moses' bidding the people rushed out with vessels and gathered the măn'-nă from the ground. They cooked it, and the taste of this food pleased them. They were glad God had supplied their need.

Now, some of the people were not careful to obey Moses.

GOD SENDING QUAILS INTO THE CAMP OF ISRAEL

When they saw they had prepared more măn'-nă than was needful for one day they kept it until the next morning. But the bread was no longer fit to eat, and they had to go out again to gather a fresh supply. And some failed to gather twice as much as usual on the sixth morning. But when they went out with their vessels on the Sabbath morning to pick up the wonderful bread they could find none. God was not pleased because they had disobeyed. And they had nothing to eat on that Sabbath.

From this time God sent măn'-nă to the Israelites every morning, except on the Sabbath, until they came to the land of Canaan.

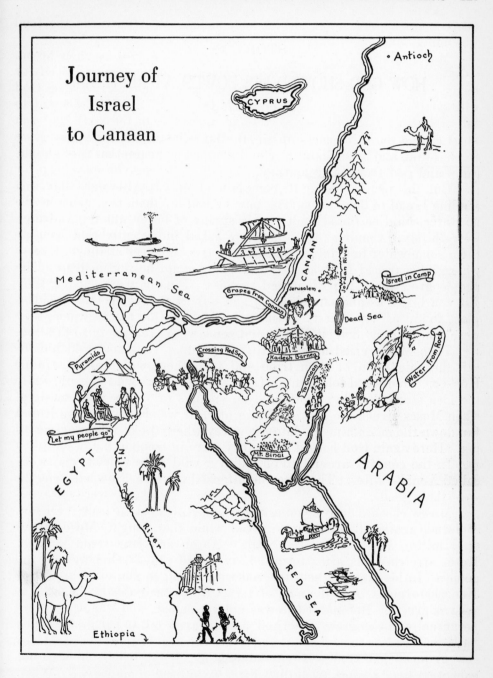

Journey of
Israel
to Canaan

STORY 10

HOW GOD SHOWED HIS POWER AT REPHIDIM

Exodus 17, 18

Leaving the Wilderness of Sin, the Israelites came to a place called Rĕph'-ĭ-dĭm, and here again the cloud stopped as a sign that they should camp and rest from their journey.

But the people began to complain at once. Although God was sending bread to them every day, now he had led them to a place where no water could be found—not even a spring of bitter water. And they were thirsty. Coming to Moses, they asked impatiently that he give them some water to drink. But Moses was as helpless as they. Everywhere he searched for water, but nowhere could he find a drop. The people grew more impatient and restless. Finally they cried, "Why did you bring us and our children and our cattle out to this dreadful place to kill us with thirst?" Instead of asking God to help them, they were complaining against Moses, and some were even ready to kill him.

Then Moses cried aloud to God for help. The Lord told him to call the chief men of each tribe and take them with him to Mount Hôr'-ĕb. There God told him to strike a certain rock with his rod, while the men stood near by. Although no springs or rivers were in sight, when Moses struck the rock a stream of clear water flowed from it and ran down the mountain-side into the valley where the people were camping. Here again God helped when they were in trouble.

In the country around Rĕph'-ĭ-dĭm a wild people lived who were called Ă-măl'-ĕk-ītes. These people attacked the Israelites, and tried to steal their goods.

Moses chose a brave young man named Joshua to lead the army of Israel against their enemies. And while they fought, Moses stood on a hilltop and watched the battle. Aaron and Hur stood by him. Moses stretched his arms toward heaven and prayed God to help his people. In his hand he held the rod with which so many miracles had been performed. And the men of Israel drove their enemies back into the wilderness. But the battle was not yet ended.

Finally Moses grew very tired, and his arms fell to his sides. Then the Ă-măl'-ĕk-ītes turned about and drove the men of Israel back. Moses saw at once that God was not helping his people when he was not holding the rod aloft. So he lifted it toward heaven once more. When

his arms grew very tired again Aaron and Hur brought a large stone
for Moses to sit upon. Then they stood, one on each side of him, and
held up his arms until evening. The battle then ended, and Joshua
returned with his men to the camp at Rĕph'-ĭ-dĭm. The people knew God
had helped them to drive their enemies away.

At this place Moses built an altar, to worship God.

One day while the Israelites were camping at Rĕph'-ĭ-dĭm some visitors from Mĭd'-ĭ-ăn came to see Moses. They were Jĕth'-rō, Moses'
father-in-law, and Zĭp'-pŏ-răh, Moses' wife, and Gĕr'-shom and Ĕl-ĭ-
ē'-zĕr, Moses' sons. Jĕth'-rō had heard how wonderfully God saved the
Israelites from Pharaoh's slavery, and he wished to talk with Moses. He
brought sacrifices to offer upon the altar which Moses had built, and
the Israelites also worshiped with him before the Lord. During his
visit Jĕth'-rō told Moses how to judge the people and how to lessen his
burden. Then he bade Moses good-by and went to his own country.

STORY 11

THE VOICE FROM A SMOKING MOUNTAIN
Exodus 19—24

Mount Hôr'-ĕb was the place where God had talked to Moses from a
burning bush. This mountain was also called Sī'-naî. In front of this
mountain lay a wilderness, which was also called Sī'-naî. When Moses
tended sheep for his father-in-law he used to lead the flocks through
this wilderness. He learned where to find grassy plains and plenty of
water. And now he brought the Israelites from Rĕph'-ĭ-dĭm to this place,
and they camped under the shadow of the great, rock-walled mountain.

While the people were busy arranging their tents and preparing
food, Moses climbed the mountain to talk with God. And the Lord
said, "Tell the people that I shall speak to them from this mountain.
On the third day I shall speak, and they shall hear my voice. Go, now,
and bid them wash their clothes and make ready to meet me."

When the Israelites heard Moses' words they grew busy at once.
Every one found something to do. Some carried water from the springs,
and others washed soiled clothing. They were getting ready for a
special time, when they might stand with Moses before God.

On the third morning a thick, dark cloud rested on top of Mount

Sĭ'-nâĭ. Terrible thunders rolled down the mountain-sides into the valley, and sharp lightnings broke through the thick cloud and flashed across the sky. The whole mountain shook. The Israelites had never seen nor heard such before, and now they trembled in their tents.

Then a trumpet sounded from the mountain-top. Perhaps an angel blew it. God had told Moses to gather the people together when they

MOSES ON THE MOUNT

should hear the sound of a trumpet. And now they gathered together near the foot of the shaking mountain and listened to hear God's voice. Moses said, "Do not come any nearer, for God has said the mountain is holy and that if you touch it you shall die."

The trumpet sounded louder, and the mountain began to smoke as though a great fire were burning on the inside. Then Moses called, and a voice answered him from the mountain-top. It was the voice of God. And this voice spoke the words of the Ten Commandments so that all the people heard. As they listened great fear came into their hearts. They hurried back into the valley. And they cried to Moses, "Let not God speak to us in this voice of thunder, for we shall die. We will hear when you speak his words, and we will obey them."

Moses answered, "Do not be afraid when God speaks. He wishes to teach you that he is a great God, and holy. He wants you to serve him only, and never to bow down to other gods, as other people do."

Still the people stood far off, for they were afraid. But Moses was not afraid. He went into the thick darkness where God was, and listened while God told him about the many laws which he wanted the Israelites to obey. And Moses wrote the words of God in a book.

When Moses came down from the mountain, he told the people all the words God had spoken; and they answered, "We will be obedient."

Early in the morning of the next day, Moses built an altar under the shadow of the great mountain, and the young men brought offerings of oxen to give to the Lord. The people assembled again, and Moses read to them from the book of the covenant. Then they said, "All that God has spoken we will do. We will be obedient." And Moses took blood from the offerings of oxen which the young men had brought and sprinkled the blood upon the altar and upon the people. He said, "This is the blood of the covenant." We remember that a covenant made by God is a promise that will never be broken if the people to whom the promise is made will be obedient. And we remember that the people worshiped God by offering the blood of animals instead of their own blood because they had sinned. Since Christ Jesus, our Savior, died upon the cross and gave his life-blood, people no longer need to worship God with blood-offerings, like they did before he died. He was the perfect offering for sin; and when we believe that he died for us, then we may be saved from our sins.

When this solemn service ended, the people went back to their tent-homes in the valley, and Moses took Aaron and his two sons, Nadab and Ă-bī'-hū, and seventy of the old men with him up the mountain. God had commanded them to worship him there. And they saw the glory of God and they were not afraid. But they did not come near to the wonderful brightness of His glory. Only Moses came near.

After this time Moses went up on the mountain again, and took Joshua with him. He commanded the people to be obedient to Aaron and Hur until he should return. For forty days he listened to God's words, and the Lord gave him two flat tablets of stone upon which he had written with his own hand the words of the Ten Commandments. These were the words he spoke in a voice of thunder to the people.

THE TEN COMMANDMENTS

Thou shalt have no other gods before me.

Thou shalt not make unto thee any graven image, or any likeness of anything that is in heaven above, or that is in the earth beneath, or that is in the water under the earth: thou shalt not bow down thyself to them, nor serve them: for I the Lord thy God am a jealous God, visiting the iniquity of the fathers upon the children unto the third and fourth generation of them that hate me; and showing mercy unto thousands of them that love me and keep my commandments.

Thou shalt not take the name of the Lord thy God in vain; for the Lord will not hold him guiltless that taketh his name in vain.

Remember the Sabbath-day to keep it holy. Six days shalt thou labor, and do all thy work; but the seventh day is the Sabbath of the Lord thy God: in it thou shalt not do any work, thou, nor thy son, nor thy daughter, thy man servant, nor thy maid servant, nor thy cattle, nor thy stranger that is within thy gates: for in six days the Lord made heaven and earth, the sea, and all that in them is, and rested the seventh day: wherefore the Lord blessed the Sabbath-day, and hallowed it.

Honor thy father and thy mother: that thy days may be long upon the land which the Lord thy God giveth thee.

Thou shalt not kill.

Thou shalt not commit adultery.

Thou shalt not steal.

Thou shalt not bear false witness against thy neighbor.

Thou shalt not covet thy neighbor's house.

Thou shalt not covet thy neighbor's wife, nor his man servant, nor his maid servant, nor his ox, nor his ass, nor anything that is thy neighbor's.

STORY 12

THE STORY OF A GOLDEN CALF
Exodus 32

While Moses was up on top of Mount Sī'-nâi talking with God, and Joshua was waiting for him on the mountain-side, the Israelites could see from their tent doors in the valley what seemed to be a flame of fire leaping up toward the sky, day and night, from the place where Moses was in the thick cloud. They knew this was a sign of God's presence on the mountain.

But when the days passed by into weeks and still Moses did not return, the Israelites began to think he would never come back to them again. They grew restless. They soon forgot the great terror which filled their hearts when God's voice thundered to them from the smoking mountain in words they understood. They seemed to forget even the words that God spoke. And then it was easy to act as though they had forgotten their promise to Moses, that they would obey the words of the Lord.

One day they came to Aaron and said, "We know something dreadful has happened to Moses, because he does not come back." They complained because Moses had led them into the lonely wilderness and left them without a brave leader to take his place. Every day they grew more restless. Finally they planned to go on without Moses. So they came to Aaron and said, "Make us gods to go before us and show us the way."

Now Aaron was not a brave man. He feared the people. He remembered the time when they wanted to kill Moses because they could find no water, at Rĕph'-ĭ-dĭm. Perhaps he thought they would throw stones at him and kill him if he refused to do as they asked. So he did not point them to the flame of fire which still leaped toward the sky from the mountain-top, where God was talking with Moses. He did not remind them of their promise to serve no other God except the One who spoke to them in a voice of thunder. Instead of bravely doing these things, he told them to bring their golden earrings, which the Egyptians had given them before they left Gō'-shĕn. Then he took the gold that they brought and melted it carefully in a fire. When it was melted together, he shaped the mass of gold into the form of a calf, or a young ox, such as the Egyptians worshiped. This calf he set up in the middle of the camp.

Then the Israelites made a great feast and began to worship the golden calf, just as they had seen their Egyptian neighbors worship oxen at their temples. This was very wicked. As they bowed themselves before the idol and sang and danced around it they broke two of the Ten Commandments which God had given them to obey. In the first command God had said, "Thou shalt serve no other gods"; and in the second command he had forbidden them to worship before anything they made, calling it a god. Now they were even crying out, "This is the god which brought us out of Egypt!" Nothing could have been more wicked.

And God saw the golden calf. He saw the Israelites bowing down and worshiping it. He heard them singing and dancing around it. And he was greatly displeased. He said to Moses, "The Israelites have sinned against me. They have broken their promise and made a god of gold. Now they are worshiping it, and crying, 'This is the god which led us out of Egypt!' Let me alone, Moses, and I will quickly destroy them all, for they are not fit to be called my people." God promised to raise up another nation from the children of Moses to be his chosen people.

But Moses loved the Israelites even though they had sometimes been unkind to him. He did not want God to destroy them all. So he prayed earnestly for God to spare their lives even though they had sinned greatly. He believed they might yet learn to serve the true God. And because Moses prayed for them, the Lord did not destroy them as he had planned.

Then Moses hurried down the mountain-side with Joshua, carrying in his arms the two wonderful tablets of stone upon which God had written the words of the Ten Commandments. It was hard for Moses to believe the Israelites had sinned so greatly. But as they came nearer the valley Joshua said, "I hear the sound of war in the camp." Then they saw the people dancing and shouting before the god Aaron made.

Moses understood now why God wished to destroy the Israelites. The sight of their idol-worship filled him with great anger. He threw the wonderful tablets of stone upon the rocks at the foot of the mountain-path and broke them in pieces. Perhaps he thought, "What is the use of keeping these tablets when the people have already broken two of the great commandments God wrote upon them?" Then he rushed into the camp and tore the idol down before the people. He broke it in pieces and threw it into the fire, he ground it into fine dust and threw the dust into the water from which the people drank. This made the water taste very bitter indeed, but Moses compelled the people to drink it.

Moses' sudden appearance in the camp broke up the merry feast. His anger quieted the people. But many of them were sorry he had come back. They wished to keep on worshiping the god Aaron had made. Then Moses called Aaron and asked, "What have these people done that you have brought this terrible sin upon them?"

And Aaron answered, "Do not be angry with me! You know these people, how their hearts are evil. And when they asked me to

make a god for them to worship I told them to bring their golden earrings. I cast the earrings into the fire, and this calf came out!''

Moses was still angry. He cried to the people in a loud voice,
''Whoever is on the Lord's side, let him come and stand by me!''
Then every man who belonged to the tribe of Levi left the Israelite
host and stood by Moses. Then Moses told these brave men to take
their swords and go through the camp and kill every person they found
who still wanted to worship the golden calf. ''Do not spare one of
them,'' he commanded. And the men killed three thousand people
that day.

This was a sad time in Israel's camp. But no one was quite so
sad as Moses. He understood how terrible was the sin of his people
and he feared that God might never forgive them. The next day he
called them together and said, ''You have done very wickedly, and in
God's sight your sin is very great. I will go up to him now and will
make an offering for your sin. Perhaps he will forgive you.''

And Moses went before the Lord and offered himself to die with
the people. But God said, ''Those who have sinned against me must
suffer for their own sins.''

Then God told Moses to cut two tablets out of stone like the ones
he had broken, and bring them up on the Mount. And God wrote on
those tablets the same words as he had written upon the others, and
God talked with Moses again for forty days and forty nights on top of
the mountain.

———•———

STORY 13

HOW GOD PLANNED TO LIVE AMONG HIS PEOPLE
Exodus 34—39; Numbers 1—5

The Israelites were glad when they heard that Moses was coming down from Mount Sī′naî with two stone tablets in his arms the second time. They went out to meet him. Although he had been gone forty
days and nights, this time they had not complained, nor wished to
worship another god. But when they saw him coming they were afraid.
They all turned back toward the camp.

Moses could not understand why they should be so frightened.
He called to them, and the rulers of the people stopped. Then they
turned around and went back again with Aaron to meet Moses. They

told him why every one was afraid of him. They said, "The skin of your face is shining with a strange light, like the sun, and we can not look upon it." Moses did not know that God's glory was shining upon his face. But he put a veil over his face, and then all the Israelites came back and listened to his words.

God had given to Moses the rules that he wished the people to obey. These rules, or commandments, Moses wrote in a book. But the Ten Commandments, which God had spoken to the people in a voice of thunder, God himself wrote upon the two tablets of stone. Whenever Moses told the people about God's words he wore a veil over his face, but whenever he talked with God he took the veil off.

Now the time had come when God wanted to let the people know that he was living among them, right in their camp. He wanted them to have a certain place where they might always worship him. He wanted them to build such a place, where the sign of his presence might dwell just as it dwelt in the cloud by day and the pillar of fire by night.

The Egyptians had temples built of stone, where they worshiped their gods. They had idols of gold and idols of silver and living animals in their temples, before which they bowed down and worshiped. This kind of worship is called idolatry.

God wanted the Israelites to be his own people. He wanted them to act differently from other people. He wanted them to worship him only, because he is the only true God. So he told Moses about his plan to dwell among the people, and he showed Moses how to build the place of worship.

When the people heard about God's plan to live among them, they were glad. They offered cheerfully to give the best of everything they had to help build a place where they might worship the Lord, their God. They brought gifts of gold and of silver, of jewels, of wood, and of beautiful linen cloth. They brought also the skins of animals. And God chose two wise men, named Bĕz'-ă-lĕel and Ă-hō'-lĭ-ăb, to teach other men how to use these gifts and make everything for the place of worship.

Now the people themselves were living in tent-homes. These dwelling-places they could easily move about from one camp to another as they journeyed toward Canaan. God told Moses to build the place of worship somewhat like a tent, with board walls and with top of cloth and animal skins, so that it could be taken apart and moved easily when the people moved their camp. This kind of place was called a tabernacle.

And God told the people exactly what kind of material he wanted them to use when they made the tabernacle. He told them what kind of furniture he wanted them to put inside the tabernacle. And he told them how to make the furniture and where to place each piece of it.

The people were careful to obey all the words of the Lord. They worked faithfully and brought more gifts than were needed for the building. Even the women helped, for they spun beautiful linen cloth and made very pretty needlework.

When everything was finished, God told Moses to set up the tabernacle in the middle of the camp. And he chose the men of the tribe of Levi to take care of the tabernacle. Moses and Aaron belonged to this tribe. God told Moses to divide the whole tribe of Levi into three groups, one group for each of Levi's sons. And God said these three groups should camp one on the north side and one on the south side and one on the west side of the tabernacle. Moses and Aaron set their tent-homes on the east side, or in front of the door of the tabernacle.

After this time, when God chose men from the twelve tribes to go out to battle against their enemies he did not take any men from the tribe of Levi. He divided the tribe of Joseph's descendants into two separate tribes, and these tribes were given the names of Joseph's two sons, Ē'-phră-ĭm and Mă-năs'-sēh. In this way he still had twelve tribes to go out to battle, and twelve tribes to camp, three on each of the four sides, around the place of worship.

STORY 14

THE TABERNACLE. WHERE THE ISRAELITES WORSHIPED GOD

Exodus 40

The tabernacle, where the Israelites worshiped God, was surrounded by an uncovered space, called a court. This court was closed in by curtains, which were made of fine linen, and hung upon brass posts. The curtains were between seven and eight feet high. At the end toward the east was an opening, through which the priests and their helpers might enter.

Near the entrance, or door of the court, stood a great altar. This was called the "altar of burnt offering." You remember that whenever people of those times wished to worship God they built altars. Upon those altars they laid their gifts and sacrifices and burned them. They always built their altars of earth or of stones piled up. This altar of the tabernacle was built differently. It was built of thin boards, because God wanted the people to carry it with them wherever they journeyed. It was like a square box without bottom or top, and covered on the inside and on the outside with brass so that it would not catch fire and be burned. Inside this altar a metal grating was fastened on which the fire was kindled. The ashes would fall through this grating to the ground. The altar was about five feet high and about seven feet square. Two long poles were fastened to two opposite sides of it, through rings at the corners, and whenever the Israelites moved their camp the priests carried the altar by placing the poles upon their shoulders.

Near the altar of burnt offering stood a large basin, or tank, called a laver. When the tabernacle was set up, this laver was filled with water, to be used by the priests for washing their hands and feet, and perhaps for washing parts of the offerings. Much water was needed for the worship of the tabernacle.

Further in the court stood the tabernacle itself. The walls of this place were made of boards covered with gold and placed on silver bases. The roof was made of four curtains, one laid above another. The inner curtain was of very beautiful cloth, while the outer curtains were made of skins of animals, to keep out the rain. The front of the tabernacle opened into the court. There was no door, but sometimes a curtain hung before the opening.

The tabernacle was divided into two rooms by a beautiful linen curtain, which hung from the roof. The first room, which opened into the court, was called the "holy place"; and the second room, which had no entrance except through the holy place, was called the "holy of holies."

In the first room were three things: a table, a golden candlestick, and a small altar. The table was covered with gold, and twelve loaves of bread were placed upon it, as if the people of each tribe were giving an offering of food to God. The golden candlestick was made of pure gold, and it held seven burning lights. The small altar was called the "altar of incense," because sweet perfumes were burnt upon it. The fire upon this altar was to be lighted from the altar of burnt offering. Everything in this room was made of gold or was covered with gold— even the board walls on each side. And the curtain-hangings and the curtain-ceiling were decorated with beautiful colors.

The second room contained only the "ark of the covenant." This ark was a box, or chest, covered entirely with gold, on the inside and on the outside. The lid of this box was called the "mercy-seat." At each end of the mercy-seat was a strange figure. These were called chĕr'-ū-bĭm. They were made of gold. The two stone tablets upon which God had written the words of the Ten Commandments were placed within the ark of the covenant.

All the furniture of the tabernacle was built so that it could be easily carried from one place to another. And the board walls were made so that they could be taken apart and moved with the furniture and the brass posts and the curtains.

When the tabernacle was set up in the middle of the camp, God moved the cloud above it and filled it with his glory. Every day the cloud rested upon the tabernacle, and every night a flame of fire leaped from its roof. And all the people saw these things, and they knew that God was living among them.

———•———

STORY 15

HOW THE PEOPLE WORSHIPED GOD AT THE TABERNACLE
Leviticus 1—10:7

After the tabernacle was set up, Moses did not need to climb Mount Sĭ'-naî any more to talk with God. Now he could enter the tabernacle, where God lived among the people, and hear the words of the Lord.

Before this time, whenever any one wished to worship God, that one would build an altar and burn his offering upon it, calling on the Lord to forgive his sins. And the Lord would hear him. But now Moses told the people that whenever they wished to worship God and pray for the forgiveness of their sins they should bring their sacrifice to the men at the door of the court, whose duty it should be to tend the altar of burnt offering. Those men, Moses said, would be called priests. And the priests would offer the sacrifices of the people before the Lord, and God would accept them.

God chose Aaron to be the high priest, and to him he gave the most important work in the tabernacle worship. Aaron's sons God chose to be priests also, and they were to be Aaron's helpers.

On the morning when the tabernacle worship first began, God told Moses to call the people together before the door of the tabernacle, and there, in the presence of them all, to anoint both Aaron and his sons with oil and to put on them the beautiful priestly robes which they should wear. God wanted the people to see that he had chosen these men to do his work in the court, and in the tabernacle where no one else except Moses was allowed to enter.

After Aaron was made high priest he offered a lamb on the altar of burnt offering as a sacrifice for the sins of the people. He did not put any fire on the altar, but God sent fire, which burned up the lamb. When the people saw this they shouted with joy and fell down on their faces, because now they knew God was pleased with their offering and with their priests.

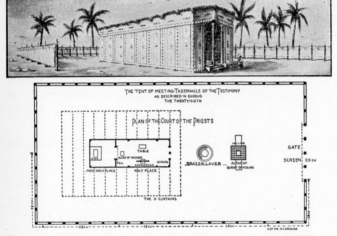

From that time the priests offered two sacrifices f o r sin upon the altar of b u r n t offering every day—in the morning and in the evening. God reminded the people by these sacrifices that sin is an awful thing.

And t h e fire which God sent on the great altar was never allowed to

THE TABERNACLE; PLAN OF TABERNACLE AND COURT

die out. Every morning at sunrise the priests raked the coals and placed fresh wood upon them, to keep the fire burning brightly. Even when the tabernacle was moved to another camping-place on their journey to Canaan, the priests would carry burning coals from the altar in a covered pan. God had lighted this fire, and they wished to keep it always burning.

Inside the holy place, you remember, was a second altar, called the altar of incense, upon which sweet perfumes were burned before the Lord. It was the duty of the priests every morning and every evening to carry a fire-shovelful of burning coals from the great altar to light the fire on the altar of incense. They carried these coals in a bowl which hung on chains. Such a bowl was called a censer. God commanded that the altar of incense should never be lighted by any other fire except from the one which he had kindled upon the great altar.

Another duty of the priests' was to keep twelve loaves of bread upon the golden table in the holy place. Each Sabbath morning they were to bring fresh loaves, and remove the stale ones. These loaves were called shewbread. No one except a priest was permitted to eat this bread.

The priests also tended the seven lamps that burned on the golden candlestick. Every day they filled the lamp-bowls with fresh oil, and they kept the lights always burning.

One day not long after the tabernacle worship had begun, a sad thing happened. Two of Aaron's sons, Nadab and Ă-bī'-hū, were preparing to light the fire on the altar of incense. They disobeyed God, and did not carry burning coals from the great altar but took other fire. And while they stood before the altar of incense in the holy place suddenly they fell down dead. Thus God punished them because they had dared to disobey his word.

Moses would not allow Aaron nor his other sons to touch the bodies of Nadab and Ă-bī'-hū. He called two men who were Levites, and cousins of the dead men, to carry the bodies away and bury them in the desert sand outside the camp.

This was a great lesson to Aaron and to his other sons. They saw that God expected them carefully to obey all of his words.

STORY 16

THE ISRAELITES JOURNEY FROM SINAI TO THE BORDER OF CANAAN

Numbers 9—12

One day while the Israelites were still camping near Mount Sī'-nâi God reminded Moses that a whole year had passed since they left Egypt. And God said, "The time has come when you must eat another Passover supper, for I want you to remember how the death-angel passed over your homes in Gō'-shĕn." Moses told the people the words of the Lord; then every family in every tribe prepared a supper like the one they had eaten before Pharaoh drove them out of his country.

Not many days after this Passover supper had been eaten, the Israelites saw the cloud lift from above the tabernacle and float slowly away toward the north. They knew the time had come when they must journey on. They had lived for nearly a year in the wilderness of Sī'-nâi, under the shadow of the great mountain, and no doubt they felt glad to start forward again toward Canaan. They followed the floating cloud on and on across the barren country for three days' journey. Then the cloud stopped, and while they rested in their tents some began to complain. God was much displeased at this, and he sent a fire among them. Many of those who complained were killed by the fire. The other people were frightened, and they cried to Moses for help. They thought they might all be killed. Then Moses prayed, and God took the fire away. Moses called the name of this camping-place Tăb'-ĕ-räh, which means, "A burning."

From Tăb'-ĕ-räh the cloud led the Israelites farther north and brought them to the second stopping-place. Here the people rested again. And here they seemed to forget the terrible punishment that had come upon those who complained at Tăb'-ĕ-räh. They seemed to forget every blessing that God had sent to them. They said, "We are hungry for meat—oh, so hungry!" And they frowned when they saw the măn'-nă lying on the ground about their camp. "We are tired of this măn'-nă," they cried; "we want meat!" They talked to each other about the fish that they had eaten while they lived in Egypt, and about the vegetables that had grown in their gardens in Gō'-shĕn. And the more they talked about these things the hungrier they became. Then instead of cheerfully gathering the fresh măn'-nă, which God sent every morning, and thankfully preparing it for food, they complained while they worked and they grumbled while they ate. Finally, like pouting children, they stood in their tent doors and wept because they had no meat.

Moses was very unhappy when he saw how foolishly the Israelites were behaving. Time after time they had complained, and just as often he had prayed for them. Now he did not want to pray for them. He told the Lord he was tired of leading such unthankful people. He even wanted to die. Poor, discouraged Moses!

God, too, was much displeased with the Israelites. He knew they were unthankful and wicked. He knew they needed to be punished again. He felt sorry for Moses because the work was too heavy for him. He told Moses to choose seventy other men to help him in his work. And God caused those men to hear His words and to speak them to the people.

Because the people desired meat, God sent them birds, quails. These he caused to come in great numbers outside the camp. When the people heard about them they rushed into the desert to gather the birds. For two days and one night they worked steadily, for God had sent enough meat to last them through one whole month. But they did not take time to thank God for his food. They thought only of satisfying their hunger. And thus they added more unthankfulness to their

sins, and God punished them severely. While they were eating the
meat God sent a sickness upon them and many died. And so here at
this place, as at Tăb'-ĕ-räh, they left behind them a graveyard where the
dead bodies of their wicked relatives were buried. They called this
place by the long name of Kĭb'-rōth-hăt-tā'-ă-väh, which means, "The
graves of lust."

When the cloud moved on, it stopped next at a place called
Hă-zē'-rōth. Here Miriam and Aaron, the sister and brother of Moses,
found fault with Moses because he had married a woman who was not
an Israelite. And they questioned why he should be the chief ruler
among the people when God had sometimes spoken to them also. They
allowed a wicked feeling of envy to grow in their hearts. They envied
Moses because he was great in the eyes of all the people. They, too,
wished to be rulers, and to be called great and wise. But God was
angry with them, and he sent a dreadful disease, called leprosy, upon
Miriam. Her skin became white like snow, and when Aaron saw what
had happened he felt sorry because they had sinned against Moses and
against God. He told Moses of his sorrow, and asked him to pray that
Miriam might be healed. Moses was ready to forgive them both, and
he prayed earnestly for Miriam. God heard his prayer, and after seven
days Miriam was well again.

When the cloud lifted from Hă-zē'-rōth, it did not stop again until
the Israelites had entered the wilderness of Pâr'-ăn, which lies just outside of the promised land of Canaan.

STORY 17

HOW TEN MEN SPOILED GOD'S PLAN

Numbers 13, 14

The Israelites left the dreary desert behind them when they came
to Kā'-dĕsh-bär'-nĕ-ă, in the Wilderness of Pâr'-ăn. Now they were very
near to Canaan, the land which God had promised to give them for
their own country. Only one more march forward would take them
across the border and into the beautiful country.

But the Israelites were not ready to enter Canaan. Although they
had always taken down their tents and prepared to march whenever
God showed by his signs in the cloud that they should go forward, now
they said, "We do not know this country that lies before us. We are
not ready to enter until we may know which way to go. Let us send

men to pass through the land and search it. When they come again, they can tell us about what they have seen and which will be the safest road for us to travel." The people did not want to trust God to lead them into Canaan. Although he had done so much for them in the past, they seemed to distrust him now. He had marvelously delivered them from Pharaoh, king of Egypt. He had divided the Red Sea before

THE SPIES RETURNING FROM CANAAN

them and brought them unharmed through its midst. He had brought them through the wilderness and protected them from the dangers of the way. He had overcome their enemies for them. He had saved their lives by giving them water out of the solid rock. He had even rained food upon them from heaven. Yet now they wanted to depend more upon themselves. And God let them have their own way.

God told Moses to choose twelve men, one man from each of the

MOSES, LEADER AND LAWGIVER

A SHEPHERD OF PALESTINE

The oldest occupation of Palestine is that of the shepherd. Abraham, Isaac, Jacob, Moses, David, Amos, and many other of the Bible characters followed this occupation. The Eastern shepherds give names to their sheep as do we to dogs and horses. The shepherd leads his flock, and every sheep recognizes and obeys at once the shepherd's voice. The tender care of the shepherd for his flock is used in the Scriptures to show God's love for his children.

twelve tribes, and send them to search the land carefully. These twelve men were called spies, because they were sent to spy out the land of Canaan. Moses told them not to be afraid, for God would take care of them. And he commanded them to bring back some fruit from the land.

For forty days the spies went here and there through the promised land. They saw strong cities and small towns. They saw fields of grain and large vineyards with ripened grapes. They saw that the land was indeed beautiful, and that it was well supplied with foodstuffs. They knew that the Israelites would not need to grow hungry for meats and for vegetables in such a bountiful land.

At the end of forty days the spies returned to Israel's camp. They brought samples of the fruits that grew in Canaan. Two of them carried one large cluster of grapes on a staff between them. Never before had the Israelites seen such splendid fruit. Then ten of the spies began to tell about the land. "It is indeed a good country," they said, "but the people who live there are stronger than we. Many of them live in cities surrounded by great walls that seem to reach to the sky. Others of them are like giants—so powerful and so tall that we looked like grasshoppers in our own eyes. We were lucky to get back alive."

Those spies did not thank God for taking care of them. They did not believe God would help the Israelites to overcome the giants and to overthrow the walled cities. They had no faith in God. And when the Israelites heard their report they began to weep. Then Caleb, one of the spies who trusted in God, quieted them and said, "Do not be afraid, for we are strong enough to take the land. Let us go up at once, for we are well able to overcome it." But the people would not listen to his words. They began to weep aloud, and all through the night the noise of their weeping was heard in the camp. When morning came they began to complain against God. "We wish we had stayed in Egypt!" they said. "We had rather died back in the wilderness than to be killed by those dreadful giants in Canaan. Why has God brought us here to die? Our wives and our children will be taken for prisoners." Then they planned to choose a captain and return again to Egypt.

When Moses and Aaron heard about the plan they fell on their faces and begged the people to obey God. And Caleb and Joshua, the two spies who had faith in God, tore their clothes as a sign of deep sorrow and cried out to the people, "Do not sin so against the Lord! He has given us all the land before us, and he has taken away the courage of those who live in the land. We can easily drive them away. Let us go forward!''

Instead of listening to Caleb and Joshua, the people wanted to throw stones at them and kill them. But God would not allow them to harm his true men. While they were going about to do the evil deed, suddenly a bright light flashed upon them from the door of the tabernacle. And God spoke to Moses out of the light and said, ''I am ready now to punish these wicked people with a terrible disease, which will kill them all. I am tired of their complaining and of their wicked plans. Although I have showed my great signs to them many times, still they will not trust me nor obey my words. I will take your children, Moses, and will make of them a great nation instead of the Israelites, and to them I will give the land of Canaan.

But Moses prayed earnestly for the people. He told the Lord that the Egyptians would hear about the death of the Israelites and they would say, ''God was not able to bring them into Canaan, so he killed them in the wilderness.'' Moses reminded the Lord of his promise to be very merciful and to forgive wrong-doing.

And God for Moses' sake forgave the Israelites and did not destroy them completely. But because they had refused to go forward at the words of Caleb and Joshua, God said they should not be allowed to cross over into Canaan at that time. None of them from twenty years of age and upward should ever go into Canaan to live because they had said, ''We had rather died in the wilderness!'' To punish them God commanded that they should turn back again into the dreary wilderness and camp there until every man who had murmured should die. Then their children might go in and possess the promised land.

When the Israelites heard about this bitter punishment they did not want to go back. They said, ''We will go forward, as the Lord first commanded us.'' And their men who had been trained for battle hurried out of the camp to fight against the men of Canaan. Moses called to them, ''Don't go! God is not with you!'' But they rushed on, paying no heed to Moses' warning, and the men of Canaan came out to meet them. The battle did not last long, for the Israelites had not obeyed God, and he would not help them. Soon the men of Canaan drove them out of their land, and the Israelites ran away from the battle into the wilderness.

STORY 18

WHY GOD CAUSED THE EARTH TO SWALLOW SOME ISRAELITES

Numbers 16, 17

One day a man named Kôr'-ăh began to think wrong thoughts about Moses and about Aaron. As time went on, he allowed those wrong thoughts to grow in his mind until they became very wicked. He told others about his thoughts, and soon many people were thinking wickedly, too.

Kôr'-ăh belonged to the tribe of Levi, to which tribe Moses and Aaron also belonged. God had chosen that tribe, you remember, to take care of the tabernacle. And he had chosen Aaron, one of that tribe, to be high priest, and Aaron's sons he had chosen to be priests. No other people except the high priest, the priests, and Moses were permitted to enter the tabernacle. And no other people except the Levites were supposed to perform service at the tabernacle, because God had made the tabernacle a holy place and he had separated the Levites from the other tribes to take care of this holy place.

Kôr'-ăh thought, "I also am a Levite, and why am I not so good as Aaron?" And Kôr'-ăh envied Aaron. And two of Kôr'-ăh's friends, Dā'-thăn and Ă-bī'-răm, who belonged to the tribe of Reuben, heard Kôr'-ăh tell about his thoughts, and they said, "We are just as able to be rulers as is this man Moses." And they went with Kôr'-ăh and with two hundred and fifty other men who despised Moses and Aaron.

Finally all these men came to talk with Moses. They said, "You are lifting yourself above us as though you were some great person. We are just as good as you." They spoke also against Aaron, for they envied both of these men. And Moses was grieved to hear their words. He knew that he had not set himself up above them as some great person. He knew God had chosen him to be their leader and he was only obeying God. He knew, too, that God had chosen Aaron to be the high priest. These men were not really talking against Moses and Aaron, but against God.

Moses told Kôr'-ăh and the men who were with him to bring censers on the next day, with fire and with sweet incense in them, just as the priests brought censers before the Lord. He told Aaron to bring a censer also, and he said they should prove which man of them God had chosen to be their high priest.

Moses' words were told through all the camp, and on the next day the rest of the Israelites came with Kôr′-ăh and his friends. And Kôr′-ăh brought them all before the door of the tabernacle. And he took Dā′-thăn and Ā-bī′-răm and the two hundred and fifty men and stood in the door of the tabernacle, and every one of them placed a censer before the Lord, and Aaron, too, placed his censer before the Lord.

God was greatly displeased, and he told Moses to go quickly away from the people for he was going to destroy them at once. But Moses fell down on his face and cried to God to spare their lives. Because of this God said he would not destroy the Israelites if they would go away from Kôr′-ăh and his friends. When they heard this the people hurried away in every direction, leaving Kôr′-ăh and his friends alone by their tents. Then Moses said, "Now we shall prove whether I have ruled these people by God's command or whether I have chosen by myself to rule over them. If the ground opens up and swallows these men we shall know that God has called me to do this work." No sooner had Moses finished speaking than the ground opened up under the feet of Kôr′-ăh and his friends and they fell screaming into the depths of the earth. The Israelites fled in terror when they heard the screams of those who perished, for they thought the earth might swallow them up also.

KORAH AND HIS FRIENDS BEING SWALLOWED
BY THE EARTH

AARON'S ROD WAS THE ONLY ONE THAT GREW

We might suppose that the people surely would be afraid to speak against the Lord any more, or against his true men. But on the very next day the Israelites began to say, "Moses and Aaron are to blame because Kôr'-ăh and all his friends were killed yesterday. Those were good people, too."

God heard their words, and he said to Moses and Aaron, "Go away from these people because I am ready to destroy them. They do not deserve to live." But Moses and Aaron fell down before the Lord again and prayed earnestly for the people. This time God would not hear their prayers. He sent a terrible sickness upon the people and they began to die everywhere in the camp. Moses was afraid they might all die. He told Aaron to take in a censer fire from the altar of burnt offering and burn sweet incense before God. And Aaron ran out among the people carrying the censer in his hand. He stood between those who had died and those who were yet alive. And God stopped the sickness that no more died of it.

Soon after this God commanded each of the twelve tribes to send Moses a rod. And he commanded Moses to write upon each rod the name of the tribe who had sent it. God said that Aaron's name should be written upon the rod of the tribe of Levi. Then God told Moses to place these twelve rods in the tabernacle before the ark and to leave them there until the next day. And God said, "The man whose rod shall grow is the man whom I choose to be my priest."

The next day Moses found eleven of the rods looking just the same as when he had placed them before the ark. But the one which had Aaron's name on it was blossoming like a growing branch upon a tree. Moses showed these rods to the people, and they knew by the sign of Aaron's blossoming rod that God had chosen him to be the high priest. God commanded Moses to keep Aaron's rod in the tabernacle so that the people might never forget to honor Aaron and his sons as God's chosen men for the priesthood.

———•———

STORY 19

THINGS THAT HAPPENED TO THE ISRAELITES DURING THE FORTY YEARS THEY LIVED IN THE WILDERNESS

Numbers 20; Deut. 2:1-15

For nearly forty years the Israelites went from one place to another in the great wilderness. They did not try again to enter Canaan, nor did they try to go back to Egypt. They waited for the time to come when God would be willing to lead them into the promised land.

During those long years of waiting only a few things happened that we may read about. Miriam, the sister of Moses and Aaron, died at Kā′-dĕsh-bär′-nĕ-ă, and was buried there. About this time the wells at Kā′-dĕsh dried up, and the people and their cattle and sheep could find no water to drink. They began to complain again, and God told Moses to take his rod and go with Aaron and all the people to a great rock not far from the camp. God said that Moses should speak to this rock in the presence of all the people. At Moses' word, God would cause water to flow out of the rock in a clear stream. From this all the people and all their animals might drink.

Moses and Aaron gathered the people together and went before them out to the great rock. Then, instead of speaking to the rock, as God had said they should, Moses spoke to the people in an angry tone and asked, "Must we bring water to you out of this rock?" Moses did not speak to the rock at all, but struck it with his rod. When no water came out he struck it again, and this time a clear stream gushed out and flowed across the sand. The people ran quickly to drink from it and to fill their vessels. The cattle and sheep also came to the stream and drank freely of the water God had sent.

God was not pleased with Moses and Aaron when they failed to do just as he had commanded them. Because of their disobedience, God said they should both die before the Israelites crossed over into the promised land.

Moses planned to lead the Israelites into Canaan from another point. To reach that point, he planned to go through the country of Ē′-dom, where the Ē′-dom-ītes lived. These people were descendants of Esau, the brother of Israel (Jacob) from whom the Israelites had descended. Both the Ē′-dom-ītes and the Israelites were descendants of Abraham and of Isaac, and Moses wished to be friendly with these people of such near kin. He sent a messenger to the king of Ē′-dom, asking him to let the Israelites pass through his country. "We will not enter your fields nor your vineyards," said the messenger, "and we will be careful to pay for the water that we drink from your wells."

But the king of Ē′dom did not feel friendly toward the Israelites. He was afraid to let so many people pass through his country. He sent word back to Moses, saying, "You must not lead your people through Ē′-dom. If you try to pass through my land, I will fight against you with my army and will drive you back again into the wilderness."

Moses did not want to fight against a people who were so near of kin to the Israelites. He changed his plans and led the people around the country of Ē′-dom—south, and east, and north toward the eastern part of Canaan. On this long, tiresome journey across bare wildernesses and rocky plains, the Israelites passed Mount Hor.

While they were camping at Mount Hor, God told Moses to take Aaron and Ĕl-ē-ā′-zär, Aaron's son, up on the mountain, and to take off Aaron's priestly robes and put them on Ĕl-ē-ā′-zär. Aaron was now an old, old man, and the time had come when he must die. And God wanted Ĕl-ē-ā′-zär to become high priest after Aaron.

With a sad heart Moses climbed the rocky mountain-side, taking his aged brother and his nephew along. And there he obeyed the words of the Lord, and there Aaron died. Then Moses returned to the camp again, with Ĕl-ē-ā′-zär, and all the people saw that Aaron did not come down with them. They saw, too, that Aaron's priestly robes were upon his son, and by this they understood that God had chosen Ĕl-ē-ā′-zär to be high priest in Aaron's place. They knew Aaron had died up on the mountain, and they mourned for him thirty days.

———◆———

STORY 20

WHY THE BRASS SERPENT HUNG ON A POLE IN THE ISRAELITES' CAMP

Num. 21: 4-9

After the Israelites left Mount Hor they came into a desert country where the hot sands burned their feet. Everything looked dreary, and Canaan seemed very far away. The people felt tired and unhappy. They began to complain again about their troubles. They said the manna no longer tasted good, and that they could find no water at all.

While they were complaining, God caused fiery serpents, or poisonous snakes which looked like fire and whose poison burned like fire, to crawl into their camp and bite many of the people. And those who were bitten died.

Now these Israelites were not so stubborn as their fathers had been, who forty years before this time had often sinned against God by complaining about their troubles. Nearly all of those old men had died. These younger men knew, when the fiery serpents came among them, that God was punishing them because they had sinned. And they were sorry for their wrong-doing. They came quickly to Moses and said, "We have sinned, for we have spoken against the Lord, and against you. We want you to pray for us, that God will take away these fiery serpents." Moses prayed, and God told him to make a serpent of brass, like a fiery serpent, and hang it on a pole and set the pole up in the middle of the camp. Then God commanded the people who were bitten by the snakes to look toward the serpent of brass, which Moses had set up. "Whoever looks toward that serpent," God said, "even though he is bitten by one of the poisonous snakes he shall not die." And the people who believed God's word and looked toward the serpent of brass were saved alive.

Many long years after this time the descendants of these Israelites and all other people in the world were troubled and dying in their sins. And God sent his dear Son, Jesus, into the world to be hung on a cross as the brass serpent was hung on a pole. And God said that whoever would look to Jesus would not die in his sins. But if any one would not look to Jesus, that one should die in his sins just as surely as the Israelite who would not look toward the brass serpent died of his snake-bite. Sin is like the fiery serpents; it stings the soul of every man, woman, boy, and girl. We can not see it as the Israelites could see the poisonous snakes in the desert, neither can we see Jesus as the Israelites saw the serpent of brass upon the pole. But we can feel the pain of guilt when sin stings our souls, and we can believe that Jesus died for our sins upon the cross. When we believe this we are looking by faith to Jesus, and thus we can be saved.

———•———

STORY 21

HOW GOD HELPED THE ISRAELITES WHEN THEY TRUSTED IN HIM

Num. 21:12—22:2

After the Israelites moved away from the camp where the fiery serpents had bitten them, they came to a wilderness near the land of Moab. Although they found no water in this wilderness, they did not murmur, because now they were willing to trust in God. And God told Moses to gather them together into one place and he would give them water.

When the people came together, Moses told the chief men of the tribes to dig a well in the sand. And while these men dug down to find springs all the people sang cheerful songs. They believed God would fill the well with good water even before they saw it bubble up from the deep springs. They pleased God by believing thus in him, and they enjoyed drinking from this wilderness well.

Near by was the country where the Amorite people lived. These were wicked people, who worshiped idols. Because their country lay between the Israelites' camp and Canaan, Moses sent a message to Sĭ'-hŏn, their king, asking him to let the Israelites pass through his land. But Sĭ'-hŏn did not want them even to come near. He took his army and went out to fight against the Israelites. He thought he would drive them away, back into the wilderness.

But God helped the Israelites and gave them a great victory. They killed the wicked king and his soldiers, and afterwards they marched into his country and took it for their own land. They drove out all the Amorites who were living in the villages, and they even went into the cities where Sĭ'-hŏn and his soldiers had lived.

Soon after this the Israelites marched on into the land of Bā'-shăn. They did not even ask Og, the king of Bā'-shăn, to let them pass through his country. He, too, was a wicked king like Sĭ'-hŏn had been, and his people also bowed down to worship idols. When Og heard that the Israelites were coming, he went out with his army to meet them and to fight against them. The Lord told Moses not to be afraid of this king nor of his army, for He would help the Israelites again. And when they fought, the Israelites killed the whole army of Bā'-shăn and took their country just as they had taken the land of the Amorites.

Now the long journey of forty years through the wilderness had come to an end. All of the old men except Moses and Caleb and Joshua had died in the wilderness. The Israelites had come again to the border of Canaan. Only the River Jordan separated them from the green hills and beautiful valleys of that promised land. They could look across the River and see the rich country, which God had promised to give to them for their own.

———•———

STORY 22

WHAT HAPPENED TO A WISE MAN WHO TRIED TO DISOBEY GOD

Num. 22:1-35

While the Israelites were setting up their tents on the plains of Moab near the Jordan River, the king of that country was wondering what he should do to make himself and his people safe. He had heard what the Israelites did to Sĭ' hŏn, king of the Amorites, and he was afraid of them. He knew their army was larger than his. He knew they had taken the land of the Amorites and the land of Bashan for their own country. He thought, "They will take my country away from me, and they may even kill me."

Finally this king, whose name was Balak, decided to send for a wise man from Mĭd'-ĭ-ăn to come and help him. So he called some of his princes and sent them with this message: "A great host of people from Egypt have come into my country and they are too many for me to fight against. I want you to come and help me, for I have heard that you are very wise, and that whomever you speak against is made weak, and whomever you bless is made strong."

When the princes of Moab came to the wise man, whose name was Bā'-lāam, they delivered the messages of their king. And no doubt they showed Bā'-lāam the money that Balak had sent to pay him for his services. But Balaam said, "I do not know whether the Lord will let me go with you or not. Perhaps he does not want me to speak against the Israelites. Stay with me tonight, and in the morning I will tell whether I may go or not."

During the night God spoke to Bā'-lāam and asked, "Who are these men in your house?" And Bā'-lāam answered, "They are princes of Moab, who have come at their king's command to ask me to help him out of trouble. The Israelites, from Egypt, have come into his land with a strong army and he is afraid of them. He wants me to speak against them in your name, so that they will become weak." But God said, "You must not go to help the king of Moab. You must not speak against the Israelites; for I have blessed them."

When morning came Bā'-lāam told the princes that God would not let him go with them. And they hurried back to tell Bā'-lāam's words to the king.

But Balak sent the second time to Bā'-lāam. This time he sent other princes, who were greater than the first ones. He sent money also, and he promised to give great honor to Bā'-lāam if only he would come to help him.

Now Bā'-lāam wished to have the money that Balak sent. He wished also to receive the honor that this king promised to give him. As he thought about these things he wanted them more than ever. He knew God had said he should not go. But he decided to try once more, so he invited these princes to stay at his house until the next morning. And while they slept he heard God's voice again. This time God told him that if the men should waken him in the morning he might go with them. Only he should be careful to speak the words God would give him to speak.

Bā'-lāam was eager to go. He did not wait to see whether these princes would call for him in the morning, but rose early and saddled the ass upon which he often rode. Then he took two of his servants and started out with the princes to see the king.

But God was displeased with Bā'-lāam. He sent his angel to trouble him, and the angel stood in the road and drew out his sword to kill Bā'-lāam. The ass upon which Bā'-lāam was riding saw the angel and turned off from the road into a field. Bā'-lāam grew angry at this and struck her a blow. Back into the road they went, and presently they came to a place where a stone wall was built on each side. Here the angel stood again with his sword drawn, and here again the ass saw the angel, while Bā'-lāam did not. The ass was frightened again, and, trying to avoid the angel, she crowded closely against the wall on the opposite side. In doing this she crushed Bā'-lāam's foot against the wall. Now Bā'-lāam was quite angry, and he struck her a cruel blow.

Farther on the road they came to a very narrow place, and here the angel stood again. This time the ass could not pass around, and, fearing the angel, she sank down on the ground beneath Bā'-lāam. At this Bā'-lāam's anger grew worse than ever and he struck a painful blow upon his faithful ass with his staff. And God gave a voice to the ass, and she spoke to Bā'-lāam. "What have I done that you should strike me these three times?" she asked.

Bā'-lāam was so angry he did not think it strange because an ass could speak. He replied, "If I had a sword I would kill you, for you are not behaving as you should." Then the ass asked Bā'-lāam whether she had not always carried him about safely since the day he bought her, and Bā'-lāam remembered that she had. And then God caused Bā'-lāam to see the angel standing before him.

Now Bā'-lāam was more frightened than the ass had been. He fell down on his face before the angel. And the angel asked, "Why have you been beating your ass? Three times she has seen me standing across your path and she has turned aside. Had she not done this I would surely have killed you, for I am much displeased with you."

Bā'-lāam cried, "I have sinned, for I did not know you were standing in the way to hinder me from going to see the king. Now I will turn back toward my home if you are displeased with my going on."

But the angel told Bā'-lāam to go on with the princes of Moab, and to be careful to speak only the words of the Lord.

STORY 23

HOW BALAAM TRIED TO PLEASE THE KING
Num. 22:36—32:9

When Balak heard that Bā'-lāam was finally coming he rushed out to meet him. He asked, ''Why did you not come sooner?'' and he told Bā'-lāam that he would give him a place of honor if only he would help in this time of trouble.

But Bā'-lāam answered, ''I cannot promise to help you even though I have come. I can speak only the words that God gives me.''

Perhaps Balak thought this wise man was trying to get more money from him by talking thus. He did not understand that Bā'-lāam could speak against people in the name of the Lord only when God wished to have him do this. Balak was an idol-worshiper, and he did not understand about the true God.

When Bā'-lāam saw all the money which Balak promised to give him he wished in his heart that he might please Balak and become a rich man. But he remembered the words of the angel, and he said, ''I can speak only the words of the Lord.''

Then the king took Bā'-lāam to the top of a mountain, from which they could look down upon the plain and see the Israelites' camp. And Bā'-lāam told the king to build seven altars on this mountain and offer to the Lord an ox and a sheep upon each of the altars. Bā'-lāam may have thought that God would be pleased with Balak's offerings and would then be willing to let him help Balak. But when Bā'-lāam went aside to hear God's words, he could hear only words of blessing for the Israelites. And he told these words to Balak, in the presence of the princes of Moab.

Now Balak was much displeased with Bā'-lāam because he had blessed the Israelites instead of speaking against them. He said, ''Instead of helping me you are helping my enemies.'' But Bā'-lāam replied again that he could speak only the words that God gave him.

Balak thought he would try again. So he took Bā'-lāam to another place where they could see a part of the Israelites' camp. And here again he built seven altars and offered oxen and sheep to the Lord as he had done before. Still God would give only words of blessing to Bā'-lāam to speak about the Israelites.

When Balak tried the third time, and Bā'-lāam still failed to speak against Israel, the king became very angry. He thought that Bā'-lāam did not want to help him. He said, ''I had planned to give you riches and honor, but your God has kept them from you. Now go in haste back to your own country. I am done with you because I see you are not my friend.'' And Bā′-lāām returned again to his home.

Although Bā′-lāām was careful to speak only the words of the Lord, yet down in his heart he wished he might please the king. Because he was a wise man he thought of another way to help Balak. Perhaps he thought Balak would still be willing to give him riches and honor. He told the king to act friendly toward the Israelites instead of trying to fight against them. And the king and all the people of Moab and of Mĭd′-ĭ-ăn, Bā′-lāām′s country, were glad to do this.

But making friends with the Moabites and with the Midianites soon brought great trouble into Israel's camp. The young men of Israel began to marry these strange young women who worshiped other gods. And these young women took their husbands to the feasts of their gods and many of the Israelites bowed down to idols.

God saw the great danger of the Israelites becoming idolators, like the nations near by, and forgetting him entirely. So he sent a plague into their camp, and many of these young people died. Then Moses took the men who were leading others into sin and caused them to be killed. After this the Israelites went to war against the Moabites and the Mĭd′-ĭ-ăn-ītes and killed many of their people. And Bā′-lāām, the man who caused the Israelites to sin, was killed in his own land. He might have been a good man if he had always tried to please God; but because he loved riches and honor he disobeyed God and finally died among the enemies of God's people.

STORY 24

THE LAST JOURNEY OF MOSES

Num. 27:12-23; Deuteronomy 34

Moses was now an old, old man. His wonderful life had been divided into three parts. First he had lived as Pharaoh's grandson in the palaces of Egypt. Then he had worked as a shepherd in the wilderness. And the last part of his life he had spent among his own people, leading them from Egypt to the land that God promised to give them for their own.

And now, although Moses was very old, he still thought of the people—*his* people—and he asked God to set some other man before them to lead them after he should die. For God had told him that soon he must die, as Aaron had died, and as all the old men had died who came out of Egypt.

And God chose a man to take Moses' place. This man was Joshua, the one who had been with Moses on Mount Sĭ'-naî and who had gone as

MOSES' FAREWELL

one of the twelve spies from Kā'-dĕsh into Canaan. Then, at God's bidding, Moses took Joshua and set him before the high priest, Ĕl-ē-ā'-zär, and laid his hands upon him and gave him some important work to do. By these acts the people understood that Joshua was soon to take up the work that Moses had done as their leader.

At this time the Israelites were living in the land that they had taken from their enemies. This land was good for pasture, and the Israelites kept many cattle and sheep. The men of Reuben's tribe and the men of Gad's tribe were all keepers of cattle. When they saw the rich pasture-lands of this country, they asked Moses to give them homes on this side of the Jordan River instead of giving them a part of the land in Canaan. At first Moses did not want to do this; but when the men promised to help the other Israelites fight against their enemies in Canaan, Moses divided the land for them. He gave a part of it to each of these tribes and a part to half of the tribe of Mă-năs'-sĕh.

After Moses had divided the country among these tribes, he called the people together and told them again about the words of command that God spoke to him on Mount Sī'-nâi. He told them many things that they needed to know before they should go into Canaan to live. He wrote all these words in a book called Deuteronomy, which is the fifth book in the Old Testament.

As the people listened to Moses' words they knew he was soon going to leave them forever. They knew he had been a faithful leader, and that he had loved them as dearly as a father loves his own children. No doubt they felt sorry because the time was soon coming when he could be with them no more.

Then one day when Moses had ended his long farewell talk with the people he walked away from his tent and away out of the camp. All alone he went, and the people stood watching him through their tears. They knew he was going away to die. But first he was going to see the land of Canaan, as God had promised him. Finally he came to Mount Nĕ'-bō. Up and up he climbed over the rocks, and higher he went until the watchers on the plain could see him no more. Then he looked from the top of that high mountain, and God showed him the country where Abraham and where Isaac had lived and died. What a beautiful country it was! As Moses looked across its wooded hills and green valleys he thought of the time soon to come when Joshua should lead the Israelites—*his* people—into that promised land.

Then God closed the eyes of this faithful old man, and folded his hands across his breast and carried his spirit away to a better land than Canaan. And God buried Moses somewhere in the plain, but no one knew where God had made the grave.

Thus ended the life of one of the greatest men this world has known, the only man who had ever talked face to face with God and whose face had shone with God's glory. And for thirty days the Israelites mourned and wept because their great leader had been taken away from them.

SUNSET ON MOUNT HERMON FROM THE GALILEAN LAKE

The Sea of Galilee was mentioned in Old Testament times by its original name of Chinnereth, or Chinneroth, meaning "harp," on account of its fancied resemblance to such an instrument. It is an expansion of the Jordan River, thirteen miles long and eight miles wide. From this point on the Sea, beyond the foot of the northern hills, is visible the dazzling whiteness of Mount Hermon, whose triple-crowned summit over nine thousand feet high is capped with eternal snow.

JOSHUA, THE NEW LEADER

PART THIRD
STORIES ABOUT JOSHUA AND THE JUDGES OF ISRAEL

Joshua; Judges; Ruth; 1 Samuel 1—8

STORY 1
HOW A WOMAN SPOILED THE PLAN OF A WICKED KING
Joshua 1, 2

On the other side of the Jordan River and several miles from the Israelites' camp stood a large city called Jericho. A high wall had been built around this city to keep out the enemies of the many people who lived there. A gate had been made in this wall through which the people of Jericho might go out of and come into the city.

When the Israelites first made their camp near the Jordan River, the people of Jericho heard about it. And they became afraid. They had heard long before this time about the Israelites. Some one had told them how God led the Israelites out of Egypt and through the Red Sea. Some one had told them how God helped the Israelites fight against their enemies, and how the Israelites captured the cities and lands of their enemies. And the people of Jericho trembled when they heard these things. They were wicked people, and their king was a wicked ruler. They did not serve the wonderful God of the Israelites; and now they were afraid that the Israelites would cross over the Jordan River into Canaan, and take their city away from them.

After Moses died, God spoke to Joshua and told him to lead the Israelites into the land of Canaan. While the people were getting ready to start, Joshua sent two men across the River to visit Jericho and learn all they could about that city. Because Jericho was such a large city, Joshua believed that the Israelites would need to capture it before they could go farther into Canaan.

When the two spies came to Jericho, they found the gate standing open, so they walked in. They came to a house where a woman lived whose name was Rahab. While they talked with her, some one hurried to tell the king of Jericho that two strange men had come inside the city and were stopping at Rahab's house. They believed these men were from the camp of Israel.

The king of Jericho said, "These men are spies, and they have come to see how strong our city is. They will do mischief to us if they

THE RIVER JORDAN

return to their people. We must find them and kill them." So the king sent his officers to Rahab's house to capture the spies.

When the officers came they could not find the men at all. Rahab had hidden them on the flat roof of her house by piling stalks of flax on top of them. Then the officers believed that possibly the spies had started back to the camp of Israel, so they hurried out of the gate and ran toward the River to overtake them and kill them. Then when they passed out of the gate, the people of Jericho closed the gate so that no more spies might come inside their city. And so these two spies were made prisoners at Rahab's house. They could not get out of the city.

But Rahab spoke kindly to the men. She said, "We know your God is helping you, and we know you are going to take our country and our city. I will make a way for you to return to your people safely, if you will promise to remember my kindness when you come with your great army to take Jericho. If you will promise to save me and my family alive, I will help you to get outside of this wall."

Because Rahab had faith to believe in Israel's God, the spies promised to save her and her family alive. Then she took them to a window of her house, which opened outside the city and above the wall. She told them to hide in the mountains near by for three days, because the officers of the king would be looking for them. Before they went away to hide in the mountains, the spies told Rahab to leave a cord hanging from her window, so the Israelites might know where to find her house, and then they would save her alive. Then she let them down by a cord to the ground outside the wall. And Rahab tied a cord, which was of scarlet color, to the window-frame.

After three days the spies returned safely to Joshua, and told him about all that had happened to them. And they said, "Surely God has given that beautiful country to us; for the people are afraid of us, and they are too weak to fight against us and drive us out of their land."

———————•———————

Story 2

HOW THE ISRAELITES CROSSED OVER A DANGEROUS RIVER
Josh. 3: 1—5: 1

It was early morning in the Israelites' camp. The two spies had returned safely from Jericho, and now all the people were ready and waiting to start on their last march toward the promised land. Joshua, their new leader, was brave; for God had spoken encouraging words to him. He knew the time had come to move forward, so he gave the command. Then the priests carrying the ark and the Levites carrying the pieces of the tabernacle led the way, and all the people followed.

But the Israelites did not go very far that day. When they came to Jordan they found a flood of water sweeping down the river and overflowing its banks. They could look across to the green hills and beautiful fields in Canaan, but the river was too deep and the waters too swift for them to wade through. So the people stopped their march and made ready to wait until the overflow waters should pass by.

Perhaps the people of Jericho knew about the overflow of the
Jordan River, and perhaps they thought, "We shall be safe from the
Israelites as long as the waters rush so wildly down that stream; for
surely our enemies will not try to cross over such a dangerous river."

But after three days' waiting, God spoke again to Joshua and
said, "Go forward!" even though the waters were still deep and the
current swift and strong.   God wanted to show his power once more to

ISRAELITES CROSSING THROUGH
THE JORDAN RIVER

his people.   And the people were
ready to obey Joshua's command.
When the priests who carried the
ark stepped bravely into the edge
of the water, a wonderful thing happened.   God stopped the water far
up stream so that it could not flow.
Instead, it piled up in a great heap.
Then all the water flowed out of the
river's bed where the Israelites
were waiting to cross over, and the
people walked across to Canaan on
dry ground.

God wanted the Israelites always to remember how he had
helped them to cross the Jordan, so
he commanded that one man from
each of the twelve tribes should pick up a large stone from the bed of
the river where they crossed over and carry that stone to their next
camping-place.   Then these men should pile the twelve stones into
a heap, to remind the Israelites of how God showed his power at the
Jordan.   And Joshua made another heap of twelve stones at the place
where the priests had stood with the ark, in the middle of the river,
while the people passed by.

After this had been done, the priests carried the ark to Canaan's
side of the river, and then when all the priests and all the people had
crossed in safety God caused the waters to flow down the stream just
as they had flowed before.

Soon the people who lived in Jericho and all their neighbors who
lived in other parts of Canaan heard that the Israelites had come into
their land.   They heard that God had dried up the Jordan River, when
its waters were overflowing the banks, to let the Israelites cross over.
And all the people in Canaan trembled because they were afraid of the
Israelites, who served such a mighty God.

On the plains near Jericho the Israelites made their camp. They called the name of their camp "Gĭl'-găl." And they went out into the fields around Jericho and gathered grain for food. Many of them had been born in the wilderness and had never eaten grain for food before. They found fruits also, and they enjoyed eating the good things that grew in Canaan.

Until this time God had been sending fresh măn'-nă from heaven every day, except on the seventh day. For forty years the people had been eating this wonderful măn'-nă. But now the time had come when they would not need to be fed from heaven any more, for they were come into a good land, where plenty of grain and fruit and vegetables grew. So no more măn'-nă fell.

STORY 3

WHAT HAPPENED TO THE STONE WALLS OF JERICHO
Josh. 5: 13—6: 27

One day after the Israelites had made their camp at Gĭl'-găl, Joshua went out to see the city of Jericho for himself. As he looked at the great stone wall that surrounded the city, perhaps he wondered how his army could ever force its way in. The gate was tightly locked, he knew; for the people of Jericho were expecting the Israelites to fight against them, and they were afraid to go outside the city wall.

Presently Joshua saw a strange man standing near by. This stranger was dressed like a soldier and he carried a bright sword in his hand. He, too, had been looking toward Jericho, and Joshua wondered whether he was a friend or an enemy of the people who lived there. So he asked, "Are you a friend of the people of Jericho or a friend of the Israelites?" The stranger answered, "I am Captain of the Lord's army."

Then Joshua was glad, for he knew that God would help him capture the city of Jericho. He believed this Captain of the Lord's army had come to lead the Israelites to their battle against their enemies. So he bowed down to the ground and worshiped before this mighty Captain. Then the Captain commanded him to take off his shoes because the ground where he stood was made holy by the presence of this holy One from heaven. Joshua quickly removed his shoes, just as Moses had done before the burning bush at Mount Hôr'-ĕb.

The Captain of the Lord's army told Joshua how the Israelites should make an attack against Jericho. And he told how God would give a great victory to the Israelites if they would carefully obey his

JOSHUA AND HIS ARMY

orders. Then he went away, and Joshua did not see him again. But Joshua knew now how to lead his army through the great stone wall of Jericho, and he was glad.

When Joshua returned to the camp at Gĭl'-găl he told the people about his visit with the Captain of the Lord's army. And all the people were ready to obey the orders which this mighty Captain had given. Perhaps on the very next day the Israelites began their attack. They did not expect to gain the victory on that first day, nor on the next; for the Lord had commanded them to go out every day for one whole week and march around the city.

THE FALL OF JERICHO

When the people of Jericho looked out of the windows of their tallest buildings they saw a host of soldiers marching around their city. Just behind the soldiers seven priests walked along, blowing rams' horns. And behind the seven priests came other priests carrying a strange-looking burden wrapped so securely that the people of Jericho could not even guess what might be inside. But the Israelites knew this burden was the ark of the covenant, which belonged to the tabernacle. And the people of Israel followed behind the priests who carried the ark. Every one walked quietly along, making no noise except with the tread of his feet upon the ground. Once around the great stone wall they marched, and then they quietly returned to their camp at Gĭl'-găl. "What can this mean?" the people of Jericho wondered. "We can not understand those Israelites. They do not fight like other men."

The next day again they saw the strange march around their city. And again on the third day, and on the fourth day, and on every day of the week. Finally they may have supposed the Israelites were only trying to make them afraid. But Rahab believed the Israelites were surely going to capture Jericho. She called her father and mother and brothers and sisters into her house. And together they looked out of the window where the scarlet cord hung, and together they watched the strange actions of the people who worshiped the true God.

On the seventh day the Israelites marched seven times around the wall of Jericho. On that morning they had risen early and prepared for their long march. They knew the day for victory had come. At the end of the seventh march around the great wall the Israelites stood still. They did not turn toward the camp at Gĭl'-găl, as on other days, but now every one looked toward the wall. Then the priests blew loudly with their trumpets and all the people shouted with a great noise. At that moment the stone wall began to tremble, then it shook, and then fell down flat. What a great miracle. The Israelites knew that God had caused the wall to tumble, because they had not even touched it. But they had obeyed God.

Joshua sent the two spies to bring Rahab and her family out of the city to a safe place. Then the soldiers of Israel climbed over the broken wall and killed all the wicked people and their wicked king. They took all the gold and all the silver that they found in Jericho, and every dish that was made of iron or of brass. These things they brought to the tabernacle at Gĭl'-găl; for God had commanded that no man should save anything for himself. Then the soldiers set the ruined city on fire, and Jericho was burned to ashes. In this way God gave a great victory to his obedient people.

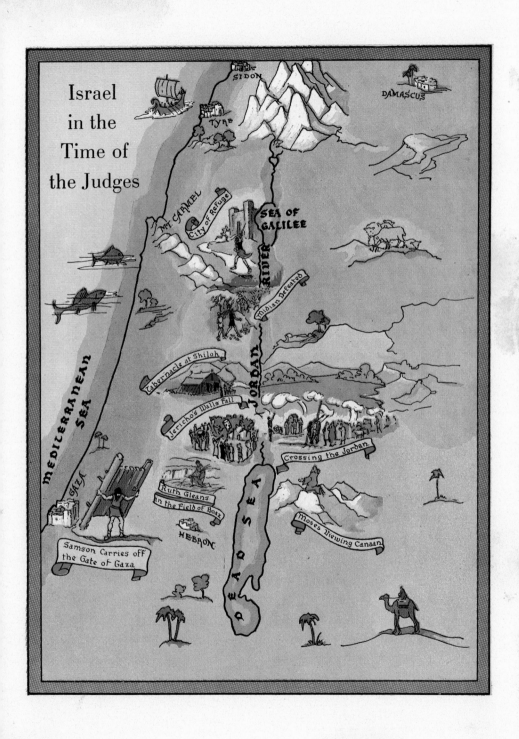

Israel in the Time of the Judges

ISRAEL IN THE TIME OF THE JUDGES

After wandering forty years in the wilderness the children of Israel arrived on the banks of the River Jordan. Moses, their leader, was now an old man. God took him up into Mount Nebo, where he saw the Promised Land. There Moses died and was buried by the angels. God rolled back the waters of the Jordan and Joshua, the new leader, and the children of Israel, walked across on dry land.

When they arrived in Canaan it was necessary to capture some of the walled cities. The first of these was Jericho.

The permanent place of worship in Canaan was established at Shiloh near the center of the land, where the tabernacle was pitched. Forty-eight cities were built throughout Canaan in which the Levites were to live and teach the people the law of God. Six cities located on hills were selected as "cities of refuge." These were places of safety for anyone who had accidentally killed another.

After many years the Israelites had trouble with the Midianites, a gypsy-like people from east of Canaan. First they grazed their herds on the land of Israel and then began stealing from them. The Israelites cried to God, who sent a deliverer named Gideon. With three hundred men Gideon defeated the Midianites by surprising them at midnight.

God raised up judges from time to time to deliver Israel from their enemies. One of these judges was Samson, the strong man, who performed many marvelous feats, including carrying off the gates of Gaza, a city belonging to their enemies, the Philistines.

During the period of the Judges, a young woman named Ruth came from the land of Moab to dwell near Jerusalem. It was in the time of the barley harvest and she gleaned in the fields of Boaz, who later became her husband. Through this marriage she became an ancestress of Christ.

STORY 4

THE STORY ABOUT A BURIED SIN
JOSHUA 7, 8

The Israelites were very happy about their victory at Jericho. From their tents at Gĭl′-găl they could see the smoke rising above the ruins of the burning city. They knew God had given them this great victory, and they brought the gold and silver and iron and brass which they found in Jericho and placed it in the tabernacle at Gĭl′-găl. These treasures belonged to God.

While the people were rejoicing about their victory and about the riches that they had brought to the tabernacle, one man among them was uneasy. He tried to act as cheerfully as his neighbors acted, but all the while he did not feel cheerful. No one who is trying to cover up a wrong deed can feel cheerful. And Ā′-chăn, for this was the man's name, was trying to hide his sin. Indeed he had buried it out of sight down in the ground beneath his tent floor. No one except possibly his sons and his daughters knew about that buried sin—so Ā′-chăn supposed. And his sons and his daughters had probably promised never to tell. None of the Israelites knew that anything was lying hidden in the ground under the floor of Ā′-chăn's tent.

But God knew all about that buried sin. And God was very much displeased with Ā′-chăn. He had commanded that no one should keep anything from the ruins at Jericho. And Ā′-chăn knew about that command. Yet when he saw a very beautiful garment in one of the houses of Jericho, he thought, "This garment is too beautiful to be burned up with this city. I will keep it for myself. No one need know where I got it." Then he saw some silver and a shining piece of gold. These he also wanted for himself, so he wrapped them carefully together and brought them to his own tent-home. There he dug down into the ground beneath his floor and buried his stolen treasure. No wonder Ā′-chăn did not feel happy!

Soon after the victory at Jericho, the Israelites made an attack against another city. This second city was called Ā′-ī, and it stood on top of a hill. The spies whom Joshua had sent to Ā′-ī came back safely and told their brave leader that only a few soldiers would need to fight against that city, because it was not nearly so large and strong as Jericho had been.

This time only about three thousand men went out to battle. But they had not been gone long when they came hurrying back, not to tell

about another great victory—oh, no!—for their enemies had chased
them away and had even killed a few of their brave men.

When Joshua heard the sad news he tore his clothes and fell down
on the ground before the ark of the covenant. He thought God had
left him alone to fight with the Israelites against their many enemies.
And now all the men of Israel were frightened because the men of Ai
had been stronger than they. Joshua prayed and asked God why this
trouble had happened. And God said,
"I can not help the Israelites when they
allow sin to lie covered up in their camp.
I strictly commanded that no one should
take anything for himself from Jericho,
and some one has dared to disobey. If
you will destroy that wicked person, I
will help you again to drive your enemies
away."

ACHAN CONFESSING BEFORE
JOSHUA

The next day Joshua searched for
the man who had disobeyed God at Jericho. And in the tribe of Judah he found
the guilty man. He took Ā'-chăn and his
sons and his daughters and brought
them to a valley outside of the camp.
There the Israelites threw stones at them
and killed them and burned them up.
And everything that belonged to Ā'-chăn,
and the stolen treasures which he had hidden away they brought out
to this valley and burned to ashes. Then they piled a heap of stones
above the ashes, that every one seeing the heap might remember how
God punished the man who tried to hide his sin.

After this God spoke to Joshua again and said, "Do not be afraid
of your enemies at Ā'-ī, for I will go with you. Take a small army as
before, but first send other men by night to hide in the woods behind
Ā'-ī. When the king of Ā'-ī and his soldiers shall see you coming with
a few men, they will rush out to drive you away as they did the first
time. Then your men who are hiding behind the city can enter the
gate and burn the city while the king and his soldiers are gone to chase
you away."

Joshua was careful to obey the words of the Lord, and when the
king of Ā'-ī and his soldiers came running out of the city to drive the
Israelites down the hill and away toward their camp at Gĭl'-găl, Joshua
raised his spear high in the air. The men who were hiding behind Ā'-ī

then came out of their hiding-place and entered the city and set fire to it. But Joshua's men ran away as if they were frightened, and the king of Ā'-ī and his soldiers followed them. Perhaps they thought, "What cowardly men these Israelites are!" But when they turned to go back home they saw that Joshua had caught them in a trap, for their home was burning behind them. And another army of Israelites was coming from the smoking ruins of their home city. So the people of Ā'-ī were destroyed, and all their gold and silver and cattle were taken by the Israelites. And God let the Israelites keep these riches for themselves.

STORY 5

THE ALTAR WHERE GOD'S LAW WAS WRITTEN UPON STONE

Deuteronomy 27, 28; Josh. 8:30-35

After the victory at Ā'-ī, Joshua led the Israelites farther north into the land of Canaan, to a place where Abraham had long years before this time built an altar to worship God. Moses had commanded Joshua to bring the Israelites to this very spot, and to build an altar there of unbroken stones, and to offer sacrifices to God upon this altar. And now, although Moses was dead, Joshua was careful to do just as he had promised.

All the men of Israel, and all the women, and all the boys and girls went with Joshua to this chosen place. They found a beautiful valley, shaped like a bowl, lying between two mountains—Mount Ē'-băl on the north and Mount Gĕ-rī'-zĭm on the south. Moses had commanded that six of the tribes, or one half of the people of Israel, should stand upon the slope of one of these mountains, and that the six remaining tribes should stand upon the other mountain-slope. Then, in the valley between, Joshua and the Levites should build the altar and offer sacrifices to God. After this the priests and the Levites should take the book in which Moses had written the laws of God and read aloud in the hearing of all the people. And they should hear again the words of the Lord which Moses had spoken to them and which they had promised to obey.

When the priests and the Levites read about the blessings which God promised to give to the Israelites if they should always obey him, the tribes on the mountain-slope of Gĕ-rī'-zĭm shouted, "Amen!" And their voices rang out across the valley to the people who stood on the other mountain-slope. And when the priests and the Levites read about the curses, or the troubles, which should come upon the Israelites if they should refuse to obey God's words, the people on the mountain-slope of Ē'-băl shouted, "Amen!" And their voices echoed back from the other mountain-side. By saying amen to the words of God's law the Israelites meant, "Let it be so."

What a wonderful meeting this must have been! And after the words of the law of God were read aloud to the people, so plainly that even the children understood them, those words were written upon stones where every one might read them. And those stones were left in the valley between the mountains; but the people returned again with Joshua and the priests and the Levites to their camp at Gĭl'-găl.

STORY 6

THE PEOPLE WHO FOOLED JOSHUA

Josh. 9: 3—27

One day a band of strange men came to the camp at Gĭl'-găl. Their clothes were nearly worn out and their shoes were full of holes. Their donkeys carried on their backs old sacks that were ready to fall in pieces. Even the skin bottles, which these men had used for carrying wine, were old and torn. And the little bit of bread that remained in their sacks was dry and moldy.

These strange men asked to speak with Joshua and with his officers, or princes. They said they had come from a country very far away, and that their people wished to be friends with the Israelites. But the men of Israel answered, "We do not know who you are. You may live here in Canaan, and we can not be friends with these people of Canaan because God has told us to destroy them all." The men then showed their moldy bread and said, "See, we brought this for our journey and it was hot when we took it from our homes. We are indeed from a far country. When we heard how your God brought you from Egypt and helped you to destroy your enemies, our people became afraid of you and they sent us to ask you to let us live and become your servants."

Joshua listened to these men. When he saw their worn-out shoes and their dry, moldy bread, he thought, "Surely they have come a long way." He felt sorry for them. He believed they were poor people and that they could do no harm to Israel. Instead of talking to God about these people and asking what to do, Joshua promised to let them live, and sent them back again to their homes.

After this had happened the Israelite soldiers went out again to battle against the people of Canaan. They had not gone very far when they came to the part of the land where the Gibeonites lived. Then they learned that the strange visitors at Gĭl'-găl had come from Gibeon. They were near neighbors to the Israelites. They had taken dry, moldy bread and worn-out shoes on purpose to make Joshua and the princes of Israel believe they had come from a country far away. But really, they were Canaanites—people whom God wanted the Israelites to destroy.

Now, it would be wrong for the Israelites to fight against the people they had promised to let live. God would not help them fight if they were breaking their word. The men of Israel were angry because they had been fooled. Joshua sent for the men who had come to Gĭl'-găl, and asked, "Why did you not tell us the truth?" The men answered, "When we saw what happened to Jericho and to Ā'-ī we were afraid. We knew you would not promise to let us live if you knew we were near neighbors, so we acted as though we had come a long distance."

Joshua said, "Because you did not speak true words to us, you and your people can never again own your houses and lands. Now you must be our slaves and do the things we tell you to do. Every day you must gather wood and bring it to the people, and every day you must carry water for us."

Although the Gibeonites had to work hard to chop wood and to carry water, yet they were glad because they were allowed to live in Canaan. They thought it was better to become servants of the Israelites than to be killed by them.

STORY 7

WHY JOSHUA SPOKE TO THE SUN AND TO THE MOON
Joshua 10—12

Not far from the place where Jericho had stood was another large city. The name of this city was Jerusalem. The people who lived here were wicked, and they were ruled by a wicked king. Other cities ruled by other wicked kings were south and west and north of Jerusalem.

After the Gibeonites became servants of the Israelites, the kings of Canaan felt angry toward them. The king of Jerusalem called four other kings and said, "Let us make war against the Gibeonites." So they gathered their armies together and marched across the hills and valleys toward the place where the Gibeonites lived

When the Gibeonites heard that a great army was coming to fight against them they were afraid. They sent a messenger to the camp at Gilgal and asked Joshua to come with his soldiers to help them. Because they were servants of the Israelites, Joshua started quickly with his army. All night they marched from Gĭl'-găl to Gibeon, and the next morning the five kings were greatly surprized to see the Israelites coming out to fight against them with the Gibeonites.

Joshua was a brave leader, and his soldiers were brave. God had told them to be brave, because he would help them to gain the victory. The soldiers from Jerusalem and from the other four cities had heard about God's power at Jericho, and they were afraid. Yet they fought; but soon they turned to run away. Then God sent hailstones from the sky and they fell upon the frightened men who were running and killed many more than had been killed in the battle. The five kings found a cave in the mountains and they ran into it to hide. But some one saw them, and sent word to Joshua. Joshua commanded that heavy stones should be rolled before the door of the cave and that soldiers should watch to see that the kings did not escape from this prison. Then the Israelite soldiers chased their enemies over the hills and through the valleys of Canaan. They did not want to let one of them get away.

When Joshua saw that the people were scattering everywhere, he thought many of the enemies might hide in the woods when night came on. Then they could come out again and fight against the Israelites. Joshua believed God wanted him and his soldiers to completely destroy these enemies and not give them another chance to fight. He knew the day would not be long enough to destroy them all, so he spoke to the sun and to the moon and commanded them to stand still. And while the sun and the moon stood still, the Israelites fought and gained a great victory. No day like that one had ever been before that time, nor has there been one since, when God listened to a man's voice and caused the sun to stand still in the sky while his people fought against their enemies.

After this great victory the five kings were taken out of the cave and killed. Then they were buried together in the cave and stones were piled in front of the door.

News of this battle soon reached the other cities of Canaan, and everywhere the people were afraid of the Israelites. Joshua felt sure God was pleased with him, and he marched on to other places and gained other victories. One by one he took the cities of Canaan until he had destroyed thirty-one kings and had taken the cities and country places where they ruled. Then the Israelites rested from war, in their camp at Gĭl'-găl.

STORY 8

HOW THE LAND OF CANAAN BECAME THE LAND OF ISRAEL
Joshua 13—19

After the Israelites had destroyed thirty-one kings in Canaan, they rested from war, in their camp at Gĭl'-găl. Joshua was growing too old to lead them out to battle any more, and there were no enemies near by to harm them. They had not yet destroyed all the wicked people who lived in Canaan, but they had taken much of the beautiful land to call their own.

But God was not pleased to have the Israelites quit fighting while the people of Canaan still lived in the land. He had promised to give all the land of Canaan to the Israelites, not just a part of it. And he was ready to help them drive out all of their enemies. He wanted them to fight until the land should be no longer a home for any people who worshiped idols. So he spoke to Joshua and said, ''You are growing too old to fight; but the land is not yet fully taken from your enemies. Now, I want you to divide this country among the twelve tribes of Israel and give each tribe a part to call its home country. Then let the tribes each drive out all wicked people who live in the part of the country that is given to it.''

Joshua and the high priest, Ĕl-ē-ā'-zär, and the old men from each of the tribes divided the land of Canaan as God told them to do. You remember that two and one half of the tribes had already taken land for their homes on the east side of the Jordan River; so only nine and one half of the tribes took this land of Canaan for their part of the promised land. After this time the land of Canaan was called the land of Israel. But there were still in this land cities where the Canaanite people lived.

One day the rulers of the tribe of Judah came to see Joshua at his tent in Gĭl'-găl. With them came an old man named Caleb. You will remember that Caleb was one of the two faithful spies whom Moses sent into Canaan with ten other men more than forty years before this time. Although Caleb was now eighty-five years old, he was as strong and brave as he had been when a young man. And now he came to ask Joshua for the piece of land that Moses promised should be given to him when the Israelites should enter Canaan to live there.

Joshua was glad to see Caleb. He remembered how faithful and true to God this old soldier had been when the ten spies brought a wrong report from the promised land. He remembered how Caleb had tried to quiet the people when they were crying for fear of the giants who lived in Canaan. And now he was ready to give Caleb any part of Canaan that this faithful old man might ask for.

There were beautiful valleys near Gĭl'-găl where the enemies had been driven away, and where green fields and fruit-trees were growing. But Caleb did not look at these places. He remembered the mountain-country where he and the other spies had seen walled cities and tall giants. Those same cities still stood on the mountain-sides, and the sons of those tall giants still lived in them. Caleb said, "Give me the mountain where we saw those giants, and the cities where the giants live. Although I am now an old man, yet if God is with me I shall be able to drive out those giants and take their cities." Brave old Caleb!

How happy Joshua felt when he saw the courage and the faith of his old friend! He spoke words of blessing to Caleb and then gave him the mountain-country and the city of Hebron where the giants were then living. And God helped Caleb to drive those giants out of the city and chase them away to the land of their enemies who lived by the seashore. Afterwards Caleb and his sons and his daughters and others of their relatives went to live in Hĕ'-brŏn.

The tabernacle had stood at Gilgal ever since the Israelites had crossed the Jordan River. Now the time came for it to be moved again. This time it was taken to a place called Shī'-lōh, and here it stayed for many long years. This place was nearer to the center of the land of Israel, and all the people of Israel were commanded to come to Shī'-lōh three times every year to worship God at the tabernacle. These three times were the times which God had chosen for the people to keep the feasts. First was the Passover feast, when they were to kill and eat a lamb as their fathers had done before they left Egypt; next was the Feast of Pentecost, fifty days after the Passover feast, when the people were to bring the first ripe fruits from their fields and lay them on the altar; and last was the Feast of Tabernacles, when the people were to gather together at Shī'-lōh and build huts of the boughs of trees and sleep out-of-doors, in these huts, to keep in mind the long years when they lived in tents in the wilderness.

Although the people of the twelve tribes went away to live in different parts of the land of Israel, yet some of the priests and some of the Levites stayed at Shī'-lōh all the time and kept the tabernacle worship just as God had told them to do when he gave them the plan for this holy place.

STORY 9

HOW GOD PLANNED TO USE SOME CITIES IN THE LAND OF ISRAEL

Joshua 20, 21

When the Israelites went away from the camp at Gĭl'-găl to live in different parts of the promised land, they had no Bibles to take with them. They had no tabernacle near by, and no longer could they see the cloud by day and the pillar of fire by night to remind them of the nearness of God. It would seem that they might soon forget about God.

But God knew how much these people would need to be reminded of him. So he planned a way for them to keep his words always in mind. He planned to have some of the Levites go with them to every part of the land.

The Levites, you remember, were chosen to care for the worship of God at the tabernacle. And they became teachers of the law of God. Only a part of them were needed at one time to serve in the tabernacle worship at Shī'-lōh. And so they changed about; for there were many Levites. Those who were not serving at the tabernacle went home to their families, who lived in the cities throughout the land. There they could teach the Israelites about God's law.

Forty-eight cities were given to the Levites to live in. And the fields outside the walls of these cities were given to them for pasture-lands. Then while the other Israelites lived in the country round about, the Levites were always near to remind them of the law that God gave to Moses.

And God told Joshua to choose six cities to be called "cities of refuge." By "cities of refuge" he meant that any person who had killed some one by accident might run to these cities and be safe. The Israelites had always believed it was right for the relatives of the dead man to kill the slayer, even though that person had not meant to do the wrong deed. But God's plan was to punish wrong-doers only when such persons did wrong on purpose.

The cities of refuge stood on high hills, and could be seen from a distance. When once a man who was running for his life should

reach the gate of such a city he would be safe. The gate-keeper would
let him pass in, but would not allow the man following him to enter.
Then the slayer would be questioned; and if it were found out that

SAFELY REACHING A CITY OF REFUGE

he had purposely killed another he would be taken outside the city
and given to those who were trying to take his life. But if he had done
the wrong deed accidentally, then he would be kept safely inside the gate.
This was the rule of the cities of refuge.

<hr />

STORY 10

THE STORY OF THE ALTAR BESIDE THE JORDAN RIVER

Joshua 22

It was a busy time at Shī'-lōh when the Israelites made ready to go
away to their own homes in different parts of the promised land. The

tribes of Judah, Simeon, and Benjamin moved toward the south country from Shī'-lōh, while the tribes of Asher, and Zĕ-bū'-lŭn, and Năph'-
tă-lī, and Ĭs'-să-<u>ch</u>är, and one half of the tribe of Mă-năs'-sēh moved toward the north country. The tribe of Dan journeyed west from Shī'-lōh,
and the tribe of Ē'-phră-ĭm stayed in the valleys near the tabernacle. You
remember that before Moses died he gave the land east of the Jordan
River to the tribes of Reuben and Gad and one half of the tribe of
Mă-năs'-sēh. Now at last all of the twelve tribes had been given parts
of the promised land in which to build their houses and plant gardens
and be really at home.

And you remember, too, that the men from the tribes east of the
Jordan River had come into Canaan with the other tribes to help drive
out their enemies. Now they were ready to return again to their wives
and children; for the great battles had been fought and many of the
enemies had been driven away or killed. Before they started away
from Shī'-lōh, Joshua called them to his tent to talk with them. He
thanked them for helping in the battles that the Israelites fought in
Canaan. He said, "Now you may return to your own land, which
Moses gave to you before he died. But when you go away across the
River, do not forget the commandments of God, which you promised
to obey. Do not forget the laws which Moses gave to all the Israelites."

Joshua sent Levites with these men to live in their cities and to
remind them of God's law. And he gave the men a part of all the gold
and silver and iron and brass and a part of all the cattle that the
Israelites had taken from their enemies.

When these soldiers came to the River Jordan and looked across
to their own country on the other side, they thought, "This river di-
vides our land from the rest of the land of Israel. But we will not
let this river cut us off from the worship of the true God at Shī'-lōh."
So they built on the high banks of the river an altar like the one on
which the priests offered burnt sacrifices to God at Shī'-lōh. Then they
marched on to their own homes.

Now God had commanded the Israelites to offer sacrifices on no
altar except the one at the tabernacle. And when the men of the other
tribes of Israel heard about the new altar that had been built on the
bank of the Jordan River, they felt angry. They believed the men on
the east side of the river were trying to worship God in their own
land instead of coming to the tabernacle at Shī'-lōh. They remembered
how God had punished all the people when only a part of them had
sinned, and now they were afraid that God would allow some trouble
to happen to them because those men had built a new altar. So they

gathered together and planned to cross the river and fight against those men who dared to disobey God's word.

Then these angry men thought, "Perhaps we had better ask those other tribes why they built that new altar before we go out to fight against them." So they chose Phĭn'-ĕ-hăs, the son of the high priest, and ten princes of Israel to go on this errand.

The men on the east side of the river were surprized when they saw Phĭn'-ĕ-hăs and the ten princes of Israel coming to see them so soon after they had left Shī'-lōh. And they were more surprized when they learned why these men had come. They said, "We do not intend to worship God on this altar which we built by the river. Neither will our children offer sacrifices on it after we die. But we built it because we were afraid that the time might come some day when your children would not want to allow our children to come to Shī'-lōh to worship the true God at the tabernacle. Then our children could show your children this altar, and your children could see that it is built like the altar at the tabernacle. They will understand that these tribes east of the river have a share in the worship of the true God at Shī'-lōh."

Phĭn'-ĕ-hăs and the ten princes were pleased when they heard these words. They hurried back to Shī'-lōh and told the people why the altar had been built by the river. And all the people were glad, because they knew that the tribes on the other side of Jordan would not try to be different from them, but that they would keep on serving the true God.

After this had happened the men went back again to their homes in the other parts of Canaan. But Joshua lived at Shī'-lōh, for he belonged to the tribe of Ē'-phră-ĭm. Now the tribe of Ē'-phră-ĭm and the tribe of Mă-năs'-sēh were both descended from Joseph, the son of Jacob, who was called Israel. And the men of these tribes had carried the coffin of their father Joseph all the way from Egypt because he had asked the Israelites before he died to bury him in the land of Canaan. Now at last they buried his coffin at a place called Shē'-chĕm, not far from Shī'-lōh, near the fields where in that long-ago time his brothers were keeping their cattle when they sold him into Egypt.

STORY 11

JOSHUA'S LAST MEETING WITH THE ISRAELITES

Joshua 23, 24

A long time after the Israelites had gone away from Shĭ'-lōh to live in different parts of Canaan, Joshua sent word to them and asked them to come together again. He wanted to talk with them once more before he should die. And the people from every tribe came together at Shĕ'-chĕm, a place not far from Shĭ'-lōh, and listened to the words of Joshua.

This brave old man knew that soon his days on earth would be ended; for he was one hundred and ten years old. He knew he could no longer help the Israelites in their battles against the wicked people who yet lived in the land. But he knew that God would be willing to help them even after he should die. So he talked to the Israelites about the wonderful victories that God had given to them when they obeyed him.

The people had never refused to obey Joshua as their fathers had refused to obey Moses. And God had blessed them because they were obedient. Now Joshua said: "You remember the good promises that God gave to you before you crossed the Jordan River and came into this land. And you see now how God has kept every one of those promises, how he has given you every good thing that he said he would give if you obeyed him. You know how he drove your enemies out of the cities and out of the country places, and caused them to leave their riches for you to enjoy. Now," said Joshua, "you see how he has blessed you because you worshiped him. But if you turn away from him and worship other gods, he will send the great troubles upon you as he said."

Joshua then talked to the people about the things that had happened to them and to their fathers before them. He even told them about Abraham, and about Abraham's sons, how God had led those old men through the very land the Israelites were now calling their own country. He spoke about the sons of Israel, who was first called Jacob. He told how those sons went down to Egypt and lived there for many years. Then he told how God chose Moses to lead the children of Israel out of Egypt's bondage to the beautiful land of Canaan. He reminded the people of the wonderful things that God did for the Israelites while he was leading them through the wilderness.

Joshua wanted the people to understand how much they had been

helped by God. He wanted them to see how good the Lord had been
to them. Then at last he said, "Today you must choose whether you
will keep on serving this God who has led you all these years, or
whether you will serve the gods of the Canaanites." And all the people
answered, "We will serve the Lord."

Then Joshua told the people that they must not keep in their
homes any idols like their wicked neighbors kept; for if they should,
God would not bless them. He said, "You must choose between the

JOSHUA'S FAREWELL ADDRESS

true God and these idols. Whichever
you choose, I and my house will serve
the true God." And all the people
promised to keep on obeying the
words of the Lord.

Joshua knew he would soon die,
and he wished to remind the Israelites of this their promise in the years
to come, when he could no longer be
with them. So he set up a great
stone under an oak-tree at Shē'-chĕm,
and whenever the people saw that
stone they remembered the promise
they had made to faithful old Joshua.

Soon after this meeting Joshua died, and the Israelites buried him
on a hillside near his home. By and by the high priest, Ĕl-ē-ā'-zär, also
died, and the Israelites buried him in the land of Ē'-phră-ĭm. Then they
made Phĭn'-ĕ-hăs, his son, to be high priest in his place. And they served
the Lord as long as the old men lived who had known Joshua and who
had seen the wonderful power of God.

———— • ————

STORY 12

HOW GOD HELPED THE ISRAELITES OUT OF THEIR TROUBLES
Judg. 1:1—3:14

After Joshua was dead, the Israelites remembered their promise
to obey the Lord. They began to fight against the wicked people who
still lived in the land; for God had told them to destroy those people
and to tear down their idols. When they fought God helped them just
as he had done while Joshua lived and led them out to battle. And
God caused their enemies to be afraid of them. Every time they went

out to battle they gained a victory, and all the while they kept gaining more cities and more land to call their own.

But after some time the Israelites grew tired of fighting. Perhaps they thought, "We shall rest a while and enjoy the good country places we have already taken. Then we can go out to battle again." But instead of tearing down the idols while they rested, they made friends with the wicked people who served these idols. They even began to let their children play with the boys and girls of Canaan; and by and by when their children grew up they married the sons and daughters of their wicked neighbors. And those sons and daughters taught the Israelites' children to bow down before the idols in the land and worship them. Thus little by little the Israelites had come to forget their promise to Joshua, that they would serve the true God, and him only.

But God did not forget his promises to the Israelites. He sent an angel to tell them that he was not pleased with them, because they had quit fighting against the wicked people of Canaan. The angel said, "Because you have not obeyed the Lord fully as you promised to do, now he will not help you when you want to drive these people away. These people will always live in your land, and they will try to teach you to do wickedly. If you refuse to serve their idols, God will bless you; but if you turn away from God, he will allow great troubles to come upon you."

The Israelites listened to the angel's words, and they felt sorry because they had not tried harder to drive out all the Canaanites while God was helping them so wonderfully. They even wept; but now it was too late, for God would not help them drive their enemies away any more. Because they had made friends with these people, now they must live among them and see their wicked doings.

However sorry the Israelites were, it was not very long until they were again forgetting, and were doing many things God had commanded them not to do. They were bowing down before the idols that stood under the beautiful trees of Canaan instead of going to Shī'-lōh to worship the true God. They were even offering sacrifices on the altars in their fields where the Canaanites worshiped other gods. It seemed so easy for them to act as did their wicked neighbors. Perhaps at first they had thought, "Three journeys each year to Shī'-lōh are too many. We will go only twice." Then maybe the next year they went only once, and by and by they did not go at all.

Although people may forget their promises, God never forgets. Whatever he says he will do, that he always does. And now when the Israelites began to worship idols, God allowed troubles to come upon them. He allowed a strong enemy from a country far away to the east to come and fight against them. The Israelites were weak, because God was not fighting for them, and they lost the victory. Then their enemies ruled over them. For eight years this cruel enemy made their lives unhappy.

When this great trouble came upon the Israelites they remembered how God used to help them. And they began to call upon God to help them again. Although they had done many wrong deeds, God heard them when they called. He saw they were in trouble and he spoke to a brave man among them whose name was Ŏth'-nĭ-ĕl. This man had married the daughters of the brave old soldier Caleb.

Ŏth'-nĭ-ĕl may never have forgotten the true God as the other Israelites had done. But while they were worshiping idols he could not help them. Now, when they turned away from idol-worship and prayed to God, he called the soldiers of Israel together and led them to battle against their strong enemy. And God gave them the victory.

After this time God used Ŏth'-nĭ-ĕl as a leader of the Israelites. He was called a judge. For forty years he ruled the people, and while he lived the land of Israel enjoyed rest from wicked nations round about them. But when he died, many of the people quit going to the tabernacle at Shī'-lōh to worship God. They would not even listen to the words of the Levites. They wanted to worship gods that they could see, like the Canaanites worshiped. So they turned again to worship idols. And troubles came upon them quickly, just as God had promised.

Not far from the land of Israel was a country called Moab. This country was ruled by King Ĕg'-lŏn. And this King looked with greedy eyes toward the rich land of Israel. He thought, "I should like to rule that country, too." One day he called his soldiers and sent them to fight against the men of Israel. And because God was not willing to help the Israelites in this battle they were beaten again. Then for eighteen long years King Ĕg'-lŏn ruled over them.

———————•———————

STORY 13

THE LEFT-HANDED MAN WHO JUDGED ISRAEL
Judg. 3:15-31

During the eighteen years that the Israelites served Ĕg'-lŏn, king of Moab, they were unhappy. Every year they had to bring much of their fruit and grain and many of their cattle to the King, and they received no money for these things. The Moabites grew richer and the Israelites grew poorer all the while. The Moabites had a brave leader and the Israelites had no leader at all. They had forsaken God, and he had forsaken them.

After suffering for a long time the Israelites began to think about the victories that God had given to their fathers. They talked to each other about those happier days when God had blessed them. They remembered, too, how they had turned away from God to serve the idols of the Canaanites. Now they took offerings for sacrifices and went to Shī'-lōh and gave them to the high priest to offer on the great altar at the tabernacle. They prayed to God earnestly and asked him to forgive their sins and help them once more. And God sent them another deliverer, or judge.

The second judge of Israel was named Ē'-hŭd. He belonged to the smallest of the twelve tribes—the tribe of Benjamin. To him the Israelites gave a present to carry to King Ĕg'-lŏn.

Now Ē'-hŭd did not feel friendly toward the wicked King who had made life so miserable for him and for his people. But he acted like a very good friend indeed. He brought the present to the beautiful summer house where the King was living, and turned to go away. Then he hurried back the second time to the beautiful palace and said, "I have a secret message for the King." So Ĕg'-lŏn dismissed his servants from the room and rose to hear what Ē'-hŭd might say.

Underneath his clothes and on his right side Ē'-hŭd carried a short sword, called a dagger. Ē'-hŭd was left-handed, and no one could see that he had a weapon with him. But when the King came near he saw a sword flash in Ē'-hŭd's left hand and he felt it cut his flesh. Then he fell on the floor and died.

Ē'-hŭd quickly locked the doors and ran away toward where the Israelites were. No one saw him leave the King's room. But after some time the servants grew tired of waiting for the King to come out. They tried the doors but found them locked. At first they supposed their King was lying down to rest, but after waiting a while longer they tried again to open the doors. This time they brought a key, and when the door was not opened they unlocked it and went inside the room. There they saw the King lying dead.

Now they knew that Ē'-hŭd had killed King Ĕg'-lŏn. But Ē'-hŭd had gotten too far away for them to catch him. They called the army of Moab and sent in haste to the land of Israel. But Ē'-hŭd had already reached home and had called the soldiers of Israel together and they came out and fought against the Moabites. In this battle Israel gained a great victory, and this victory brought them freedom again. After this time they enjoyed rest from their enemies for eighty years.

The next people to trouble the Israelites were the Philistines, their neighbors in the land of Israel. These were people whom the Israelites should have driven out of the land while God was helping them. Now they could never drive them away. But God sent Shăm'-gär to help them gain a victory over the Philistines, and he killed six hundred of them with only an ox-goad for a weapon. Shăm'-gär was the third judge of Israel.

STORY 14

TWO BRAVE WOMEN WHO HELPED THE ISRAELITES OUT OF TROUBLE

Judges 4, 5

In the land of Israel, not very far from Shī'-lōh, a brave woman lived whose name was Dĕb'-ŏ-răh. Although many of the Israelites had turned away from God again to worship idols, this brave woman loved the true God and worshiped him.

Because Dĕb'-ŏ-răh was faithful to God, sometimes God spoke to her, and told her about things that would happen by and by. And Dĕb'-ŏ-răh told the people the words that God spoke to her. Then when the very things happened that Dĕb'-ŏ-răh told about, the people began to look with great respect upon this good woman. They called her a prophetess. And they came to visit her from every part of the land. Often they found her sitting under the shade of a palm-tree, which stood near her country home, and there they talked to her about their troubles and asked her what they should do. And Dĕb'-ŏ-răh became the fourth judge of Israel.

At this time the Israelites were in trouble again. They were being ruled by a hard-hearted king, named Jā'-bĭn, who lived in the north part of their country. Perhaps Jā'-bĭn was the son of one of the Canaanite kings whom their fathers had not driven out of the land. Now because they were bowing down to idols God was allowing this wicked king to rule over them.

King Jā'-bĭn had a large army, and many of his soldiers rode in iron chariots drawn by horses. From these chariots they shot arrows and threw spears at their enemies. And the Israelites feared the iron chariots more than they feared a host of men. The leader, or captain, of Jā′ bĭn′s̓ army was named Sĭs′-ĕ-rä. He, like the King, was very cruel.

For twenty years the Israelites suffered under the rule of King Jā′-bĭn. Especially did the tribes in the north part of the land feel his cruel strength. Finally they began to cry aloud to God for help.

Then God spoke to Dĕb′-ŏ-räh and told her what to do. She sent at once for Bâr′-ăk, a brave man who lived in the north country near the city of the wicked King Jabin. When he came, she told him about God′s words.

Although Bâr′-ăk was brave, yet he felt a shiver of fear when he heard Dĕb′-ŏ-räh′s̓ message; for he remembered the iron chariots of King Jā′-bĭn′s̓ army. He knew, too, that the other men of Israel were not so brave as he. What should he do? Finally he thought of a plan, so he said to Dĕb′-ŏ-räh, "If you will go with me to the battle against Jā′-bĭn′s̓ army, I will go; but if you will not go with me, then I will not go." Bâr′-ăk knew the soldiers of Israel believed Dĕb′-ŏ-räh was a true prophetess of God, and he knew they would act bravely if she would go with them. He believed that he, too, would feel stronger if Dĕb′-ŏ-räh were near by to encourage his faith in God.

Dĕb′-ŏ-räh was ready to go with Bâr′-ăk; but before they started she said, "God will give the honor of this victory to a woman, and not to you." Bâr′-ăk may have thought that Dĕb′-ŏ-räh spoke of herself; but in that he was mistaken. When they reached the north country, Bâr′-ăk called ten thousand soldiers from the tribes of Năph′-tă-lī and Zĕ-bū′-lŭn and went with them to Mount Tā′-bôr, the place God had chosen for their camp. Dĕb′-ŏ-räh went with them.

Soon Sisera heard that the Israelites were making ready to fight, so he gathered his soldiers together and started out in haste toward Mount Tā′-bôr. As he went he may have thought, "How can those weak Israelites dare to come out to battle against me and my soldiers?"

From the camp at Mount Tā′-bôr, Dĕb′-ŏ-räh and Bâr′-ăk could see the little river of Kī′-shŏn winding like a silver ribbon in the valley far below them. Presently they saw a swarm of people gathering along the river′s bank. This was Sĭs′-ĕ-rä′s̓ army. And they saw the hundreds of iron chariots, which the men of Israel feared so greatly. But Dĕb′-ŏ-räh cried out to the soldiers in the camp, "This is the day when the Lord has delivered Sĭs′-ĕ-rä into your hands. Already the Lord has gone out to battle; now go down at once!"

Bâr′-ăk and his soldiers obeyed quickly, and rushed down the mountain-side toward Sĭs′-ĕ-rä′s̓ army. And God sent a great fear into the hearts of the enemies, and they began to run away. Then God caused a flood of water to sweep down the little river and overflow its banks.

Many of Sĭs'-ĕ-rä's men were drowned in the flood, and all the others were killed. Sĭs'-ĕ-rä himself left his iron chariot and ran away as fast as he could go. What a coward he had become!

Now one of the Kē'-nīte people, named Hē-bĕr, had moved his tents away from his kinsmen to a lonely place near the border of this valley where the battle was fought. And Jā'-ĕl, Hē'-bĕr's wife, saw Sĭs'-ĕ-rä coming in great haste toward her tent. The people who live in tents do not allow strange men to enter the tents of their women, and no doubt Sĭs'-ĕ-rä knew this custom. He thought his enemies would not expect him to hide in Jā'-ĕl's tent, so he ran there to be safe. And when Jā'-ĕl asked him to come inside, he believed she was friendly toward his people. He called for a drink of water because he was very thirsty, and Jā'-ĕl gave him a bottle of milk. That was even better than water. Then, because he was very tired he lay down to rest, and Jā'-ĕl covered him with a large rug. Soon he fell asleep.

"Now," thought Jā'-ĕl, "this is my chance!" So she stepped softly into the tent and killed the sleeping man. What a cruel deed! But Jā'-ĕl knew how wickedly Sĭs'-ĕ-rä had behaved and she wanted to help the Israelites out of their trouble. When she knew Sĭs'-ĕ-rä was dead she ran out, and she saw Bär'-ăk passing by. He was following after Sĭs'-ĕ-rä and trying to catch him and kill him. She called Bär'-ăk and said, "Come with me and I will show you the man you seek." And she brought him into the tent where Sĭs'-ĕ-rä lay dead.

So it was Jā'-ĕl, a woman, instead of Bär'-ăk, the soldier, who killed Sĭs'-ĕ-rä and ended some of Israel's greatest troubles. After Sĭs'-ĕ-rä's death King Jā'-bĭn was not strong enough to rule over the Israelites, and they enjoyed freedom again. Dĕb'-ŏ-räh wrote a song about this victory, and she and Bär'-ăk sang it together as they thanked God for helping them. You may find the words of that song in the fifth chapter of Judges.

————◆————

STORY 15

HOW A BRAVE MAN TORE DOWN AN ALTAR OF BAAL

Judges 6

Dĕb'-ŏ-räh judged Israel for forty years, and during that time the people were not troubled any more by their enemies. But after she died they grew careless again and soon forgot about God's goodness to them. They made images of the gods that the Canaanites worshiped, and served them. They even built altars and offered sacrifices to the gods, just as their wicked neighbors were doing all around them. God was much displeased with them, and he forsook them entirely.

About this time the Israelites began to have trouble with the Mĭd'-ĭ-ă-nītes. These Mĭd'-ĭ-ă-nītes came from the country east of the land of Israel. They lived in tents like gypsies, and roamed about wherever they could find pasture and water for their cattle and sheep and camels. The land of Israel had much beautiful pasture-land, and streams of clear water, so the Mĭd'-ĭ-ă-nītes came with all their tents and cattle and sheep and camels and camped along the borders of Israel. The Israelites were too weak to drive them away, and the Mĭd'-ĭ-ă-nītes grew bolder all the while. First they allowed their flocks and herds to graze on the pasture-lands of Israel; then they began to rob the Israelites of the food that grew in Israel's fields and vineyards; and finally they even crowded the people out of their homes and drove them away to hide in dens and caves in the mountains. Like grasshoppers they filled the valleys of eastern Israel with their tents and ate up everything that the Israelites had raised in their gardens and fields. What a time of trouble this was!

As at other times when trouble came upon them, now the Israelites remembered God and cried again to him for help. But God knew they had forsaken him and brought this great trouble upon themselves. He sent a prophet to remind them of the wonderful things that he had done for their fathers and yet they had forsaken him and turned to other gods. Now those gods could not help them.

One day after the prophet had spoken to the people, an Israelite named Gideon was threshing wheat by a wine-press, to hide it from the Mĭd'-ĭ-ă-nītes lest they come and take it away from him. While he worked, an angel came and sat down under an oak-tree near by. Presently Gideon looked up and saw the angel. He did not seem to know at first that his visitor was from heaven. But as they talked together the angel told Gideon that he should deliver the Israelites from their enemies. Gideon answered, "How can I do such a great work? for I am of a poor family, and am the least in my father's house." Then the angel told him that by God's help he would be able to do this great work.

Gideon had been so greatly discouraged because of the troubles and poverty of his people that he was not very quick to believe the angel's word. Perhaps he thought it seemed too wonderful to be true that God would use him to bring about such a deliverance. So he asked for a sign from the angel. "If you will remain here until I return again and bring you a present," he said, "then I will believe that you have surely spoken to me the words of God.'' And the angel waited until Gideon returned with some food. Then, instead of eating it, the angel told Gideon to place the meat and bread upon a rock near by, and to pour out the broth. Gideon obeyed, and the angel touched the meat and bread with the staff that he carried in his hand. Like a flash the rock flamed up in fire and burned the meat and bread. And the angel disappeared out of sight.

When Gideon knew he had been talking to a messenger from God he was afraid; but God spoke to him and comforted him. Then Gideon built an altar at that place and called it by a name which meant, ''The Lord send peace.''

Now the people where Gideon lived were worshiping the idol called Bā'-ăl. Even Gideon's father had an altar of Bā'-ăl standing in his yard. God told Gideon to tear this altar down and destroy the trees near by where the people bowed before the images of Bā'-ăl.

Gideon was a brave man, yet he knew the people would be angry if they should see him tearing down their idol, so he waited until night, and then he called ten servants to help him. They took one of his father's oxen and tore the altar of Bā'-ăl in pieces. Then they cut down the trees where the idols had stood and built a large altar to the true God. On it they placed the wood from the trees to make a fire, and they killed another ox that belonged to Gideon's father and offered it for a sacrifice to God.

When the people of the neighborhood came the next morning to worship Bā'-ăl they found his altar torn down and all the places to bow before him lying in ruins. ''Who has done this?'' they asked angrily, and some one answered, ''Gideon, the son of Joash.'' Then they hurried to Jō'-ăsh and demanded that he bring out Gideon at once. ''He has torn down Bā'-ăl's altar, and we want to kill him,'' they said.

But Jō'-ăsh answered bravely, ''If Bā'-ăl is a god, let him help himself. Why should you try to save him?'' And the people, when they saw that Bā'-ăl could not harm the one who destroyed his altar, were no longer angry with Gideon. Perhaps they felt foolish because they had been worshiping such a god.

After this had happened Gideon sent messengers to the different parts of the land and called the soldiers of Israel together. But first he wanted to be very sure that God would be with him before he should try to drive the Mĭd'-ĭ-ă-nītes away. So he asked again for a sign from God. This time he placed a piece of wool at nightfall on a smooth floor where no roof had been built overhead. He asked God to cause only the fleece of wool to become wet with dew. When morning came he found the ground dry everywhere, but the fleece of wool was covered with dew.   Gideon wrung a bowlful of water out of it.

Still Gideon was not satisfied.   He prayed that God might not be

CALL OF GIDEON

angry with him if he should ask the third time for a sign.   Now he placed the fleece of wool out as before, and he asked God to cause the dew to lie everywhere except on the fleece.   And when morning came the fleece was dry while the ground about it was wet.   Then Gideon believed that surely God was ready to help him.

STORY 16

HOW THE MIDIANITES WERE SURPRIZED AT MIDNIGHT
Judges 7:1—8:28

Gideon's message to the people of Israel brought thirty-two thousand men from different parts of the country to his command. They pitched their camp beside a great spring called the well of Hâr'-ŏd, on Mount Gĭl-bō'-ă. The Mĭd'-ĭ-ă-nītes were camping in the broad valley below them.

When Gideon's army had gathered together, God spoke to their brave leader and said, "You have too many soldiers; for when the Mĭd'-ĭ-ă-nītes are defeated the people will think they have gained the victory in their own strength. I want them to know surely that I am leading them to the battle." And God told Gideon to send home every man who was afraid to fight against the enemy.

Gideon obeyed God's command, and more than two thirds of his soldiers left the camp and returned to their homes. They were cowards, and cowards never can act bravely when dangers come. No doubt Gideon and the ten thousand men who remained were glad because the cowards had gone away before the battle started.

Still God was not satisfied with the size of Gideon's army. He wanted fewer men than these. So he commanded Gideon to take the army down to the water and divide them there. Those who laid aside their weapons and bowed down at the water's edge to drink God told Gideon to separate from those who held their weapons in one hand and drank water from the other hand. And all the men except three hundred threw their weapons on the grass and knelt down to drink. We know they were not very watchful of the enemy, or else they would not have carelessly laid aside their weapons in a time of danger to satisfy their thirst. By the three hundred watchful men God wished to frighten the Mĭd'-ĭ-ă-nītes out of the land. He told Gideon to send the others back to the camp.

Now Gideon's army looked very small. Indeed, it no longer looked like an army; for only a handful of men remained. But Gideon knew God had promised to help, and he was willing to obey every word God spoke to him.

When darkness came over the valleys and hills, God told Gideon that the time had come to go down and surprize the enemy's camp. But first he told Gideon to take only one servant and steal quietly through the shadows to the edge of the camp and listen. There he would hear something that would make him braver and stronger for the attack.

Again Gideon carefully obeyed the Lord, and when he came near the Mĭd'-ĭ-ă-nītes' camp he heard one man telling another about a strange dream that he had dreamed. "In my dreams I saw a cake of barley bread come tumbling into our camp, and it overturned one of the tents." The other man said, "Your dream means that Gideon, the

GIDEON'S ARMY BLOWING THEIR TRUMPETS

son of Jō'-ăsh, will come against us with his sword and drive us away; for his God has delivered us into his power." When Gideon heard these words he thanked God and hurried back to his waiting men.

A busy time was now before them. First Gideon divided the men into three companies, with one hundred men in each company. Next he gave each man a trumpet on which to blow at the time of the attack. And last of all he told every man to carry an empty pitcher with a burning torch hidden inside the pitcher. So with trumpets in one hand

and pitchers in the other hand Gideon and his three hundred brave soldiers marched quietly down the mountain-slope toward the enemy's camp. Here they parted, and very quietly they took their places around the camp. Then they waited for Gideon's signal.

Now the Mĭd'-ĭ-ă-nītes, except their watchmen, were all sleeping soundly. At midnight Gideon gave his signal, and when his soldiers heard his trumpet they all blew a loud, long blast. Then they cried aloud on every side of the camp, "The sword of the Lord and of Gideon!" And every one broke his pitcher at the same time. What a glare of light flamed up from the smoking torches around the camp!

The sleeping Mĭd'-ĭ-ă-nītes were awakened with a start. "What can this great excitement mean?" they wondered. Then they thought, "Gideon has come with a great army and has surprized us. He will kill every one of us if we do not run away at once." So away they ran through the darkness, stumbling over each other, and falling upon each other's swords. Many of them died from being trampled upon and wounded by their own people. Others hurried away toward the Jordan River, beyond which lay their own country.

Gideon and his brave men followed the fleeing Mĭd'-ĭ-ă-nītes, and other soldiers of Israel came hurrying out to help drive their enemies away. They killed the two kings of Mĭd'-ĭ-ăn and the princes, and many of their men. After this time the Mĭd'-ĭ-ă-nītes did not trouble Israel any more. And the people of Israel wished Gideon would become a king and rule over them. But Gideon said, "I will not rule over you, and neither shall my son rule over you; for God is your King." And Gideon judged Israel at God's word for forty years.

STORY 17

THE MAN WHO MADE HIMSELF KING OVER ISRAEL
Judges 8 : 32—10 : 5

When Gideon refused to be made king over Israel, the people returned to their homes, and he went back to live again in Ŏph'-răh, the place where God first spoke to him. Here the people from every part of the land came to talk with him about their troubles; for he was the judge of Israel.

After Gideon died, one of his sons, named Ă-bĭm'-ĕ-lĕch, remembered that the Israelites had at one time wanted to make his father the king of their country. But he remembered that his father had refused to be made a king. "Now," thought Ă-bĭm'-ĕ-lĕch, "I will become their king." So he talked with the men who lived in Shē'-chĕm, a city not far from Ŏph'-răh, and they were well pleased with him. They gave him money from the temple of their idol, and with it he hired some wicked men to go with him back to the home of his father's people.

Now Ă-bĭm'-ĕ-lĕch feared that his brothers, the sons of Gideon, might not want him to rule over them, so he planned to kill them all. But one of them, the youngest, whose name was Jō'-thăm, ran away and hid in the mountains. The others he killed.

After this wicked deed was done, Ă-bĭm'-ĕ-lĕch went again to Shē'-chĕm, and the men from that city took him out to a country place and, under an oak-tree, crowned him for their king. Although they knew how cruelly he had treated his brothers—the sons of the great man who once saved their land from their enemies—yet they gave honor to Ă-bĭm'-ĕ-lĕch.

When Jō'-thăm heard that Ă-bĭm'-ĕ-lĕch had been made king by the men of Shē'-chĕm, he knew God was not pleased. He knew that Ă-bĭm'-ĕ-lĕch had sinned again, and that the people of Shē'-chĕm had also sinned. So he climbed the mountain that stood near Shē'-chĕm and spoke in a loud voice, that all the people in the valley might hear his words. He told them a parable, or story, about the trees. This is what he said:

"The trees went out one day to make for themselves a king. First they asked the olive-tree to rule over them. But the olive-tree replied, 'Shall I leave my olive-oil, with which honor is given to God and man, and become merely a ruler of trees?' And the olive-tree would not be their king.

"Next they asked the fig-tree to rule over them. But the fig-tree replied, 'Shall I quit bearing fruit for mankind, and give myself to become only a ruler over the trees?' And the fig-tree would not be their king.

"Then they asked the vine to rule over them. But the vine also refused to leave the work that God had given to it. So at last they spoke to a bramble-bush, on which sharp thistles grew. And the bramble-bush replied, 'If you will trust yourselves under my shadow, then I will become your king. But if you will not trust in me, then fire will come out from me and destroy you all, even the beautiful cedar-trees!'"

Then Jō'-thăm explained the meaning of the story, or parable. He said that the men of Shē'-chĕm were like the trees that wanted a king to rule over them. And Ă-bĭm'-ĕ-lĕch was like the bramble-bush, on which sharp thistles grew. Ă-bĭm'-ĕ-lĕch would bring much sorrow to them, and just as the fire would burn up both the trees and the thorn-bush too, so the sorrows caused by Ă-bĭm'-ĕ-lĕch would finally mean death to him as well as to the people of Shē'-chem.

After telling this story and explaining its meaning, Jō'-thăm ran away and hid in another part of the land. He knew Ă-bĭm'-ĕ-lĕch would surely kill him if he could find him.

For three years Ă-bĭm'-ĕ-lĕch ruled over Israel as king. Then God allowed an evil spirit to trouble Ă-bĭm'-ĕ-lĕch and the men of Shē'-chem. They no longer felt kind toward each other. Finally the Shē'-chem-ītes planned to kill Ă-bĭm'-ĕ-lĕch; but when their governor heard about the plan he sent a secret messenger to Ă-bĭm'-ĕ-lĕch to warn him about the wicked intentions of his people.

Not long after this Ă-bĭm'-ĕ-lĕch came with an army against Shē'-chem and destroyed the city. Then he went to another city near by and began to fight against it. The people of that city fled into a tower and bolted the door on the inside, and climbed to the topmost part for safety. Ă-bĭm'-ĕ-lĕch attempted to set the tower on fire; but while he was in the act a woman on the top of the building threw a stone down upon his head and crushed his skull. Ă-bĭm'-ĕ-lĕch knew then that he would die, and he did not want to be killed by a woman. Because he was a strong soldier he thought it would be dishonorable to have it said of him that a woman had caused his death. So he commanded the young man who carried his armor to kill him quickly with his sword. And thus it was that Ă-bĭm'-ĕ-lĕch and all the men of Shē'-chem were killed as cruelly as they had killed the sons of Gideon.

After Ă-bĭm'-ĕ-lĕch died, the people of Israel were judged for twenty-three years by a man named Tō'-lă, who belonged to the tribe of Ĭs'-să-chär. Then Jā'-ĭr, a man who lived on the east side of the Jordan River, became the next judge, and for twenty-two years the people came to him to have their disputes settled and their troubles removed.

———•———

STORY 18

HOW A GIRL SUFFERED FOR HER FATHER'S RASH PROMISE
Judges 10: 6—12: 7

In the land of Israel east of Jordan there lived a man named Jĕph'-thăh. His brothers despised him and drove him away from their

father's home, so he went to live in the land called Tŏb. Here he
became a strong man, and his brave deeds were told by many people.
Finally even his brothers heard about them.

At this time the Israelites were in great trouble again. They had
quit going to the tabernacle at Shī'-lōh to worship God. Everywhere in
the land they were bowing down before the gods that other nations
worshiped. And the very nations whose gods they were serving began
to trouble them. They began to make war against the Israelites and
to take away their riches. The Ammonites came from the east and the
Philistines came from the west and ruled over the Israelites. The
Ammonites even threatened to take away the homes of the Israelites
and to drive them out of their country. This was an unhappy time
indeed for the people who had once enjoyed the blessings of God.

After suffering for eighteen years under the rule of their enemies,
the Israelites remembered how God had long ago given them all the
land and had made them stronger than all the nations who lived around
them. So they cried to God for help, and they expected God to send
a deliverer, just as he had done at other times when they were in
trouble.

But God was much displeased with the people. He was not willing to help them, because they had turned away from him to worship
the gods of other nations. He said, "Let the gods that you have chosen
instead of me help you out of your trouble. I will not be your God
when trouble comes upon you if you will not worship me when you
have rest from your enemies."

Now the Israelites became very sorry for having sinned against
the true God. They saw that the gods they were serving could never
help them at all. They knew the true God whom their fathers had
worshiped could deliver them out of the power of their enemies. So
they tore down their idols and began to serve the Lord. They confessed their sins to the Lord and asked him again to help them.

When the Lord saw that the people were really sorry for their sins,
he began to pity them. He saw them gather their soldiers together at
a place called Mĭz'-pēh to fight against the Ammonites. But they had
no leader.

Finally someone remembered Jĕph'-thăh whose brave deeds had
been told through all the land. They sent quickly for him to come
to lead them to the battle against the Ammonites. But Jĕph'-thăh was
not willing to come. Not until his brothers had promised to treat him
kindly would Jĕph'-thăh return again with his family to his old home
and help his people out of their trouble.

Jĕph'-thăh knew that unless God would be with him he could not gain a victory over the Ammonites. So he asked God to help him, and he promised to give as a present to God the first thing that should meet him on his return home from the battle. This was not a wise promise; for Jĕph'-thăh did not know what might come first to greet him on his return.

The Ammonites sent a message to the Israelites at Mĭz'-pēh and wanted them to give up all the land east of the Jordan River; they said this land belonged to them first. But Jĕph'-thăh sent back an answer that God would be the judge, for he had given the land to the people of Israel. Then the battle began; and the Israelites won the victory.

News of the victory reached Jĕph'-thăh's home before he returned with the army to Mĭz'-pēh. And everybody was glad because God had helped them again. Jĕph'-thăh's daughter, his only child, came hurrying out to meet her father, singing for joy. But her song ended quickly when she saw her father's troubled face. He had remembered his promise to the Lord. Now he believed that he must give his only child as an offering to God. How sorry he felt because he had made such an unwise promise! He tore his clothes and cried out in distress. Then he told his daughter about the promise that he had made.

The people of other nations sometimes gave their children to their gods; but the law of Moses forbade the Israelites doing such a thing. Perhaps Jĕph'-thăh had never heard that part of the law read, and he had often heard about the cruel custom of his heathen neighbors. He believed that he would need to keep his promise, although it was not a wise one. And his daughter urged him to keep it, because God had given him the victory over their enemies. But first she asked for two months time to spend alone with her friends in the mountains, weeping because she must soon be taken away from them. Afterwards she returned again to her father that he might fulfil his promise to God.

Jĕph'-thăh judged Israel for six years after his victory over the Ammonites, and then he died.

STORY 19

THE STORY OF A STRONG MAN WHO JUDGED ISRAEL
Judges 13—16

About twenty-five years passed before the Israelites as a nation again forsook God and turned to idol-worship. Perhaps the fathers and mothers never did set up the old idols they had torn down; but when their sons and daughters grew to manhood and womanhood they wished to have gods like their heathen neighbors'. So they made idols like the gods that their neighbors worshiped, and placed the idols in their cities and under the trees in their dooryards. There they bowed down before them, and served them in the same wicked manner as did their heathen friends.

Not all of the Israelites, however, began to worship idols again. Some here and there throughout the land of Israel continued to fear God and to serve him. But their numbers were few. And when trouble came upon the land because the people as a nation had forsaken God, the few who still served him suffered with those who deserved to be punished.

After a while the Philistines began to trouble Israel. These people lived by the seacoast, and they were strong and cruel. For forty years they ruled over the tribes of Israel whose land joined their country. They worshiped a god whom they called Dā'-gŏn, and they set up his idol in the temple of their chief city, Gā'-ză. This hideous-looking idol had the face and hands of a man, and the body of a fish.

One of the tribes whose land joined the country of the Philistines was the tribe of Dan. Belonging to this tribe was a man named Mă-nō'-ăh, who with his wife feared God and served him. These people had no children. One day an angel appeared to Mă-nō'-ăh's wife and told her that God would give her a son. He said this son should become a great man some day, that he would begin to deliver their land from the rule of the Philistines.

No doubt Mă-nō'-ăh and his wife were made happy by the promise of this angel. And when the child was born to them they named him Samson. They were careful to obey the words of the angel, who had told them never to allow their son to drink wine. Neither should they ever cut his hair for the angel said he should become a Nazarite.

Now a Nazarite was a person who either gave himself to do some special work for God or else was given by his parents at the time of his birth. And the sign by which a Nazarite was known from other people was his long hair, which grew from year to year without being cut. If he should cut his hair, or if he should drink wine, then he no longer could have God's blessings upon his work.

When Samson grew up, his body became very strong. His will also became strong, and hard to bend. That is, whenever he wished to do a certain thing he would not listen to a'dvice from any one; he wanted to do as he pleased. Perhaps his parents had allowed him to have his own way when a child, and when he became a man he still wished to have his own way. Sometimes he behaved much like a naughty child; and this wrong behavior at last got him into great trouble. It even cost his life.

SAMSON KILLING A LION

Although Samson was careful never to drink wine nor to cut his hair, yet he was not careful always to choose good people for his friends. He visited the Philistines, and when he grew to manhood he even wished to marry one of them. His parents were sad, because they feared that he might begin to worship Dā'-gŏn if he should marry a Philistine woman. But Samson wanted to have his own way, and he had it.

No sooner was Samson married than his troubles began. His wife's friends displeased him, and he became angry with them. He went back to his own home and left his wife at her father's house. When he did not return for many days, his father-in-law gave his wife in marriage to another man.

By and by Samson's anger cooled off and he decided to go again and live with his wife. Probably he felt ashamed because he had left her in an angry mood. Wishing to gain her good-will again, he took her a present. But when he came to her father's house he learned that she had become the wife of another man.

Now Samson was very angry indeed. He started toward his home, but stopped long enough on the way to catch three hundred foxes and tie their tails together, two and two, placing between the tails of each two a firebrand. Then he lit the firebrands and turned the foxes loose,

SAMSON KILLING THE PHILISTINES WITH A DRY BONE

yelping and snarling, into the corn-fields of the Philistines. Of course the corn was all burned up, and even the olive-trees and the grape-vines were destroyed by the fire.

Then it was the Philistines who became angry. They asked, "Who has done this mischief?" and some one told them that Samson was trying to punish them because his wife had been given to another man. Hearing this, the Philistines blamed Samson's father-in-law for the trouble, and they set fire to his house and burned him and his daughter to death.

When Samson heard what had happened to his wife and her father, he rushed down to their city again and killed many of the people who lived there. Then he hurried away and climbed to the top of a high rock in the land that belonged to the tribe of Judah. The Philistines followed after him and came with an army of one thousand men to capture the man who was giving them so much trouble. The men of the tribe of Judah asked, "Why have you come into our land?" And the Philistines said, "We have come to take Samson and to bind him and carry him back to our own land to be punished." Then the men of Judah climbed to the top of the rock and bound Samson with new cords, and tied his hands fast. In this condition they brought him down and gave him to his enemies.

Just when the Philistines thought they had almost ended their troubles, Samson broke the cords off his arms and hands and picked up a dry bone, which lay on the ground near by, and began to strike violently at the people around him. With this weapon he killed them all.

Afterwards Samson became very thirsty and he thought he might die. He prayed to God and asked for water. Then God caused water to come, and Samson drank from it and received strength once more.

Samson showed his great strength again when he visited the Philistines' chief city, Gā'-ză, and the men of that city locked the gates to keep him for a prisoner. He rose up during the night and, finding the gates locked, tore them apart from the city wall and placed them, posts and all, upon his shoulders. For twenty miles he carried them across the fields and hills, and placed them on top of a hill in the tribe-land of Judah. How surprized the men of Gā'-ză were to discover, on the next morning, that their prisoner had fled and had taken the gates of their city with him!

STORY 20

HOW SAMSON CAME TO HIS DEATH

Judges 16: 4-31

Although Samson knew that the Philistines hated him, yet he dared again and again to go among them. He knew their fear of his great strength made them quite harmless.

And, strange as it may seem, the Philistine women pleased Samson more than did the women of his own people. Some time after the cruel death of his wife, Samson met and loved another young woman among the Philistines. Her name was Dĕ-lī'-lăh.

When the rulers of the country heard that Samson was coming often to visit Dĕ-lī'-lăh, they offered to give her much money if she would find out for them the secret of Samson's great strength. They believed they would then be able, by Dĕ-lī'-lăh's help, to capture him and put him in prison. Dĕ-lī'-lăh loved pretty things that money can buy. She loved her own people better than she loved the strong man who came often to visit her. And she consented at once to help the rulers in their plan to capture Samson.

When Samson came again to visit at her home, Dĕ-lī'-lăh received him as kindly as at other times. Perhaps she talked to him with flattering words, to please him. Then finally she asked him to tell her whether his great strength could possibly be taken away from him by human hands. Samson replied that if he should be tied securely with seven green twigs his great strength would leave him and he should be powerless, like other men.

Dĕ-lī'-lăh quickly sent a messenger to the rulers, telling what she had learned; and they sent her seven green twigs like those of a willow-tree. With these she bound Samson securely while he lay asleep. Then she called to him in frightened tones, "Wake up, Samson! the Philistines are coming to take you!" But Samson did not seem at all frightened when he found himself tied with the green twigs. He sprang up and broke the twigs as easily as if they had been burned by fire.

Then Dĕ-lī'-lăh was disappointed. She knew Samson was not serious when he told her about the green twigs. She pouted and told him that he was only making fun of her. She asked him again to tell her about the secret of his strength; and Samson pretended to be very serious when he told her that if he should be bound tightly with new ropes, then he should no longer be strong.

Dĕ-lī'-lăh believed he was telling the truth this time, so she sent word again to the rulers, and they came, bringing the new ropes. While Samson slept, they hid near by and waited until Dĕ-lī'-lăh should tie him fast and then waken him, as she had done before. But this time when Samson was awakened, he broke the strong, new ropes as easily as if they had been threads, and ran away.

We should think Samson might know by this time that Dĕ-lī'-lăh was not his friend. But perhaps he thought he was having some fun. So he went again to visit Dĕ-lī'-lăh, and again she coaxed him to tell the secret of his wonderful strength. This time Samson told her that if his hair should be woven like threads in a loom where cloth is made, then he could not free himself. But when Dĕ-lī'-lăh wove his long hair in a loom and fastened it securely to the weaving-frame with a large pin, Samson rose up and tore the frame apart as easily as he had freed himself at other times.

Dĕ-lī'-lăh began to think that she should not be able to get the money

that the rulers offered to give to her if she would find out the secret of
Samson's great strength. She felt very unhappy. Day after day she
pleaded with Samson, telling him that surely he did not love her at all.

Because Samson did love Dĕ-lī'-lăh he began to feel sorry for her.
He did not want to make her so unhappy. Finally he told her the
truth—that he was a Nazarite, and that because his long hair had never
been cut he was a powerful man. "If I should let my hair be cut short,
then the Lord would leave me," he said, "and then I should become
weak and helpless before my enemies."

Dĕ-lī'-lăh was sure now that Samson had told her all the truth.
She sent her messengers secretly to the rulers and told them what
Samson had made known to her. And they came again to hide and
wait until Dĕ-lī'-lăh should call for them. While Samson slept a man
came and shaved off his long hair. Then Dĕ-lī'-lăh called him again and
told him that his enemies had come to take him. Samson opened his
eyes and saw that the Philistine rulers were already in the room. He
sprang up and said, "I will go out as at other times." But alas! this
time he could not go out, for the Lord had departed from him and he
was helpless in the hands of his enemies.

The Philistines rejoiced greatly because at last they had gotten
hold of Samson. They bound him and took him to Gā'-ză, the city where
he once tore down the gates and got away. Now they locked him in a
prison, and to make very sure that he would not bother them again they
put out his eyes. Then they chained him with fetters and made him
turn a heavy millstone to grind grain, just as though he were a beast.

Poor, unhappy Samson! At last, when all was too late, he realized
that Dĕ-lī'-lăh, the woman he loved, was not his friend. He realized that
he had made a sad mistake when he kept company with a Philistine
woman. He knew she had tempted him to displease God by telling the
secret of his wonderful strength. And he had yielded to the temptation.
Now he must suffer the remainder of his life, and always be blind. There
in the prison he prayed to God and promised again to become a Nazarite,
even though he was blind. And God heard his prayer.

Now the rulers of the Philistines planned to offer a great sacrifice
to their god, Dā'-gŏn, to thank him for giving them power over Samson.
So they made a feast in the temple of their god, and many people came
to praise Dā'-gŏn and to rejoice over Samson's defeat. Finally they
brought Samson into the court of the temple, to amuse them. No doubt
they thought he looked very funny with his long, shaggy hair and beard,
for he had never been shaven in the prison. They may have forgotten
that the secret of his great strength lay in his long hair, or they may

have supposed that he could no longer do harm because he was blind.

Samson knew that the temple was crowded with people. Even on the flat roof three thousand men and women were standing together, looking down into the court where Samson was leaning against a pillar, praying. They did not know that he was asking God to help him once more. They were laughing at his misery. Then suddenly the roof began to crack and fall in pieces, and the whole temple of Dā'-gŏn fell down. Samson had asked the boy who led him to take him to the

SAMSON PULLING DOWN THE PHILISTINE TEMPLE

great pillars that supported the roof. And, standing between these pillars, he had placed his arms around them and had bowed forward with all his might. God had heard his prayer, and had given him back his great strength. And thus Samson died with the Philistines, in the ruins of their temple.

For twenty years Samson had judged his own people. He had been the strongest man of whom the world had known. And by his great strength he had set his people free from the rule of their enemies.

When the news of this great act of Samson's reached the land of Israel, Samson's brothers hurried to Gā'-ză and found his body and carried it back to their own land. They buried him in the same place where his father, Mă-nō'-ăh, had been buried. And it was known everywhere throughout the land that Samson killed more Philistines at his death than he had killed during all the years of his life. And perhaps even Dĕ-lī′-lăh, too, died among the others in the temple of Dā′-gŏn.

———•———

STORY 21

THE YOUNG WOMAN WHO FORSOOK IDOLS TO SERVE GOD

Ruth 1—4

Ruth was a young girl who lived in the country of Moab. Her father and mother and all her relatives worshiped idols. Her neighbors worshiped idols, too. In fact, Ruth had never heard about the true God. Her nation, the Moabites, had never served God. They served a hideous-looking idol named Chē′-mŏsh. This idol was sometimes called a fire-god, because he was worshiped with fire. His image was made of brass, with a hollow place on the inside, in which fire was built. Then, when the brass image became red-hot, the sacrifices were placed in the outstretched arms. Sometimes even children were offered as sacrifices to this god. Ruth had often seen her people bow down before Chē′-mŏsh. She, too, had been taught to fear and worship him.

Then one day some people from the land of Israel came to live near Ruth's home. Because so little rain had fallen in their own land these people could not raise food enough to eat. So they had come to Moab, where plenty of rain fell, and there they decided to stay until the famine should end in their own country.

After a while Ruth became acquainted with this Israelite family. She soon learned that they worshiped a different God from the god of the Moabites. Finally the man, whose name was Ē-lĭm′-ĕ-lĕch, died, leaving his wife, Nā′-ō-mī, and her two sons alone in a strange land. When the sons grew to manhood they married girls of Moab. One of the girls was named Ôr′-păh, and the other one was named Ruth—the Ruth of our story.

Now Ruth went to live with Nā′-ō-mī, her mother-in-law. Ôr′-păh, too, lived with them. And there these young women learned about the God of the Israelites. Instead of teaching her young husband to serve Chē′-mŏsh, the fire-god, Ruth learned to serve the true God.

Ten years passed by, and Ruth's husband died. His brother also died, leaving his mother alone with her two daughters-in-law. Now Nā′-ō-mī was very sad. She was too poor to care for herself, and when she heard that the famine had ended in her homeland she decided to return again to her own people. With a sad heart she started away from the strange country where her husband and sons lay buried.

Ôr'-păh and Ruth loved Nā'-ō-mī, and they wished to go with her to the land of Israel. But after they started Nā'-ō-mī urged them to turn back and leave her to go alone. She knew the journey would be long and tiresome for them, and she knew they had no friends waiting to welcome them there. Once she had been a stranger in Moab, and she remembered how it felt to live among people of a different nation. She told them they might be happier with their own people.

After a while Ôr'-păh kissed her mother-in-law good-by and turned back; but Ruth clung only more tightly to the dear old lady who had helped to teach her about the true God. She said: "Do not try to force me to turn back, for I will never leave you alone. Where you go, I will go; from this time your people shall become my people, and your God I choose to be my God."

Nā'-ō-mī saw how truly Ruth loved her, and she did not talk to her any more about going back to her own mother's home. Together these two women walked on and on, over the fields and hills. At last they came to the city of Bethlehem, where Nā'-ō-mī had once lived so happily with her husband and two little boys.

The people of Bethlehem were glad to see Nā'-ō-mī again. But they noticed quickly how trouble and sorrow had changed their old friend. They asked each other, "Can this be Nā'-ō-mī?" And when she heard them she said, "Do not call me Nā'-ō-mī now, but call me Mâr'-ă; for God has taken my loved ones away from me, and my life has become bitter indeed." The word "Nā'-ō-mī" means pleasant, and the word "Mâr'-ă" means bitter; and Nā'-ō-mī thought her name should be changed because her happiness had been changed to sorrow. And Nā'-ō-mī told her friends how Ruth had chosen to come with her and to worship the God of Israel.

At this time the grain was ripe in the fields, and the reapers were busy cutting it with sickles and binding it in bundles. The custom of the Israelites was to leave some stalks of grain in the fields for the poor people to gather. And Ruth went out to glean some grain for herself and for her mother-in-law.

Now it happened that Ruth began to glean in the field of a very rich man, named Bō'-ăz. This man lived in Bethlehem, and his servants worked in his fields. While Ruth was busy at work, Bō'-ăz came to talk with his servants. He saw the strange young woman and he asked who she was. The master of his servants replied, "This is the young Moabitess who came with Nā'-ō-mī from her own land. She asked me whether she might glean after our reapers, and I gave her my consent.''

Bō'-ăz had heard how Ruth forsook her idol-worship and began to serve the true God. He had heard, too, how kind she had been to her mother-in-law. And now he saw her toiling patiently among strange people, trying to find food for herself and Nā'-ō-mī. And he admired the beautiful young woman. He told the reapers to treat her kindly,

RUTH AND NAOMI

and to let some grain fall on purpose for her to gather. And he spoke kindly to her, and told her to come back every morning to glean in his fields. He invited her to eat lunch with his servants and to relieve her thirst from their water-pitchers.

Ruth was very thankful for this kindness. She bowed with her face to the ground and said, ''Why are you so kind to one who is a stranger?''

And Bō'-ăz replied, ''I have been told about your kindness to your mother-in-law since your husband died, and I have heard how you left your own people and their idols to worship the true God. And now may the true God reward you with many blessings.''

Ruth told Nā'-ō-mī about the kindness of Bō'-ăz when she returned at evening with her garnered sheaves, or bundles. And Nā'-ō-mī said, ''This man is a relative of my husband's. Stay in his field as long as the harvest lasts.''

At the end of the harvest the bundles were taken to the threshing-floor, where the kernels of grain were separated from the chaff and straw. Then a feast was held, and the rich and the poor rejoiced together because God had given them food for another year. Nā'-ō-mī sent Ruth to the threshing-floor when Bō'-ăz held a feast. She told Ruth

RUTH

THE VILLAGE WELL IN BETHLEHEM

Throughout the centuries the springs that feed the wells in Bethlehem have given forth their sparkling waters. Today as in the days of Ruth the women come with their jars and carry home water for their household use. The village well is the place ideal for the exchange of news, the very center of a little social life.

RUTH GLEANING IN THE FIELDS OF BOAZ

to speak to Bō'-ăz about their kinship, and to ask him to treat them kindly for the sake of her husband and his father, who had died in Moab.

Bō'-ăz had seen how well Ruth behaved, how quietly and carefully she worked, and he had admired her conduct very much. Now he saw that he loved her. And when she told him about Nā'-ō-mī's words he promised to treat them kindly.

Not long after this time Bō'-ăz married Ruth, and took her to live in his own house. And he took care of Nā'-ō-mī, too, as long as she lived. And Nā'-ō-mī became the nurse of the baby boy which God gave to Bō'-ăz and Ruth. This little boy they named Ō'-bĕd.

Because Ruth chose to serve God, he blessed her and gave her a happy home in the land of Israel. And she became the great-grand-mother of David, who was one of Israel's bravest kings. From her descendants long years afterwards was born the wonderful Child who became the Savior of the world.

STORY 22

THE LITTLE BOY WHOSE MOTHER LENT HIM TO THE LORD
1 Sam. 1:1—3:18

In the land of Israel, not very far from Shī'-lōh, there lived a man named Ĕl-kā'-năh. This man feared God, and every year he went to Shī'-lōh, taking his offerings for sin to the priests at the tabernacle. He did not go alone, but took his family with him, and they worshiped God together.

But Hannah, Ĕl-kā'-năh's wife, was very unhappy because God had never given her a child. Even though Ĕl-kā'-năh loved her dearly and gave her much honor, still Hannah would not be comforted. One year when she went with her husband to offer sacrifices at Shī'-lōh she prayed and asked God to give her a baby boy. She promised to lend the little boy back to God if only he would answer her prayer.

And God answered Hannah's prayer. He rarely denies unselfish prayers, and Hannah had prayed unselfishly. Even before another year passed by God gave Hannah and Ĕl-kā'-năh the baby boy she had promised to lend again to him. And Hannah named him Samuel, which means, "Asked of God." We are sure that she nursed him care-fully and loved him very dearly. But she did not forget her promise to the Lord.

When Samuel was yet a very little fellow, Hannah packed his clothes in a neat bundle one day and took him to Shī'-lōh. There she brought him to the high priest, whose name was Ē'-lī. She told Ē'-lī how she had prayed for this child, and how she had promised to lend him to the Lord as long as he should live. Now she wanted Samuel to live near the tabernacle and learn how to help the high priest.

THE INFANT SAMUEL

Ē'-lī knew God was pleased to have Hannah do this, and he promised to take care of her little boy and to teach him to serve God. Then Hannah and her husband returned to their own home at Rā'-măh, leaving Samuel at Ē'-lī's tent, near the tabernacle at Shī'-lōh.

Every year after this time when Ĕl-kā'-năh came to offer his sacrifices at Shī'-lōh, Hannah came too, and every year she brought a new coat for her little boy. How glad she must have been to see him growing taller! And how thankfully she must have listened while Ē'-lī told about the many things that little Samuel was learning to do about the tabernacle! Her heart was very glad because God had answered her prayer. And God gave her other children besides Samuel.

Now Ē'-lī had two sons, who were priests. But they were wicked men. They did many things that displeased God greatly. They behaved so wrongly that many good people in Israel dreaded to go to Shī'-lōh with their offerings. And Ē'-lī knew they did wrong; but still he allowed them to be priests at the tabernacle. Sometimes he told them that they should act differently, but he had allowed them to misbehave for so many years that now they would not listen to his words. But Samuel did not learn to do wrong, like those wicked men.

One day God sent a prophet to speak to Ē'-lī and warn him about his sons' wrong-doing. He said they would surely be punished. And because Ē'-lī had allowed them to act as priests when they were wicked men, the prophet said that Ē'-lī would also be punished. The office of the high priest would be taken away from his house forever. None of his children after him should work at the tabernacle.

After the prophet went away, God one night spoke to Samuel. Now it had been a long, long time since any one had heard God's voice. Samuel did not understand that God was speaking to him. He was only a child yet, and he did not know very much about God. When he heard a voice calling him through the darkness, he believed that Ē'-lī wished to speak to him. So he rose quickly from his bed and ran to Ē'-lī. "Here am I," he said, and he stood ready to do whatever Ē'-lī might ask. But Ē'-lī was surprized at his coming. He said, "I did not call for you, my boy. Lie down again." And Samuel obeyed.

Soon the voice spoke again, "Samuel!" And Samuel rubbed his sleepy eyes and hurried again to Ē'-lī's bedside. "Here I am," he said, "for I heard you call." But once more Ē'-lī replied, "I did not call; return again to your bed."

When the voice spoke the third time to Samuel, and when Samuel ran the third time to Ē'-lī, then the old man understood that perhaps God was wishing to speak to his little friend. So he told Samuel to return again to his bed and listen for the voice. And when God should call again he should say, "Speak, for thy servant heareth."

Samuel went back and lay down again, and soon he heard the voice of God calling, "Samuel! Samuel!" And he answered, "Speak, for thy servant heareth." And God talked with Samuel that night, and told him that he was soon going to punish Ē'-lī and his sons just as the prophet had said.

When morning came Samuel was afraid to tell Ē'-lī about the words of the Lord. Perhaps he had lain wide awake for a long time, wondering how he could tell this message to the dear old man who had been so kind to him. But Ē'-lī knew that God had spoken to the child. And when Samuel did not come near to tell him about God's words he called the lad to him. Samuel came as he had done during the night, and said, "Here am I." And at Ē'-lī's request he told all the words of the Lord. And Ē'-lī bowed his head and said, "It is the Lord: let him do what he wills."

STORY 23

THE STORY OF THE STOLEN ARK

1 Sam. 3: 19—4: 22

As Samuel grew older, God spoke to him again and again. And Samuel was always faithful to speak God's word to the people. By and by the Israelites from every part of the land began to say to each other, "Surely Samuel is a prophet of God!"

But in many parts of Israel at this time the people were worshiping idols. While some, like Samuel's parents, still feared God and worshiped him at Shī'-lōh, many others had turned completely to serve the idols made of wood or silver, or gold. And God's displeasure rested upon them. Like Ē'lī's wicked sons, they were soon to be punished by their enemies because of this great sin.

The Philistines, their old-time enemies, planned to fight against the Israelites again. So they went out to battle and killed many of the Israelites. After the battle the chief men of Israel met together and talked things over. They saw God had not helped them at all. And finally they decided to send for the ark of God at Shī'-lōh, and bring it into their camp. They knew God had blessed their fathers long ago when the ark was in the camp, and they believed by bringing it into the camp again they would surely cause God to look kindly upon them once more.

Instead of praying earnestly and asking God to help them, the Israelites hurried to Shī'-lōh and told Ē'lī's wicked sons about their plan. And these priests replied at once, "We will take the ark and go with you to the battle." They, too, believed that God would surely take care of his ark. And they supposed that God would protect the people where the ark of God was taken.

When the priests came back with the Israelites to their camp, all the soldiers gave a glad cry. They shouted so loudly that the sound of their rejoicing was heard in the camp of the Philistines. And their enemies wondered, "What has happened in the camp of Israel to cause such rejoicing after we have defeated them in battle?" Presently some one told them that the ark of God had come into their camp.

The Philistines were idol-worshipers. They believed the ark was like an idol, or god, and that its presence in the camp of Israel would add greatly to the strength of the Israelites. They remembered the things they had heard long ago about how the God of the Israelites had

brought great troubles upon Egypt. They were afraid of such a wonderful God. They trembled, because they thought the Israelites would
surely gain the victory over them and rule over them cruelly afterwards.

Before the next battle began the captains of the Philistine army
told their men to fight bravely to the very end. They said, "We must

TELLING ELI THE ARK HAS BEEN STOLEN

defeat the Israelites in this battle and save our country." And the
soldiers did their very best.

The Israelites had started out bravely enough, with Ē'-lī's sons
carrying the ark of God into their battle-line. But soon they saw that
their enemies were stronger than before. And soon Israelite men began
to fall on every side. Even the priests were killed, and the ark of God
was taken away from the Israelites.

This was the greatest sorrow that had ever come upon the people
of Israel. To have the ark of God taken away from them—what could
seem worse? Every soldier left alive fled from the battle-field in great

fear. He knew now that God surely had forsaken his people because of their sins. One of those who ran away came to Shī'-lōh with his clothes torn as a sign of sorrow, and told the sad news to the people of the city.

E'-lī sat near the tabernacle, by the roadside, waiting to hear news from the ark. He felt troubled because his sons had taken it away from the tabernacle. But he was now very old and blind, and his sons did much as they pleased. And so they had taken the ark away with them to the battle.

When the messenger came into the city and told how the Philistines had defeated the Israelites again, and had even killed E'-lī's sons and stolen the ark of God, the people of Shī'-lōh cried aloud for sorrow. And E'-lī heard their sad cry. He asked, "What has happened?" And the messenger came to him and repeated all his words.

E'-lī listened sorrowfully to the account of the defeat. He even heard about the death of his sons without uttering a cry. But when the messenger told him that the ark of God had been stolen by the Philistines, he fell backward from his seat and died. For forty years he had judged Israel, as well as being the high priest. And he died at the age of ninety-eight years.

———————•———————

STORY 24

HOW THE ARK OF GOD TROUBLED DAGON AND HIS WORSHIPERS

1 Sam. 5:1—7: 2

The Philistines rejoiced greatly over the victory they had gained. They believed their god was greater even than the God of the Israelites, whose ark they had taken. They carried the ark from the battlefield to one of their chief cities, and set it up in the temple beside Dā'-gŏn, the fish-god.

But troubles began at once for Dā'-gŏn and for his worshipers. The next morning when the people of the city came to the temple they found their god lying face downward on the floor before the ark. They set him up in his place and went away. The next morning they came again, and this time they found Dā'-gŏn lying on the floor in the same humble position, but now his head and his hands were broken off his body. What a pitiful condition poor Dā'-gŏn was in! Surely he could not protect himself before the ark of the God of Israel.

Nor did the troubles end here. The people of the city began to have boils and sores, which caused them much suffering. And all the Philistines in the country near by also suffered from these terrible boils. Finally they decided that the ark of God in their temple was bringing this trouble upon them. Their rulers gathered together to plan what to do. They said, "We will not let the ark of the God of Israel stay with us, for he is against us and against Dā'-gŏn, our god." So they sent the ark away to another of their cities.

Gath was the second place to which the ark was taken, and the people of that city soon began to suffer from boils and sores just as the people of Ăsh'-dŏd had, where the ark had been in Dā'-gŏn'ṡ temple. And many of the men of Gath died.

Now the Philistines were becoming afraid of the ark. They sent it on to another city, called Ĕk'-rŏn. But the people of Ĕk'-rŏn cried out in fear when they saw it being carried into their city. They said, "Have you brought this ark here to kill us and our children?"

God was much displeased because the Philistines had stolen the ark away from Israel. He was punishing them, and again in this city he caused many of the people to die, and a great cry of sorrow rose from the homes of the people whose relatives were killed.

Now the Philistines were in very great trouble. They did not know what to do with the ark. They were afraid to keep it among them any longer lest they all die. At last they decided on a plan. And this is what they did:

First they built a new cart, then they took two young cows that had never before worn an oxen's yoke and hitched them to the cart. They set the ark in the cart and put with it a box containing a present of golden jewels for Israel's God. After they had tied the calves at home they brought the young cows to the road that led toward the land of Israel and let them go. For they said, "We shall see whether they will return home to their calves or whether they will take the ark back to Israel. If they return home we shall believe our troubles have just happened by chance; but if they go straight on to the land of Israel we shall know surely that Israel's God has troubled us." This did not seem like a fair test; yet the cows started at once toward Israel, and did not stop until they reached the country of Bĕth-shē'-mĕsh.

The men of Bĕth-shē'-mĕsh were busy at work in their wheat-harvest when they saw the new cart coming up the highway from Ĕk'-rŏn. They noticed at once that the ark of God was in the cart and they were glad. Seven months had passed since the ark had been stolen from Israel. Perhaps the Israelites feared they might never see it again. Now the cows turned from the road and entered a field. They stopped beside a great stone.

The men of Bĕth-shē'-mĕsh came quickly to the place and removed the ark from off the cart. They brought axes and chopped the cart in pieces, then built an altar and laid the wood upon it, and offered the two cows in sacrifice to God for returning the ark again to their land. Some Levites had come with them to do this work as they had seen it done at the tabernacle in Shī'-lōh.

All might have gone well had the men of Bĕth-shē'-mĕsh not been too curious. But they wished to see what was inside the ark. Perhaps they wondered whether the Philistines had stolen the tables of stone, which Moses had so very long ago put inside this gold-covered box. So they lifted the lid, called the mercy-seat, and looked inside. This was very wrong, for God had commanded that no one except the priests should touch the ark, and the men of Israel knew this command. Because they disobeyed, many of them died.

Now even the people of Israel were in trouble because of the ark. They sent quickly to their neighbors at Kĭr'-jăth-jē'-ă-rĭm, asking them to come and take the ark away. And when they came they took it to the house of a man named Ă-bĭn'-ă-dăb, and it was kept in that place for twenty years. Ă-bĭn'-ă-dăb was a Levite, and they placed the ark in the keeping of Ĕl-ē-ā'-zär, his son.

After this time the worship of God was never again restored in Shī'-lōh. Samuel returned to his parents' home at Rā'-măh, and he became the last of Israel's fifteen judges.

STORY 25

HOW SAMUEL JUDGED THE ISRAELITES
1 Samuel 7, 8

After Ē'-lī's sons, the priests, had been killed, and Ē'-lī had died, no one remained at the tabernacle to offer sacrifices on the altar of burnt offering every morning and evening. So Samuel went back to live again at his father's house in Rā'-măh, and by and by the tabernacle at Shī'-lōh was no longer used.

Now the Israelites were being ruled by the Philistines. And everywhere they were mourning because the Lord seemed to have forsaken them entirely. They were thinking, too, of Samuel, the boy who used to help Ē'-lī, the high priest, at the tabernacle. They remembered how God used to talk to Samuel, and they believed he would find a way to help them out of their troubles.

Samuel began to visit the people in different parts of the land. He talked to them about God, and told them that if they wished to be delivered from the rule of the Philistines, first of all they must forsake their idols, tear them down, and begin to serve God with their whole hearts.

What a cleaning-up time followed! Everywhere the people tore down the idols of Bā'-ăl and Ăsh'-tă-rŏth, the gods of the heathen before which they had often bowed down. And everywhere they began to call upon God to help them. They were much in earnest; and Samuel was well pleased to see them do these things. Then he sent word to the people to come together in a great meeting at a place called Mĭz'-pēh, and there he would pray for them.

While the meeting was being held at Mĭz'-pēh, the Philistines heard that the Israelites had come together at that place. They supposed that the Israelites were preparing to fight against them, and they sent word quickly to their bravest soldiers to come at once. Then they marched toward Mĭz'-pēh to fight with Israel.

But the Israelites had brought no weapons to fight with. They had come to weep and confess their sins before God. They had not thought about fighting against their enemies at this time. And now, when they saw the Philistines coming over the hills in line for a battle, they trembled. What could they do? They begged Samuel to pray for them in this great need. They knew God could help when they were helpless to defend themselves. And Samuel took a lamb and offered it as a burnt sacrifice to God, and prayed earnestly for help. And his prayer was heard.

The Philistines did not get near enough to the helpless Israelites to use their swords and spears, for God sent a terrible thunder-storm, and so frightened them away. They dropped their weapons and ran in every direction, trying to find shelter from the storm. While they were seeking places to hide, the men of Israel ran out and picked up their weapons and chased them. They killed many, and drove the others back to their own land.

This was a great victory for the Israelites; and Samuel rejoiced with them. He set up a stone pillar on the battle-field and called it Ĕb'-ĕn-ē'-zĕr, which means, "The Stone of Help," because God had so wonderfully helped them.

The Philistines did not return again into the land of Israel during the years that Samuel lived and judged the people. They even restored the cities which they had taken away from the Israelites.

Samuel was the last of the fifteen judges who ruled the people of Israel. He made his home at Rā′-măh, and built an altar at that place. But often he went to other parts of the land to talk with the people about the Lord. When he grew too old to travel about so much, his two sons helped him judge the Israelites. They were not kind to the people as their father had always been. They would decide matters of dispute in favor of the persons who gave them money. And soon the people became dissatisfied with these money-loving rulers.

For a long time some of the Israelites had wished to have a king rule over them, as their neighbors were ruled. And now they decided to tell Samuel what they wanted. So they sent their messengers to talk with Samuel at his home and tell him how greatly they desired a king.

Samuel was much displeased when he heard the request of the people. He

SAMUEL'S FAREWELL ADDRESS

had tried always to rule them as he believed would please the Lord, and now they were dissatisfied with his work. He told the Lord about the request of the people, and asked what he should do. And God said, "Let them have a king. They are not forsaking you when they ask for a king, but they are forsaking me. Now give them what they desire. Only warn them first of the sorrows that will come to them when a king is their ruler."

Samuel told the people the words of the Lord. And he warned them carefully of the troubles that would come when a king should rule over them. Still they said, "We want a king." And Samuel said, "Return to your homes, for God will give what you have asked."

SAUL ANOINTED BY SAMUEL

PART FOURTH

STORIES ABOUT THE THREE KINGS OF UNITED ISRAEL

1 and 2 Samuel; 1 Kings 1—12; 1 and 2 Chronicles 1—11

STORY 1

THE TALL MAN WHOM GOD CHOSE TO BECOME ISRAEL'S FIRST KING

1 Samuel 9, 10

Samuel did not look about for the man who should become the first king of Israel. He waited until God should choose a man for the place. And then one day God spoke in his ear and said, "Tomorrow about this time I will send a man to you from the tribe of Benjamin, and I want you to anoint him to become the king of my people. He will be captain of their army, and he will save them from the Philistines."

This man whom God had chosen was named Saul. He was a young man, and his father's name was Kish. His father was a very rich man. He owned wide fields and green pastures in the land of Benjamin, and many cattle and sheep and asses.

One day some of Kish's asses wandered away from his pasture and were lost in the woods. Where they went no one knew, so Kish sent Saul and a servant to look for them. And what a searching-time they had! For two days they went from one place to another, hunting the lost asses; but nowhere could they find a trace of them. Finally Saul said, "Let us return, for my father will think that we, too, are lost."

The servant did not want to return until they had found the lost animals. He said, "Let us first stop in this city near by and ask the man of God to tell us where our asses may be found. He is a prophet, and whatever he says always happens." But Saul was unwilling to stop, because he had no present to give to the prophet. His servant, however, had a piece of money, and when Saul knew this he was ready to seek the man of God at once.

As the two men were climbing the hill leading to the city gate they met some young girls with empty pitchers, going out to draw water. They asked the girls where they might find the man of God. And the girls told them that Samuel had come to worship God with the people there, and that the people had prepared a feast and were waiting at the place of sacrifice for him to ask a blessing upon the food before they should begin to eat. Saul and his servant hurried on, and in the gate they met an old man whom they also asked where they might find the prophet.

This old man was Samuel himself, and he had come to the gate to wait for Saul. He had never seen Saul before. But God told him that Saul was the one he promised to send from the land of Benjamin. And God caused Samuel to know what Saul was seeking.

Samuel answered Saul and said, "I am the prophet you are looking for. And today you must go with me to the feast that these people have made. Do not search any more for your father's asses, which were lost three days ago, because they have been found. And now you are the man to whom all Israel is looking."

Saul was much surprized to hear Samuel's words. He said, "I am a Benjamite, of the smallest tribe of Israel. Surely the people do not want me for their king." But Saul went with Samuel to the feast. And in the best room he sat at a table among the most important guests. Samuel ordered the best food to be set before Saul, and he told the young man that he had kept this food especially for him.

After the feast, Samuel took Saul to a quiet place on a house-top and told him many things that would soon come to pass. And Saul wondered about these things. When Saul and his servant started home the next morning, Samuel walked a little way with them. And before he turned back Samuel asked the servant to go on ahead because he wished to speak to Saul alone. Then he took some oil and poured it on Saul's head, and kissed Saul, and said, "I am doing this because God has anointed you to become the captain of his people, the Israelites."

Then Samuel gave three signs to Saul, that Saul might believe his words. He told him that two men would meet him at a certain place and tell him that his father's asses had been found, and that his father was now sorrowing because Saul had not yet returned. Farther on three men would meet him, and they would give him two loaves of bread. And last of all, a company of prophets would meet him and he would join their company and prophesy with them. Samuel said that God would change Saul into a different man. And after these words Samuel turned back toward the city, and Saul journeyed on.

The three signs that Samuel had given came to pass; and Saul's heart was changed by the Spirit of God and he prophesied with the young men who met him on the way. Then he stopped with his servant at a place of sacrifice, and his uncle met him there. "Where have you been?" his uncle asked; and Saul told him about their search for his father's asses, and about his visit with Samuel. But he did not tell that Samuel had anointed him to become Israel's first king.

Soon after these things had happened, Samuel sent messengers throughout the land to call all the men of Israel together at Mĭz'-pēh, the place where God had given them a great victory over the Philistines. And when they met together, Samuel talked to them about the wonderful ways God had blessed them and helped them out of their troubles. He spoke to them about the things that God had done for their fathers and for their grandfathers long ago. "Now," said he, "you are asking for a king to rule over you instead of letting God be your ruler and king. You are not honoring God when you ask for a king; but God will give you the desire of your heart. He will choose for you a king today."

And when the twelve tribes came before the Lord, the strong tribes passed by, and God did not choose any one among them. But from the weakest tribe he chose a family, and from that family he chose a man, and that man was Saul.

Every one wished to see the man God had chosen, but Saul could not be found. He had hidden himself from the crowd. Then God told where he was hiding, and the people ran, and found him. They brought him out, and every one saw that God had chosen a handsome young man who stood head and shoulders taller than any other man in the crowd. And the people shouted with a loud cry, "God save the king!"

Afterwards Samuel told the people what kind of kingdom they should have, and he wrote all his words in a book. Then he dismissed the assembly, and every man went away to his own home. Saul, too, returned to his home at Gĭb'-ĕ-ăh, and a company of men who loved their new king went with him.

But some of the people were not satisfied with the man God had chosen. They had wished to choose a man for themselves. And they looked with anger upon Saul. These men were idol-worshipers, and they did not fear God. But Saul pretended not to notice their angry looks and their unkind actions. He went back quietly to work in his fields as he had been working before Samuel anointed him to become the ruler of his people.

STORY 2

HOW THE EYES OF SOME OF SAUL'S PEOPLE WERE SAVED
1 Samuel 11, 12

Not long after the meeting at Mĭz'-pēh, the Ammonites, a fierce people who lived near the desert country, came with their king, Nahash, to fight against one of the cities of the Israelites. This city was Jā'-bĕsh, on the east side of the Jordan River.

The men of Jā'-bĕsh knew they could not drive the Ammonites away. They thought, "It would be better for us to let the Ammonites rule over us than to try to fight against them, for they will kill us in the battle. We will send them a message and promise to serve them if only they will spare our lives."

Nahash, the Ammonite king, sent this message back: "We will spare your lives; but in seven days I will come with my soldiers and put out the right eyes of all your people."

This cruel threat filled the men of Jā'-bĕsh with alarm. "We must have help from our people in other parts of the land," they said. So they sent swift messengers across the Jordan River to Gĭb'-ĕ-ăh, the city where Saul lived. And the people of Gĭb'-ĕ-ăh wept with a loud noise when they heard about the trouble that had come upon the Jā'-bĕsh-ītes.

Saul was just returning from the field with his cattle when he heard the cry of his neighbors. He asked why they wept, and some one told him the message that had come from Jā'-bĕsh. Until this time Saul had behaved quietly, as he did before he had been anointed to be the captain of the Lord's people; but now the spirit of a king stirred his soul and he prepared at once to help the distressed Israelites on the other side of the Jordan River. First he killed two oxen and divided their bodies into twelve parts. Then he sent one part to each of the twelve tribes, with this message: "Whoever will not come out to fight with Saul and Samuel, his oxen shall be cut in pieces."

Everywhere the soldiers of Israel left their homes and came hurrying to Saul, and soon he had a very large army. Together they marched across the hills of Benjamin till they came to the Jordan River. Here they waded through the water and climbed the bank on the other side. Before very many hours' marching they came upon the army of the Ammonites.

From morning until noonday the fought against these cruel people, and many of the Ammonites ran away. Saul's army destroyed the others, and the men of Jā'-bĕsh were saved from much suffering. Nahash did not return again to fight against the Israelites.

POOLS OF SOLOMON ON THE HEBRON ROAD

Some twelve miles south and west of Bethlehem, on the way to Hebron, the traveler reaches the reputed pools of King Solomon. These three large reservoirs are of very uncertain age, but it is positively known that both the Saracens and the Romans made use of them, and it is quite possible that the Roman reservoirs were enlargements of pools originally prepared by King Solomon. Under the British rule in Palestine the pools have been once more brought into use.

SAUL REJECTED BY THE LORD

After this victory the Israelites crossed the River again, and they stopped at the place where their fathers had camped long ago, when first they entered the land of Canaan. The name of this place, you remember, was Gĭl'-găl. Here they sacrificed to the Lord, and here Samuel gave up his rule as a judge over them; he gave it to King Saul, who from this time would be their leader. But Samuel continued to be a prophet among the people and to give them warning from God.

The Israelites were now well pleased with their King. They saw that he was brave, and they praised him. They wanted to kill the wicked men who were angry because God had chosen Saul to be their king. But Saul did not permit them to harm those men. He said, "No man shall be put to death today, for God has given us this great victory."

Many of the soldiers who had come at Saul's command to fight for the men of Jā'-bĕsh had left their fields of wheat almost ripe enough to gather in the grain. At this time of year rain seldom fell in their land, and so the sky above them was clear and cloudless on this day.

While the people were all rejoicing together with their new King at Gĭl'-găl, Samuel stood near by looking on with sad eyes. How he pitied these people who had refused to let God rule over them any longer! Now he felt that he must give them one more warning.

Samuel began his warning by reminding the people that he had given them what they asked for. "Now," said he, "your king walks before you; and I am old and gray-headed. I have lived among you since a child, and you know my life. Tell me, have I ever judged you wrongly?"

The people answered, "No."

"Have I ever taken away your oxen, or your asses?" asked Samuel. And again the people replied that he had not.

"Have I ever taken gifts of money from you when you wanted me to be unfair with your neighbor?" he asked. "If I have, now I will restore those gifts to you." But no one could accuse Samuel of having done wrong while he judged them.

"Now," said Samuel, "the Lord is witness to this truth against you."

And all the people answered, "He is witness."

Samuel then told the people that God had cared for them as a father cares for his own children; that he had even delivered them from their cruel enemies after they had turned away from him to serve idols. He reminded them of the victories that God had given to their fathers when Gideon and Jĕph'-thăh ruled over them as judges. He told them how God wanted to be their King. He showed them how greatly they had sinned against God when they had asked for a man to be their king.

Still God was not ready to leave them alone and helpless before their enemies if they would serve him and, with their king, obey his commands. But if they would turn away from serving God and from listening to his voice, then even their king should not be able to save them. All these words Samuel spoke in their hearing, and then he said, "See, God will now do a great thing before your eyes. I will call upon him, and he will send thunder and rain, to show you that your wickedness is great in asking for a king."

When Samuel prayed, the sky suddenly grew dark with heavy clouds, and the thunder roared so loudly that the men became afraid. The rain fell fast, and the thunder continued to roar. Great fear came into the hearts of these men who only a short time before were rejoicing with their new King, Saul. Now they were afraid of God, and of Samuel, his prophet. They cried, "Pray for us, that we shall not be killed by this storm; for we have sinned more against God than our fathers. We added to their sins when we asked for a king."

Samuel comforted the people by telling them that God would not destroy them if they would be careful to serve him. He said, "It has pleased the Lord to make you his people." And Samuel promised to pray for them as long as he should live, and always to teach them the good and the right way.

STORY 3

KING SAUL AND HIS PEOPLE IN TROUBLE
1 Samuel 13

After Saul had been King over Israel for two years, he chose three thousand soldiers to be ready at any time for a battle. He took two thousand with him to a place called Mĭ<u>ch</u>′-măsh, and left one thousand with his son Jonathan, at Gĭb′-ĕ-ăh.

Now, the Philistines had begun to cause much trouble again in the land of Israel. They were not at all afraid of King Saul. They even placed some of their soldiers in forts, or garrisons, throughout the land, and those soldiers, instead of Saul, ruled the Israelites.

Not far from Gĭb′-ĕ-ăh, on a hill, was a ruling Philistine garrison. Jonathan and his soldiers fought against that garrison and drove the Philistines away. Then the other Philistines heard what Jonathan had done and they became angry. They gathered a very large army of thousands of chariots and horsemen and came to fight against King Saul.

The Israelites had believed that if only they had a king like other nations they could drive all their enemies away. Now God had allowed them to have a king; but their enemies were troubling them as much as before. The Philistines had even taken away their swords and spears and would not let them make any more weapons. Only a few of the men of Israel were prepared to fight.

King Saul sent swift messengers through the land to call the soldiers of every tribe together. Because he was King, they came when he called; but they came trembling with fear of the Philistines. They knew they could not fight without weapons even if they had a king to lead them out to battle.

When Samuel heard about the trouble, he sent word to King Saul that he would come and offer sacrifices to God at Gĭl'-găl and pray for the King and for his people. Then God would show him what they should do.

King Saul and his men hurried to Gĭl'-găl to meet Samuel; but when they arrived he was not there. They waited for several days; still he did not come. All the time the Philistines kept sending more soldiers to their camp, until it seemed that their numbers could not be counted. Saul's men became more frightened than ever. Some of them began to steal away and to cross over the Jordan River, to hide in the country on the east side, where two and one half of the tribes lived. Others hid in caves, and in thickets near by, and some crept in among the rocks or crawled into deep holes in the ground.

Finally Saul became afraid that all his men would leave him. So, instead of waiting longer for Samuel, he offered a burnt sacrifice upon the altar at Gĭl'-găl just as Samuel would have done. Now God had forbidden any one except his priests or the Levites to offer a sacrifice, and although Saul was King of Israel, God did not want him to do such a thing.

While the sacrifice was yet burning, Samuel arrived, and when he saw what Saul had done he was much displeased. He asked, "Why have you done this?" and Saul replied, "Because my people were afraid and were scattering to different parts of the land, and you were so long coming I feared the Philistines would attack us before you should arrive. I was forced to do this thing."

Samuel knew that Saul was not forced to disobey God. He knew the King was trying to make an excuse for his wrong-doing. And he

said, ''You have acted foolishly, for you have not kept the commandment of the Lord. And because of your disobedience, some day God
will take away the kingdom from you and give it to another man who
will obey him.''

Instead of telling Saul what to do about the Philistines, Samuel
turned and went away. Then Saul counted his soldiers and found
that only six hundred were still with him. He marched with them back
to his old home at Gĭb'-ĕ-ăh, where Jonathan had been stationed at the
first, and the Philistines camped near Mĭch'-măsh.

STORY 4

HOW THE FAITH OF A BRAVE YOUNG PRINCE BROUGHT A GREAT VICTORY
1 Sam. 14:1-46

Under a pomegranate-tree at the edge of Gĭb'-ĕ-ăh farthest from the
Philistines' camp sat the King of Israel talking with the grandson of
the high priest Ē'-lī. They were probably talking about the ark of God,
which had been taken away from Shī'-lōh to a battle against the Philistines when Samuel, the gray-headed old prophet, was only a young
man. How many changes had come to Israel since that sad day when
the ark of God had been stolen! And still the Philistines were fighting
against the Israelites, and still they were ruling them.

While King Saul and his companion were talking together, two
men from Saul's army slipped quietly away. They were Jonathan,
Saul's son, and the young man who carried Jonathan's shield and sword
and spear. Jonathan had said, ''Come, let us go over to the Philistines' camp. It may be that the Lord will work for us; for he can
save his people by a few as easily as by many soldiers.'' Jonathan
had strong faith in God, and he was a brave young man. His armor-
bearer, too, was brave, so they started out together, telling no one of
their plan.

God was well pleased with Jonathan, and he caused the Philistines
to become afraid of the young Prince. In a very short time he and his
armor-bearer had killed twenty men. Then God sent a great trembling among the Philistines, and the ground shook beneath their feet.
Things began to totter and fall, and the Philistines believed that a strong
enemy had come suddenly to fight against them. They heard the cries
of those whom Jonathan and his armor-bearer were killing, and now
they seized their weapons and made ready to fight.

But instead of attacking their enemies, the Philistines began to fight against each other. And the cry of battle rang out across the valley and reached the city of Gĭb′-ĕ-äh.

King Saul had appointed some men to watch the camp of the enemy by day and by night, and to be ready to send him word whenever the Philistines were forming a line for battle. When the watchmen saw the excitement in the Philistines' camp, they sent messengers to tell him that something strange was happening to their enemies. "Men are stirring about in every direction," the messenger said, "and some are falling and others are running away."

Saul called his soldiers together quickly and counted them to see if any had gone from them. Then he saw that Jonathan and his armor-bearer were missing. So he and the other men prepared for battle and ran out to join in the fight. Then, too, the Israelites who had been hiding in caves and in thickets among the rocks crept out to see what this noise meant. And then they hurried out to join in the fight against the Philistines.

And what a fight they had! The Philistines, their strong enemies, now ran like cowards from the battle and into the woods. The men of Israel chased after them like swarms of angry bees. And as they ran other Israelites came out to join in the chase.

But after a while the men of Israel grew very faint and weak because they had eaten no food all that day. Saul had commanded them to eat no food until evening, because he did not want to stop long enough in the chase to take a bite. If any man should disobey him, that man should be put to death, he had said. And because the soldiers feared Saul they would not eat. They grew so faint from the chase that many of their enemies got away, whom they might have overtaken and killed.

Jonathan did not know about his father's command, and as he was passing through the woods with a band of men he found some wild honey and ate of it. Then one of his companions said, "Your father forbade us to touch food before evening." But it was too late, for Jonathan had already eaten.

When Saul heard about Jonathan's act, he said, "You have disobeyed, and now I must keep my word even though you are my son. I must put you to death."

But the people who stood by refused to let their King do such a cruel deed. They cried, "God forbid that Jonathan should be killed for this act. Was not God with him today when he brought us this great victory over our enemies?" And they saved the young Prince alive.

HOW SIN ROBBED SAUL OF HIS KINGDOM
1 Sam. 14:47—15:35

The Philistines stayed in their own country, by the sea-coast, after they had been driven away from Mĭ*ch*'-măsh, and King Saul went out to fight against other nations who had been troubling the Israelites. God helped him to be victorious in those battles, and his soldiers began to honor him as a brave leader.

All the while King Saul kept a close watch over the Israelites, and whenever he saw a strong-looking young man who acted bravely in the presence of danger he took that young man and placed him in his regular army. In this manner he kept making his army larger and stronger, and finally he chose Abner, his cousin, to become the captain of it.

But when everything began to go nicely, King Saul seemed to forget that God had given the kingdom to him and that he could easily take it away again. Instead of always being careful to obey all of God's commands, Saul allowed a feeling of pride to creep into his heart and to crowd out some of the fear of God. He allowed wrong thoughts to enter his mind and to make him believe that he was wise enough to decide for himself what was the right thing to do.

While these changes were going on in the King's heart, one day a message came to him from God. Samuel, the gray-headed old prophet, came to him and said, "God wants you to take your army and go out to battle against the Ă-măl'-ĕk-ītes. Those are the wicked people who fought against Moses and the Israelites when they came out of Egypt, and God has not forgotten their sin. Because they have continued to do wrong, now God wants you to destroy them all. Not one must you save alive, nor even their oxen and sheep and camels and asses must you keep for yourselves; for God commands that they all be killed."

Saul gathered an army of two hundred and ten thousand men and started for Ăm'-ă-lĕk at once. And he sent messengers to the Kē'-nītes who lived among the Ă-măl'-ĕk-ītes, telling them to leave the country, because God was going to punish their neighbors. The Kē'-nītes had been kind to the Israelites when they came from Egypt, and now Saul and his soldiers were kind to them.

When the battle began, Saul's army fought bravely and destroyed all the Ă-măl'-ĕk-ītes except the king, Agag, whom Saul took to a safe place. Then after the battle ended Saul and the soldiers looked about upon the flocks and herds that had belonged to the Ă-măl'-ĕk-ītes, and they saw many valuable cattle and sheep and playful little lambs. "We will save the best," they said, "and kill the others." So they returned again to the land of Israel, bringing Agag, the king of the Ă-măl'-ĕk-ītes, and the best of the cattle and sheep and lambs.

God told Samuel what Saul had done, that he had dared to disobey the command given, and Samuel knew that Saul had turned away from serving God. Sorrow filled the heart of the old prophet, and he wept and prayed all night. Early the next morning he rose and started out to meet the returning King of Israel.

When Saul saw the prophet coming, he thought, "I will tell him that I have obeyed the Lord's command, and he need not know that King Agag is yet alive and that we have saved the best of the flocks and herds. We have obeyed nearly all of God's command, and it would have been too bad to destroy the best things."

But Samuel could not be fooled so easily. The pleasant words of greeting from the King did not hide the traces of a guilty conscience upon the King's face. Saul had done wrong, and now he was trying to cover up his sin and to make Samuel believe that he had done all of God's command. "I have performed the commandment of the Lord," he said; but the old prophet's keen eyes looked straight into his. "Then what is the meaning of the noise of bleating sheep and lowing cattle that I hear?"

"Those have been spared to sacrifice to the Lord," answered the King. "They were the best of the flocks and herds, and my soldiers thought it would be better to keep them alive. So we have brought them to sacrifice to God."

Now, Saul was trying to place the blame for the disobedience upon his soldiers; but Samuel understood that Saul himself was the guilty one. Poor Saul! he had forgotten how God spoke often to Samuel, telling of things that would happen. He had forgotten that he could not fool the prophet of Israel.

Samuel told Saul what God had spoken to him that night. Still Saul tried to excuse himself and blame his soldiers for sparing the best things; but Samuel told him plainly that God had turned away from him. "It is better to obey God than to sacrifice to God," said the old prophet.

"I have sinned," cried the King at last, "because I feared the people and obeyed their voice." Not yet was he willing to admit that he sinned by his own choice. He wanted Samuel to forgive him; but Samuel turned to go away. Then Saul caught hold of Samuel's mantle and tore it, and Samuel said, "The Lord has torn the kingdom of Israel away from you today and has given it to your neighbor, who is a better man."

Because of Saul's earnest request that he should worship with him at Gĭl'-găl, Samuel went this last time with the King whom God had rejected and offered sacrifice upon the altar at Gĭl'-găl for the sins of the people. Then he called for Agag to be brought out before the people, and there he killed the wicked ruler, whose life Saul had wished to save. After doing this, he returned to his own home at Rā'-măh, and never again visited Saul. He mourned and wept as if Saul had died, because he knew God would not bless Israel while Saul ruled over them.

STORY 6

WHY GOD SENT SAMUEL TO BETHLEHEM

1 Sam. 16:1-13

When Samuel returned to Rā'-măh from Gĭl'-găl, perhaps he thought that his work on earth was ended. No longer could he carry messages from God to Israel's King, because God had rejected Saul and would send no more messages to him. So Samuel laid aside his cane and wept, not because his work had ended, but because Saul had proved himself unworthy to be the leader of God's people.

As the days passed by, Samuel's sorrow for Saul did not cease, and his gray head bowed lower upon his breast. Finally God spoke to him, and said, "How long will you mourn for this unworthy man whom I have rejected as the ruler of my people? Now I have chosen another to take his place."

Samuel raised his head and listened to God's voice. Then his trembling hands reached again for the cane he had thrown aside, for God gave him some more work to do before he should die. "Fill your empty horn with oil," God said; "for I am going to send you to Bethlehem to anoint the one whom I have chosen to be Israel's king in place of Saul."

At first Samuel feared to go. He said, "Saul will hear of it, and he will surely kill me." But God told him to take an offering for a sacrifice and prepare a feast for the people of Bethlehem, then to invite an old man named Jesse, who lived near the city, to come with his sons to the feast. "One of his sons I have chosen," the Lord said, "and I will tell you which one of them shall be Israel's next king."

Samuel was no longer afraid to obey God. He rose from his place of weeping and filled his empty horn with oil. Then he took a meat-offering and started toward Bethlehem.

When the rulers of the city saw Samuel coming toward them they were afraid. They asked, "Why have you come?" Samuel told them that he had come to worship God at that place; and when they saw his offering for the sacrifice they made themselves ready to enjoy the feast that would follow. And Samuel invited Jesse and his sons to attend the feast, too.

Now Jesse had eight sons, but only seven came to the feast. The youngest was not yet grown to manhood, and he kept his father's sheep in the fields outside the city. When Ē-lī'-ăb, the eldest son of Jesse, came, Samuel thought, "Surely this must be the man whom God has chosen." For Ē-lī'-ăb was a tall, handsome young man, and Samuel was pleased with his appearance.

But God said, "This is not the man. You are judging by the outward appearance; I am looking at the heart."

Jesse then brought his other sons to Samuel, and one by one they passed before the prophet. But Samuel shook his head and said, "God has chosen none of these. Have you no other son?"

And Jesse replied, "I have one more, but I did not bring him to the feast. He is my youngest, and he is now in the field caring for my sheep."

Samuel told Jesse to send for the shepherd-boy at once, because God had chosen him to do a great work. And they waited while a messenger hurried away to bring the lad to Samuel.

David, the shepherd-boy, was surprized to see a messenger running toward him from over the hills near Bethlehem. He knew a religious feast was being held that day in the city, for his father and his brothers had been invited to attend. And when he left them early in the morning they were making preparations to go. Now he wondered what had happened that they should be sending word to him out in the field alone with the sheep. Had some one been killed? or were the Philistines coming to fight against their city?

David rose quickly and drew his shepherd-coat about him. Then, picking up his rod, he hurried to meet the breathless runner. "You are wanted in Bethlehem at once," gasped the runner. "Samuel, the old prophet, wishes to see you, and your father has sent word that you must leave your sheep and come in haste."

Samuel waited patiently, and when at last a rosy-cheeked, bright-eyed youth, clad in a shepherd's garb, entered the room, the Lord said to

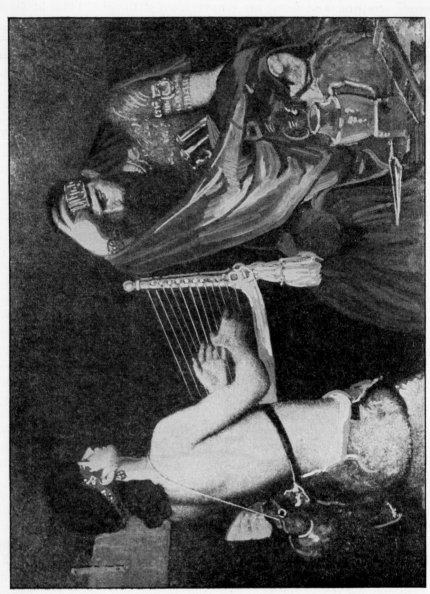

DAVID PLAYING BEFORE SAUL

Samuel, "Arise and anoint this youth, for he is the one whom I have chosen." So Samuel poured oil from his horn upon the head of David, as God had commanded. And the shepherd-boy understood by that act that God had chosen him to become some day the leader of Israel.

After the feast had ended, Samuel returned again to Rā'-măh, and he did not grieve any more about Saul. He knew God had chosen a better person to sit upon the throne of Israel.

<hr>

WHY JESSE SENT DAVID TO VISIT KING SAUL
1 Sam. 16:14-23

Saul did not take off his kingly robes and lay aside his crown when Samuel told him that God had rejected him from being king of Israel. He tried to act is if nothing had happened, and he kept on ruling the people. As long as he lived he ruled them.

So David did not become king at once after Samuel anointed him. He returned again to the fields near Bethlehem to watch his father's sheep. But God sent his Spirit upon David's heart that day, and afterwards David thought much about God. One day he wrote a beautiful poem, which we call the twenty-third Psalm. In the first verse of this poem he said, "The Lord is my Shepherd, I shall not want." He believed that just as tenderly as he cared for his sheep, so the Lord cared for him.

As a shepherd-boy David lived much in the out-of-doors, and he learned to love the country scenes. The hills and valleys, the trees, grasses, and flowers all reminded him of the God who had made them. And many times as he looked at these things he felt gladness in his heart and he sang for joy.

David sang so well that in later years he was called the Sweet Singer of Israel. He also played well on a stringed instrument called a harp.

After Saul refused to obey God's words, God took away the good spirit which he had given to him. And a bad spirit came to trouble him. Sometimes this spirit made Saul feel very unhappy, and he would act strangely, as if he did not know what he was trying to do. At such times if he could hear sweet music the bad spirit would go away, and Saul would feel cheerful again.

One day the servants who waited on Saul told him that it might be well if he could have a musician brought to the palace. Then whenever the evil spirit should trouble him and cause unhappy feelings to enter his heart, the musician could play, and thus drive the sadness away. Saul believed this plan would be a good one to try, so he commanded his servants to find a musician and bring him to the palace.

One of his servants had lived in the land of Judah, and had known Jesse, the Bethlehemite, and his sons. He had often heard David play on his harp, and he had thought David's music would surely please the King. Now he told Saul about David, the shepherd-boy, who played on the harp and sang so sweetly. And Saul sent at once to Jesse, asking him to let David come to Gĭb′-ĕ-ăh to visit the King's palace.

Jesse called David from the field and told him about the King's message. Then he prepared a gift and sent it with his son to the King's house. And David came to see Saul, and he stood before Saul, with the other servants.

Not long afterwards a second message came to Jesse from the King. This time Saul asked Jesse to let him keep David with him for a while, because he was well pleased with him.

Saul did not know that David had been anointed to become king in his place. If he had known this he would have been jealous of David, and he might have even tried to kill him. Because he did not know, he listened often to the soft, sweet music that David made with his harp, and he felt glad again. After a while the evil spirit did not seem to trouble him at all, and then he allowed David to return again to his father's home at Bethlehem.

———————

STORY 8

HOW DAVID KILLED THE GIANT GOLIATH
1 Sam. 17:1-54

The Philistines began to trouble Israel again, and they prepared to fight against King Saul and his army. They marched into the land of Israel and pitched their tents along the side of a mountain. King Saul and his soldiers made their camp across the valley from the Philistines, on the side of another mountain.

But the battle did not begin at once. The Philistines did not seem to be eager to fight. They sent one of their soldiers out into the valley to talk to the men of Saul's army. This soldier was a giant, and his name was Gō-lī′-ăth. He called to the men of Israel and said, "Why have you come out to fight a battle with the Philistines? I am a Philistine. Now choose one of your men and send him to fight with me. If I kill him, then you shall become our servants; but if he kills me, then my people will become your servants.''

But the men of Israel were afraid of Gō-lī'-ăth. None of them would dare to go out to fight against him. How frightful he looked as he stood in the valley before them, nearly twice as tall as an ordinary man! Even the tall King of Israel, who stood head and shoulders higher than any of his soldiers, would have looked small beside this mighty giant.

Every morning and every evening Gō-lī'-ăth would come out into the valley between the two camps, walking with long steps, and there he would call to the Israelite soldiers. And every morning and every evening the men of Israel would tremble when they saw him coming. Forty days passed by, and still the Philistines waited for King Saul to send some one to fight against their champion.

While this was happening, David was busy at home caring for his father's sheep, as he had been before he went to visit King Saul. One day while he was watching them he saw a lion spring out of the woods and snatch a little lamb. He hurried after the lion and tried to save the lamb. Then the lion became angry and dropped the lamb, and turned to attack David. But God gave wonderful strength to the shepherd-boy, and he seized hold of the lion's beard, and killed him. Another day a hungry bear came out of the woods and stole a lamb. Again David ran fearlessly to rescue the lamb and God helped him to kill the thief.

Three of David's brothers were soldiers in Saul's army. Jesse, their old father, thought often of them and wondered how they were getting along. One day he called David from the field and told him to get ready to visit his brothers in the camp of Israel. ''Take this parched grain and these ten loaves of bread to them,'' he said, ''and take these cheeses to their captain. Learn for me how your brothers are getting along, and bring back the message which they send.'' Jesse did not know that when he should send David away this time his son would never come back again to take care of his sheep.

Bright and early the next morning David started out on this errand to the camp of Israel. When he reached the place, the sun had risen in the sky, and the soldiers were forming a line for battle. The Philistines were also forming a line, ready to begin the fight. David ran quickly to find his brothers, and to tell them about their father's gift, which he had brought to them and to their captain.

While the brothers were talking together, suddenly the soldiers around them looked anxiously toward the enemy's camp. Their faces grew pale with fright. As David turned about to see the cause for their alarm, he wondered, ''What can this mean?'' And this is what he saw:

A tall giant, the giant Gō-lī'-ăth, dressed in clothes that were covered

DAVID KILLS A LION

with pieces of brass so that no sword could touch his body, was coming toward the camp of Israel again. On his head he was wearing a helmet of brass that fitted closely, like a hood. Gō-lī'-ăth knew the soldiers of Israel were afraid of him, and he called loudly to them as he had been doing every morning and every evening for forty days.
And David heard his voice ring out like an angry peal of thunder, and he saw the soldiers of King Saul turn and run away like frightened sheep.

When David saw these things, the Spirit of God stirred his heart and filled him with courage. ''Why should this wicked Philistine trouble us?'' he asked, bravely. ''I will go out and kill him.'' The soldiers who stood near were surprised to hear David's words. They told him how Gō-lī'-ăth had been coming out for many days, and how frightened they were of him. But David was firm in his belief that God would give him strength to kill such a wicked man, and the soldiers ran to tell King Saul.

Ē-lī'-ăb was much displeased when he heard David talk thus with the soldiers, and he called his brother aside and asked, "Why have you left those sheep in the field and come out here to see the battle?"

But David answered, "What have I done that you should be angry with me?" Then a messenger came from King Saul, calling for David, and he hurried away to speak with the King.

Saul had not seen David for some time. And he had never before seen him dressed in the clothes of a shepherd. Now he did not know him. How disappointed he felt when he saw only a shepherd-boy come before him, with no weapons at all! But David spoke bravely to him and said, "Do not be afraid any longer of this giant. I will go out and kill him."

"You are only a youth," answered Saul, "and you are not strong enough to fight against such a mighty soldier as this Philistine giant."

But David told him how he had killed both a lion and a bear while caring for his father's sheep, and he said, "This giant shall be as one of them, for he has dared to speak mockingly of God's people, and God will give him over into my hands." Then Saul was ready to let David go to fight the giant; for he saw that David had faith to believe God would help his people.

But David had no armor and no shield to protect his body from the giant's sword. He had no soldier-clothes at all. So Saul took off his armor and dressed David with it, and put his helmet upon David's head. Then he gave his sword to David, and the shepherd-boy looked like a grand soldier, dressed up in the clothes of a king.

"Now you are ready," said Saul.

But David replied, "I can not go with these clothes and with this sword. I have never used them before, and I am not prepared to fight with them." So he took them off, and picked up his shepherd's staff and ran down to the brook near by to find some smooth stones. These he put into his shepherd's bag, and then he took out his leather sling and started to meet the giant.

Gō-lī'-ăth was much surprized when he saw David coming toward him with no weapons. He became very angry; for he thought the Israelites were making fun of him. He said, "Am I a dog, that you have come to fight against me with that staff?" And he cursed David by the gods of the Philistines, and cried out, "Come to me, and I will

DAVID AND HIS SLING

soon tear you in pieces and will give your flesh to the birds and to the wild beasts.''

But David called back, ''You have come to me with a sword, and with a spear, and with a shield; but I come to you in the name of the Lord of hosts, the God of the armies of Israel, which you have mocked. Today the Lord will deliver you into my hand, and the flesh of the soldiers of the Philistines will become meat for the birds and for the wild beasts, that all people who hear of this may know that there is a God in Israel. And all people will know that the true God does not save with swords and spears.''

Then David ran forward and took a stone from his bag and placed it in his sling and threw it fiercely at the giant. And the stone hit the giant in his forehead, stunning him so that he fell face downward upon the ground. What a crash rang through the valley as Gō-lī′-ăth's heavy armor struck the earth! Then David hurried to the place where the giant lay.

The Philistines did not wait to see what would happen next; for now they knew God was helping the men of Israel, and they

DAVID SLAYS THE GIANT

turned to run back to their own land. They did not even wait to take down their tents and to gather their belongings together, but every one of them started out as fast as he could go. And Saul's army chased after them, and followed them to their own country. When Saul and his men came back, they took everything that the Philistines had left in their tents. And there was great rejoicing that day among the men of Israel, for they knew God had delivered them from their strong enemies.

STORY 9

HOW SAUL BECAME DAVID'S ENEMY

1 Sam. 17: 55—18: 30

When David went out to fight against Gō-lī'-ăth, few of the men in Saul's army knew him. Even the King himself wondered where this brave young shepherd had come from. He asked Abner, the captain of his army; but Abner had never met David before. As they two watched David approach the giant so fearlessly and overcome him so easily, the King told Abner that he must find out whose son this brave young man was.

Jonathan was standing near his father when David returned from killing the giant. And Abner met David and brought him to the King. "Whose son are you?" asked Saul.

And David replied, "I am the son of Jesse, your servant, who is a Bethlehemite." Perhaps Saul remembered then how this same handsome youth stood before him and played beautifully on a harp when the evil spirit used to trouble him. Now he would not let David go back to Bethlehem to care for his father's sheep any longer. He needed brave young men like that to be in his army, so he kept David, and gave him the command of one thousand soldiers. And he said that hereafter David should live in his palace at Gĭb'-ĕ-ăh.

Jonathan was glad when he heard his father's words to David; for he loved the rosy-cheeked young shepherd and he wished to become his friend. He took off his princely robe and gave it to David, and he also gave him his sword and his bow. Then he promised David that day always to love him; and David was pleased to have the prince of Israel speak so kindly to him. In later years he realized that God had caused Jonathan to love him so dearly, and he thanked God for giving him such a noble friend.

When Saul made David to be captain over a thousand men, the soldiers loved their brave young leader. They were ready to go anywhere with him to battle, for they saw that God was with him. The servants of Saul also were pleased when David came to live at the palace. Everywhere David went the people loved him.

But David soon found out that he had one enemy. Saul, the King, began to look unkindly upon him. You remember that after Saul had disobeyed God an evil spirit began to trouble him. This evil spirit came at different times to make him feel unhappy. And now, after the great victory over the Philistines, when Saul was returning from

the battle-field with David and the other soldiers this evil spirit began
to trouble him again. The women of Israel came out of the cities to
meet the returning army and they played on three-stringed instruments
and danced for joy, because God had given Israel the victory. They
sang words like these:

> "Saul has slain his thousands,
> And David his ten thousands."

King Saul was displeased with this song. He saw that the women
were giving greater praise to David than to him, and a jealous feeling
crept into his heart. Perhaps he remembered Samuel's words, that

KING SAUL THROWING HIS SPEAR AT DAVID

God would take the kingdom from him and give it to a better man
than he. Now he saw that God was with David, and he began to hate
David. The evil spirit returned to trouble him more than ever.

On the next day David played on his harp before the King again.
But this time the beautiful music only made Saul unhappier. He took
his javelin, or spear, and threw it at David, intending to kill him. But
David saw it and stepped aside quickly, and the javelin did not touch
him. Twice Saul threw the spear at him, and both times David escaped
being harmed with it. Then Saul was sure that God was with the young
man, and he felt afraid of David. He wanted to kill him, but he feared
to try any more.

Now, Saul had two daughters, and this gave him the thought of another plan to get rid of David. He called the young man to him and said, "I am going to send you out again to fight against the Philistines. If you will fight bravely and defeat them, I will give my elder daughter to become your wife when you return."

David answered that he was not worthy to become son-in-law to the King; but he hurried away to the battle-field, glad that he could prove himself a brave man.

Now, Saul hoped that the Philistines would surely kill David, because he had killed their giant; but David returned unharmed and with greater honors as a captain. And the people praised him more than ever. But David found that Saul had not kept his promise; for Mḗ'-răb, the King's daughter, had become the wife of another man.

Then Saul heard that his younger daughter, Michal, loved David, and he thought again that he might get rid of him by sending him out to fight against the Philistines. This time he said that David should kill one hundred of the Philistines.

David knew it would be an honor to become son-in-law to the king, and he knew that Michal loved him. So he called his soldiers and hurried quickly to do as Saul had bidden him. And he killed two hundred instead of one hundred men. When he returned safely again, Saul kept his promise and gave Michal to be his wife. But he feared David more than ever, and tried to think of some other plan by which to destroy this one who he believed would some day take his throne.

STORY 10

HOW JONATHAN AND MICHAL SAVED DAVID'S LIFE

1 Sam. 19:1—20:2

Wrong thoughts, like weeds, will quickly grow
When in one's mind they're given place,
And soon their ugly selves will show
To bring their owner much disgrace.

At first King Saul had tried to cover up his wrong thoughts about David. He had tried to act friendly at the very time when he was planning some way to cause David's death. But those plans failed, and he was disappointed.

Then Saul grew bolder. He had allowed the wrong thoughts to remain so long in his mind that they had become too big to cover up.

So he called Jonathan and his servants and told them that they should kill David.

How sad Jonathan felt when he heard this! He loved David and he was grieved to see his father becoming so jealous and hateful toward him. Instead of trying to kill David he ran to him and said, "You must hide quickly, lest one of my father's servants kill you. He is seeking your life." Jonathan promised to speak to his father to try to persuade him to think kindly toward David. "If he will listen to my words," said Jonathan, "I will send and bring you again to the palace."

David felt very thankful to Jonathan for his kindness, and he ran away to hide in a safe place outside the city. After he had gone, Jonathan spoke to his father about David, and reminded him of the times when David had risked his own life to save the kingdom of Israel from the power of the Philistines' rule. He told him that David had given much brave service to their country, and had never done anything deserving of death. Saul listened to Jonathan, and he became ashamed of his jealous feelings. He said, "David shall not be killed."

Jonathan hurried out to David's hiding-place to tell him the glad news, and he brought David back with him to live again in Gibeah. And David appeared before the King as he had done in other days, and Saul did not try to harm him.

Soon afterwards war broke out with the old-time enemies—the Philistines—and Saul sent David out to fight against them. Once more he drove them back in terror to their own land, and returned from the battle with greater honors than ever. And once more the evil spirit of jealousy crept back into Saul's heart.

David came to play on his harp before Saul; but the troubled King did not care for his sweet music. He sat thinking how much he wished to be forever rid of the handsome young musician whom everybody seemed to love. Suddenly he picked up his javelin and aimed it at David, intending to strike him to the wall with the sharp point. But David was watchful, and he stepped aside quickly and ran out of the room.

Saul was determined to get him now, so he sent messengers to David's home to guard the house and capture David in the morning. But Michal, David's wife, heard that the messengers were coming and she urged David to make his escape. She let him down from a window, and he crept past the guards through the darkness and ran out into the open country.

When morning came, the soldiers told Michal that her father had

sent for David; but she said he was sick and could not come. In the
night she had put an image in David's bed and had covered it over
nicely, and the bed looked as though a man were lying in it. The soldiers
told Saul that David was ill, and Saul commanded them to carry him
in the bed to the palace. Saul believed that surely David could not
escape if he were ill. But when they came with the bed, Saul found
only an image in it, and David was nowhere to be seen. Saul knew his
daughter had fooled him because she loved David and wished to save
his life.

David had run away to Rā'-măh, where Samuel lived, and had told
the old prophet about his troubles. And Samuel took him into a place
near by, called Nâî'-ōth, where the young prophets lived.

Now Saul was very angry, and he sent through the country to find
where David had gone. When he heard that David was with Samuel at
Nâî'-ōth, he sent messengers to capture him there. But the messengers
did not capture David. They stayed in Nâî'-ōth with Samuel and with
David and worshiped God at that place. Saul sent other messengers,
and they did the same. At last Saul said, "I myself will go, and I will
capture David." But when he came to the place and heard the others
praying and worshiping God he had no strength left to harm David.
He bowed down to the earth and worshiped, too. And he stayed a night
and a day at that place; but David fled away and hurried back to Gĭb'-
ĕ-ăh to speak with Jonathan.

STORY 11

WHY A LITTLE BOY PICKED UP ARROWS FOR A PRINCE
1 Samuel 20

One bright morning Jonathan, the prince of Israel, called a little
boy to him and said, "Come with me out to the field near the city.
I am going to shoot with my bow and arrows, and I want you to watch
where the arrows fall. Then you can run and pick them up and bring
them back to me."

So the two started off together, walking out of town into a wide
field. How proud the little boy felt to be walking along beside a prince!
Perhaps he even tried to take steps as long as Jonathan's. Perhaps
his eyes sparkled when he saw the shining bow that Jonathan carried.

Finally they came to a great rock in the field, and Jonathan stopped
to fit an arrow into his shining bow. Then he aimed carefully at an
object far off, and shot the arrow. How swiftly it darted through the

air! The little boy watched to see where it should fall and then he ran gleefully to pick it up. As he ran, Jonathan shot another arrow farther away, and called after him, "Is not the arrow beyond you?"

When the arrows had all been shot, and picked up from the grass, Jonathan told the little boy that he might carry the shining bow and the arrows back to the city. And perhaps the boy thought that would be the greatest fun of all.

Now Jonathan had not told the boy why they had come out to shoot in the field that morning. And the boy did not know that some one was hiding behind the great rock while Jonathan was shooting with his bow and arrows. But all the while David was hiding behind the great rock, listening to hear what Jonathan should tell the child. And after Jonathan sent the boy away, David came out from his hiding-place and fell on his face to the ground, bowing down before Jonathan three times. Then Jonathan ran to meet him, and the two friends wept and kissed each other.

DAVID AND JONATHAN

You remember that Saul was trying again to kill David, and that he had gone to Naioth for this purpose. But the Lord would not let him kill David there. And while Saul worshiped the Lord at Nâi′-ōth, David ran away and came back to talk with Jonathan. He told Jonathan how Saul was trying to kill him. And Jonathan felt very sad. He wanted to help his friend whom he loved so much. He asked, "What can I do to help you?" And David said, "Tomorrow will be a feast-day and Saul will expect me to eat at his table, because I am his son-in-law. I can not go, for I fear he will kill me there. Let me hide in the field, and if Saul becomes angry because I am not present at the feast you will know that he is trying to take my life; but if he speaks well of me, then you will know that it will be safe for me to return again."

Jonathan promised to let David know whether his father was still angry or whether he would be kind. He told David to hide behind the great rock, and he said he would come out in the morning and bring a little boy along to pick up the arrows which he would shoot. If he should say, "The arrow is beyond you!" then David would know that Saul was very angry; but if he should tell the boy to find the arrow at one side, then David would understand that Saul was no longer displeased.

Saul was very angry when David failed to come to the feast, and he even threw his javelin at Jonathan because he thought Jonathan was too friendly with David. And Jonathan knew that David's life was in great danger, so he rose from the table and would not eat any food that day. He hurried out to the field with the little boy, to let David know that he must go away from that place and never let Saul find him again.

Because David and Jonathan loved each other very dearly, they were sorry to part. They did not know whether they should ever see each other again. Jonathan knew that some day God would cause David to become the king of Israel. He asked David to promise that he would always be kind to him and to his children. And David was glad to make such a promise to his faithful friend.

Then the two men parted, and Jonathan went back to the city. But David went away to seek a hiding-place somewhere in the land of Israel.

————•————

STORY 12
THINGS THAT HAPPENED WHILE DAVID HAD NO HOME
1 Sam. 21:1—22:5

In the land of Israel was a little city called Nob. This city was the home of the priests who cared for the tabernacle of God. After the ark had been taken away from the tabernacle at Shī'-lōh and stolen by the Philistines, and after Ē'-lī, the high priest, and his two wicked sons had died, the tabernacle was moved to Nob. The ark was not restored to the place in the tabernacle where God planned that it should be kept, still the priests were caring for the tabernacle every day just as faithfully as it had been cared for when the ark was there. A man named Ă-hĭm'-ĕ-lĕch was now the high priest, and he wore the same breastplate that Aaron, the high priest, had worn.

One day Ă-hĭm'-ĕ-lĕch was surprized to see David come hurrying toward the tabernacle. He wondered what this brave captain might want; for he knew that David had won many battles against the Philistines and he knew the people of Israel loved him. He knew, too, that David had married the King's daughter and that now he belonged to the royal family of the kingdom of Israel. But he did not know that Saul hated David and wished to kill him. He did not know that David had left his home at Gĭb'-ĕ-ăh without taking a bite of food to eat and without even taking a weapon with which to protect himself in times of danger.

David was careful not to tell the high priest about his troubles. But he asked for bread, because he was hungry, and Ă-hĭm'-ĕ-lĕch gave him five loaves that had been kept in the holy place of the tabernacle because he had no other to give. Then David asked for a sword, and Ă-hĭm'-ĕ-lĕch said, ''I have none here except the one which belonged to the giant Gō-lī'-ăth, whom you killed.'' David was glad to take that one, for it was a great sword.

Ă-hĭm'-ĕ-lĕch did not know that he was helping a man whom the King of Israel hated. But when he was talking with David, another man came near and heard their conversation. He saw David take Gō-lī'-ăth's sword and go away. This other man's name was Dō'-ĕg. Dō'-ĕg was not an Israelite; but he lived in the land of Israel, and Saul had made him the chief over all the caretakers of the King's cattle.

When David saw Dō'-ĕg at the tabernacle he was afraid this man would go back to Saul and tell that David had been talking with the high priest. He knew Saul would send men to hunt all through the land of Israel to find him. Poor David! he did not know where to go to hide, so he hurried away toward the homeland of Saul's enemies, the Philistines, and came to the city of Gath.

Ā'-chĭsh was king of Gath at that time, and his servants knew David. They remembered how the women of Israel had rejoiced after David killed the giant, and how they had sung about David's great victory. The Philistines wanted to keep him for a prisoner; and when David heard them talking he felt sorry that he had come to their city. He thought now that Ā'-chĭsh would surely try to kill him, so he began to act as though he were a crazy man. Ā'-chĭsh was afraid of him and quickly sent him away.

From Gath David went back into the land of Israel and came to a place known as the wilderness of Judah. Here he found a cave among the rocks, the cave of Adullam, and in this cave he lived for many days. When his friends heard about his hiding-place, they came to see him there. His parents, too, and his brothers left their home near Bethlehem and came to live with David in the cave. They were afraid of King Saul, and they also feared the Philistine soldiers who had come into the land and had captured the city of Bethlehem.

David's father and mother were very old, and he felt sorry to see them driven away from their home with no place to live except in a cave. So he took them to Moab, the land where his great-grandmother

Ruth used to live among her own people. And he asked the king of
that country to let them live there until he could find a better place for
them. Then he went back again to Adullam.

Other men from the land of Israel kept coming to David until he
had a little army of about four hundred. He became their captain, and
they loved him very dearly. One time three of those men heard him
say that he longed to have a drink of water from the old well near the
gate of Bethlehem. There he used to draw water to drink when he
was a shepherd-boy, and he remembered how good that water tasted.
But David knew the Philistines now ruled the city and he knew it would
be dangerous to go there to get a drink. He would not try to go. He
would not send any one on such a dangerous errand.

These three men crept away through the shadows when evening
came and hurried to Bethlehem. There near the gate they found the
well, and they drew some water to carry back to give to their captain.
They returned to the cave safely and brought the water to David.
When David heard how they had risked their lives to try to please him,
he knew they loved him very much indeed. But he said, "I can not
drink this water; it is too precious. You have risked your lives to
bring it to me, and now I will give it as an offering to God." So he
poured it on the ground before the Lord as a precious gift.

STORY 13

HOW A WICKED SERVANT OBEYED A WICKED KING

1 Sam. 22: 6-23

One little sin brings many more—
It pushes through the half-closed door
Of careless minds and hearts;
The host of other sins come, too,
They find the door and scramble through.
Then trouble quickly starts.

King Saul had allowed the sin of jealousy to creep into his heart.
Then the sin of hate pushed its way in and threw the door wide open
to the terrible sin of murder. What a wicked heart Saul carried about
with him! No wonder he felt unhappy.

After David went away from Gĭb'-ĕ-ăh, Saul tried very hard to find
him. But no one seemed to know where David had gone. No one seemed
ready to help the unhappy King. Even Jonathan, the King's son, was
David's friend.

About this time a message came to the King telling that David and a small army were living in the great cave, Adullam. Because Saul was seeking to kill David, he supposed at once that David was trying to kill him. "Why should he have a band of soldiers with him if he were not trying to plan a way to take the kingdom?" reasoned the unhappy man. And Saul began to pity himself. He began to feel so sorry for himself because none of his soldiers would help him capture David.

One day while Saul sat under a tree near his palace in Gibeah he thought about his troubles and wondered what to do. He spoke to his servants and told them how distressed he felt because none of them would help him. He told them that even Jonathan had refused to defend his own rights, but was letting David have the first place in the hearts of all the people of Israel.

Dō'-ĕg, the man whom Saul had appointed to be chief over all his herdmen, was there that day, and he stepped up boldly and told the King that he had seen David at the tabernacle, in Nob, talking with the high priest. He told how Ă-hĭm'-ĕ-lĕch had given food to David, and also the sword that once belonged to Gō-lī'-ăth.

Saul felt sure that Ă-hĭm'-ĕ-lĕch, the high priest, had tried to help David get away to a safe hiding-place. He sent quickly for Ă-hĭm'-ĕ-lĕch and for all the priests who lived at Nob, and they came wondering what service they might do for their king. They knew nothing of the whereabouts of David; they did not even know David had run away from the King.

When the priests came, Saul called Ă-hĭm'-ĕ-lĕch and spoke sharply to him. He asked why Ă-hĭm'-ĕ-lĕch had given food and a weapon to an enemy of Israel.

How surprised Ă-hĭm'-ĕ-lĕch was to hear these words! He answered, "Who is so faithful among all your servants as David, your own son-in-law? Does he not go wherever you send him? and is he not loved by all your people?" Ă-hĭm'-ĕ-lĕch did not know that the evil spirit of jealousy had driven the King to hate David for these very reasons.

Now Saul's anger grew fierce, and he cried, "You and all the other priests have helped David to get away from me, and you shall be punished for this act. You must die." Saul did not stop to think that these priests were God's men, the very ones whom God had chosen to care for the tabernacle. Even if he had thought of this he would not have checked his wicked anger. He commanded his soldiers to kill Ă-hĭm'-ĕ-lĕch and all the other priests who were standing by.

But Saul's soldiers feared God more than they feared to disobey their wicked King, and they said, "We can not kill the priests of the Lord." Then Saul turned to his wicked servant, Dō'-ĕg, and told him to kill the priests. And Dō'-ĕg obeyed. Not only did he kill the priests, but he hurried away to Nob and killed every man, woman, and child whom he could find in the city.

But one of Ă-hĭm'-ĕ-lĕch's sons, named Ă-bĭ'-ă-thär, fled from the city and came to David, bringing the sad news of Saul's command and the cruel way in which it had been obeyed. And David took Ă-bĭ'-ă-thär and kept him safely from the fate of his brothers. Afterwards Ă-bĭ'-ă-thär became the high priest, and he was with David through all the years of trouble until David became a very old man.

STORY 14

HOW DAVID SPARED SAUL'S LIFE
1 Samuel 23—27

Not far from David's hiding-place was a city called Kē-ĭ'-läh, and the people who lived there were being troubled by the Philistines. David heard about their trouble, and at once the spirit of a king stirred his heart. He wanted to help them, so he asked God if he should take his little army and go out to drive the Philistines away. God told him to go; but his soldiers were afraid to go with him. He prayed the second time, and God gave courage to all his men.

When Saul heard that David had driven the Philistines away from Kē-ĭ'-läh and had marched with his soldiers into the city, he thought, "Now is my chance; I will capture my enemy, for he has gotten himself into a trap." Saul believed it would be easy to capture David inside the walls of Kē-ĭ'-läh, and he planned to send an army to take him there.

But God warned David of the danger he was in, and told him to leave the city. So David called his soldiers and hurried away into a thick woodland to hide. There he was when Jonathan found him one day and told him not to be afraid. "God will not let my father hurt you," he said, "for you will yet be king over Israel and I shall be next to you."

David felt glad when he heard Jonathan's comforting words. How he loved his friend! For a long time they talked about the happy days to come when David would be king and they could work together as faithful friends. Then they bade each other good-by, and Jonathan went away. This was the last time they ever saw each other, for Jonathan was killed not long afterwards in a battle with the Philistines.

David went from one place to another to hide in the mountains and in the woods. Everywhere he went Saul followed after him with an army of three thousand men. At last Saul's army came to the wilderness of Ĕn-ġē'-dī, where David was hiding with his men in a great

KING SAUL IN DAVID'S CAVE

cave. Saul did not know that they were inside the cave, and he wished to rest for a while, so he went into the cave and lay down to sleep.

David and his soldiers were standing in the dark shadows at the sides of the cave when Saul entered, and they saw him lie down to rest. But he did not see them. When he fell asleep David crept up softly and cut off a part of his robe. Then he went back into the shadows again to wait until Saul should waken.

David's soldiers wanted to kill Saul. They knew he was a wicked

King, and that God was much displeased with him. But David remembered that God had once chosen Saul to rule his people, and he believed it would be a great sin to kill one whom God's prophet had anointed, so he would not let his soldiers harm the sleeping man.

When Saul awoke and went out of the cave, David followed and called after him. Saul was surprized to hear David's voice behind him, and when he turned and saw that David had been in the cave while he lay asleep he knew then that David was not his enemy at all. He knew that David would have killed him if he were an enemy. David showed him the piece of cloth that he had cut from Saul's robe, and told how his men had urged him to kill Saul. But he said, "I will not hurt you, for you are the Lord's anointed. Why should you believe that I am seeking your life?"

Saul was ashamed of himself when he heard David's kind words and saw that David really did not mean to do him harm. He wept for sorrow when he remembered how much he had once loved David, and he said, "You are a better man than I, for you have done good to me while I was trying to kill you. Today the Lord let me fall into your hands, and you have spared my life. I know that some day you will be the king of Israel."

After their talk together, Saul took his army and returned to his home at Gĭb'-ĕ-ăh. Perhaps he thought he would never again trouble David, but the evil spirit soon came back into his heart and he grew as hateful as ever. David had been afraid to go home, and now Saul started out to find him again.

David was hiding in the country that belonged to the Ziphites, and they sent word to Saul to come and take him there. So he came with an army of three thousand men and pitched his camp in the wilderness of Ziph, at a place called the hill of Hă-chĭ'-lăh. David sent spies to be on the watch, and they brought back word to him that Saul had come.

"Now," thought David, "I will go by night and visit Saul's camp. Perhaps I can show him again that I do not wish to harm him." So he took a young man along, named Ăb'-ĭ-shâî, and they two entered Saul's camp while all the soldiers were sleeping soundly. Even Saul's brave captain, Abner, was fast asleep; for God had put a deep sleep upon them all. David and Ăb'-ĭ-shâî went into the center of the camp, and there they found Saul lying with his spear stuck into the ground near his head, and with a bottle of water standing by.

Ăb'-ĭ-shâî wanted to kill Saul, but David said they had not come for that purpose. He told Ăb'-ĭ-shâî that some day God would permit Saul to be killed, perhaps in a battle, but that it would be wrong for him to kill one whom God's prophet had anointed to be king of Israel.   He told Ăb′-ĭ-shâî that he might take Saul's spear and the water-bottle; and then they walked quietly out of the camp.   No one heard them come and no one heard them go away.

When the two men climbed to the top of a hill outside the camp, David cried loudly to Abner, the captain of Saul's army.   And Abner awoke with a start.   He knew David's voice and he was afraid.   David told him that he was not fit to be the King's chief captain because he had not watched to keep an enemy out of the camp.   He said, "Some one has come into your camp to kill Saul, and you have been asleep.   They have stolen the spear and the water-bottle of your master.   Send one of your soldiers now to get them."

Saul, too, was awakened by David's voice,

DAVID SPARES SAUL'S LIFE

and he cried out, "Is that your voice, my son David?"   Again he felt ashamed when he found out how easily David might have harmed him.   He knew he had sinned greatly, and he asked David to return to Gĭb′-ĕ-ăh, for he would not try any more to take his life.

But David remembered the other times when Saul had become sorry for his jealous behavior, and he was afraid to believe the promise that the King made.   Instead of going back to live in Gĭb′-ĕ-ăh, he took his soldiers and went to the land of the Philistines, where he lived until he heard about Saul's death.

THE UNHAPPY ENDING OF SAUL'S LIFE

1 Sam. 28: 3—31: 13

Troubles that are left unmended
Never can be rightly ended.

Troubles began for Saul when he disobeyed God and tried to do just as he pleased. And they grew bigger when he allowed wrong thoughts to fill his mind and cause him to do wrong deeds. By and by, after many years of trouble, he became an old man. And what a miserable old man he was! Nowhere could he feel contented and happy.

About this time the Philistines were causing him much trouble. They were stealing from his people and they were even stealing cities away from his rule. They were growing bolder all the while; and Saul knew he was not able to drive them out of the land of Israel. He remembered the times when he used to send David to fight against them. He remembered how God used to bless David and always help him to gain the victory. Now he had no one to send, so he had to go himself.

Saul gathered all the soldiers of Israel together and led them out to the battle-field where Gideon had led three hundred brave men to a great victory many years before. But Saul did not feel courageous, as did Gideon. He was afraid when he saw the hosts of the Philistines gathering in the valley. He wondered what to do. No priest of the Lord could he find in the land to tell him of God's will; for he had commanded all the priests to be killed, and the only one who escaped had fled to David's company. Samuel, the faithful old prophet, was dead and buried; and God would not speak to Saul.

There were people living at that time, as there are people today, who believed they could speak with the dead. Such people are wicked, and God had commanded the Israelites to destroy any they might find in their land. Saul had commanded his people to destroy them. But when he could find no one to tell him what to do he thought of Samuel. How he wished that he might speak to the dear old man once more! Samuel used to talk to God and understand God's will. "Surely he could help now," thought Saul. And Saul wondered whether he could find some one who could speak to Samuel even though the prophet was dead.

Not far from Saul's camp was a village called Endor, and a woman lived there who said she talked with the spirits of the dead. We call such a person a witch. Some of Saul's servants told him about the witch who lived at Endor, and Saul decided to visit her. He knew she would be afraid of him, so he dressed in the clothes of a poor man that she might not know who he was. Then he took two of his men with him and went to Endor that very night.

The woman was frightened when three men stopped near her door in the dark shadows and asked her to speak with the spirit of a man who had died. She said, "Saul, the king of Israel, has commanded that every one be killed who speaks with spirits; are you asking me to do this thing and so place myself in danger of losing my life?" Saul

A RECENT PICTURE OF ENDOR, THE PLACE WHERE SAUL FOUND THE WITCH

told her not to be afraid to do just as he asked, for she would not be punished.

When the woman tried to call Samuel's spirit from the dead, she saw something that frightened her terribly. And she knew at once that the old man who was waiting to hear Samuel's words was King Saul himself. She cried, "Why have you fooled me?" Saul told her not to be afraid, and asked what she had seen. Then she described the form of an old man wrapped in a mantle; and Saul cried, "It is Samuel."

Instead of receiving any help or comfort, Saul heard words that night that frightened him more than ever. The messenger who spoke to him said that on the next day he and his three sons should be killed, and that the Philistines should gain a great victory over his people. When the voice ceased speaking, Saul lay helpless upon the ground. The woman prepared some food for him to eat. Then he rose up and went away with his two companions.

On the next day the battle began, and the Philistines overpowered the men of Israel and killed many of them. Saul's three sons fell dead on the battle-field—Jonathan and his two brothers. And Saul himself was wounded. When he saw that he must die, Saul feared that the Philistines would come and torture him. So he commanded his armor-bearer to kill him, but the armor-bearer said, "I can not kill the Lord's anointed." Then Saul fell upon his own sword, and died.

STORY 16
WHAT HAPPENED TO DAVID'S HOME AT ZIKLAG
1 Sam. 29: 1—2 Sam. 2: 3

When David went with his soldiers to live in the land of the Philistines, he became friendly with Ā'-chĭsh, the king of Gath. God caused this heathen king to be kind to David and his men, and to give them a city to live in. The name of this city was Ziklag.

At the time of Saul's death, David and his soldiers were making their homes at Ziklag. Ā'-chĭsh wanted David to go to the battle against Saul, and had him in his army; but the other rulers of the Philistines were afraid of him. So David took his men and went back to the land of the Philistines.

When they came near to Ziklag they saw that an enemy had been there and had burned the city. All their belongings were stolen, even their wives and children. David called Ă-bī'-ă-thär, the high priest, and he asked God whether they should follow after the enemy and try to overtake them. God told them to go, so David took his six hundred men and started to follow the trail of the enemy.

Because they had no food to eat, a part of David's men became too weak to go very far on the trail. These stopped by a brook to rest, while the others went on with their brave captain. As they went they found an Egyptian, nearly dead, lying in a field, and they gave him water to drink. For three days this Egyptian had lain without a drop of water and without food. After he ate some bread and drank water he was able to speak with David and his men. He told them that a band of Ă-măl'-ĕk-ītes had passed by that way and had left him behind when he fell sick. He said they had been in the land of the Philistines and had burned the city of Ziklag. David said, "Can you show us which road they have taken?" The Egyptian promised to go with David and help him find the Ă-măl'-ĕk-ītes if David would not allow the Ă-măl'-ĕk-ītes to take him again for their servant. And David took the Egyptian with his men.

The Ă-măl'-ĕk-ītes were camping in a valley and enjoying a feast when David and his soldiers found them. They fell upon the company and rescued their wives and children and all the goods the Ă-măl'-ĕk-ītes had stolen from the land of the Philistines and from the land of Judah. They killed many of the Ă-măl'-ĕk-ītes and drove the others away into the wilderness.

When David returned to the men who were resting by the brook, he divided with them the goods that he and his men had taken away from their enemies. And they hurried back to their places in the land of the Philistines.

Now Ziklag was burned, and they had no homes to live in. While they were wondering what to do, a messenger came running from the battle-field to tell about the death of Saul and of his sons. The messenger said he was an Ă-măl'-ĕk-īte and that he had found Saul leaning upon his spear nearly dead. Thinking David would be pleased to hear that his enemy, Saul, was killed, the Ă-măl'-ĕk-īte told David that he had killed Saul and had brought Saul's crown to him.

But David was not pleased. He tore his clothes as a sign of sorrow, and cried, "Were you not afraid to kill a man who was the Lord's anointed?" The Ă-măl'-ĕk-īte had expected David to give him a present because he had killed Saul. But David commanded his soldiers to kill the stranger.

David mourned about the death of Saul and of his dearly loved friend, Jonathan. He seemed to forget that Saul had ever been unkind to him. He tried to remember only the good things that Saul had done. He wrote a poem about their death, and one of the verses reads thus:

> Saul and Jonathan were lovely and pleasant in their lives,
> And in their death they were not divided:
> They were swifter than eagles,
> They were stronger than lions.

After Saul's death, David asked the Lord what to do. He no longer had a home in the land of the Philistines, because the city of Ziklag had been burned. The Lord told him to go back to his own land again; so he took his family and all his soldiers and their wives and children and went back to the land of Judah, to live in Hē'-brŏn.

STORY 17

WHEN THE SHEPHERD-BOY BECAME THE KING OF ISRAEL
2 Sam. 2: 4—6: 18

Many years had passed since God sent Samuel to Bethlehem to anoint the shepherd-boy for Israel's king. During those years David grew to manhood and became a mighty captain. He led his brave soldiers to many battles, and God always gave them victories over their enemies.

After David went to live at Hĕ'-brŏn, the men of Judah came to anoint him to be their king. For a few years the other tribes followed Saul's son Ĭsh-bŏsh'-ĕth; but when they saw how God was blessing David, they sent their chief men to him with this message: "We are all your brothers, and we know God has chosen you to become the ruler of his people." Then they anointed him to be king over all the land.

David set up his kingdom in the city of Jerusalem. First he had to drive away the Jĕb'-ū-sītes, a strange people who had lived at that place since the time of Joshua. Then he chose Mount Zion, one of the hills inside the wall of Jerusalem, and on this hill he built his royal palace.

Now, the Philistines were ruling over many places in the land of Israel and they were not pleased when David took the throne. They gathered their armies together and came to fight against him in a valley near Jerusalem. David did not rush out to meet them, but first asked God what he should do. And God told him to go out to the battle. He called his soldiers and went out and defeated the Philistines, driving them away in such haste that they left the images of their gods behind. David and his men found the images and burned them to ashes.

After this battle the Philistines came again to fight against David. They pitched their tents in the same valley as where the first battle had been fought. David prayed again, and God told him not to go out this time as he had gone before, but to take his army off to one side and wait under the mulberry-trees for God's sign. When he should hear a sound in the tops of the trees, then he should hurry out to the battle, for God would go before him and would give a great victory. David was careful to do exactly as God said, and God helped him to drive all the Philistines out of the land. Never again did they come back to bother Israel while he was the king.

David wanted to bring the ark of God to Jerusalem. He had heard how it had been taken away from Shī'-lōh to battle against the Philistines long years before Saul became the king. He knew God's plan was to keep the ark inside the tabernacle, so he built a new tabernacle after the pattern of the old one, which had stood at Nob, and then he sent word to the people in every part of the land telling them that he was going to bring the ark to Jerusalem.

Thirty thousand men came, a great army of men, to see the moving of the ark from its resting-place at Kĭr'-jăth-jē'-ă-rĭm to the King's city. They built a new cart to carry it, and tried to move it as the Philistines had done when they sent it back to the land of Israel. But God did not want his people to handle the ark in that manner. He had commanded that no one except the priests should even touch the ark. But the people had forgotten God's command.

David and a company of musicians walked before the cart, playing on harps and other stringed instruments and singing praises to God. The other people followed, every one feeling happy because the King was trying to worship God in the right way. Suddenly every one stopped, and the music ceased. One of the oxen that helped to draw the cart perhaps had stumbled, for the ark tottered as if ready to fall to the ground. The driver, seeing the danger the ark was in, reached out his hand to steady the ark, and immediately he fell down dead.

"What can this mean?" every one wondered, and David was frightened, too. He knew God had been displeased with some part of their plan, and he did not know what to do, so he left the ark at the home of a man who lived near by. Then he and all the people of Israel went back to their homes.

David began to inquire about God's plan for moving the ark from one place to another, and he learned that God intended for the priests to carry the ark on their shoulders. After several months had passed, word came to David that God was blessing the man at whose home near the roadside the ark had been left. And David sent again to bring the ark to Jerusalem.

This time David called for the Levites and commanded them to carry the ark. And again he and other musicians went before the ark, singing and playing on stringed instruments. And they brought the ark safely inside the city walls and placed it in the new tabernacle, which David had built. Then they offered burnt offerings and peace-offerings before the Lord.

WHAT HAPPENED TO A LITTLE LAME PRINCE WHEN HE GREW UP

2 Sam. 4:4—9:13

Mĕ-phĭb′-ŏ-shĕth is a very long name for a very small boy. But Jonathan, the prince of Israel, thought it a very good name for his little son, and soon the child grew old enough to answer when they called that name.

One day Jonathan kissed his little boy good-by and went away to the battle at Mount Gĭl-bō′-ă. He never came back again; for in that battle against the Philistines he was killed. And his father, King Saul, was killed, too. Many others of the soldiers of Israel were killed by their enemies that day.

When news from the battle reached the city Gĭb′-ĕ-ăh, every one became excited. And every one in the King's household became very much afraid. Even the servants were afraid. They knew their own lives would not be safe after their master, the King, had been killed by the Philistines, for the Philistines would send soldiers to Gĭb′-ĕ-ăh to take that city and to destroy every one they could find who belonged to Saul's family. And so the servants and all the people who lived in the palace ran away.

Mĕ-phĭb′-ŏ-shĕth was not big enough to run very far, for he was only five years old. He could not understand why every one was hurrying away so fast. He grew tired, and perhaps he began to cry. Then his nurse picked him up and carried him in her arms. But while she was running along with the other servants she stumbled and dropped the little Prince to the ground. Both his feet were hurt so badly in that fall that he was never able to run about and play with other children again. He was taken to the home of a kind man who lived on the other side of the Jordan River, and there he lived till he grew to be a man.

After David became the king of Israel he remembered his dear friend Jonathan, who had been killed by the Philistines. He remembered how Jonathan had planned to live near him after he should become king. And he remembered his promise always to be kind to this faithful friend and to his children.

But Jonathan was dead, and David missed him when he came back to live again in Israel. He remembered the promise he had made to Jonathan, and he began to look about to find where Jonathan's children had gone.   He could find none in Gĭb'-ĕ-ăh, and after a long time he heard about Mĕ-phĭb'-ŏ-shĕth, the lame prince who was living in the country of Israel on the other side of the Jordan River.   So he sent after Mĕ-phĭb'-ŏ-shĕth and had him brought to the palace at Jerusalem.

Mĕ-phĭb'-ŏ-shĕth was now a grown man, and he had married a wife. Perhaps he felt afraid when the messenger came from Jerusalem, saying that David had sent for him.   But he hurried to the palace to speak with the old-time friend of his father.   When he came before David he bowed down to the ground in a very humble manner.   And David said, ''Mĕ-phĭb'-ŏ-shĕth, do not be afraid of me, for I wish to show kindness to you for your father's sake.   I want to give back to you all the land that once belonged to your grandfather, King Saul, and I want you to come and live in my palace and sit at my table every day.''

Then David called an old man who had been a servant of King Saul, and he told this servant to take care of the lands and fields that now belonged to Mĕ-phĭb'-ŏ-shĕth.   And this old man and his sons became servants of Mĕ-phĭb'-ŏ-shĕth.

The lame Prince brought his wife and his little son, whose name was Mĭ'-chă, from their home cn the other side of the Jordan River, and they lived with him at Jerusalem among the children of the King.   As long as Mĕ-phĭb'-ŏ-shĕth lived, David was kind to him, for his friend Jonathan's sake.

STORY 19

DAVID'S SIN AND HIS PUNISHMENT
2 Sam. 11:1—12: 26

Temptations come to one and all;
The rich and poor alike may fall
In Satan's traps, set ev'ry day
To catch the feet that go astray.

David was a wise man, and he loved God.   But he was often tempted to do wrong things, and sometimes he allowed the temptations to lead him into trouble.   One day a very strong temptation came to him and he forgot that God could see everything he was doing.   He forgot that God could even hear his thoughts, and he planned to cover up his wrong deed.

But God sent a faithful prophet to speak to the King and to tell him how greatly he had sinned.   The prophet said, ''Because you have displeased God you shall have many sorrows in your home-life.   First your baby son whom you love so dearly shall die. Other troubles will come in later years.''

David wept when the prophet spoke to him. He felt very unhappy because he had displeased God. He asked God to take away his sin and to give him a clean heart, for he knew that his heart was not right. And his prayer was heard in heaven because he was truly sorry for his wrong deed.

Not long after this had happened the baby in David's home became very sick. And David remembered the words of the prophet.

THE PROPHET SPEAKING TO KING DAVID

When he saw that the child was growing worse instead of better every day, he thought, "I will fast and pray very earnestly, and maybe the Lord will spare the life of my darling.'' So David refused to eat any food, and he lay down with his face on the ground, to pray to God. His servants urged him to take food; but he would not eat.

Although God had forgiven David's sin, he did not take away the punishment which that sin had brought. He allowed David to suffer pain because he had done wrong, and after seven days of sickness the baby died.

David's servants were afraid to tell him the sad news about the baby's death. They said to each other, "If our King has been so greatly distressed that he would not eat while his child was ill, how can we tell him that the child is dead?'' But David heard them whispering, and he asked, "Is the child dead?'' And they answered, "He is dead.''

Then David rose from the ground and washed himself in clean water, and dressed in his kingly robes, as in other days. He went first to the tabernacle to worship God, and afterwards he came to his home and asked for food. His servants were surprised, and they asked why he had fasted and wept and prayed while the child lived. He answered, "I fasted and prayed then because I thought the Lord might spare my darling's life; now I know that the child can not come back to me, but some day I shall go to be with him.''

Israel under Saul, David, and Solomon

ISRAEL UNDER SAUL, DAVID, AND SOLOMON

Saul, the first king of Israel, was rejected of God because of disobedience, and David, a shepherd boy, was anointed king. However, it was many years before he came to the throne. He lived in Saul's palace awhile and played the harp before Saul.

A giant, Goliath, of the Philistines, challenged Israel. David accepted the challenge and killed the giant.

David and Saul's son, Jonathan, became fast friends.

Once when Saul was in trouble he went to the witch of Endor, who said she could talk with the spirits of the dead.

After the reign of Saul and David, Solomon, David's son, came to the throne. David had desired to build a beautiful temple in which to worship God, but God chose Solomon, David's son, to do this. Cedars were brought from the Lebanon Mountains to Jerusalem for use in building the Temple. Solomon was known throughout the world for his wealth and wisdom. Visitors came from many lands, among them the Queen of Sheba.

After this baby died, God gave David and his wife another child, and they named him Solomon. God loved this child, and he told David that some day Solomon should sit upon his throne and become the king of Israel.

———— • ————

STORY 20

THE WICKED PRINCE WHO TRIED TO STEAL HIS FATHER'S KINGDOM

2 Samuel 15—17

Ăb'-să-lọm was one of the handsome princes who lived at the palace in Jerusalem. But he was not like his father, David. When he grew to manhood he thought often about the time to come when his father should die and there should need to be a new king in Israel. Ăb'-să-lọm wished to become the new king. Perhaps he did not know that God had already chosen his younger brother, Solomon, to be the third ruler of the kingdom.

As time passed by Ăb'-să-lọm grew tired of waiting for his father to die. Finally he planned to steal the kingdom away while his father was yet alive. First he began by acting very friendly toward all the people who came to visit Jerusalem from other parts of the kingdom. He won their hearts by kindly doing services for them. Because he was young and very handsome they became attracted to him. Then when he treated them very kindly they thought he would make a great king indeed.

While this was happening David was busy attending to his duties as a king. He did not know that Ăb'-să-lọm was stealing the hearts of many of his people. So when Ăb'-să-lọm came to him early one morning and asked permission to go that day to Hē'-brŏn to worship God there, David said, "Go, my son." He was glad to hear that Ăb'-să-lọm wished to worship God.

But Ăb'-să-lọm's plan was not to worship God at all. He used that for an excuse to go away from Jerusalem without causing his father to grow uneasy. He had already planned to meet with the people of Israel at Hē'-brŏn and to become their king at that place. Then he would return with them to Jerusalem and sit upon his father's throne.

Perhaps Ăb'-să-lọm planned to take his father by surprise when he should return to Jerusalem to claim the throne. But a messenger hurried to tell the King what was taking place at Hē'-brŏn, and David un-

derstood at once what would happen if his son should return and find
him there. So he quickly called his faithful servants and told them of
Ăb′-să-lom′s̱ wicked doings. "Let us flee from the city at once," he
told them; "for if Ăb′-să-lom and his followers find us they will try to
take our lives."

This was a sad hour for David. Now his own son, whom he loved
from babyhood, had risen up against him, ready to take his life. Poor
David! again he remembered the words of God's prophet, who said
that troubles would come in his own household because he had sinned
so against God. And David felt very humble. He covered his head and
removed his sandals from off his feet. Then he walked away from
his beautiful palace, away from the city of Jerusalem, weeping as he
went. And his faithful servants followed, with their heads covered
too. They wept with David when they thought about the unkindness
of Ăb′-să-lom.

Now the priest Ă-bī′-ă-thär, who fled to David when Saul had commanded all the priests of God to be killed, was living in Jerusalem.
He and another priest named Zā′-dŏk, with their two sons, took the ark
of God and prepared to follow David, too. But David told them that
they could help him more if they would remain in the city and send
him word about the doings of Ăb′-să-lom. So they returned with the
ark to the tabernacle.

Another of David's friends, a very wise man named Hū′-shâi, who
often helped the King, hurried to join the fleeing company. He tore
his coat and put dust upon his head to show the people how sorry
he felt for David. But when he met David, the King said, "Hū′-shâi,
I want you to go to Jerusalem instead of following me. There you
can learn about Ăb′-să-lom′s̱ plans and tell the priests. And the priests
will send their sons to tell me what I must do." So Hū′-shâi left David
and went into Jerusalem, while the King and his followers journeyed
on toward the wilderness near the Jordan River.

When Ăb′-să-lom and his friends came to the palace at Jerusalem
they saw at once that David and his faithful servants had run away.
They were surprised to find that Hū′-shâi had not gone with them, and
they asked why he remained behind. But Hū′-shâi pretended that he
wished to please Ăb′-să-lom as he had pleased David. And because Hū′-
shâi was a very wise man, Ăb′-să-lom was glad to keep him in his court.

At once Ăb′-să-lom and his friends began to plan how they should
capture David and win all of David's servants to become the servants
of the new King. They decided that it would be wise to send an army
out that very night to search for David and kill him.

But Hū'-shâî said, "Your plan is not good. David is a mighty soldier, and his servants, too, know how to fight bravely. They will defeat your few men. First you must gather a large army together, and then go out after the.old King." Hū'-shâî spoke thus because he wished to give David more time to get far away to a safe hiding-place. And Ăb'-să-lǫm thought Hū'-shâî's advice was best to follow, so he sent messengers to call the soldiers of Israel together; and while the army was gathering, Hū'-shâî sent word to David by the sons of the priests, telling him to flee across the Jordan River at once.

When the sons of the priests started to go to David with Hū'-shâî's message, a young man saw them, and he hurried to tell Ăb'-să-lǫm. Then Ăb'-să-lǫm sent soldiers to catch the messengers; but they hid in a well until the soldiers had gone back again to the city. Then they ran on to tell David the words of Hū-shâî, and David took his servants and went to the city of Mā-hă-nā'-ĭm, on the other side of the Jordan River.

* * *

STORY 21

HOW THE WICKED PRINCE WAS HUNG IN THE BOUGHS OF A GREAT OAK-TREE

2 Samuel 18, 19

Ăb'-să-lǫm believed that his soldiers would try harder to capture David if he should go with them. So he led them out from Jerusalem, riding on a mule as was the custom of kings. And a great host of men followed, all armed and ready to fight against the servants of David.

Now, David was being cared for by kind friends in the city of Mā-hă-nā'-ĭm. His servants would not let him go out to the battle, so he divided them into three companies and sent them away to meet Ăb'-să-lǫm and his men in a thick woodland called the woods of Ē'-phră-ĭm. Then he waited by the gate of the city to hear the first news that should come from the battle-field.

Before letting his men start David urged them to be kind to Ăb'-să-lǫm if they should find him in the woods. Even though Ăb'-să-lǫm was an ungrateful son, David could not forget his love for the young man. And he waited with an anxious heart to hear what the result of the meeting in the woods should be.

David's servants were successful in the battle. Many of Ăb'-să-lǫm's soldiers were killed, and many others were scattered and lost in the thick woods. As Ăb'-să-lŏm was riding through the woods trying to escape from David's servants, his mule ran under the boughs of a great oak-tree, and Ăb'-să-lŏm was caught by his head in the thick boughs. His mule ran away, leaving him hanging there alone. One of David's servants was near by and saw him; but he remembered David's words, and would not hurt the young prince. He ran quickly to tell his captain Jō'-ăb, what he had seen. And Jō'-ăb asked, "Why did you not kill Ăb'-să-lŏm at once?" The servant answered, "Because I heard David command us to spare the young man's life."

Although Jō'-ăb was the chief captain of David's army, he was not always careful to obey the orders that David gave to him. He was a cruel man, and sometimes he did things that grieved his master very much. When Jō'-ăb heard that Ăb'-să-lŏm was hanging in the boughs of a tree he hurried to the place and found the young Prince yet alive, and Jō'-ăb killed him. The young men who carried Jō'-ăb's armor came to help him kill Ăb'-să-lŏm, and they took Ăb'-să-lŏm's body down from the tree and threw it into a deep hole in the ground. Then they covered the hole with a heap of stones.

Ăb'-să-lŏm's soldiers soon heard that their leader had been killed, and they ran away from the battle. They had nothing left to fight for, and they were afraid of David's servants, so they hurried quickly to their own homes on the other side of the Jordan River.

Jō'-ăb sent a young man named Cū'-shī to carry the news of the battle to David. After he started, one of the priests' sons asked permission also to run as a messenger to David. But Jō'-ăb said, "You have nothing to tell." Still the priest's son begged to go, so Jō'-ăb gave his consent. But he did not send a message with this man. And this man ran faster than the first; but when he came to David he could not tell what had happened in the woods.

Cū'-shī then came forward and bowed low before David, saying as he did so, "Tidings, my lord the king." And David knew he had a message from the battle. How eagerly the old King listened to Cū'-shī's report of the victory, which his servants had gained over Ăb'-să-lŏm's army! Then he asked in anxious tones, "Is the young man Ăb'-să-lŏm safe?"

Now Cū'-shī knew that David loved the wicked young Prince, and it was not easy to tell what had happened to Ăb'-să-lŏm. So he said kindly, "Let the enemies of my lord the king, and all who rise up to harm you, be as the young man is." And David understood by these words that Ăb'-să-lŏm was dead.

Instead of rejoicing because of the victory, King David covered his face and began to weep aloud because of his son's death. Again and again he cried, "O my son Ăb'-să-lọm! my son! my son! I would rather have died myself!" And all the people who heard David weeping were made sad that day. No one felt like rejoicing over the victory, for they were afraid that their King would be displeased.

Finally Jō'-ăb came and spoke to David. He said, "The people will think that you love your enemies and hate your friends. They have risked their lives to save you from harm, and now you only weep, because your ungrateful son has been killed. You do not thank the people who have been true to you in this time of trouble." So David ceased his weeping and went out to speak again to his brave servants.

Not long afterwards David and his servants and all who had come with him returned again to live in Jerusalem. And David showed much kindness to the friends who had cared for him while his life was being sought by this wicked son.

STORY 22

WHY THE DEATH-ANGEL VISITED JERUSALEM
2 Samuel 24; 1 Chronicles 21

Under the rule of David the kingdom of Israel grew from a weak, oppressed nation into a very powerful one, such a powerful one that the heathen people who lived in other lands were made to see God's blessings upon David and his servants.

Now God had intended that his people, Israel, should always trust him to care for them and to deliver them from their troubles. He did not want them to trust in their own strength, as the people of other nations trusted. But when the kingdom of Israel grew so strong that neighboring kingdoms were afraid to oppose it, then the temptation came to David to trust in his army as did the kings of mighty nations around him. The more he thought about this temptation the greater his desire grew to know just how many soldiers he had in his kingdom. He wanted to know how large an army he could raise if it should become necessary for him to begin a great warfare.

God saw that David was forgetting to trust in him. And God was not pleased with this desire of the King. Neither was Jō'-ăb, the captain of David's army, pleased when he heard of the King's plan. He said, "This thing is not right." But he obeyed his master, and went out with other captains to count the number of soldiers in the land.

Early one morning not long after David had sent the captains away on an errand, God sent a faithful prophet to speak to the King. He said, "Your desire to count the number of the soldiers of Israel is not right. You have brought God's displeasure upon your people, and they must be punished for this sin."

David listened to the prophet, and he began to understand why Jŏ'-ăb had not wanted him to carry out his plan. He saw how he was causing his people to trust in their own might and wisdom instead of depending wholly upon God to help them, as in other days. So David humbled himself and prayed to God for forgiveness.

While God was ready to forgive, yet he knew that the people everywhere must know that David's plan had been unwise. So he sent his prophet, Gad, to speak again to the King. And Gad came to David and said, "God has sent me to tell you that you must choose one of these three things for a punishment because of your sin: First, a famine of seven years. Second, a warfare of three months in which your enemies shall gain the victories over you. Third, a pestilence lasting three days, when many people in your land shall die."

David felt very sorry when he saw that his people would have to suffer because he had led them to do wrong. He told the prophet that it was hard for him to decide which of the three things to choose, as his people would need to suffer in each of them. But he said, "It will be better to fall into the hand of the Lord than into the hand of our enemies, for the Lord has great mercy." So David chose the three days' pestilence.

Then God sent a great pestilence through the land of Israel, and many of the mighty soldiers whom David had trusted to help deliver his kingdom in times of trouble died of the pestilence. Everywhere in the land there was death and sorrow, and David's heart was made very sad. When the angel of death came to strike the soldiers who lived in Jerusalem, God caused David to see the angel standing with his sword drawn over the city. And the King cried to the Lord when he saw the angel, and said, "I have sinned, and I have done wickedly; but these sheep, what have they done? Let your angel strike me instead of these innocent people."

God heard David's prayer, and he did not allow the angel to destroy any more people. He told David to build an altar on the spot where he had seen the angel standing. And David called his nobles, and hurried to obey God's command.

Now the angel had stood on the top of a mount called Mŏ-rī'-ăh, which was inside the walls of Jerusalem. And a man named Ă-raû'-năḥ owned a threshing-floor at this very place. He was busy threshing his grain when he saw the King and his nobles coming toward him, so he left his work and ran out to bow down low before David. He had not seen the angel standing near by. David told Ă-raû'-năh at once that he had come to buy the threshing-floor as he wished to build an altar upon it. Ă-raû'-năh said he would gladly give it to the King; but David refused to take it without paying the full price.

After building the altar, David laid burnt offerings and peace-offerings upon it and prayed earnestly to God. And God answered by sending fire from heaven to burn up the offerings David had given **for** his sin.

David was pleased when God sent the fire to burn up his offering, and he prepared at once for the building of a temple for God upon Mount Mō-rī'-ăh. Long before this time he had wished to build such a house for the worship of God, but the prophet had told him that God did not want him to build the temple. Now David planned to get everything ready that his son Solomon might build this beautiful place. And God was pleased with David's plan.

———————•———————

STORY 23

WHY SOLOMON RODE UPON THE KING'S MULE

1 Kings 1:1—2:12

David was now an old man, and he could no longer go out among his people. Day after day he lay upon his bed in the beautiful palace at Jerusalem, waiting to die. He had ruled Israel for many years, and God had blessed him with much honor and with great riches. Now his people knew that soon he must die, and they were wondering who should be the next king to sit upon his throne.

One of Solomon's elder brothers thought he would rule the people in his father's place. Perhaps he knew that God had chosen Solomon to be the next king; but he was proud like Ăb'-să-lǫm, and he did not care to please God. He wished to become the king instead of Solomon. So he prepared chariots for himself and appointed fifty young men to run before him as he rode through the streets of Jerusalem. People looking on would believe that he was a great ruler whom every one should respect, so he thought. Because David had always allowed him to do just as he pleased. Ăd-ō-nī'-jăh believed he could easily become king in his father's stead

One day Ăd-ō-nī'-jăh called his friends together and made a great feast for them in a valley just outside the walls of Jerusalem. Jō'-ăb, the captain of David's army, and Ă-bī'-ă-thär, the high priest, were with Ăd-ō-nī'-jăh. They planned to make him king of Israel after the feast should be ended, and they were rejoicing together and having a very good time indeed.

But Nathan, the prophet of God, was troubled. He knew God had chosen Solomon to sit upon David's throne, and he feared that David did not know of Ăd-ō-nī'-jăh's plan to take this place instead of Solomon. So Nathan came to Băth'-shĕ-bă, Solomon's mother, and told her what was happening in the valley just outside the city wall.

Now David had promised Băth'-shĕ-bă that her son, Solomon, should be the king after him, and she, too, was troubled when she heard about Ăd-ō-nī'-jăh's doings. She hurried to David's bedside and asked if he had forgotten about his promise to make Solomon the next king of Israel. David said that he remembered the promise very well, and that God had chosen Solomon for the throne. Then Băth'-shĕ-bă told the old King that Ăd-ō-nī'-jăh and his friends were planning to take the kingdom away from Solomon.

While Băth'-shĕ-bă was speaking, Nathan called to see David. He asked if David had given permission to Ăd-ō-nī'-jăh to take the throne after him. Then he told about the feast which was being held in the valley that very day, and he said, "The people are eating and drinking with your son Ăd-ō-nī'-jăh, and they are calling him their king."

David remembered the troubles that his wicked son Ăb'-să-lŏm had caused, and he feared that Ăd-ō-nī'-jăh would cause much trouble, too. So he thought that before his own death it would be wise to have the young Prince Solomon anointed as king. He told his servants to bring his own mule from the stable and place Solomon upon it, then to go with him to Gī'-hŏn, where the priest Zā'-dŏk should anoint Solomon with oil. Then he commanded that all his servants should blow their trumpets and cry aloud, "God save King Solomon!" Afterwards they should bring him back to the city and place him on the throne.

Nathan called the priest and one of David's brave soldiers and they quickly obeyed the King's orders. And many people of the city saw Solomon riding on his father's mule, with his father's servants attending him, and they began to shout for joy, because they knew Solomon had been made the king that day. The noise of their rejoicing was heard in the valley where Ăd-ō-nī'-jăh and his friends were feasting.

Jō'-ăb, the captain of David's army, heard the sound of trumpets and he said, "There is an uproar in the city." Being a brave soldier,

DAVID TELLING SOLOMON TO BUILD THE TEMPLE

DAWN OF DAY OVER JERUSALEM

The pilgrim of Palestine returns again and again to enjoy this panorama of the Holy City—its domes, spires, and housetops, all burnished under the light of the morning sun. A giant old olive tree, one of the number which still grace Mount Olivet, frames the scene. The view extends across the Valley of the Kedron toward Mount Moriah, upon which stands the famous Dome of the Rock, on the reputed site of Solomon's Temple, and upward into the heart of Jerusalem.

he wished to go at once to find out the cause of the excitement in Jerusalem. But while he was speaking a messenger came to tell what had
taken place.

Ăd-ō-nī'-jăh was frightened when he heard that his father had made
Solomon to be the king of Israel. His guests, too, were afraid, and
they hurriedly left the scene of their feasting and returned to their own
homes. But Ăd-ō-nī'-jăh was afraid to go home. He knew Solomon
would hear what he had been doing, and he feared the new King would
cause him to be killed. So he ran to the tabernacle and caught hold of
the altar of God.

When Solomon heard that Ăd-ō-nī'-jăh had run to the tabernacle for
safety, he sent for his brother at once. Solomon was a peace-loving
man and did not intend to put any one to death. The servants told
Ăd-ō-nī'-jăh that the new King would deal kindly with him if he would
behave himself rightly, and Ăd-ō-nī'-jăh promised to do just as Solomon
had asked. Then Solomon permitted him to return safely to his own
house.

David did not live very long after these things happened. Before
he died he called Solomon to his bedside and urged him to obey God
always. He spoke to him about many things that should be done, and
urged Solomon to carry out his plans for the temple building in Jerusalem. In all, David had reigned as a king for forty years.

———•———

STORY 24

HOW GOD SPOKE IN A DREAM TO SOLOMON
1 Kings 3: 3-15; 4: 29-34; 10:1-13

God will help the ones who try
  In their work to please him well;
Others then will glorify
  Him, and of his goodness tell.

Solomon was not like his elder brothers, Ăb'-să-lǫm and Ăd-ō-nī'-
jăh. Instead of wishing to seem great in the eyes of every one, he felt
that he was too much like a child to know how to rule wisely over his
people. He remembered that God had helped his father, David, and he
wanted God to help him, too.

One day soon after he became King, Solomon took one thousand
burnt offerings to Gibeon, where a great altar stood, and there he sacrificed them to God. All day long he watched them burning; and while

the smoke rose from the altar toward the sky, he sent an earnest prayer up to God for help. When darkness came he lay down to rest, but still he longed to have God speak to him. Finally sleep came to his weary eyes, and while he slept he had a wonderful dream. He saw God standing near his bedside, and he heard God's voice saying, "Ask whatever you wish, and I will give it to you."

Solomon was just a young man, and there were many things that he might have desired. If he had been a selfish young man he would have asked for pleasure, or for great honor and riches. But Solomon did not ask for these things. At once he thought of the great work that was his to do, and he remembered how childlike he felt. So he answered, "O Lord my God, you have made me to be King instead of my father, David, and I am only a child; I do not know how to rule these people. They are the people whom you have chosen to call your own, and now I ask you to give me an understanding heart so that I may know how to rule them well, and that I may know right from wrong."

God was well pleased with Solomon's desire, and he said, "Because you have asked for wisdom instead of asking for selfish things, I am going to give you much wisdom, until you will be known in every nation round about because of your great understanding. And I will also give you what you have not asked for: great riches and honor I will give you, so that no king in any other land while you live shall be as wise and rich and honorable as you."

Solomon awoke and knew he had been dreaming. But he felt sure that God had spoken to him while he lay asleep, and he rose and went back to Jerusalem to the ark of God. There he offered more burnt offerings and peace-offerings, and made a feast to all his servants. And he began at once to judge so wisely that all his people were sure God was blessing their new King with great understanding. And they feared him and served him with willing hearts.

Soon the wisdom of Solomon was talked about in other countries. Down in Egypt, where many wise scholars lived, none were so wise as the new King of Israel. And visitors came from every land to hear him speak wise proverbs, and to hear the wonderful songs which he wrote. In the Bible many of his proverbs and songs are written, and we may read them in the books called Proverbs, Ecclesiastes, and the Song of Solomon.

One day after Solomon had been King for a long time, and after he had built the temple that David planned and many other beautiful houses, a visitor came from a far-off country to see him. This visitor was a woman, and she was queen of a country called Shē'-bă. In her

home country she had heard much about the wise King who ruled in
Israel, and she wished to find out for herself if he were quite as wise
as people believed him to be.

There were no railway-trains nor automobiles nor aeroplanes in
that long-ago time, and the Queen of Shḗ'-bă had to travel the distance
across the sandy desert with a slow caravan of camels, like the Arabs

SOLOMON'S DREAM

use for crossing the desert lands today. But when she came at last
to the end of her tiresome journey and saw all the splendors of Solomon's kingdom—his beautiful palaces and the wonderful temple, which
he had built for God's worship, the great host of servants who waited
on him, their rich garments and daintily prepared foods—when she saw
all these things and heard the wise answers that Solomon gave to all
her questions, then she was glad she had come to see these things for
herself. She said, ''I did not believe all the things I heard in my home
country, but now I see that not half of your greatness and wisdom had

been told to me." And she blessed the God of Solomon, who had given him such great wisdom and riches and honor.

The Queen of Shē'-bă brought rich presents to Solomon from her country, and he gave gifts to her from his kingdom. Precious gifts they were; and she stored them away for safe-keeping when she started with her train of servants on the long, dangerous journey back to her own land.

———•———

STORY 25

THE TEMPLE OF THE LORD, WHICH SOLOMON BUILT ON MOUNT MORIAH

1 Kings 5:1—9:9

While David was King of Israel he planned to build a beautiful house near his palace in Jerusalem and call it the temple of the Lord. He planned to build it just like the tabernacle had been built by Moses and his helpers in the wilderness, only this was to be a house of wood and stone instead of a tent.

But God did not want David to build such a place. He said, "You have been a man of war and you can not build a house for my presence to dwell in. Your son Solomon, who shall reign after you, will be a man of peace, and he shall build the temple." So David did not begin the work of the building, but he planned many things for the time when this work should be done. And before dying he explained his plans carefully to Solomon and urged the young King to carry them out.

Not long afterwards Solomon wrote a letter to Hiram, the king of Tyre, a country by the seashore. In that country many beautiful cedar- and fir-trees grew up on the Mountains of Lĕb'-ă-non, and Solomon wished to get wood from some of tnese trees to use in building the temple. He told Hiram about his purpose to build the house of God which his father, David, had planned to build, and asked permission to buy some of these trees.

Hiram had been a dear friend of David's, and now he was glad to help David's son. He allowed Solomon to send men to that country to work with his, Hiram's, servants in the Mountains, cutting down the great trees. After the trees were cut, the men dragged them to the seashore and threw them into the water, and they were floated down the coast to a place not very far from Jerusalem. Here they drew the wet logs from the sea and sawed them into boards.

While this work was going on, Solomon had other men digging great stones out of the earth and cutting them into shape for the foundation-stones of the new building. He ordered that every stone should be cut to fit another, so that all of them might be ready to go into their proper places when they should be brought to Jerusalem.

So great was the task of building the temple that Solomon appointed thousands of men to help in the work. They made every part ready to be put together with other parts without using nails or hammers. And they worked seven years on the building before it was finished.

DEDICATION OF SOLOMON'S TEMPLE

The temple stood on top of the mount, Mō-rī'-ăh, where David had seen the angel stand with the drawn sword stretched over the city. There, you remember, he bought the threshing-floor from Ă-rău'-năh and built upon it an altar to worship God. At the same place where his altar stood, the great altar of burnt offerings for the temple was built. This great altar was made of rough stones that had not been cut to fit each other, for so God had commanded his people to build the altars upon which they should offer their sacrifices to him.

Only the priests were allowed inside the inner court and the rooms of the temple, but around these Solomon commanded that a wide outer court should be built, and the men of Israel were permitted to walk in this outer court. No person other than a Jew, however, was allowed to pass inside the outer wall of the great building.

When the building was finished, Solomon called all the men of Israel to come to Jerusalem from every part of his kingdom. Then he went with them to the house of God and offered many sacrifices upon the great altar of rough stones. The ark of God was brought from Mount Zion and placed in the holy of holies, that inner room behind the great curtain, where only the high priest might go. And other furniture that belonged to the tabernacle was placed in the temple just as God had commanded it to be placed in the tent-house that Moses had built. When the priests had carried the ark of God and other furniture into the building, God filled the temple with a cloud just as he had filled the tabernacle with a cloud many years before. And all the people knew by this sign that God was pleased to let his presence dwell in the house that Solomon had built.

Solomon knew that God was greater than the house that he had built for him. He knew that God's presence filled all the heavens, and that God does not dwell in only one place, but that his presence is everywhere. He prayed a beautiful prayer to God in the presence of all the people, and asked God to let his blessings always rest upon that place. He asked that God would always hear the prayer of every one who should pray for forgiveness in that house. And when Solomon had ended his prayer, and all the people had finished their worship, he dismissed them and sent them back to their homes.

God spoke to Solomon in a dream again after the temple was finished. This time he said, "If you will walk before me as David, your father, did, with always a desire to keep my laws and to do my commands, then I will bless your children after you forever. But if you will forsake me, you or your children, to worship other gods, then I will despise this house that you have built for my name. And I will allow other nations to take away your kingdom and to bring much sorrow to your people."

STORY 26

THE LAST DAYS OF KING SOLOMON
1 Kings 11

Solomon ruled Israel for many years after he had built the beautiful temple of the Lord. During those years his kingdom rose to its greatest glory and power, and his fame was told in countries far and wide.

But Solomon's last days were not his best days. In the beginning of his reign he followed closely the good example of his father, who loved and served God. But as he grew older he married daughters of kings from other countries and brought them to live in his palaces at Jerusalem. These strange young princesses were idol-worshipers, and instead of learning to serve the God of Israel they brought their heathen gods to Jerusalem and worshiped them there. Solomon loved these young women and he thought it would be unkind not to do for them whatever they should ask. So when they requested him to build temples for their gods, he did so. That was not all; he even went with them into these heathen temples and bowed down before the heathen gods.

It seems strange that a man who had received so many great blessings from the Lord God of the whole earth should ever bow down before wood and stone to worship gods that can neither see nor hear, much less answer prayer. But Solomon, with all his great wisdom, seemed to forget the very One to whom he owed himself and all his wonderful success as a king. No wonder God was displeased with him. No wonder God allowed enemies to rise up to trouble Solomon in his last days. And finally God told him that the kingdom of Israel should be taken away from him forever, and that only one of the twelve tribes would honor his son as their ruler.

In his great wisdom Solomon had planned and erected many great buildings besides the temple and his palaces in Jerusalem. He had caused large storehouses to be built in different parts of his kingdom in which his servants stored away the grain and fruits which they gathered from the fields. He had many beautiful places in the land of Israel. All this work cost money, and he had taxed his own people and the nations that served him to raise the money for his building-work. This caused the people to become restless and to feel dissatisfied with him.

At this time there was a young man among Solomon's servants named Jĕr-ŏ-bō'-ăm. This young man toiled so faithfully that Solomon made him overseer of all his building-workmen. One day God sent a prophet to speak to Jĕr-ŏ-bō'-ăm as he was leaving Jerusalem.

Ă-hī'-jăh, the prophet, met Jĕr-ŏ-bō'-ăm in a field just outside Jerusalem, and stopped the young man to speak to him. Then he did a very strange thing indeed. He took off his new mantle, or cloak, and tore it into twelve pieces. Ten of the pieces he gave to Jĕr-ŏ-bō'-ăm, saying as he did so, "Take these; for surely the Lord God of Israel will tear the kingdom of Israel out of the hand of Solomon and will give ten tribes to you, because Solomon has turned aside to worship other gods. One tribe will the Lord leave for Solomon's son, for he will not forget his promise to David, that his children's children shall sit upon his throne in Jerusalem."

JERUSALEM FROM THE MOUNT OF OLIVES, AS IT IS TODAY

Solomon heard what the prophet had done; but instead of repenting of his wickedness as David did, he tried to kill Jĕr-ŏ-bō'-ăm. Knowing about the King's intention, Jĕr-ŏ-bō'-ăm ran away from the land of Israel and went to live among the people of Egypt. There he stayed until he heard that King Solomon had died.

PART FIFTH
STORIES ABOUT THE DIVIDED KINGDOM

1 and 2 Kings; 1 and 2 Chronicles; Jonah; Jeremiah

STORY 1

THE FOOLISH YOUNG PRINCE WHO LOST HIS FATHER'S KINGDOM

1 Kings 12:1-24

> Kindness pays in ev'ry dealing:
> Harsh words always bring distress,
> Hatred, and much bitter feeling—
> They were never known to bless
> Those in sorrow or in grief.
> 'Tis kind words that bring relief.

The young Prince Rē-hō-bō'-ăm grew up in the palace at Jerusalem during the years when the kingdom of Israel was in its greatest glory. He had seen all the wealth and splendor of his father, Solomon, and he had heard his father's rare wisdom spoken and sung throughout the court. He had lived in sight of the beautiful temple of the Lord, and he had seen people come from every part of the land to worship God at that place.

But Rē-hō-bō'-ăm had not learned to worship God. His mother, who had been a heathen Princess before she married Solomon, had not taught her son the religion of the Israelites. She had taught him to worship the gods in the idol-temple that Solomon had built for her at Jerusalem. And now Rē-hō-bō'-ăm was an idol-worshiper like his mother.

After Solomon died, Rē-hō-bō'-ăm was the next one chosen to sit upon David's throne. But the men of Israel were in no hurry to crown him. First they sent to Egypt and brought back the young man Jĕr-ŏ-bō'-ăm, who had run away after Solomon heard what the prophet Ă-hī'-jăh had told him in the field near Jerusalem. They took Jĕr-ŏ-bō'-ăm for their leader, and met with Rē-hō-bō'-ăm in the city of Shē'-chĕm, which was north of Jerusalem and nearer to the center of the land. Then they talked with Rē-hō-bō'-ăm and told him about their feelings; for they wanted the new King to promise certain things before they would accept him in the place of his father.

273

But Rē-hō-bō'-ăm was not ready to give an answer at once. He was not a thoughtful young man like his father had been. He cared more for pleasure and for riches than he did for wisdom. He did not know about the unhappy feelings of his people, for he had never been poor and driven to heavy work. He told the people to wait three days and then come again to hear his answer.

After the people went away, Rē-hō-bō'-ăm wondered what he should tell them when they should return. He decided to call the old men who

REHOBOAM TAKING THE YOUNG MEN'S COUNSEL

used to help his father rule the great kingdom, and ask them what he should say in answer to the people's request. Now this was a wise thing to do; for these old men understood how restless the Israelites were becoming during the last days of Solomon's rule, and they told the young prince to speak kindly to the people and promise to make their work easier.

But Rē-hō-bō'-ăm was not pleased with the old men's advice. He was very proud, and he thought it would not become him as a rich young Prince to speak kindly to servants, so he sent the old men away and called for the idle young princes who had grown up as his companions in Jerusalem. Them he asked what to do, and they urged him to speak roughly to the people and threaten to make their work harder than ever because they had dared to ask for easier services. "Teach them that as a king you will do just what you please," they said; and Rē-hō-bō'-ăm thought their advice sounded good, so he accepted it.

At the end of three days the people came again with Jĕr-ŏ-bō'-ăm to hear what Rē-hō-bō'-ăm would answer them. And he stood up in their presence and spoke harsh words, saying he would deal more severely with them than Solomon had dealt. He thought they would fear him and respect him if he should act like a stern ruler.

But Rē-hō-bō'-ăm was mistaken about his people. When they heard his answer, they cried, "Then we will not have you to rule over us. We will return to our own homes and we will fight before we will become your servants." And nearly all of them went away. Only the men of the tribe of Judah stayed to anoint Rē-hō-bō'-ăm as their king.

Rē-hō-bō'-ăm believed that the other people would soon become willing to acknowledge him as their king, too, so he sent one of his officers to them to collect money as his father had done. But the angry men took the officer and threw stones at him until he died. Then Rē-hō-bō'-ăm knew that the people were much displeased with him, and he feared them greatly. He called for his chariot, and rode in haste to Jerusalem to get away from them.

After he came to Jerusalem, Rē-hō-bō'-ăm decided to send soldiers from the tribe of Judah to fight against the men of the other tribes and compel them to return to his kingdom. But God sent a prophet to tell him not to send these men to fight against the other men of Israel, for there would never again be one kingdom as there had been under the rule of David and of Solomon. And Rē-hō-bō'-ăm listened to the prophet's words and kept the soldiers at home.

STORY 2

THE STORY ABOUT TWO GOLDEN CALVES
1 Kings 12:25—13:6

The people of the ten tribes who refused to crown Rē-hō-bō'-ăm for their king gathered in another great meeting and chose a ruler for themselves. They chose Jĕr-ŏ-bō'-ăm, and he set up his kingdom at Shē-chĕm.

Jĕr-ŏ-bō'-ăm remembered the words that the prophet Ă-hī'-jăh had told him, and he knew it was God who caused the people to choose him for their king. He remembered, too, that the prophet had said God would bless him very much if he would try to rule the people wisely and if he would seek to do right as David had done.

But Jĕr-ŏ-bō'-ăm had never trusted God so fully as David trusted him. He believed he should try to help himself as much as possible without expecting God to help him when he helped himself. He had seen the idol-temples that Solomon built for his heathen wives at Jerusalem. Perhaps he even knew that sometimes Solomon himself went into those temples to worship. Then when he had fled from Solomon to hide in Egypt he saw the worship of the Egyptians. These people, you remember, worshiped animals, and believed that cattle and cats and such things were sacred. They built large temples for sacred oxen, and worshiped them with sacrifices.

Jĕr-ŏ-bō'-ăm was afraid to let his people go down to Jerusalem to worship God in the beautiful temple, which Solomon had built. He thought they might wish to become one nation again with the people of Judah if they should go often to the temple. So he thought he would try to change their religion.

First he collected much gold; then he had it melted together into one great mass. From this mass he had two images of calves molded. These he set up before the people. Then he said, "It is too far for you to go all the long way to Jerusalem to worship God; you may worship him here in your own land. I will build two places of worship; one at Bethel, in the southern part of the land, and the other at Dan, in the northern part of the land. And I will set up one of these golden calves in each place, for these are the gods which brought your fathers out of the land of Egypt."

Then Jĕr-ŏ-bō'-ăm built houses for the golden calves, one in Bethel and one in Dan. He made altars at those places to offer sacrifices to the gods; and he chose men to be priests, just as the Levites were chosen to be priests in the worship of the true God. He also appointed feast-days at the same time of year as the feasts were held at Jerusalem, because he did not want his people to go down to worship at Jerusalem at any time.

This was a great sin, and God was much displeased with Jĕr-ŏ-bō'-ăm. He would have kept the people of Israel from uniting again with the people of Judah even if they had continued to go to worship at Jerusalem. But Jĕr-ŏ-bō'-ăm had not trusted God to keep the kingdom; he was trying to keep it for himself.

God sent a prophet to Bethel to cry out against the evil that Jĕr-ŏ-bō'-ăm had done by causing the people to worship the golden calves. When the prophet came, Jĕr-ŏ-bō'-ăm was burning incense at the altar that he had built at that place. The prophet came bravely up to the altar and told about some dreadful things that would happen upon it some day. He said that God would give a sign to prove the words were true that he had spoken about the altar. The sign was to be that the altar would suddenly fall apart and the ashes would pour out upon the ground.

Jĕr-ŏ-bō'-ăm became angry when he heard the prophet's words, and he commanded his servants to catch the man. He, too, reached out his hand to seize the man of God, but when he did so his hand became stiff and the flesh dried onto the bone. He could not move the hand at all.

Period of the
Divided Kingdom

Northern Kingdom — Israel
Southern Kingdom — Judah

Just at that moment the stones of the altar fell apart, letting the ashes pour down upon the ground, and Jĕr-ŏ-bō'-ăm knew that God was causing these things to happen.

Now the wicked King of Israel was very much frightened, indeed. He forgot that he had wanted to hurt the man of God, and he began to beg earnestly that the prophet would call upon the Lord and pray that his withered hand be made well. When the prophet prayed, God was merciful to Jĕr-ŏ-bō'-ăm and caused his hand to be restored as well as it had been before.

———•———

STORY 3

WHY A PROPHET WAS KILLED BY A LION
1 Kings 13: 7-32

The prophet who spoke to Jĕr-ŏ-bō'-ăm at the altar of Bethel had been warned by the Lord not to eat nor drink in that place, but to return at once to his own home, by a different road from that which he had traveled when coming to Bethel. So when Jĕr-ŏ-bō'-ăm urged him to stay a while and rest from his journey, the prophet answered that he could not because God had warned him not to eat nor drink in that place. Even the offer of a reward from the King did not cause the prophet to remain in Bethel.

When he turned to go away, some young men who were standing near hurried home to tell their father about the words that this man of God had spoken to the wicked King. Now their father was also a prophet, and he wished very much to see this brave man who dared to talk so boldly to the wicked ruler. He asked his sons which way the prophet of Judah had gone, and they told him. Then he called for his ass, and they saddled and brought the animal to him.

As the old man hurried along the way to overtake the prophet from Judah he decided to tempt him to disobey God. Presently he came upon a man sitting under an oak-tree by the roadside. He stopped his beast and asked, "Are you the prophet from Judah?" The man replied, "I am." "Then come with me," he said, "for I want you to eat bread at my home." But the prophet answered, "I can not go, for God has commanded me not to eat nor drink in this place."

The old man then told a lie to the prophet. He said, "An angel told me to bring you back to my home in the city of Bethel to eat bread." The prophet believed this lie, and he rose and went back with the old man to the city. But while he was eating and drinking God spoke to him and rebuked him for his disobedience. He told the prophet that he would surely be punished, for he had known what he was supposed to do and he did not need an angel to speak other words than God's words to him.

The prophet rose from his meal and started once more for his homeland. But he had not gone far outside the city when a lion came out of the woods and killed him. The lion did not try to eat his flesh, but stood quietly watching his dead body. And the ass upon which the prophet had been riding stood near by as if waiting for his master to rise up again and mount him. He did not seem to be afraid of the lion.

By and by some people came along the road, and they saw the lion and the ass and the body of a dead man lying between them. These people hurried to the city and told what they had seen. And the old man who had called the prophet back to eat bread at his house, said, "This must be the prophet whom the lion has killed. I will go and see for myself." So he commanded his sons the second time to saddle his ass, that he might ride out to see what had happened to the prophet from Judah. And he found the lion, and there, too, lying torn beside the road, he saw the prophet's body.

The old man was sorry when he saw what had befallen his friend. He picked up the dead body and placed it upon the ass and took it back to the city, and there he buried it in the grave that he had prepared for himself. Then he mourned for the dead man. And he commanded his sons to bury him, when he should die, in the same grave with the prophet who had been faithful to cry aloud against the sins of Jĕr-ŏ-bō'-ăm, but who had failed to obey all the words of the Lord.

WHAT THE BLIND PROPHET TOLD THE QUEEN OF ISRAEL
1 Kings 14:1-20

King Jĕr-ŏ-bō'-ăm and his wife, the Queen, had a dear little son whom they called Ă-bī'-jăh. He was a good child, and they hoped that some day he would become a strong man. But one day the child became sick, and for many days afterwards he lay upon his bed not caring any more to run about and play like other children.

When weeks passed by and still the little Prince lay suffering, his parents feared that he might die. Finally Jĕr-ŏ-bō'-ăm decided to ask a prophet of God whether his little boy would ever be well again. But he was afraid to have the Lord's prophet know that he was sending to find out. He knew he had not pleased God when he made the golden calves. He was afraid the prophet would reprove him for his wrong-doing. So he told his wife to go to visit Ă-hī'-jăh, the old prophet who had given him the ten pieces of a torn garment and had told him that he should become the first king of Israel.

Ă-hī'-jăh was now an old man, and he was blind. Jĕr-ŏ-bō'-ăm's wife dressed herself, in shabby clothes and pretended that she was some poor woman in trouble. Then she took ten loaves of bread and some cakes and a bottle of honey as a gift for the prophet, and started on her journey. Her heart was very heavy, for she loved her child and she was afraid he might never be well again. She hurried along the dusty road, wishing to finish her errand as soon as possible and return again to the bedside of the little Prince.

Although Ă-hī'-jăh was blind, yet the Queen did not deceive him. God had caused him to know that he would have a visitor and who his visitor would be. When the Queen came to the door, he said, "Come in, wife of Jĕr-ŏ-bō'-ăm, why are you trying to make me believe that·you are another woman? I have sad news to tell you today."

Jĕr-ŏ-bō'-ăm and his wife had forgotten that God might speak to a blind prophet as easily as to one who could see. So now the Queen was surprised to hear Ă-hī'-jăh's words. She came into the room and gave her offering to the blind old man. Then she listened while he told her the words of the Lord.

"Go home again to your husband," said he, "and tell him that God has said he must be punished because he has refused to do right and to rule his people wisely. He has made idols of gold and has caused his people to serve them and to cast the Lord behind their backs

COLONNADES OF HEROD, AND THRESHING FLOOR OF SAMARIA

In the days of the Divided Kingdom, Samaria was the capital of the Ten Tribes. In 722 B.C., the city was captured after a siege of three years by Shalmaneser, king of Assyria, and the kingdom of the Ten Tribes was ended. Later Alexander the Great took the city. In 109 B.C., Samaria was demolished entirely. The city was rebuilt and greatly embellished by Herod the Great, who named it Sebaste. Here are two columns of the original Street of Colonnades which encircled Herod's capital. All that remains on the site of the city today are a few ruins and a little village.

16

OFFERING SACRIFICES OF THANKSGIVING IN
ASA'S GOOD REIGN

Now instead of having blessings he shall have sorrows. This sick child, whom he loves, shall die, and shall be buried in honor and mourned by the people of the kingdom. But his other sons and daughters shall be killed and the kingdom shall be taken away from Jĕr-ŏ-bō'-ăm's house forever."

The prophet said that the little Prince would die at the moment when the Queen should enter her home city, and she would never see him alive again. So when she turned away from Ă-hī'-jăh's home her heart was very sad. Just as she entered her home city, little Ă-bī'-jăh took his last breath, and when she came to his room he was lying dead upon his bed.

The words of the prophet came to pass, and after Jĕr-ŏ-bō'-ăm died his son who took the throne was killed by another wicked man. Then all the children of Jĕr-ŏ-bō'-ăm were killed and their dead bodies were thrown out into the streets and into the fields for the wild dogs and the birds to eat. This was the dreadful punishment for Jĕr-ŏ-bō'-ăm's sin of idolatry in the kingdom of Israel.

———•———

STORY 5

THE STORY OF A KING WHO TRIED TO DESTROY IDOL-WORSHIP

1 Kings 15:8-24; 2 Chron. 14:1—16:14

A thoughtful young prince was growing up in Jerusalem during the years that Rē-hō-bō'-ăm and his son Ă-bī'-jăh ruled the kingdom of Judah. This young prince was Ă-bī'-jăh's son and Rē-hō-bō'-ăm's grandson. His name was Ā'-să.

When Ă-bī'-jăh died, after ruling Judah only three years, Ā'-să became the new King. And Ā'-să began at once to rule his people wisely. He had seen that the cause of all their trouble had been due to their forgetfulness of the true God, and now he endeavored to turn his people's minds back to the right kind of worship. He began by commanding his servants to tear down and destroy every idol they could find in the land, and to break in pieces the altars that had been built to worship strange gods.

One day Ā'-să learned that his own grandmother, who had been Queen since the time that Rē-hō-bō'-ăm ruled in Judah, was worshiping an idol. Ā'-să thought, "This will never do at all. My grandmother can no longer be Queen, for she sets the wrong kind of example before my people.'' So he refused to allow her to be Queen any longer, although she was an old lady. And he tore down her idol, stamped it in the dust, and then burned it near the brook outside the city. He wanted his people to forsake their idols entirely and turn to serve the true God.

For ten years King Ā'-să had peace in his country. During that time he strengthened his kingdom and ruled wisely. And his people loved him. Then God allowed a strong army from the country of Ē-thĭ-ō'-pĭ-ă to come against his kingdom and try to destroy it. Ā'-să's soldiers could not drive this enemy away. But Ā'-să believed it would be just as easy for God to drive away a strong enemy as a weak one, so he prayed earnestly, and God heard his prayer. The Ē-thĭ-ō'-pĭ-ăns were defeated before Ā'-să's men and they ran back toward their own land. Ā'-să and his soldiers followed them and found many valuable things that these frightened strangers had thrown away in their haste to escape. God caused his fear to fall upon the people who lived in the country places where Ā'-să and his soldiers followed after the Ē-thĭ-ō'-pĭ-ăns, and from these places Ā'-să's men gathered many sheep and cattle to take back to Jerusalem. So this was a great victory for the King of Judah and his people.

After this victory God sent a prophet to speak to Ā'-să and urge him to be always true. The prophet said, ''The Lord is with you now, for you are trying to please him. If you will ask his help at any time, he will bless you; but if you forsake him as your fathers have done, then he will forsake you.'' And Ā'-să decided to keep true to God.

Soon the people who lived in the kingdom of Israel began to hear that God was blessing the King of Judah, and they went again to worship the Lord in Jerusalem. They brought many animals for sacrifice, and they joined with Ā'-să's people in seeking God with their whole hearts. And God was well pleased with them. For many years he did not allow an enemy to trouble the land of Judah.

But Bā-ăsh'-ă, the king of Israel, grew jealous of Ā'-să because some of his people had gone to live in Judah. He planned to build a strong city at the southern part of his country and station soldiers there to prevent any of his people from going down into Judah to worship God. Neither did he want any of the people from Judah to come up into his kingdom, for fear they would teach his people to love God and try to go to Jerusalem to worship.

King Ā'-să heard about Bā-ăsh'-ă's plan and he was much displeased. He tried to think of a way to prevent Bā-ăsh'-ă from carrying out his plan. But he did not ask God to help. Instead, he took some gold and silver coins out of the money-box in the temple and sent them as a gift to a heathen king who lived north of the kingdom of Israel. He asked that king to trouble Bā-ăsh'-ă's country on the north and cause him to leave his work at the southern part of his land. The heathen king did as Ā'-să requested, and Bā-ăsh'-ă left his work and hastened up to drive his enemy away. While he was gone, Ā'-să and his soldiers destroyed all the work that Bā-ăsh'-ă had done in trying to build the strong city of Rā'-măh.

God sent a prophet to tell Ā'-să that he had done wrong by asking a heathen king to help him instead of asking help from the Lord. "Because you have done this," the prophet said, "you shall have wars as long as you live." But Ā'-să did not believe the words of the prophet. He became angry and commanded his servants to cast the prophet into the prison-house.

Some years later King Ā'-să became diseased in his feet, and he suffered a great deal. But he did not ask God to heal him of his disease. He spent much money hiring doctors, who tried to cure him, but they could not. After two more years Ā'-să died and he was buried in his own sepulcher, or tomb, in Jerusalem. He had ruled as King longer than any of the kings of Judah before him.

STORY 6

WHY BIRDS FED A PROPHET BY A BROOK NEAR JORDAN
1 Kings 16: 29—17: 24

Things were not going well in the kingdom of Israel, where the people were worshiping the golden calves instead of the true God. Each new king who sat upon the throne did just as wickedly as the king who ruled before him, and sometimes even worse. Finally, in the last years that Ā'-să ruled in Judah Ahab took the throne of Israel.

Now Ahab was not fit to be a king. He did more evil in the sight of the Lord than any king who had ruled before his time. Not only did he worship the golden calves which Jĕr-ŏ-bō'-ăm had made, but he married Jĕz'-ĕ-bĕl, a wicked princess, who brought her heathen religion into his land. And Ahab built temples for her gods and went into the temples to worship the gods with her. Ahab's wife brought much distress into the land of Israel. She was not satisfied to see her husband worshiping her idols; she wanted to destroy all the true religion out

ELIJAH BEING FED BY THE RAVENS

of the land. She brought many priests of Bā'-ăl from her home country and commanded that all the prophets of the Lord should be killed. And her wickedness was great before the Lord.

One day Ahab was much surprized to see a strange-looking man, dressed in a hairy mantle, standing before him. This man was the prophet Ē-lī'-jăh, and God had sent him to speak to the King of Israel. Before the King had time to ask his visitor what he wanted, Ē-lī'-jăh said to him, "As the Lord God of Israel lives, before whom I stand, there shall be neither dew nor rain any more in all your land until I announce it." Then Ē-lī'-jăh turned and walked away as suddenly as he had come.

At first Ahab paid no attention to what Ē-lī'-jăh had spoken. But when the days began to pass and no more dew formed on the ground, Ahab remembered Ē-lī'-jăh's words. He sent men out to search everywhere for this strange-looking prophet; but they could not find him. And Ahab grew alarmed. He knew there would be a famine in his country if there should be no more dew nor rain, so he sent to other countries, asking the kings to help him find the man who had brought trouble and sorrow upon him and upon his people.

Now God had told Ē-lī'-jăh where to go to hide from King Ahab. And Ē-lī'-jăh had walked rapidly away from the King's palace to a hiding-place by the Brook Chē'-rĭth. Here, when the rains no longer fell, he could drink water from the Brook that trickled over the rocks at his feet. And here the birds brought bread and meat to him every morning and every evening, just as God had said they would do.

But when the days passed by and no rain fell anywhere in the land, the water of the Brook began to dry up. Ē-lī'-jăh saw that it was not going to last much longer, and perhaps he wondered what he should do. Then God spoke to him again and told him to leave his hiding-place and go to a heathen city called Zăr'-ĕ-phăth. God said that a widow would take care of him in that city. And although Ē-lī'-jăh had to cross through the land of Israel, he was not afraid to obey God's voice.

Near the gate of Zăr'-ĕ-phăth Ē-lī'-jăh noticed a poorly dressed woman gathering sticks to burn. He saw by her dress that she was a widow, and he thought, "Perhaps this is the widow to whom the Lord has sent me." So he spoke to the woman and asked her for a drink of water. Although she did not know him, the widow started into the city to get water for him to drink. Then Ē-lī'-jăh called her and said, "Please bring me a little food also, for I am very hungry."

Now the widow stopped and turned around to speak to the stranger who was asking for both water and food. She said, "I have no bread to give you. I have only a handful of meal and a little oil in my house, and I was picking up sticks when you came, intending to make a fire to bake my last bit of food for myself and my son before we die of hunger."

"Do not be afraid," said Ē-lī'-jăh; "do just as you had planned, but first make a little cake for me and then bake cakes for yourself and

ELIJAH RESTORES THE WIDOW'S SON

for your son. For the Lord God of Israel has commanded that your barrel of meal and your bottle of oil shall not become empty as long as the famine lasts."

The widow hurried into the city to do as Ē-lī'-jăh had commanded, and she found that she had plenty of meal to bake three cakes instead of only two. And every day after that time she baked cakes from her handful of meal and from her little drop of oil. And always she found just enough meal and just enough oil to feed herself and her family. And she kept Ē-lī'-jăh, the prophet, in her home for many months.

Now Ē-lī'-jăh was very thankful to the poor widow who showed such kindness to him. And when one day her son took very sick, and died. Ē-lī'-jăh felt sorry for her. She came to tell him about her trouble and said, "O man of God, have you come here to remind me of my sins, that I should be punished in this way?" And Ē-lī'-jăh answered, "Give me your son." He picked up the breathless body of the young child and carried it upstairs to the loft, where he hid himself. Then he placed the child upon his bed and prayed earnestly to God and said, "O Lord my God, let this child's soul come to him again." And the Lord heard Ē-lī'-jăh's prayer and restored life into the child. Then Ē.lī'-jăh took him in his arms and carried him down-stairs again to give him to his mother.

The widow was very happy when she saw that her son was alive once more. She said, "Now by this I know that you are a man of God, and that the words of the Lord in your mouth are true words."

STORY 7

HOW GOD SHOWED HIS GREAT POWER ON MOUNT CARMEL
1 Kings 18:1-40

After Ē-lī'-jăh's visit to King Ahab there was no rain nor dew in all the land of Israel nor in the countries near by for over three years. During that time the grass on the hillsides had withered and died and the fields everywhere had begun to look like waste-lands where nothing could ever grow again. The farmers could raise no crops or vegetables, and the people in the land were suffering from hunger. Many of their animals had died, and even the horses and mules that belonged to the King were gaunt, hungry-looking beasts.

Now Ahab was very sure that there might never be rain again until Ē-lī'-jăh would return to announce it. And he wished to find where Ē-lī'-jăh had gone, so that he could send and bring him back to his palace. Perhaps he thought he would punish Ē-lī'-jăh in some cruel manner to force him to let rain come again. So he commanded his messengers to search everywhere for the missing prophet. But always the messengers returned with the same report: "We have found no trace of him." No one seemed to know the least thing as to Ē-lī'-jăh's whereabouts.

One day Ahab called his chief servant Ō-bă-dī'-ăh, a good man, and said, "We must find pasture-land somewhere for these horses and mules or else they will die. Now, we will divide the land, and you go one way while I go the other way to search for springs of water where grassy spots may be found.'' So they two separated, each going in a different direction.

Ō-bă-dī'-ăh had not gone far when to his surprize he met a stranger dressed in a hairy mantle. He knew at once that this stranger was Ē-lī'-jăh, and he fell on his face before him, crying, ''Are you my lord Ē-lī'-jăh?'' The stranger replied, ''I am. And now hurry back to Ahab and tell him that I have come.''

Ō-bă-dī'-ăh was very much afraid to obey the prophet's command. He feared that Ē-lī'-jăh would disappear as soon as he should turn back to speak to the King, and then he knew Ahab would become so angry that he might kill him. So he told Ē-lī'-jăh how carefully the King had searched for him, not only in the land of Israel, but also in the neighboring kingdoms. And he said, ''The King knows that I, his servant, fear the Lord, and if I tell him that you have come and then he can not find you, he will believe I have hidden you as I hid the prophets of the Lord whom Jĕz'-ĕ-bĕl, the Queen, tried to kill. And he will surely take my life.''

Ē-lī'-jăh spoke encouraging words to Ō-bă-dī'-ăh and promised to show himself to King Ahab that very day. So the servant turned and ran hurriedly back to overtake his ruler and to tell him that Ē-lī'-jăh had come.

When Ahab heard that Ē-lī'-jăh had been found, no longer was he interested in finding pasture-land for his starving animals. Now he wanted to see the strange-looking prophet who, he believed, had dared to bring so much trouble upon him and upon his people. So he hurried back with Ō-bă-dī'-ăh to the place where Ē-lī'-jăh had met him.

Because Ē-lī'-jăh knew God had sent him to speak to the angry King he was not at all afraid when Ahab came near and asked, ''Are you the man who has been troubling my country?''

Ē-lī'-jăh answered, ''No, I am not the man who has been troubling your country; you and your father's house are the guilty ones. You have forsaken the commandments of the Lord God and have worshiped the gods of the heathen, and by doing so you have brought this trouble upon yourselves.''

Ē-lī'-jăh instead of Ahab, seemed to be the chief speaker in this meeting, just as he had been in their first meeting over three years before. Now he told the King to call all the prophets of the idol Bā'-ăl, whom Jĕz'-ĕ-bĕl had brought into the land, and bring them to Mount Carmel, and all the people of the kingdom, too. And Ahab hastened to do just as the prophet said.

ISRAEL UNDER THE DIVIDED KINGDOM

After the death of Solomon, the kingdom was divided. The northern kingdom was called Israel and the southern kingdom Judah. Because the kings and their subjects forsook God, God sent prophets to warn them. The first of these prophets was Elijah, who appeared to the wicked Ahab, king of Israel, and told him that no more rain should fall in Israel until he would announce it. At the end of three years Elijah prayed for rain, on Mt. Carmel, and God sent rain. Following this, because of threats of Jezebel, Ahab's wife, Elijah fled to the wilderness south of Judah, where he lay down under a juniper tree to die. But God, through an angel, encouraged him and he went on.

Elijah established a school for prophets at Bethel. Elisha, one of the young prophets, took Elijah's place when God called Elijah home. Elisha performed many miracles, one of which was restoring a dead child to life.

Another prophet in the northern kingdom was Jonah, who because he disobeyed God, was punished by him. The prophet Amos reproved Israel for worshiping a golden calf instead of the true God.

When the great host of curious people came together at the meeting-place, there they saw the man whom their King had been searching for during the dreary years of famine. And they listened quietly while Ē-lī'-jăh spoke to them.

"Why are you following first one god and then another?" asked the prophet. "If the Lord be the true God, why not follow him? but if Bā'-ăl be the true God, then do not turn again to follow the Lord."

The people were not ready to answer Ē-lī'-jăh, so he told them that he had come to prove to them that very day which is the true God. He said, "I and the prophets of Bā'-ăl have met with you here. I am only one, and Bā'-ăl's prophets are four hundred and fifty men. Now I ask that you bring two bullocks for sacrifices, and we will build two altars and will prepare our sacrifices and lay them on the altars, and the God who will answer by fire, let him be the God."

Ē-lī'-jăh's words pleased the people, and they quickly brought the offerings for the sacrifices. They wished to see what would happen next.

Ē-lī'-jăh then told the prophets of Bā'-ăl to choose which bullock they wanted, and he took the one that was left. He told them to build their altar and offer their bullock first, and call upon Bā'-ăl to send fire from heaven to burn up the sacrifice that they offered.

There were many of Bā'-ăl's priests, and it did not take them long to prepare everything ready for the offering of their bullock. But when they began to pray to Bā'-ăl, no answer came. They cried earnestly from morning until noonday, and still no fire fell. Ē-lī'-jăh stood by, watching. He knew Bā'-ăl could never send fire from heaven, and he said to the prophets, "Perhaps you should cry louder, for Bā'-ăl may be sleeping. Or he may be gone on a journey, or he may be talking with such a loud voice that he can not hear your prayers." The prophets cried louder than ever, and danced about their altar, cutting themselves with sharp knives until the blood streamed down their bodies. They thought perhaps their god would be moved with pity if he should see them suffering; but still no answer came from Bā'-ăl and no fire fell from the sky.

By and by, when the time came for the evening sacrifice at the temple in Jerusalem, Ē-lī'-jăh called the people to come near and watch while he should rebuild the altar of the Lord, which had been torn down at that place. He chose twelve rough stones and piled them together for the altar. Then he dug a deep ditch around the altar, and after he had laid wood upon the altar and the sacrifice-offering upon the wood he commanded the people to bring four barrels of water and to pour them over the sacrifice. They obeyed, and he sent them again and again for more water, until they had emptied twelve barrels of water upon the altar, and it had soaked the wood and the meat and had run into the deep ditch, filling it to the brim.

When everything was ready Ē-lī'-jǎh called upon the Lord, and fire fell from the sky and burned up the sacrifice and the wood, and even licked up all the water in the ditch.

The people stood by, looking on in amazement. They had never seen such a wonderful sight before. Now they knew that Ē-lī'-jǎh's God was the true God, so they fell on their faces and cried, "The Lord, he is the God! The Lord, he is the God!"

STORY 8

THE LITTLE CLOUD THAT BROUGHT A GREAT RAIN
1 Kings 18: 40—19: 3

Ē-lī'-jǎh knew that his work was only begun when God sent the fire which burned up the sacrifice on Mount Carmel. He commanded the people to capture every one of the wicked priests of Bā'-ǎl and to take them down the mountain-side to the Brook Kī'-shǒn. There he and the people killed them all.

Ahab looked on in silence, not knowing what to do. He could not protect the wicked priests because all his people believed that Ē-lī'-jǎh's God was the only true God. He wondered what his wife, Jěz'-ě-běl, would do when she should find out that Ē-lī'-jǎh had made fun of her god, Bā'-ǎl, and that he had caused all of her priests to be put to death. While he was thinking about these things Ē-lī'-jǎh came near and said, "Go back upon the mountain, Ahab, and enjoy the feast, which the people have spread, for the famine is now ended and soon there will be a great rain."

Ahab could see no sign of a cloud in the evening sky, but he turned at Ē-lī'-jǎh's words and went up to the place of feasting. And Ē-lī'-jǎh climbed to the top of the Mount and knelt down there to pray. No one was with him now except his servant, and Ē-lī'-jǎh bowed his face to the ground and prayed earnestly that God would send rain. Then he sent his servant to look toward the sea for some sign; but the servant returned and said that he saw nothing. Ē-lī'-jǎh prayed again, and again he sent his servant to look for a sign from God; but the servant returned as before and said, "There is nothing." Seven times Ē-lī'-jǎh

MT. CARMEL, WHERE THE PRIESTS AND PROPHETS MET

prayed and seven times he sent his servant to look for a sign from God. And the seventh time the servant came back and said, "A little cloud like a man's hand is rising out of the sea."

Ē-lī'-jăh took this for a sign from God that his prayer for rain had been heard and would be answered. He sent his servant to tell Ahab that he should make his chariot ready at once and hasten back to his home in Jĕz'-rĕel, before the rain should overtake him.

Ē-lī'-jăh wrapped his hairy mantle about his body and ran down the mountain-side to go to Jĕz'-rĕel, too. He was very happy because God had shown such wonders in Israel that day. He believed that now the people of Israel would be ready to worship the true God and forsake Jĕz'-ĕ-bĕl's wicked religion. As he ran the strong winds blew and the sky grew darker with the coming storm. Soon the rain began to fall in torrents, and the brooks overflowed their banks and the dry, thirsty ground drank in the fresh water. But Ē-lī'-jăh did not mind the rain at all. He was very happy because God had heard and answered his prayers.

Ahab knew that Ē-lī'-jăh too had come to Jĕz'-rĕel, for he had seen the prophet running before his chariot. Now he hurried to his palace to tell Jĕz'-ĕ-bĕl all that had happened on the Mount. However displeased the King had been with Ē-lī'-jăh's doings that day, he did not feel able to punish the man of God. But he believed that his wicked wife could plan some way to punish him, and in this he was not mistaken.

Jĕz'-ĕ-bĕl flew into an angry rage when she heard how Ē-lī'-jăh had caused all her priests to be killed. She sent a messenger hurriedly to the prophet, saying, "Tomorrow at this time if I have not made your life as the lives of my priests whom you have slain then let the gods kill me, too." And Ē-lī'-jăh, hearing these words, rose up quickly and ran with his servant out into the dark, stormy night to escape from the wrath of the wicked Queen.

STORY 9

WHAT AN ANGEL FOUND UNDER A JUNIPER-TREE IN THE WILDERNESS

1 Kings 19: 3-21

One day God sent an angel on an errand into the wilderness south of Judah. Down there in the wilderness, all alone, was a man who was very unhappy, and God wanted the angel to comfort him. So the beautiful angel hurried on his errand, glad for a chance to help some one in trouble. And presently he saw a juniper-tree, and under the tree he saw a man lying on the ground fast asleep. This man was Ē-lī'-jăh, the prophet, who had run away from the angry Queen of Israel.

Now Ē-lī'-jăh was very unhappy indeed. He had not expected that his great victory on Mount Carmel would come to such a sudden end. He had hoped that Jĕz'-ĕ-bĕl would see how God was striking a terrible blow at her false, wicked religion; but Jĕz'-ĕ-bĕl had not paid the slightest attention to what God had done. She had tried to vent all her wrath upon the man who had dared to set up another God in place of Bā'-ăl. And Ē-lī'-jăh was disappointed, and very unhappy.

"Where shall I go to hide?" thought Ē-lī'-jăh, as he ran out of the gate of Jĕz'-rēel that dark, stormy night. "I can not return again to the widow's home in Zăr'-ĕ-phăth, for some one will surely find me there. I can not hide in Judah, for the King of Judah is friendly with Ahab and he will deliver me into the hand of my enemy." So Ē-lī'-jăh and his servant had run southward. As they passed through Judah, Ē-lī'-jăh had left his servant in Judah, but he himself had run farther south into the great wilderness. And there, under the boughs of a juniper-tree, he had stopped to rest from his flight, and there he was, fast asleep, when the angel found him.

THE ANGEL FINDING ELIJAH

The angel did not waken Ē-lī'-jăh at once. First he kindled a fire, and baked a cake upon the coals. Then he touched the sleeping man and roused him, saying, "Rise up and eat." And Ē-lī'-jăh opened his weary eyes and saw the food upon the coals near by and a bottle of water standing at his side. He was hungry, very hungry, and he ate the food and drank the water. Then he lay down again and slept, for he was still tired and still very unhappy.

The angel came the second time to comfort Ē-lī'-jăh. And the second time he provided food and awakened the slumbering man, urging him to rise and eat. And when Ē-lī'-jăh rose up the angel said, "You have a long journey before you, and unless you take this food you will not have strength enough to go so far." Then the angel went away.

Ē-lī'-jăh ate of this wonderful food that the angel had prepared and he was not hungry again for forty days. He went on the strength of that food to the mountain where God first spoke to Moses, in the burning bush. And, finding a cave in the mountain, he crept into it to hide. For Ē-lī'-jăh was still very much discouraged.

While Ē-lī'-jăh was resting in the cave the Lord came near and said to him, "What are you doing here?" And Ē-lī'-jăh told the Lord what had happened in Israel, how the people had forsaken God's law and thrown down God's altars and even killed God's prophets. "I am the only one left," said the unhappy man, "and now they seek my life." God told Ē-lī'-jăh to come out of the cave and stand on the Mount before him. And Ē-lī'-jăh rose up to obey God's voice.

Now God caused a great and strong wind to sweep across the mountain and break the rocks in pieces. But Ē-lī'-jăh knew God was not in the great and strong wind. Then God sent an earthquake, which shook the ground under Ē-lī'-jăh's feet. But he knew God was not in the earthquake. After the earthquake ceased, God caused a terrible fire to break out, and the flames leaped up toward the sky and burned up many of the trees on the mountain-side. But Ē-lī'-jăh knew God was not in the fire. After the fire passed by and everything grew quiet on the mountain-side, Ē-lī'-jăh heard a still, small voice. And he knew that was God's voice, so he wrapped his hairy mantle about his face and stood in the door of the cave to listen.

God's voice asked the question again: "What are you doing here, Ē-lī'-jăh?" And the prophet answered as he had answered the first time, telling God about the sad conditions in Israel, and that he was the only one left who served God in all the land. But God said, "You are mistaken, for there are seven thousand people in Israel who have never worshiped Bā'-ăl." And God sent Ē-lī'-jăh back again to do the work of a prophet in the land of Israel, and to anoint a young man named Ē-lī'-shă to become the next great prophet after he should die.

Ē-lī'-jăh was not afraid to go back again to Israel, because he knew God was sending him there to work for him. And now he knew there were others living in Israel who loved and served the true God. He found the young man, Ē-lī'-shă, plowing with oxen in his father's field, and he anointed him to become the next great prophet, as God had commanded. Then Ē-lī'-shă broke his plow in pieces and killed the oxen, sacrificing them to God, and left his field to become the servant of this wonderful man who heard and obeyed God's voice.

AHAB AND THE BEGGAR KING

1 Kings 20

King Ahab had an enemy named Bĕn-hā′-dăd, who ruled over Syria, the country just north of Israel. Now this ruler was a very bitter enemy indeed. He hated the people of Israel and wished to take them for his slaves.

Bĕn-hā′-dăd and thirty-two of his friends, who also were kings, decided to make war against Ahab. They brought their armies together and came down into the land of Israel, to make their camp near Ahab's capital city, Să-măr′-ĭ-ă. While they were making their plans to capture the city and take Ahab away for a prisoner, God sent a prophet to tell Ahab that he would give him the victory over his enemies in the battle.

Ahab had only a very small army compared with the great host that had come from Syria; but he believed God would help him, and his few men went out bravely to make an attack upon Bĕn-hā′-dăd and his men. They found him and the kings drinking wine, and they soon put the whole army, with its drunken leaders, to flight. They killed many of the Syrians, and only a few of the entire host of the armies of the foreign kings ever reached their homes alive.

After this victory, God sent the prophet again to speak to Ahab, and to tell him that the Syrians would come back the next year to renew the fight. So Ahab prepared his army for another attack. And at the end of the year the Syrian army came again, in numbers as great as before. This time they did not pitch their tents near the city of Să-măr′-ĭ-ă, but on the plains in the north country of Israel. They believed that the cause of their defeat in the other battle was due to the fact that the God of Israel was a god of the hills, and Să-măr′-ĭ-ă was built upon a hill. Now they planned to fight in the valley, and they believed their gods would give them the victory.

Ahab gathered his soldiers in battle-line and started out to meet his enemy again. Now his soldiers looked like only a handful compared with the Syrian host. But Ahab was not afraid of the great host; for God's prophet had told him that because the Syrians believed Israel's God was only a god of the hills, now they should be defeated again to prove to them that Israel's God was able to help his people fight on the plains as well as on the hills.

When the battle began the men of Israel fought bravely and killed many of the Syrians. The other Syrians with their King, Bĕn-hā'-dăd, ran into a city near by, called Ā'-phĕk. They thought they could protect themselves from the men of Israel when once they were inside the city walls. But they did not know that it was God whom they were fighting against instead of only a few men. And no one can run away from God. When they came into the city the wall fell down upon them and killed many thousands.

Bĕn-hā'-dăd was not hurt, for he had hidden in a place where the crumbling walls could not reach him. But he was afraid to come out of his hiding-place lest the King of Israel find him and punish him severely—just as severely as he had intended to punish the King of Israel. After a while some of his servants came to him and urged him to come out of his hiding-place and meet Ahab. They told him to act humbly, and perhaps Ahab would treat him kindly.

Then some of those servants dressed themselves in sackcloth and tied ropes around their heads and came bowing down before Ahab just as if they were most willing to become his servants. They told him that their King, Bĕn-hā'-dăd, had sent them to ask that his own life might be spared.

Ahab seemed glad to hear that Bĕn-hā'-dăd was yet alive, and he spoke kindly to the men. He told them to bring their King from his hiding-place, and they hurried back to tell Bĕn-hā'-dăd about his words. Then they brought their King before Ahab, and Bĕn-hā'-dăd acted very humbly indeed. He did not seem at all like the proud King who had tried so hard to overthrow the kingdom of Israel. Ahab felt sorry for him and took him up into his own chariot to talk with him. Then he allowed Bĕn-hā'-dăd to return again to Syria.

But God was not pleased with Ahab for permitting this wicked King to escape with no punishment. He sent a prophet to speak with Ahab to tell him that he had done wrong. The prophet dressed himself like one who had been in the battle, and covered his face with ashes. Then he stood by the roadside and waited for Ahab to pass by with his chariot.

When the King's chariot came along the prophet cried out, and Ahab stopped to see what the poor man wanted. "During the battle a man brought a prisoner to me and told me to watch him closely," began the prophet. "He said that if the prisoner should escape I should have to give my own life for his. But while I was very busy attending to other duties the man got away, and I can not find him. Now what shall I do?" he asked the King.

"You must pay for his life with your own," answered Ahab. Then the prophet took the ashes off his face and Ahab saw who he was. And the prophet said, "Because you allowed Bĕn-hā'-dăd to escape without punishment when God gave him into your hand, now God will punish you instead, and you must pay your life for his life." Ahab listened sadly to these words, for he knew they had come from God. He saw when too late that he had made a great mistake by letting his enemy have freedom, and he rode back to his palace in Să-mâr'-ĭ-ă with a heavy heart.

STORY 11

HOW A KING'S POUT COST A MAN'S LIFE

1 Kings 21

> Listen, children, girls and boys!
> Pouting never pays!
> You may think it brings you joys
> By its easy ways,
> But it robs you, like a thief,
> And at last it brings you grief.

Who would have believed that a grown-up man would pout? But Ahab, the king of Israel, did it; and here we have the story:

Ahab had built a summer house in the little city of Jĕz'-rēel, which was north of Să-mâr'-ĭ-ă, his capital city. And around this summer house he had made wide, grassy lawns and gardens of beautiful flowers and trees. He had taken much time to make this summer house and its surroundings very beautiful, and whenever he came to Jĕz'-rēel he tried to think of some way to add to its attractiveness.

One day while the King was walking through his gardens and admiring their beauty, he noticed that just across the fence was a fine vineyard. Now the vineyard belonged to a man named Naboth, and Ahab thought, "I should like very much to have that vineyard for my own! I will speak to Naboth, and ask him to exchange it for another that I will give him in its place. Or I will pay for it with money."

Ahab hurried around to the other side of the fence to speak to Naboth. He said, "You have a good vineyard here, just outside my palace grounds. I should like to have it to make of it a garden. What shall I pay you for the place?"

But Naboth did not care to sell his vineyard. He said, "My father lived here, and my grandfather, and even my great-grandfather. I can not let you have this ground, for it is my inheritance." And he would not take another vineyard in exchange for that one, neither would he take money from the King, for he wished to keep the vineyard for himself.

When Ahab saw that Naboth could not be persuaded to part with the vineyard he turned and walked away. But he kept thinking, over and over, "I want that vineyard of Naboth's!" And the more he

thought about wanting the vineyard the unhappier he became because Naboth would not part with it. Finally Ahab went back to his home in Să-măr′-ĭ-ă, still very much disturbed in his mind because he could not get what he wanted.

When Ahab reached his home he went straight to bed. There he lay all day with his face to the wall, pouting! He would not eat, and he did not care to talk to any one. At last Jĕz′-ĕ-bĕl came into his room and asked, "What is the matter, Ahab, that you are so sad you will not eat?" And Ahab told her all about his experience at Jĕz′-rêel with the man who would not part with his vineyard.

Ahab knew that his wicked wife, Jĕz′-ĕ-bĕl, would find a way to get possession of that vineyard.

NABOTH REFUSING TO SELL HIS VINE-
YARD

And he was not at all surprized to hear her say, "Get up from your bed at once and eat some food. Stop thinking about your troubles, for I will get that vineyard for you."

Jĕz′-ĕ-bĕl's plan to secure the vineyard was very cruel. She wrote letters to the rulers of Jĕz′-rêel and sealed them with her husband's seal. In the letters she commanded the rulers to take Naboth and have him stoned to death on a false accusation. She told the rulers to have two very worthless men testify that they had heard Naboth speak wickedly of God and of King Ahab. For such an act as this the law commanded that a man should be put to death, and she knew the people who believed the words of the two men would be willing to throw stones at poor Naboth.

Not long afterwards a messenger came to Jĕz'-ĕ-bĕl, saying, "Naboth is stoned, and is now dead." And Jĕz'-ĕ-bĕl called Ahab and told him to go at once to Jĕz'-rĕel and take possession of the vineyard that he wanted, for the owner was no longer alive to refuse him. And Ahab climbed into his chariot and rode rapidly to Jĕz'-rĕel, thinking as he went, "Now I can have that vineyard, after all!"

But Ahab did not get much happiness out of that vineyard. While he was walking about between its long rows of grapevines, planning how he would change the place into a beautiful garden, suddenly he came face to face with the prophet Ē-lī'-jăh. And he stopped short, and said, "Have you found me, O my enemy?"

Ē-lī'jăh answered, "I have found you. And now God has sent me to ask if you have killed and also taken possession. O wicked man! the wild dogs licked the blood of poor Naboth, whom you have killed. And in the very same spot the wild dogs will some day lick your blood because you have done this great evil in the sight of the Lord."

Ahab trembled as he listened to the prophet's words. And he heard Ē-lī'-jăh say that not one of his children should go unpunished. And Jĕz'-ĕ-bĕl, the wicked Queen, should die an awful death,

ELIJAH MEETING WICKED AHAB

more terrible than the others, for she had caused Ahab to do so much evil in the land of Israel.

Naboth's vineyard was no longer a delight to Ahab. He tore his kingly robes as a sign of his grief, and dressed himself in sackcloth. Then he refused to eat food again, but this time he was not pouting, for he was trying to show God that he was sorry for his wrong-doing. And when God saw that Ahab was repenting, he told Ē-lī'-jăh that he would not allow Ahab's wife and children to be destroyed until after Ahab himself should die.

STORY 12

WHEN FIRE FELL FROM THE SKY AND BURNED UP SOME WICKED MEN

2 Kings 1

After King Ahab died, one of his sons became the King of Israel in his place. And this new King was wicked, like his father had been before him. He did not try to please God, but worshiped Bā'-ăl, the

RUINS OF THE BEAUTIFUL PALACE AT SAMARIA

idol that his mother had brought into the land of Israel. And he hated the people who tried to please God.

But Ā-hă-zī'-ăh, this new King, did not rule the people very long. One day after he had been King only a short time, he fell down through a lattice in his beautiful palace at Să-mâr'-ĭ-ă. And the fall hurt him so badly that it made him sick. For days and days he lay upon his bed suffering misery. He wondered whether he should ever be well again. Finally he called some of his men and told them to go down to the land of the Philistines and ask the god of those people whether he should be healed of the disease.

Ā-hă-zī'-ăh did not want to ask a prophet of the true God about his sickness. But the true God knew all about Ā-hă-zī′-ăh, and why he was sending to the god of the Philistines. And the Lord sent an angel to speak to Ē-lī′-jăh, the faithful prophet, and tell him what Ā-hă-zī′-ăh had done. The angel told Ē-lī′-jăh to go out and meet the messengers of the King who were going to the land of the Philistines, and to tell them that God had said Ā-hă-zī′-ăh would never be cured of his disease.

As the messengers were hurrying on their errand they were met by a stranger, who said, "Is there no God in Israel, that you must go down to the land of the Philistines to inquire of that idol whether your master will be made well of his sickness? Go back and tell him that the Lord God has said he will never be able to rise up from his bed again."

Ē-lī′-jăh turned and went away as suddenly as he had come, and the messengers decided to go back at once and tell the King what Ē-lī′-jăh had told them. So they hurried back to the palace, and when they entered the sick-room Ā-hă-zī′-ăh said, "Why have you come back so soon?"

"A strange-looking man met us," they answered, "and he asked if there is no God in Israel that you must be sending to the Philistines to inquire about your sickness. He said that because you are doing this you will never be cured of your disease, but will die from it."

The King knew that it must have been Ē-lī′-jăh, the prophet, who had spoken to his messengers. And he was greatly displeased with Ē-lī′-jăh. He wished to capture him and possibly put him into a prison-house. So he sent a company of soldiers to take Ē-lī′-jăh and bring him to Să-mâr′-ĭ-ă.

When the soldiers and their captain found Ē-lī-jăh he was sitting on top of a hill. The captain called to him and commanded him to come down. But Ē-lī′-jăh knew that the soldiers were wicked men, and he knew their King was angry with him and was planning to punish him because he had obeyed God. So Ē-lī′-jăh did not come down from the hill. He said, "If I am a man of God, as you have said, then let fire come down from heaven and destroy you all." And fire fell from the sky and burned up the captain and his men.

When this company of soldiers and their captain did not return with Ē-lī′-jăh, the King sent another company to capture him. And this second company was destroyed just as the first had been. Then the King was more angry than ever. He sent the third company, and commanded their captain to bring Ē-lī′-jăh back to Să-mâr-ĭ-ă.

The captain of the third company knew what had happened to the other captains and to their soldiers, and he was afraid of Ē-lī′-jăh and of his God. He did not stand at the foot of the hill and command the prophet to come down, as the other captains had done. He climbed to the top of the hill and fell down on his knees before Ē-lī'-jäh, and begged the prophet to spare his life and the lives of his soldiers. And the angel of God who often spoke to Ē-lī'-jäh now told him not to be afraid to go down with the captain to Să-mâr'-ĭ-ă, to see the King. So Ē-lī'-jäh rose up and wrapped his mantle around his shoulders and followed the captain back to Să-mâr'-ĭ-ă, to see the King.

When Ē-lī'-jäh came to the palace he walked boldly into the sick-room to speak to the King. He was no more afraid of meeting Ā-hă-zī'-ăh now than he had been of meeting the wicked Ahab in Naboth's vineyard. And he told Ā-hă-zī'-ăh the same words that he had told to the messengers.

God did not let the King harm Ē-lī'-jäh; but God caused Ē-lī'-jäh's words to come true. And not long afterwards Ā-hă-zī'-ăh died, and Jĕ-hôr'-ăm, his brother, ruled Israel in his place.

STORY 13

THE STORY OF A GREAT WHIRLWIND

2 Kings 2:1-18

Ē-lī'-jäh, the prophet, was now an old man. He had been a wonderful man. He had worked hard to destroy the worship of Bā'-ăl out of the land of Israel, and he had tried to turn the people back to serve the true God. But now he was old, and his work on this earth was ended. He was ready to go to heaven.

God had chosen another brave man to do the same kind of work as Ē-lī'-jäh had begun. This man was Ē-lī'-shă, the friend of Ē-lī'-jäh, who often went with him on his journeys. And Ē-lī'-shă knew the time had come when God was going to take away the old prophet. Ē-lī'-shă loved Ē-lī'-jäh very much, and he felt unwilling to let the old prophet leave him.

But the time had come when God wished to take Ē-lī'-jäh up to heaven. And Ē-lī'-jäh seemed eager to go. He visited the schools where the young prophets were studying about God, and perhaps he bade them all good-by. Then he urged Ē-lī'-shă to stay with them. But Ē-lī'-shă answered, "I will not leave you." So they went on together, and the young prophets followed far behind; for they knew that Ē-lī'-jäh, their faithful old teacher, was going to heaven that day. And they wished they might see him go.

When the two men, Ē-lī'-jäh and his friend, came to the River

Jordan, the old prophet took off his mantle, wrapped it together, and struck the waters of the Jordan with it. The waters parted at once, and a dry path appeared through their midst. Then the two walked across to the other side.

The young prophets soon lost sight of what was taking place on the other side of the river. They were too far away to hear Ē-lī'-jäh ask

Ē-lī'-shă what he should do for him before he should be taken away. And they were too far away to hear Ē-lī'-shă ask that a double portion of the old prophet's spirit might rest upon him. Ē-lī'-jäh knew that only God could bestow such a gift upon Ē-lī'-shă. So he answered his friend, "If you see me when I am taken away, then you shall know that God will give you a double portion of my spirit."

On and on the two men went, when suddenly a chariot of fire and horses of fire pushed between them and separated them. Then a great whirlwind came, and Ē-lī'-shă saw his dear old friend leave this world and start upward toward heaven in

ELIJAH GOING TO HEAVEN IN THE WHIRLWIND

the whirlwind. Ē-lī'-shă knew that Ē-lī'-jäh was leaving him forever. He looked upward and cried, "My father! my father!" Then the great whirlwind and the chariot and horses of fire and the old prophet Ē-lī'-jäh disappeared in the clouds, and Ē-lī'-shă could not see them any more.

But lying on the ground at Ē-lī'-shă's feet was the old mantle that Ē-lī'-jäh used to wear. And Ē-lī'-shă picked it up and started back to the land of Israel.

The young prophets stood watching by the side of the River long

after they had lost sight of the two men. And when Ē-lī'-shă came back
alone, they saw him. They saw him wrap Ē-lī'-jăh's mantle together,
just as the old prophet himself had done, and they saw him strike the
waters with it. Then they saw the waters part, just as they had parted
before when Ē-lī'-jăh struck them. And the young prophets said, "The
spirit of Ē-lī'-jăh is resting upon Ē-lī'-shă." So they hurried out to meet
him and bowed down at his feet, just as they had bowed down before
the old prophet who had gone up to heaven in the whirlwind.

Ē-lī'-shă was now master, or teacher, of the young prophets. And
the young men wished to send some of their number across the Jordan
to look for the body of Ē-lī'-jăh. They thought that perhaps the old
prophet's body might be left on top of one of the mountains in that
land. Ē-lī'-shă said, "Do not send, for you can not find Ē-lī'-jăh's
body." But when the young prophets kept urging him to let them send
of their men, finally he said, "Let them go."

For three days the servants searched everywhere for the body of
Ē-lī'-jăh. But they could find no trace of him. Then they came back,
and Ē-lī'shă said, "Did I not tell you that you should not send?" And
Ē-lī'-shă stayed for a while with the young men at the school of the
prophets in Jericho.

STORY 14

WHY TWO HUNGRY BEARS KILLED SOME CHILDREN FROM BETHEL
2 Kings 2:19-25

In the land of Israel was a city called Bethel, and in this city Jĕr-ŏ-
bŏ'-ăm, the first king of Israel, had set up a golden calf for his people to
worship instead of the true God. And for long years afterwards the
people of Bethel worshiped the golden calf and other idols. They did
not love God and they did not teach their children to love him.

But there were other people living near Bethel who loved God.
And they wished to see the true religion again planted in their country.
So they started a school in the city of Bethel, which they called a
"school of the prophets," like the school down at Jericho. And Ē-lī'-
jăh used to visit that school. Ē-lī'-shă had been with him the last day
when he visited the young men at that place.

Now after Ē-lī'-jăh had gone up to heaven in a great whirlwind,
Ē-lī'-shă took up the work of the old prophet and went from one place to

another, visiting the schools of the prophets and teaching the people of Israel to worship the Lord only. He also carried messages from the Lord to the kings of the land, just as Ē-lī′-jăh had done before him. And he had much work to do.

Ē-lī′-shă stayed in Jericho for a while after Ē-lī′-jăh was taken from him. And one day the men of that city came to him and said, ''You see that our city is built in a pleasant place, but the water that we must drink is not good. It causes much sickness and death.'' Ē-lī′-shă told them to bring him a new bottle with some salt in it. And when they did so he took the salt from the new bottle and threw it into the springs where the people went to draw their water. Then he said, ''From this time forth there shall be no more deaths caused by these waters, for God has healed them.'' And after that day the waters became pure and sweet.

Then Ē-lī′-shă started on his journey north and west to visit the school of the prophets at Bethel. As he came near to the city he met a host of children. Possibly they were going out to the country to have a picnic. They had seen Ē-lī′-shă before, and they remembered that he was the same man who used to come to their city with Ē-lī′-jăh to visit the school of the prophets. They had heard that Ē-lī′-jăh had gone to heaven in a whirlwind, but they only laughed. They did not believe that people would go to heaven in that way. Their parents were idol-worshipers, who were unfriendly toward the prophets of the true God. And no doubt these children had heard their parents speak unkindly about Ē-lī′-jăh and Ē-lī′-shă.

Now the children began to make fun of Ē-lī′-shă. They danced about him and mocked him and cried, ''Go up, bald head! go up!'' This was very wrong, for no one should make such fun of persons. And they were telling him to go up as Ē-lī′-jăh had done, for they did not like to have him visit their city.

Ē-lī′-shă knew these children would never grow up into good men and women. He knew they would worship idols and bring much sorrow to Israel if they should live. So he prayed to God that he would punish them for their wrong-doing. And as he went on his way into the city two hungry bears came out of the woods and caught the wicked children and killed forty-two of them. This was a terrible punishment, but it was God's way to teach those children who ran away to safety that it is very wrong indeed to make such fun of any one.

After Ē-lī′-shă's visit at Bethel he went to Mount Carmel, the place where God had so wonderfully answered Ē-lī′-jăh's prayers, and then he went back to Să-mâr′-ĭ-ă, the capital city of Israel.

STORY 15

ELISHA'S MIRACLE THAT SAVED TWO BOYS FROM BECOMING SLAVES

2 Kings 4:1-7

In the land of Israel there were both rich people and poor people, just as there are in every land today. And Ē-lī'-shă, the prophet, visited the poor as well as the rich. He listened to their troubles and comforted them, as a true friend will do. And the poor people whom he visited loved him. They were glad to see him coming toward their humble homes, and always made him feel that he was a welcome guest.

In one of the humble homes where Ē-lī'-shă sometimes visited, two bright-eyed little boys lived. They were brothers, and their father was one of the young prophets who loved and served the true God. These two little boys were happy even though their parents were poor. Every day they could run and play, and do chores about the house for their mother. They did not know that a great sorrow was coming into their home, which would rob them of their dear father. But one day the sorrow came. Their father grew sick and died, leaving them alone with their poor, widowed mother.

Then another sorrow came. One day a stern, rich man stopped at the door of that humble home and asked for the money that the father had borrowed before he took sick and died. Because the poor widow had no money to give him, the rich man said, "Then I will take your two boys to be my slaves." But he did not take the boys at once. He told the widow that he would give her a little time to collect enough money to pay the debt.

After the rich man had gone away the mother wondered what she should do. She had no money, and she did not know where she could earn enough to pay the debt. In her trouble she remembered the prophet Ē-lī'-shă, so she hurried to him and told her pitiful story.

Ē-lī'-shă listened, and he felt sorry for the poor woman. He wished to help her, so he asked, "What do you have in your house?" And the woman answered, "I have nothing except a pot of oil." The prophet knew that would be enough to help if she would obey him, so he told her to go home and borrow empty jars and bowls and pots from her neighbors. He urged her to borrow very many. "Take all those empty vessels to your home," he said, "and after you have shut the door, pour the oil from your pot into the empty vessels. When one vessel is full, set it aside and fill another.''

The widow hurried home and borrowed empty vessels from all her neighbors. When she had brought a great many into her humble home she called the boys into the room and shut the door, just as Ē-lī'-shǎ had told her to do. Perhaps the sons wondered, ''What is mother going to do now?'' Then she told them about Ē-lī'-shǎ's words, and they were eager to help her fill the empty jars and bowls.

THE MIRACLE OF THE WIDOW'S OIL

Never before had the boys seen so much oil as their mother poured out of her pot into the neighbors' vessels. They knew God was causing the oil to increase, so there would be enough to fill every empty jar. They carried the empty vessels to their mother, and helped to set them aside after they were filled with oil. How hard they worked! Finally their mother said, ''Bring me another jar''; but there was no other jar to bring, for all were filled with oil.

This wonderful oil was just like the oil that the poor widow had poured out of her own vessel. It did not disappear, like a dream, but it stayed in the pots and jars and bowls. And the widow hurried away again to speak with Ē-lī'-shă. She wanted to tell him what had happened to her pot of oil. And she wanted to ask him what she should do with all the oil that now stood in her humble home.

Ē-lī'-shă knew the widow would come again, and he was waiting to see her. He told her to go home and sell all the oil in her neighbors' vessels, and take the money to pay off the debt that her husband owed the rich man. And he said there would be money left for her and for her sons.

We are sure it was a very thankful woman who hugged her boys to her breast after the debt was paid. She knew the God of Israel took notice of poor people and their needs. And she was glad to teach her boys to love and serve such a God, who, through the miracle of his prophet, Ē-lī'-shă, had spared them from becoming slaves.

STORY 16

THE STORY ABOUT A LITTLE BOY WHO DIED AND BECAME ALIVE AGAIN

2 Kings 4: 8-37

Ē-lī'-shă went from one place to another, teaching the people to love and serve the true God. He visited in the homes of the rich as well as in the homes of the poor. And one day he came to the little city of Shū'-něm, where a rich woman and her husband lived, and their servants. The woman and her husband had no children. This woman invited Ē-lī'-shă and his servant into her home, and she cared for them as long as they stayed in Shū'-něm. She believed Ē-lī'-shă was a prophet of the true God, and she wished to show her respect to such a great man by entertaining him and his servant.

Ē-lī'-shă often passed through Shū'-něm on his journeys, and he stopped each time to rest at this kind woman's home. One day the woman said to her husband, "Let us build a room for this prophet, and place in it a table, a candlestick, a bed and a chair, that he may rest here with us whenever he comes to our city." So they built a special room for Ē-lī'-shă and his servant.

Not long afterwards Ē-lī'-shă passed that way again, and he was pleased to see the nice room that his kind friends had built for him.

He wished to repay them for their kindness, so he sent his servant to speak to the woman to ask her what they might do for her. But she told the servant that she needed nothing at all, for she was happy to live among her own people and she did not care for a special favor from any one, not even the king.

Ē-lī'-shă's servant noticed, however, that there were no little children playing about in that home, so he came back and told his master. And Ē-lī'-shă told the woman that because she had been so kind to him and to his servant, God would give her a little son. The woman thought this promise seemed too good to be true. But God had heard Ē-lī'-shă's words, and God gave her and her husband a baby boy.

A few years passed by and the child grew old enough to follow his father about. One day he went with his father out to the harvest-field, where the servants were cutting the ripe grain. As he ran here and there, playing in the warm sunshine, suddenly he became very sick. He called his father and cried, "My head! my head!" And his father told a servant to carry the child home.

When the servant came, bringing the sick little boy, the mother was alarmed. She took the child in her arms and held him on her lap until noon. Then he died. Now what should she do? she wondered. First she carried her dead child to Ē-lī'-shă's room and laid him on the prophet's bed. Then she called for a servant and prepared to go at once to find Ē-lī'-shă to bring him back to Shū'-nĕm.

It was a long ride to Mount Carmel, where Ē-lī'-shă and his servant were staying that day. But the woman did not think about the distance, for she thought only about the great sorrow that had come to her, and she believed the prophet could help her in her time of trouble. Perhaps as she hurried on the way she prayed that God would help her find the prophet.

Ē-lī'-shă saw the woman coming far down the road, and he sent his servant to meet her. He told the servant to ask if it was well with her, and with her husband, and with her child. So the servant ran forward and asked her the questions Ē-lī'-shă had bidden him. And the woman answered, "It is well." But she hurried on till she came to the place where Ē-lī'-shă was, and then she fell down at his feet and seemed to be in great distress.

Ē-lī'-shă was troubled; for God had not shown him what had happened to grieve the good woman who had been so kind to him. Finally the woman cried, "Did I ask you for a child?" Then the prophet knew that something had gone wrong with the little boy. So he told his servant to take his staff and hurry on to Shū'-nĕm and place the staff across the face of the child. But the woman was not satisfied. She said, "I will not go back with only the servant. You, Ē-lī'-shă, must come too."

Ē-lī'-shă's servant reached Shū'-nĕm first and found the body of the dead child lying on his master's bed. He placed his master's staff across the child's face, but no signs of life appeared. Then he went out of the room and started back to meet Ē-lī'-shă and the woman. When he came to them he said, "I have obeyed your words, but the child is not awakened."

Soon Ē-lī'-shă came and saw that the little boy was dead. He understood the grief of the mother, and he felt sorry for her. He shut the door of his room and began to pray earnestly that God would cause life

ELISHA RESTORES A BOY TO LIFE

to come into the child again. After praying he went up to the child and lay with his face upon the child's face and his hands upon the child's hands. And as he lay there the child's body grew warm. He rose up and walked about in the room, then went back again and lay upon the child as before. And then the child sneezed seven times, and opened his eyes.

Ē-lī'-shă called his servant at once, and told him to bring the woman. And when she came to his room he said, "Take up your son." She looked and saw that her child was alive again, but she bowed thankfully at Ē-lī'-shă's feet before she took the boy away.

ELISHA'S KINDNESS TO THE POOR

2 Kings 4:38-44; 6:1-7

There came a time when food was scarce in the land of Israel and the poor people had little to eat. During this time Ē-lĭ′-shă came to visit the young prophets who lived at Gĭl′-găl. And while he was there one of the young men went out to the field to gather some vegetables and green things to cook for dinner. By mistake he picked some poisonous gourds, which grew on a vine in the field, and he threw the gourds into the cooking-vessel with the other food.

When the men sat down to eat they discovered that their food was poisoned. Some had already eaten, and they cried to Ē-lĭ′-shă and said, "O man of God, there is death in the pot!" But Ē-lĭ′-shă did not seem to be alarmed. He called for some meal and threw it into the cooking-vessel that held the poisoned food. Then he commanded them to dish up the pottage and feed it to the hungry people. And the people ate, and they did not suffer any harm from the poisoned gourds.

While Ē-lĭ′-shă was staying with the poor people at this place, one day a man brought him a present of twenty loaves of barley bread and some ears of new grain in the husks. Ē-lĭ′-shă knew that the young prophets would enjoy eating this food, so he commanded a servant to prepare the loaves and the grain to serve to the prophets for their dinner. The servant was amazed. He knew there were one hundred hungry men to be fed, and he knew the barley loaves were very small. He knew the gift of food had been intended for only one man, and now Ē-lĭ′-shă was asking that it be given to one hundred men.

Ē-lĭ′-shă saw how astonished the servant was to hear his request. But he said again, "Give this food to the hungry people, that they may eat." Then he told the servant that God would bless the food, and that it would increase until there would be enough for all, and some left over. And the servant obeyed Ē-lĭ′-shă's command, and set the food before the hungry men. He saw that every man had as much as he wished to eat, and afterwards he picked up the scraps that they had left. And he knew that God, at Ē-lĭ′-shă's word, had increased the food in a wonderful way.

At another time a company of the young prophets went down to the Jordan River to build new homes for themselves. And Ē-lĭ′-shă was with them again. They cut down the trees along the River's bank to use in building their new homes. While they were busy at work an ax-head flew off from one man's ax and dropped into the River. At this place the River was deep or muddy, and the poor man could not see where the ax-head had fallen. He did not know what to do, for he had borrowed the ax and he was too poor to buy a new one for the owner. So he came to Ē-lī'-shă and told what had happened.

Ē-lī'-shă listened to the poor man's story, and then said, "Show me the place where the ax-head sank into the water." The man led him to the spot where the accident had happened, and Ē-lī'-shă cut down a stick and threw it into the water at the same place. Then as the men watched they saw the ax-head rise from the bottom of the river and float like a piece of wood. And Ē-lī'-shă told the man to reach out and pick it out of the water, before it should float down the stream.

This was another miracle that Ē-lī'-shă performed, for he made iron to swim. And the young men who saw the miracle wondered at the mighty power of God which was shown by this faithful prophet

———·———

STORY 18

HOW A LITTLE SLAVE-GIRL HELPED A HEATHEN MAN TO FIND THE TRUE GOD
2 Kings 5:1-27

The people who lived in the country just north of Israel were called Syrians. They were heathen people and had never been taught about the true God. They worshiped a god called Rimmon, and built temples for this god in their cities.

While Ē-lī'-shă was the prophet in Israel, the Syrians sometimes came down in small companies to steal from the Israelites. They would steal anything valuable that they could find and carry the stolen goods back to their own land to sell. They even stole children, and sold them for slaves to the rich people of Syria.

One time a robber band of Syrians came into the land of Israel and stole a little girl away from her mother's home. They stole other things, too, and then went back to sell them to their own people. They sold the little girl to the rich captain of the Syrian army, a man named Nā'-ă-măn, and Nā'-ă-măn brought the child to his wife to become her servant.

Nā'-ă-măn's wife was kind to her little servant, and after a while the child began to like her new home. Of course she missed her dear mother; but little slave-girls must be brave. And soon this little girl learned how to do many things for her mistress, and she learned to love her.

When the little slave-girl had been in Nā'-ă-măn's home for a while she found out that a dark cloud of sorrow hung over that beautiful home. She found out that her master, Nā'-ă-măn, was a leper. She saw that all the Syrians honored Nā'-ă-măn as a very great man indeed. Even the King of Syria respected Nā'-ă-măn, and chose to walk with him rather than with any other great men in his kingdom when he went into the temple of Rimmon to worship the idol there.

But Nā'-ă-măn was a leper. Now, a leper is a person who has a disease called leprosy, which causes the skin to become white and decays the flesh. At first the leper suffers no pain, but after the disease begins to work into the body of the leper, then the fingers and the toes and the ears and nose and even the arms and legs drop off. So leprosy is a terrible disease. And finally the person dies.

One day the little slave-girl found her mistress looking very sad. And she wished to comfort her, so she said, "If my master, Nā'-ă-măn, could be with the prophet who is in Samaria he could make him well of this dreadful disease." Before the little girl was stolen from her mother's home, perhaps she had seen Ē-lī'-shă when he went to visit the people who lived in the northern part of Israel. At least, she knew about the great miracles that Ē-lī'-shă had done, and perhaps she had heard how he brought the little boy at Shū'-něm back to life when he died. She may have told her mistress about these things.

Nā'-ă-măn's wife became interested at once. She hurried to tell her husband what the little girl had said, and Nā'-ă-măn told the King. Now, the King loved Nā'-ă-măn, and wished to see him cured of the leprosy, so he said, "I will write a letter to the King of Israel and ask him to cure you of this disease. And I will send you to Să-mâr'-ĭ-ă at once."

Because the King of Syria knew nothing about the true God, he supposed that the King of Israel could command the prophet to heal whomever he wished. And he sent a great present of money and beautiful clothes to give to the King after he should cause the prophet to cure Nā'-ă-măn. He sent this present of gold and of silver with Nā'-ă-măn and his servants, and they drove rapidly down to the land of Israel to see the King.

Nā'-ă-măn's prancing horses and great chariot stopped before the palace in Să-mâr'-ĭ-ă, and a messenger delivered the letter that the Syrian King had written to the King of Israel. Then Nā'-ă-măn and his servants waited anxiously outside the gate for an answer from the King.

THE CAPTIVE MAID TELLING ABOUT THE PROPHET

Perhaps they thought he was sending for the prophet to come to the palace and cure Nā'-ă-măn there.

But the King of Israel was not preparing to do some great deed. He was greatly troubled when he read the letter that Nā'-ă-măn had brought. He said, "Does the King of Syria think I am God, that I can kill and make alive? Why has he sent this leprous man to me that I should make him well? Surely he is only trying to find an excuse to make war against my country." Then he tore his clothes to show that he was in distress, for he did not know what to do. If he had been a good King, one who served the true God of Israel, then he might have thought at once of the good prophet, Ē-lī'-shă; but the King of Israel was worshiping idols and he did not love and serve God. He did not honor God's prophet as he should have done.

And still Nā'-ă-măn and his servants were waiting for an answer from the King. They wondered why he was so slow. They did not know how greatly their letter had troubled him. And while they waited, Ē-lī'-shă sent to the King and asked, "Why have you torn your clothes? Send the leprous man to me, that he may know there is a prophet in Israel."

The King of Israel was glad for this way out of his trouble, and he hurriedly sent Nā'-ă-măn and his servants to Ē-lī'-shă's house. And Ē-lī'-shă sent his servant down to speak to Nā'-ă-măn, to tell him that if he wished to be cured of this disease he should go down to the muddy waters of the Jordan River and dip himself seven times.

Nā'-ă-măn was a proud man, and he was much offended when Ē-lī'-shă would not come out to speak with him. He turned angrily away from Ē-lī'-shă's gate and started back to Syria. "Why should I go down to that muddy river and bathe?" he stormed. "If bathing can make me well of this disease, then I will bathe in the clear waters of our rivers at home."

But Nā'-ă-măn's servants knew that bathing alone would never cure their master of the leprosy. They knew he should obey the prophet's words if he wished to be cured. And they felt sad to see him turn away in anger from Ē-lī'-shă's gate. One of them came to Nā'-ă-măn and said, "If this prophet of Israel had come out and told you to do some great thing, would you not have done it? Then why not do this simple act and be cured of your disease?"

Although Nā'-ă-măn was proud, yet he was sensible enough to listen to his servant. And he saw at once that he was acting foolishly by refusing to do as Ē-lī'-shă had commanded. So he told his driver to turn toward Jordan, and he went down into the river and dipped his body

under the water seven times. And his leprosy disappeared so completely that not one sign of it remained.

Now Nā'-ă-măn was very happy. He was glad because he had obeyed
Ē-lī'-shă's words, and he hurried back to Ē-lī'-shă's house. This time the
prophet came out and spoke to him. And Nā'-ă-măn said: "Now I know

NAAMAN IN THE RIVER JORDAN

there is no God in all the earth
but in Israel. Let me give you
a present to show how thankful
I am because you have cured
me of this disease." But Ē-lī'-
shă would take no present. He
wanted to teach this stranger
from a heathen land that God's
gifts can not be bought with
money. Then Nā'-ă-măn asked
if he might take some earth
from the land of Israel and
carry it back to Syria. With
this he wanted to build an altar
where he could worship the
true God in his own country.

He thought God would not be pleased with an altar that had been built
of soil from a heathen country. And he promised that hereafter he
would no longer worship the idols, which can neither see nor hear nor
help in times of need. Then he turned and started toward his homeland.

Now Ē-lī'-shă's servant had seen the gifts that Nā'-ă-măn wished to
give to his master, and he was unhappy because Ē-lī'-shă had refused to
take them. He thought of all the things which that money could buy,
and the longer he thought about these things the more he wanted to
get the money. After Nā'-ă-măn started away, and Ē-lī'-shă went back
into his house again, this servant decided to try to get some of the
money. So he ran to overtake Nā'-ă-măn, and when Nā'-ă-măn saw him
following he stopped his chariot and turned to meet the servant.

Gĕ-hā'-zī, for this was the servant's name, said, "After you left
my master's house two young men came who are in need, and my master has sent to ask you to give them some silver money and some new
clothes." Nā'-ă-măn believed the story, and was glad to give the money
and the clothes to Gĕ-hā'-zī. He gave even more than Gĕ-hā'-zī asked
for, and sent the gift back with two of his servants.

Gĕ-hā'-zī was careful that Ē-lī'-shă should not see him. He left the
gift in a secret place and sent the servants away. Then he came into

the house where Ē-lī'-shă sat, and Ē-lī'-shă asked, "Where have you been?" Gĕ-hā'-zī answered, "I have not been away." But Ē-lī'-shă knew the words were not true. He knew about Gĕ-hā'-zī's sin, and he said, "My heart went with you when you followed Nā'-ă-măn and brought back that present." Then he rebuked Gĕ-hā'-zī for the great wrong that he had done, and he said, "Because you have desired riches more than to please God, the leprosy of Nā'-ă-măn shall come upon you." And from that hour Gĕ-hā'-zī was always a leper.

STORY 19

A LITTLE BOY WHO BECAME KING, AND HOW HE RULED IN JUDAH
2 Chron. 22:11—24:27

Jō'-ăsh was only seven years old when he became the king of Judah. As a little Prince he had never been allowed to run about and play wherever he wished. He had been watched very carefully, lest his own grandmother, the wicked Queen Ăth-ă-lī'-ăh, should hear about him and try to kill him.

Jō'-ăsh's father, who had been the king of Judah, was dead. And all of his brothers and sisters were dead, too. After his father had been killed, by an enemy, in the land of Israel, his grandmother had killed his brothers and sisters so that there should be no one left except herself to sit upon the throne. She had not known about the baby Prince, Jō'-ăsh, whose aunt had hidden him away in a safe place, with his faithful nurse.

For six years Ăth-ă-lī'-ăh ruled the people as Queen. But many of the people were displeased to have her rule over them. They knew the throne of David belonged to David's descendants, and not to strangers, like this cruel woman. For Ăth-ă-lī'-ăh was the daughter of a heathen, and she was a heathen, too. She never went to worship in the beautiful temple of the Lord, which stood so near her palace, but she worshiped in an idol's temple. She even caused her sons to break down some of the beautiful parts of the temple and use those parts to decorate the temple of her heathen god.

While Ăth-ă-lī'-ăh was busy ruling the people, the high priest, Jĕ-hoi'-ă-dă, was busy planning a way to crown Jō'-ăsh king of Judah. Now Jĕ-hoi'-ă-dă was an uncle of the little Prince, and it was Jĕ-hoi'-ă-dă's wife who had rescued the Prince when he was a baby. These kind people loved the Lord, and they had taken care of little Jō'-ăsh and his faithful nurse during the years while the Queen was ruling in Judah.

When Jō'-ăsh had grown from babyhood into a bright-faced little lad, his uncle called for men from different parts of Judah to come to the temple at Jerusalem. He gave them swords and spears, and told them to stand as guards about the temple court. Then when a great crowd of people gathered in the outer court, the high priest brought out the little Prince and placed him beside a pillar where the people could see him. How glad they were to know that one of David's descendants had been saved from the cruel hand of the Queen! They watched while the high priest and his sons anointed little Jō'-ăsh with oil and placed the crown upon his head. Then they shouted with a glad cry, "God save the King!"

CROWNING THE BOY JOASH

Queen Ăth-ă-lī'-ăh did not know what was taking place at the temple of the Lord. But when she saw the people gathering in the temple court and when she heard them rejoicing, she feared that trouble was coming upon her. So she ran into the temple, right through the crowd of people, and there she saw the little King standing by the pillar, with a crown upon his head.

The high priest saw her, and he commanded the men with swords and spears to catch her and carry her away. And they took her out to a gate of the city and killed her there. Her friends, the idol-worshipers, became afraid, and they did not oppose the high priest and the new King.

Until Jō'-ăsh grew to manhood, his uncle, the high priest, ruled the people. But he kept Jō'-ăsh and taught him how to rule the people aright. And as long as he lived, he helped Jō'-ăsh to be a good King.

When Jō'-ăsh became a man he wished to repair the temple of the Lord. Many years had passed since Solomon had built the temple, and it had grown old. Then, too, Ăth-ă-lī'-ăh had caused her sons to tear down some of its beautiful parts and use those parts to decorate the temple of her god, Bā'-ăl. Now Jō'-ăsh wanted to replace those damaged parts and make the temple look as good as when it was new. At first he told the priests and the Levites to go through the land and ask the people for money to use in repairing the Lord's house. But the money came so slowly that way, and finally he decided to place a large box, or chest, at the door of the temple where every one who came there to worship might see it. In the lid of this box was a hole, and he wanted the people to drop their money-gifts through the hole into the box.

Jō'-ăsh's plan worked well, for the people were glad to help make the temple look as good as new. They brought much money, and soon the workmen were busy repairing every worn-out place in the great building. They even made new ornaments of gold and silver to beautify the Lord's house.

Jĕ-hŏî'-ă-dă, the high priest, lived to be a very old man. And as long as he lived Jō'-ăsh ruled wisely. But after he died the people who loved to worship idols grew friendly with Jō'-ăsh and persuaded him to do wrong deeds. Finally they caused him to forget God. And in his last days Jō'-ăsh did many things that displeased the Lord. He even commanded wicked men to throw stones at one of Jĕ-hŏî'-ă-dă's sons, who was a prophet of the Lord. After this prophet was killed God permitted the Syrians to come down to Judah and rob that country and kill many of the idol-worshipers who had led Jō'-ăsh into sin. Then Jō'-ăsh became sick with great diseases, and while he lay suffering upon his bed some of his servants came into the room and killed him.

———•———

STORY 20

HOW ELISHA LED HIS ENEMIES INTO A TRAP
2 Kings 6: 8-23

The King of Syria began to look with greedy eyes upon the little kingdom of Israel, just south of his own country. He planned to attack the cities of Israel one at a time, and steal them away from the rule of King Jĕ-hôr'-ăm. So he sent his soldiers to make an attack on one of the cities.

When the soldiers came to the city they were surprised to find that Jĕ-hôr'-ăm had the place strongly guarded. They went back to their King, and he sent them to attack another city. And again they found that Jĕ-hôr'-ăm had a strong guard waiting to protect the city and drive them away. Several times they tried to capture cities in Israel, but every time they found that the King of Israel was ready to drive them back.

The King of Syria began to wonder how King Jĕ-hôr'-ăm seemed to know so much about his plans. He believed that one of his own soldiers was helping the King of Israel, by telling him in time to prepare himself to defend his cities. And the King of Syria thought, ''I must find that guilty man and punish him.'' So he called all of his soldiers together and told them that one of them must be helping the King of Israel.

It is a terrible thing to be found guilty of helping the enemies of one's own country, and when a ruler finds such a man he always punishes him severely. But none of the Syrian soldiers were being untrue to their King. One of them, however, knew who was telling Jĕ-hôr'-ăm about their King's plans, and he said, ''O King, I know who your enemy is. None of us are deceiving you, but there is a prophet in Israel named Ē-lī'-shă, and whatever you plan to do against the kingdom of Israel he tells King Jĕ-hôr'-ăm. Then Jĕ-hôr'-ăm sends his soldiers to protect his cities from your attack.''

The King of Syria knew he could never fight successfully against Israel while Ē-lī'-shă was there to tell about his plans. So he sent men to find out where the prophet was living. Then he decided to send his whole army to take that single man and bring him back to Syria as a prisoner. The men returned and said that Ē-lī'-shă was staying in Dō'-thăn, and the King of Syria prepared his chariots and horses and a host of soldiers to go after him.

One morning a few days later, when the servant of Ē-lī'-shă rose early and went out-of-doors he was frightened to see a host of soldiers coming from every side. They were coming straight toward Dō'-thăn, and the servant guessed at once that they were Syrians and that they were coming to capture his master, Ē-lī'-shă. He ran into the house and cried, ''Alas, my master! what shall we do?''

Ē-lī'-shă did not seem to be frightened at all. He answered quietly, ''Do not be afraid, for there are more with us than there are with the Syrians.'' The servant could not understand. He saw only himself and his master, and he knew there were thousands of Syrians, coming from every side to take them for prisoners. Then Ē-lī'-shă prayed and asked God to cause the servant's eyes to see their protectors. And the servant saw a multitude of horses and chariots of fire in the mountains to take care of Ē-lī'-shă. He knew God had sent them to protect his master, and he was no longer afraid.

When the Syrians came near to Dō'-thăn, Ē-lī'-shă asked God to cause them to become blind. And God sent blindness upon everyone. Then Ē-lī'-shă went out to them and told them he would show them the way

to the city where they would find the prophet.   And he led them
to the city of Să-mâr′-ĭ-ă.   Then he prayed that God would open their
eyes again, and they looked about and saw that they were inside the
walls of the city where their enemy, King Jĕ-hôr′-ăm, lived.   And they
were afraid.

Jĕ-hôr′-ăm was surprized when the prophet led such a multitude of
blind men into his city.   He thought Ē-lī′-shă had brought them to be
prisoners, and he asked, "Shall I kill them?"   But Ē-lī′-shă answered,
"No.   You must set bread and water before these men, for they are
hungry and they must be fed.   Then we must send them away."

Jĕ-hôr′-ăm was not a good man, but God caused him to respect Ē-lī′-
shă and obey his words. He prepared a great amount of food and gave it
to the Syrians, and after they had eaten he sent them back to their
own land.   And they did not try again to harm the good prophet.

———•———

STORY 21

WHERE FOUR LEPERS FOUND FOOD FOR A STARVING CITY
2 Kings 6:24—7:20

A time of great trouble had come to the land of Israel.   Bĕn-hā′-dăd,
the king of Syria, had led his great army into the land and had camped
around the walls of Să-mâr′-ĭ-ă, where Jĕ-hôr′-ăm lived.   Day after day
he waited outside the walls for the people of that city to open the gate
and let him come in to capture them and their King.   But the people
were afraid to open the gates.

Bĕn-hā′-dăd knew that if he waited long enough the people of
Să-mâr′-ĭ-ă would starve for food, because they had no way to bring food
inside the city.   He believed they would then be willing to open the
gate.   So he made a camp and made ready to stay there for many
days.   And while he waited, sure enough the food-supply grew less
and less inside the city walls, and the people began to get very hungry.
They were willing to pay great sums of money for only a handful of
food, and finally they could find nothing to eat except the flesh of horses
and donkeys.

One day while King Jĕ-hôr′-ăm was walking about through the
streets of Să-mâr′-ĭ-ă he learned that his people were even killing and
eating their own children.   He was terrified, and tore his clothes and
dressed himself in sackcloth.   Then he said, "Ē-lī′-shă, the prophet, is
to blame for this famine, and I am going to kill him."   Instead of

appreciating the good prophet who had helped him many times before, the King blamed Ē-lī'-shă for allowing this trouble to come upon Israel. Yet it was his own sins and the sins of his people that had brought about this trouble.

Ē-lī'-shă knew that Jĕ-hôr'-ăm was sending a man to take him and cut off his head. But he told his friends to stop the man at the door and wait until the King himself should come. And soon Jĕ-hôr'-ăm came, leaning upon the arm of an officer. Ē-lī'-shă spoke boldly to him, and said, "Tomorrow about this time there shall be food for the hungry people in the city, and the food will be sold in the gate of the city for a small sum of money." The officer who came with the King did not believe Ē-lī'-shă's words. He said, "If the Lord would make windows in heaven, could this thing be true?" Ē-lī'-shă replied that the officer should see with his eyes, but he should not eat any of the food. And then the King decided to let Ē-lī'-shă live at least one more day, to see if his words would come true.

That very evening four lepers came to the gate of Să-mâr'-ĭ-ă and sat down. They were very tired and hungry. Although these men were Israelites they had not been allowed to live among their own people, because they were lepers. Now they wondered what to do. They knew of the famine inside the city walls, so they decided to go out to the camp of Bĕn-hā'-dăd and give themselves up for prisoners. But when they came to the camp they found no one in sight. Every tent was empty. On and on they went, from one tent to another, but they did not see a Syrian anywhere. They found much food, and ate greedily of it. Then they began to gather the treasures of gold and silver and rich garments, which the Syrians had left in the camp, intending to hide them in a safe place.

Finally the lepers thought of the starving people in Să-mâr'-ĭ-ă, and they said to each other, "We do wrong when we fail to report to the people what we have found in this camp." So they hurried to the city gate and told the gatekeeper about the good news. And soon the lepers' message was being told in every part of the city.

Now, God had caused the Syrians and their King to hear a strange noise, which sounded like a strong army coming upon them through the darkness, and they feared that Jĕ-hôr'-ăm had sent for the kings of other countries to come and drive them away. They were not prepared to meet and fight a strong army, and they did not want to be defeated. So they left their tents and their food and everything in the camp, and ran on foot toward their homeland. As they ran they dropped the treasures that they had tried to carry back to their own country, and the road was strewn with rich garments and empty vessels.

As soon as King Jĕ-hôr'-ăm heard what the lepers had found in the camp, he rose up in the night and sent servants to search in the country for the missing army. He thought that Bĕn-hā'-dăd and his soldiers were only hiding somewhere near by, waiting for the starving people to crowd out of the city in search for food. But the servants soon returned, and told the King that they had found no trace of Bĕn-hā'-dăd's army anywhere. They told him how the road was strewn with garments and vessels, just as if the enemy had run away in great haste.

On the next day Ē-lī'-shă's word came true, for the people gathered much food from the empty tents of the Syrians and brought it to the gate of the city to be sold. And Jĕ-hô'-răm told the officer on whose arm he had leaned, to sit in the gate and have charge of the people as they came and went; but the officer could not control them, for they were so hungry that they crowded like starving animals, and they pushed him down and trampled over him until he died. Perhaps before he died he remembered that Ē-lī'-shă had said, "Your eyes shall see the food, but you shall not eat of it."

STORY 22

THE PROPHET WHO TRIED TO RUN AWAY FROM GOD
Jonah 1—4

During the years that Ē-lī'-shă was the prophet in Israel, the Syrians were a strong nation, and they often warred against the Israelites. But after Ē-lī'-shă died the Syrian nation grew weaker, and by and by did not trouble Israel any more at all.

Then a new enemy arose, from the far east country. This new enemy was the Assyrian king, who was conquering many little countries round about. And all the while he was sending his armies nearer and nearer to the border-land of Israel, and the Israelites were beginning to fear him.

Nĭn'-ĕ-vēh was the capital city of Assyria, and the home of the great king. And Nĭn'-ĕ-vēh was a great city. It had stood for hundreds of years, and it had grown larger and larger until thousands and thousands of people lived inside its high walls. These people did not serve the true God, but worshiped idols. And year after year they became more wicked, until finally God thought he would destroy them all.

But God is very merciful. He knew the people of Nĭn'-ĕ-vēh had not known about him as had the people of Israel, for no prophets had ever come to warn them about their wrong-doings. So he decided to send them a prophet from Israel to tell them that their city would be destroyed because of their awful sins.

Jonah was the prophet whom God chose to send to Nĭn'-ĕ-vēh. But Jonah did not want to go to that wicked city so far from his homeland. He knew the Assyrians were enemies of the Israelites, and he thought it would be better if God would destroy their city than to give them a chance to repent of their sins. So Jonah thought, "I will not go to Nĭn'-ĕ-vēh. I will take a ship down at the great Sea, and I will sail away toward the west country. instead of going toward the east country. Then maybe I can get so far away that God will not talk to me any more about going to preach to those wicked people of Nĭn'-ĕ-vēh."

Jonah went down to the seaside and found a ship ready to sail away. He paid his fare, climbed on board the ship, and started with the sailors to go to a city called Tarshish, far to the west. He thought he was very safe now, and he feared no longer that he should have to go to Nĭn'-ĕ-vēh. Indeed, he felt so safe that he went down into the ship and soon fell fast asleep.

But God knew all about Jonah's plans, and God was not willing for his prophet to disobey him. He had called Jonah to go to preach to the heathen people in Nĭn'-ĕ-vēh, and he sent a storm on the Sea which threatened to wreck the ship. The sailors became frightened and they called on their gods to quiet the winds; but the winds blew harder than ever. They did not know what to do. Finally the captain went down into the ship and found Jonah lying there asleep.

The captain woke Jonah and told him to call upon his God for help in this time of trouble. But Jonah did not feel much like asking God to help him when he was running away from the work that God had told him to do. No doubt his conscience began to trouble him greatly: and when he saw the strong waves dash against the ship and toss it about like a chip on the water, he feared that he should never again see dry land.

When the storm continued to rage, the sailors decided that one of them on board the ship must be the cause of the trouble, so they decided to cast lots and see on which one the lot would fall. And the lot fell on Jonah.

Jonah was a stranger among them, and the sailors wondered what terrible thing this stranger had done. They gathered round him and asked, "Tell us, who are you and what is your business?" And Jonah told them that he was from the land of Israel and that he worshiped the God who had made the sea and the dry land. At once they were afraid, for they did not know about such a great God, and they thought surely he was angry. Jonah told them how he had tried to run away from God, and they believed that God was trying to punish him. Jonah, too, believed that God had sent the storm on his account.

"What shall we do to you that the storm may cease?" asked the frightened m e n when they saw that their ship would soon be dashed in pieces if the wind and waves continued to toss it about. And Jonah answered, "T h r o w me overboard in the water, and then the storm will end." The sailors did not wish to treat Jonah so cruelly, but when they saw that all would be lost if they allowed him to remain on board the vessel, they picked him up and threw him into the sea. Then the waves grew quiet, and the wind grew calm, and Jonah disappeared out of sight.

But God was not yet finished with Jonah. He had prepared a great fish, and the fish swallowed Jonah and carried him about for three days

JONAH PREACHING IN NINEVEH

and three nights before throwing him out onto the land. By that time Jonah was very willing to go to Nĭn'-ĕ-vēh and preach God's message to the people there.

When Jonah entered the city he began to cry out: "Within forty days Nĭn'-ĕ-vēh shall be destroyed!" On and on he went, for Nĭn'-ĕ-vēh was a great city, and in every street where he passed he cried out the same words. And the people stopped to listen to his strange message. They had never seen a prophet of God before. Some of them

ran to tell their King about Jonah's words, and the King was frightened. He rose from his throne and laid aside his rich garments and
dressed himself in sackcloth. Then he sat down in ashes and became

JONAH UNDER THE GOURD-VINE

sorry for his sins. He commanded all the people of the city to do as
he was doing, and to cry earnestly to God to spare their lives.

After Jonah finished preaching he went outside the great walls and waited to see the fire fall from the sky to burn up the enemies of the Israelites. But forty days passed by and no fire fell. Because the people believed Jonah's message and repented of their sins God did not destroy their city. Then Jonah became very much displeased. He feared that people might call him a false prophet, and he wanted to die instead of go back to his own country again.

God taught Jonah a lesson by allowing a gourd-vine to grow up in one night and make a shelter for him from the burning heat of the sun. Then God caused a worm to destroy the gourd, and Jonah became very unhappy. Again he wished that he might die. So the Lord spoke to Jonah and said, "You were sorry to see the plant die, though you did not make it grow. And should I not have more pity on the people of Nĭn'-ĕ-vēh than you have on a plant?" Jonah learned that God looks upon people of every nation as being precious in his sight, even though they do not know how to worship him.

STORY 23

THE SAD ENDING OF THE KINGDOM OF ISRAEL
2 Kings 17

The people of Nĭn'-ĕ-vēh believed God's prophet and were ready to ask God to forgive their sins. They repented, and they were not destroyed. But the people of Israel did not believe the faithful prophets whom God sent to them, one after another. Some of them, of course, believed; but many of them did not. Their kings refused to worship God in the right way, and kept the golden calves, which the first king of Israel had made.

Many years passed by, and God saw that the Israelites would never return to worship him as they had done in the days of David and Solomon. Nineteen kings had ruled in the land of Israel, and many times God had helped those kings out of trouble. Still they would not lead their people back to the true worship.

At last God allowed an enemy to carry them all away to a strange land. Hoshea was king in Israel when the great Assyrian army came down into the land and took possession of it. For a while Hō-shē'-ă and his people paid a large sum of money each year to the Assyrian nation, and they were allowed to live in their own land. But when Hō-shē'-ă refused to pay the money and sent to the king of Egypt for help, the king of Assyria sent his army again, and the army took Hō-shē'-ă and all his people away from their homes and led them into heathen cities to keep them for slaves. This was the terrible punishment that their sins of idol-worship had brought upon them. And they were never again allowed to return to live in their homeland.

The Assyrian king now ruled over all of the country where the ten tribes of Israel used to live. He wanted to have some people in that land, so he took some heathen people from cities in the east country and brought them to live in the cities of Să-mâr′-ĭ-ă. He told them to work the fields and keep the vineyards, and pay him money from the crops they raised in Israel.

The new people in Israel were idol-worshipers. They did not know about the true God at all. After they had been in the land for some time they became afraid of the God of that land, for lions would come out of the woods and kill some of them when they went out to their fields to work. They believed that the God of Israel was sending the lions among them because they did not know how to worship him. So they sent messengers back to Nĭn′-ĕ-vēh to tell the king about their troubles. They asked him to send a priest of the Israelite slaves back to Israel, that he might teach them to worship the Israelites' God.

The king sent a priest of the Israelites, and he went to live in Bethel. He told the strange people about the true God, and they, too, tried to worship him. But they continued to worship their own gods, and their religion became a mixture of right and wrong. Even today some of the descendants of those people are living in Să-mâr′-ĭ-ă, and their worship is a mixture of idolatry and the religion of the Jews.

———— • ————

STORY 24

THE GOOD KING HEZEKIAH

2 Kings 18—20; 2 Chronicles 29—32

After the people of Israel were carried away into captivity by the king of Assyria, only the tribe of Judah remained of the twelve tribes that had entered the promised land under the leadership of Joshua (see Part Third, Story Two). And Hĕz-ē-kī′-ăh was the king of Judah at that time.

Now the kingdom of Judah was very weak when Hĕz-ē-kī′-ăh took the throne. For many years it had been ruled by men who were not serving the true God, and they had even shut up the temple of the Lord.

Hĕz-ē-kī'-ăh began at once to restore the true religion. He called for the priests and the Levites to come to Jerusalem to cleanse the temple. Then when everything was ready for worship at the house of God, he sent invitations to the people in every part of the land of Judah and Israel, and commanded them to come to the Feast of the Passover, which they had not kept for many long years.

Some of the people only laughed when they received Hĕz-ē-kī'-ăh's invitation to attend the Feast. They had worshiped idols for so long a time that they did not care to return to Jerusalem again, to worship the true God. But many from the land of Judah came gladly, and there was a great meeting.

Hĕz-ē-kī'-ăh destroyed the idols out of his land, and tried to teach his people to do right. He found in Jerusalem the brass serpent that Moses had made in the wilderness. He saw that the people were burning incense before this brass serpent, just as if it were an idol, so he cast it into the fire. He tore down the altars that had been built to worship heathen gods, and did much to strengthen his kingdom.

The King of Assyria had gained power over Judah before Hĕz-ē-kī'-ăh took the throne. Every year the people of Judah had to pay Assyria a large sum of money. But Hĕz-ē-kī'-ăh was displeased to have his people oppressed by this heathen King. He decided to quit paying the money. He built up the walls of Jerusalem until they were very strong. Then he gathered an army and made ready to fight against the Assyrians.

But Hĕz-ē-kī'-ăh's army was only a handful compared to the hosts of Assyria. The enemies came into the land of Judah and took one city after another. Then they marched toward Jerusalem, and Hĕz-ē-kī'-ăh knew that his soldiers could not keep them away. He saw when too late that he had made a sad mistake when he refused to pay the money that the Assyrian King required of his people. So he sent word to the angry King, promising to resist him no more and to pay whatever that King should require.

The King of Assyria thought: "Now is my chance to spoil this little country of Judah." So he demanded a heavier tax than he had ever asked before. And Hĕz-ē-kī'-ăh took all the gold and silver that was in his palace, and all that he could find among the people, and even the gold and silver from the temple of the Lord to pay this tax. Still the King of Assyria was not satisfied. He sent a message, saying, "I am going to destroy your city and take you and your people away to a far country, just as I have done to your neighbors who lived in Israel.

The gods of other nations did not help them when I came against them, and your God will not be able to save you."

Hĕz-ē-kī'-ăh was afraid when he heard this message. He knew that his army was not strong enough to drive away such a powerful enemy. He took the letter that this King had written and went into the temple to pray. There he spread the letter before the altar and asked God to help him and his people out of their trouble. Then he sent some of his princes to visit the good prophet Isaiah and ask him to tell them about God's will.

Isaiah answered, "The Lord has said that the King of Assyria shall not come into this city, nor shall he even shoot an arrow against it. But he shall go back to his own country by the way that he came, and there he shall be killed with a sword."

That same night an angel of God visited the camp of the Assyrian King and caused a terrible sickness to fall upon the soldiers. By morning many of them lay dead. All of the leaders in the army were among the dead men, and the King rose up and hastened back to his own land. Never again did he return to fight against Hĕz-ē-kī'-ăh, for God had heard and answered the prayers of the good King. And years after this, while he was worshiping in the temple of his god in Nĭn'-ĕ-vēh, two of his own sons killed him.

At one time Hĕz-ē-kī'-ăh became very sick, and there was no cure to be found for his sickness. Isaiah, the prophet, came to him and said, "God has commanded that you get ready to leave this world, for you must die."

Hĕz-ē-kī'-ăh did not feel that he could leave his people. He turned his face to the wall and prayed earnestly that God would make him well again. Then he wept bitter tears, and reminded God how faithfully he had tried to rule the people. And God heard Hĕz-ē-kī'-ăh's prayer.

Isaiah was returning to his home when the Lord spoke to him again, saying, "Go back to the King and tell him that I have heard his prayer and seen his tears; and now I will add fifteen years to his life. On the third day he shall be able to go up to the temple to worship."

Hĕz-ē-kī'-ăh was glad to hear Isaiah's second message. He asked for a sign from the prophet, and Isaiah answered, "The sign shall be according to your choice. Shall the shadow on the sun-dial go backward or shall it go forward ten degrees?" The sun-dial was the instrument by which the King might know the time of day; for he had no clocks as we have now. And Hĕz-ē-kī'-ăh asked that the shadow might go backward, as it would not seem like a sign for the shadow to move for-

HEZEKIAH SPREADING THE LETTER BEFORE THE LORD

ward. So Isaiah prayed, and the shadow moved backward ten degrees.

And Hĕz-ē-kī'-ăh was healed of his disease, according to God's word, and he lived for fifteen years more. During that time he built up his kingdom and became very rich. He grew proud of his riches; but God rebuked him, and he humbled his heart again. When he died all the land mourned for him, because they knew he had been the best king Judah had known.

STORY 25

THE STORY ABOUT A FORGOTTEN BOOK
2 Chronicles 34, 35

It was house-cleaning time in the temple of the Lord. Many years had passed since this building had been repaired by the boy king, Jō'-ăsh, and during those long years the temple had been much neglected. It had even been mistreated, for one king had set up altars for the idol of Bā'-ăl right in the courts of the Lord's house. Now that king was dead, and his grandson, Jō-sī'-ăh, was ruling the people of Judah. And because Jō-sī'-ăh was trying to do right he had given the command that God's house should be repaired and made ready for the proper kind of worship.

Many skilful workmen were hired to help repair the temple. And the heathen altars were torn out of the temple courts and carried outside the city, where they were burned with fire. While this work was going on, the high priest was setting things in order in the rooms of the temple. And there, hidden away beneath some rubbish, he found a strange book.

This strange book proved to be the same one as Moses had written before he died. It was called the Book of the Law, for in it Moses had written the words of the law, which God gave to the Israelites. And Moses had commanded that the book should be read in the hearing of all the people once every seven years. But now many years had passed by since the book had been read. And during those years the book had been entirely forgotten.

The high priest carefully removed the dust from this precious book and called for a servant of King Jō-sī'-ăh. Shā'-phăn, the servant, came quickly, and the high priest told him to carry the book to the King.

Now, Jō-sī'-ăh had never heard the words of God's law before this time. He asked his servant to read aloud from the book, and Shā'-phăn read about God's promise to bless the people if they should serve him faithfully. Then he continued to read, and Jō-sī'-ăh heard about God's promise to punish the people if they should forsake him and turn to worship idols. Jō-sī'-ăh was alarmed. He knew the people had disobeyed God's law, and he feared the awful punishments, which God promised to send upon them. He tore his clothes and wept bitter tears. Then he sent servants to a woman named Hŭl'-dăh, who was a prophetess, to ask her about God's plan to punish the people for their great sins.

Huldah told the servants that God would surely send all the great punishments upon the people just as he had promised to do if they should forsake his law and worship idols. But because Jō-sī'-ăh, the king, had humbled his heart and had wept tears of sorrow for their sins, Hŭl'-dăh said that God would not let the punishment come upon the land during his lifetime.

Jō-sī'-ăh did not try to forget about the words of God's law. He wanted all his people to hear them, too. So he called for a great meeting at Jerusalem, and when the people came together he read to them out of the book. Then he promised God to keep that law and to serve God with all his heart. He commanded his people to keep the law, too. And they obeyed their King.

Afterwards Jō-sī'-ăh prepared to keep the Passover Feast, which the Israelites were commanded in God's law to keep once every year. He assembled the people from every part of the land, and when they came together he gave from his own flocks many lambs for the Passover supper. And the people rejoiced together, and kept the Feast for seven days. Not since the days of the prophet Samuel had there been such a great Passover Feast as this one.

Jō-sī'-ăh ruled the people for thirty-one years. He began to rule when he was only a child, eight years old. Of course some older men had charge of the important affairs of the kingdom until he grew to manhood. But Jō-sī'-ăh longed to be a good king when he was only a boy. And at the age of sixteen he began to seek God earnestly, and God helped him to rule wisely.

At the end of Jō-sī'-ăh's good reign the king of Egypt went out to fight against the Assyrian king, and he marched through the land of Judah. Jō-sī'-ăh was not pleased to have him pass through the country so he called out his army and prepared to fight against him. Now the king of Egypt did not wish to fight against Jō-sī'-ăh, and he sent word for Jō-sī'-ăh to return home from the battle-field; but Jō-sī'-ăh would not go. He dressed himself in the clothes of a common soldier and went out to battle anyway. And in the midst of the fight he was shot by an archer and wounded so severely that his servants brought him back to Jerusalem in a chariot. Soon afterwards he died, and the people buried him among the honorable kings of Judah. The prophet of God wept for him, because he knew that Jō-sī'-ăh was the last king who would ever try to keep the words that Moses wrote in the Book of the Law.

STORY 26

THE WEEPING PROPHET, AND HIS GREAT WORK
Jeremiah 1—52

While Jō-sī'-ăh was the king in Judah, God called a young man named Jeremiah to be a prophet. At first Jeremiah thought he could never obey his call, for he was a shy, timid young man. He told the Lord that he could not speak to the people because he was only a child. But God answered, "Do not say you are only a child; for you must go to every person to whom I send you, and you must tell them every word I bid you." Then the Lord touched Jeremiah's mouth and said, "I have put my words in your mouth, and I have set you over the nation to do a great work for me."

Jeremiah was no longer afraid to obey when God promised to be with him and help him out of his troubles. For Jeremiah knew he would have many troubles. He knew how the prophets before him had been cruelly treated because they dared to speak God's words to the sinful people. He knew that he, too, might have to suffer many things.

While Jō-sī'-ăh was king in Judah, Jeremiah was treated kindly. But after Jō-sī'-ăh died the people soon turned back to idol-worship again. They did not care for the true God, and they refused to listen to his faithful prophet. The king of Egypt took their new king away as a prisoner, and made them pay great sums of money every year. Then he placed another of Jō-sī'-ăh's sons upon the throne of Judah.

Jō-sī'-ăh's sons were not good men like their father. They forsook God and allowed idols to be set up all through the land. They even treated God's prophet unkindly because he warned them about the dangers that God would send upon them as punishments for their sins.

One day Jeremiah told his dear friend Bâr'-ŭch the words that God spoke to him, and Bâr'-ŭch wrote the words in a book. Then he took the book and went out to read it among the people. Soon the princes of Judah heard about it, and they called for Bâr'-ŭch and asked him to read to them. They were frightened when they heard what Bâr'-ŭch had written; for they believed God's words, and they knew their land would soon be taken away from them. They asked Bâr'-ŭch to let them have the book to read to the King. But first they told Bâr'-ŭch to hide himself and Jeremiah, lest the King be angry when he hear the words of God and try to punish them for putting the words into the book.

Jĕ-hói'-ă-kĭm, Jō-sī'-ăh's son, was the king at that time. He was sitting in his palace when the princes came to him, bringing the book that Bâr'-ŭch had written. And he listened while they read. But as soon as they finished reading a page he called for the book and took his penknife and cut the page out. Then he threw it into the fire. This he did with every page that Bâr'-ŭch had written. He would not believe the words of the Lord. And he wanted to punish Jeremiah and his friend; but he could not find them.

The princes sent word to Jeremiah and Bâr'-ŭch, telling them how the King had treated the book, and once more the prophet and his friend wrote down the words of God. And the words that they wrote were true; for not long afterwards a great king from the east country, of Chăl-dē'-ă, came and took some of the people away to Babylon. And Jĕ-hói'-ă-kĭm was placed in a prison-house and kept for a prisoner as long as he lived.

But Jeremiah's troubles were by no means ended. After the death of Jĕ-hói'-ă-chĭn, son of Jĕ-hói'-ă-kĭm, who had reigned just a little over three months, a new king, Zĕd-ē-kī'-ăh, another son of wicked Jĕ-hói'-ă-kĭm, was soon ruling the people of Judah, and he was more wicked than his father had been. He caused Jeremiah to be cast into a prison-house because he spoke the words of God. And the men who put him into the prison tied ropes about his waist and lowered him into a deep hole beneath the prison floor. Such a hole is called a dungeon, and there the prophet was kept for some time.

In the dark, dreary dungeon Jeremiah was very unhappy. He had no comfortable place to rest, and he had only dry bread and water to eat and drink day after day.

While this trouble was happening to Jeremiah, the people of Jerusalem were also in distress. The king of Babylon had come again, with a strong army, and was camping around the walls of their city. They could not go away, and none of their friends could come to help them. And their food-supply was growing smaller every day. Soon they would have nothing left to eat.

The King of Judah was afraid of this army outside his city. He

called for Jeremiah to tell him what to do. So the men let ropes down
into the dungeon and pulled the prophet out again to send him to the
King. And Jeremiah told the King that God was going to allow the

JEREMIAH BEING CAST INTO THE DUNGEON

army to capture that city and break down its walls and even destroy
the beautiful temple of the Lord. But he said that God would not let
the Chăl-dē′-ăn king, Něb-ū-chăd-něz′-zär, kill the people of Jerusalem if
they would willingly offer themselves to become his prisoners. Then
they would not need to starve to death inside the city.

Jeremiah asked the King not to send him back into that dark dungeon again. So afterwards he was kept in the court of the prison, and treated more kindly. But he was not allowed to go about through the city and talk to the people.

The people of Jerusalem and their King were not willing to give themselves up as prisoners to Nĕb-ū-chăd-nĕz'-zär, as Jeremiah had told them to do. So weary months passed by, and they stayed inside the walls of Jerusalem and suffered from hunger and thirst. Jeremiah suffered with them, for he could not escape. At last, when all the food was gone, the King decided to slip away from Jerusalem during the night. He thought the Chăl-dē'-ăn army and King Nĕb-ū-chăd-nĕz'-zär might not see him.

But King Zĕd-ē-kī'-ăh had not gone far from the city when he was captured by his enemies, the Chăl-dē'-ăns. They put heavy chains on his hands and feet, and then put out his eyes and led him away to Babylon. Many of the people of Judah were taken with him, and only a few of the poorer people were left in the land. Nĕb-ū-chăd-nĕz'-zär and his army broke down the walls of Jerusalem and set fire to the temple of the Lord. They first took out all the vessels of gold and silver that they found in the temple, and carried those precious vessels to their own land.

Jeremiah was allowed to remain in the land of Judah among the poorer people. And he lived to be an old man. But as long as he lived he faithfully warned the people according to all the words that God spoke to him. Because he lived during such a time of trouble, Jeremiah was a sad-faced man. He talked more about the sorrows of his people than about their joys. And often he wept because of their sins. For this reason he was called the "Weeping Prophet."

KING NEBUCHADNEZZAR BOWING BEFORE DANIEL

PART SIXTH

STORIES ABOUT THE JEWS

Daniel; Nehemiah; Haggai; Ezra; Esther; Malachi

STORY 1

HOW THE PEOPLE OF JUDAH LIVED IN A STRANGE LAND

2 Chron. 36:14-21

When the city of Jerusalem was finally broken up, the Chăl-dē'-ăn army started back on their long journey to Babylon. They took with them Zĕd-ē-kī'-ăh, the king of Judah, and a host of his people for prisoners. Old men and women, young people, and even children were among the number who marched as prisoners to Babylon.

Day after day this host of people walked on and on, stopping only at night to camp by the roadside and rest from their weary journey. And at every camp they knew they were farther away from their home and nearer the land of strangers.

The captives were called "Jews"— a word that means "the people of Judah." And the Jews of today are descendants of those very people who marched as prisoners from Jerusalem to Babylon so long ago.

When at last the weary journey came to an end, the Jews found that their new ruler treated them more kindly than they had hoped. He gave them fields and houses in that strange land, and permitted them to work for themselves just as they had done in their own country. He even took some of them into his capital city and trained them to become his nobles and rulers.

God did not forget the people after they were carried away to Babylon. He sent messages to them from his faithful prophet Jeremiah. And he promised to bring them back again to their own country if they would try to please him while they were living among strangers. The people listened to these messages, and some of them rejoiced to hear Jeremiah's letters read. They longed for the time to come when they would return to the land of their fathers.

In the land of Babylon the Jews refused to worship idols. They saw around them the idolatry of their heathen neighbors, the C̲h̲ăl-dē'-ăns̈; but they remembered how God was displeased with idol-worship, and they were trying now to please him. They often met together in little groups and talked about the land of Judah and the beautiful temple of the Lord, which had been destroyed. And when they talked about these things they wept for sorrow.

Sometimes the C̲h̲ăl-dē'-ăns̈ would ask the Jews to sing for them. Perhaps they had heard that the Jews were lovers of music, and were skilled musicians. But the Jews hung their harps away and refused to sing. They would answer, "How can we sing the Lord's song in a strange land?" They thought the beautiful songs of joy and victory that David and other musicians had written would sound out of place in a strange country.

Now the Jews were careful to teach their children about the true God. They were glad when the priests and the Levites came to talk to them about Moses' law. And as the days and the years passed by they did not forget the hope which Jeremiah had given them—the hope of returning again to Judah.

In the land of Babylon another man began to hear messages from God and to speak those messages to the people. This man was Ē-zēk'-iĕl, who was one of the captive Jews. He had been among the first captives, when Jĕ-hoi'-ă-c̲h̲ĭn was taken to Babylon. And he afterwards warned the other people in Judah about God's punishment upon them for their disobedience. Ē-zēk'-iĕl saw wonderful visions from God, and he encouraged the people to believe that the time would come when they might return again to their own land.

----•----

STORY 2

FOUR BRAVE BOYS WHO STOOD BEFORE A GREAT KING
Daniel 1

In the king's palace at Babylon a company of young boys were being entertained. These young lads were strangers in Babylon. But they were not strangers in a king's court, for they had lived in a royal palace in their home country.

Among this company were four bright-eyed, handsome youths who seemed to be more thoughtful than their friends. These boys were Daniel, Hăn-ă-nī'-ăh, Mī'-shā-ĕl, and Ăz-ă-rī'-ăh, and they had come from Jerusalem with the first captives whom Nĕb-ū-c̲h̲ăd-nĕz'-zär had carried away from Judah. They had been princes in Judah during the rule of King Jĕ-hói'-ă-kĭm, and they served the God of Israel.

King Nĕb-ū-chăd-nĕz'-zär had commanded his chief officer of the palace to choose this company of young boys and to teach them the learning of the Chăl-dē'-ăns. He wished to have them well trained, that when they should become grown men they might be able to help rule the great

kingdom of Babylon. And he had appointed his servants to carry choice food from his own table to set before them every day, that they might eat of it and grow into sturdy manhood.

Now, Daniel and his three friends wished to keep the law that God gave to the people of Israel; and that law forbade them to eat of certain kinds of food. But the heathen nations, like the Chăl-dē'-ăns, had no regard for that law, and they prepared food that the Jews called unclean. They also cooked their food in certain ways that the law of Moses condemned. Daniel and his three friends knew about these differences between the Chăl-dē'-ăns and their own people. And they decided to refuse the King's food, lest it should be the kind of food that Moses in his book had forbidden the Israelites to eat.

DANIEL REFUSING THE KING'S FOOD

God knew about the desire of Daniel and his friends. And God caused the chief officer of the King's palace to love these young boys. When the food was brought before them from the King's table, Daniel stood up and bravely told the officer about his desire not to eat of that food, lest he should be breaking the law of his God. He also pleaded for his three friends, Hăn-ă-nī'-ăh, Mī'-shā-ĕl, and Ăz-ă-rī'-ăh, that they, too, might be allowed to refuse the King's food.

At first the officer was afraid that the King might be displeased if the boys refused to eat food from his table. He said, "When you appear before Nĕb-ū-chăd-nĕz'-zär and he sees that you are not looking so well and strong as the other young boys, then he will think that I have not cared for you as I should have done. And he will kill me."

But Daniel said, "Try us for ten days with the kind of food we desire to eat, and then see if we do not look as well fed as the other young men." Because the officer loved these boys he agreed to do as Daniel had asked. And for ten days he fed them vegetable food and bread instead of the meats and wine from the King's table.

At the end of the ten days the officer saw that Daniel and his friends were even healthier-looking than their companions. So he continued to give them the food that they desired. And God blessed these boys with much wisdom, so that they quickly learned the language and the wisdom of the Chăl-dē'-ăns.

When three years had passed the King requested that the young boys should be brought before him. He examined them with hard questions, and he saw that Daniel and his three friends were wiser by ten times than were any of the wisest men in all his kingdom. Nĕb-ū-chăd-nĕz'-zär was well pleased with these young Jews. He gave them places of honor among his own people, and they continued to live in Babylon for many years.

<hr>

STORY 3

HOW DANIEL BECAME A GREAT MAN IN BABYLON
Daniel 2

After young Daniel and his three friends were numbered among the wise men in Babylon, one night the King had a very strange dream. When he awoke from the dream he could not go to sleep again. And the dream troubled him greatly. He believed that surely that dream must have a deep meaning, and he decided to call the wise men in his kingdom and have them explain the meaning to him.

Morning came at last, and Nĕb-ū-chăd-nĕz'-zär arose from his bed. But now he could no longer recall his dream. This fact troubled him, too, for he knew the dream had been strange and he believed it had a deep meaning. He sent at once for the wise men who had often stood before him, and when they came he told them about his troubled thoughts regarding the strange dream which he could no longer remember. He asked them to tell the dream and the meaning of it.

The wise men were puzzled at this request from their King. They thought he was being unreasonable, for they did not know what he had dreamed about. So they asked him to tell the dream first, and then they would tell the meaning. "I have forgotten the dream," replied the King, impatiently, "and if you are as wise as you claim to be you can tell me what it was. Then you can tell its meaning."

When the wise men insisted that no human being could do such a thing as tell what some one else had dreamed and forgotten, the King became very angry with them. He said, "Unless you tell this dream and its meaning you shall all be killed." Even this cruel threat could not enable the wise men to know the dream, so they turned away from his presence in great fear.

Nĕb-ū-chăd-nĕz'-zär then called the captain of his guard and commanded him to kill all the wise men in Babylon. So Ăr'-ĭ-ŏch, the captain, took his sword and prepared himself to do the terrible deed. When he came to Daniel's house he found that the brave young man and his three friends had heard nothing about the King's command. They had not appeared with the other wise men before Nĕb-ū-chăd-nĕz'-zär.

When Daniel heard what had happened he begged the captain to delay the cruel work until he might first speak with the King. Then he hurried to the palace and went boldly in to tell Nĕb-ū-chăd-nĕz'-zär that he would find out the dream and its interpretation if only a little time were given him to prepare. And Nĕb-ū-chăd-nĕz'-zär granted him a little time.

Daniel knew that no living person could be wise enough in himself to do what the King had required; but Daniel knew also that secret things are known by the great God of all the earth, whom he and his three friends were serving. So the four young men prayed very earnestly that God would cause Daniel to know this dream, and that night God showed Daniel in a vision what the dream had been and what it meant.

Now Daniel was very thankful to God. He knelt down and prayed a beautiful prayer of thanksgiving. Then he went quickly to Ăr'-ĭ-ŏch, the captain of the King's guard, and said, "Do not destroy the wise men, but bring me in to speak with the King; for I can tell the interpretation of his dream." Ăr'-ĭ-ŏch was glad, and he took Daniel and brought him to the palace. Then he told the King that he had found a man among the captives from Judah who could make known the strange dream and its meaning.

Daniel told Nĕb-ū-chăd-nĕz'-zär that the power to make known his dream was given by the great God in heaven, for no wise man of earth could know such secrets and reveal them. Then he said: "O King, when you lay down to sleep on your bed you wondered what should come to pass in future years. Then you fell asleep, and in your dream God showed you what would happen hereafter. And this was your dream: You saw a great image, exceedingly bright, standing before you. The head of this image was of gold, the breast and arms were of silver, the waist and hips were of brass, the legs were of iron, and the feet were part of iron and part of clay. Then you saw a stone that was cut without hands roll toward this great image and strike the feet of it. And the stone broke the feet, and the whole image fell to the ground in broken pieces, and it became like dust, which the wind can blow away. Then while you looked in wonder, the stone grew until it became a great mountain, which filled the whole earth.''

Něb-ū-chăd-něz'-zär listened eagerly to the young man's words. Then Daniel continued: ''Now I will tell you what this dream means, for God intends to teach you something by it. This great image represents four great kingdoms of earth. Your kingdom is the first, and the head of gold represents this kingdom. After you there will come another king not so great, and he is like the breast and arms of silver. The third kingdom is shown in the dream by the parts of brass, and the fourth by the iron legs and the feet. This fourth kingdom will be very strong at first, but afterwards it will become weaker; for the iron in the feet was mixed with clay.

''In the days of these kings,'' said Daniel, ''God will set up a kingdom which shall never be destroyed, and his kingdom is represented in your dream by that stone cut out without hands, which smote the great image till it fell. God's kingdom will increase until it fills the whole earth, and it will break in pieces every other kingdom. This, O King, was your dream, and this is the meaning of it.''

Něb-ū-chăd-něz'-zär was astonished at the wisdom of this young Jew. He believed that Daniel was a wonderful person, like a god, and he fell on the floor before Daniel to worship him. But Daniel had told him that the God in heaven had made known the dream and the meaning to him so Něb-ū-chăd-něz'-zär said, ''Of a truth, your God is a God of gods, and a Lord of kings, and a revealer of secrets.'' Then Něb-ū-chăd-něz'-zär gave many great gifts to Daniel, and made him the ruler of all the province of Babylon, and the chief of all the wise men in his kingdom. He did not allow his captain to destroy the wise men, after Daniel had revealed the meaning of his dream.

At Daniel's request the King placed Hăn-ă-nī'-ăh, Mī'-shā-ĕl, and Ăz-ă-rī'-ăh, in honorable offices of the province, among the governors of the land. And the names of these young men were known to the King as Shā'-drăch, Mē'-shăch, and Ă-bĕd'-ně-gō.

STORY 4

WHAT THE KING SAW IN THE FIERY FURNACE

Daniel 3

Nĕb-ū-c̣hăd-nĕz'-zär, the king grew in power until he became the greatest king in the world at that time. Year after year he added new countries to his kingdom, and in every country the people feared him greatly. These things caused him to become very proud, and to think himself a wonderful man indeed.

Then Nĕb-ū-c̣hăd-nĕz'-zär decided to make a god and compel the people of every country to worship that god. So he built a great image, ninety feet high, and covered it with gold. This image he set up on the plain of Dū'-ră, which was near Babylon. There it could be seen at a great distance.

THE THREE WHO REFUSED TO WORSHIP THE IMAGE

After the image had been set up, the King sent a command to the princes and rulers and officers in every nation, that they should come to the great gathering on the plain of Dū'-ră. And they dared not disobey. When they çame together, Shā'-drăc̣h, Mĕ'-shăc̣h, and Ă-bĕd'-nĕ-gō, Daniel's three friends, were among them. For some reason Daniel himself was not there.

King Nĕb-ū-c̣hăd-nĕz'-zär was pleased to see such a vast company of men assembled on the plain before the image. He wished to have every one of them bow down and worship the god that he had made, so he caused one of his servants to cry out in a loud voice and say: "O people, nations, and languages, to you it is commanded that when the sound of music is heard you must fall down upon your knees before this great image of gold, which the King has set up. But if you refuse to fall down and worship the image, then you shall be thrown into a furnace of fire."

Soon afterwards the music began to play, and the people fell down on their knees, trembling in fear of the great King who had given such a stern command. All the people except three men bowed with their faces to the ground. These three stood up boldly, and would not kneel at all. They were Shā′ drăch, Mē′-shăch, and Ă-bĕd′-nĕ-gō.

Because Nĕb-ū-chăd-nĕz′-zär had given these young men positions of honor in the kingdom, some of the Chăl-dē′-ăns were jealous of them. And now these jealous Chăl-dē′-ăns watched to see if Daniel's friends would kneel before the image. When they saw the young men standing bravely alone among all the kneeling princes and nobles, they hurried to tell Nĕb-ū-chăd-nĕz′-zär.

And Nĕb-ū-chăd-nĕz′-zär was surprized to hear that these men had dared to disobey his command. He knew they were good rulers, and he did not wish to destroy them in the furnace of fire. He thought perhaps they might have misunderstood, so he sent for them at once, and told them that he would give them another chance to obey. But they bravely answered: "O King, we will not accept another chance. We will not bow before your image, for we will not worship any god except the one true God. And our God is so great that he can deliver us from the fiery furnace that you have prepared. But even if he will not deliver us from any such a death, we will not worship any other god."

Nĕb-ū-chăd-nĕz′-zär could not understand why these Jews should refuse to worship the image, and he was very angry indeed. He believed these young men were too stubborn to obey him, and he no longer wished to spare their lives from the cruel furnace. He commanded his servants to throw more fuel into the fire and make it seven times hotter than it had been before. Then he called the mightiest men of his army and gave them orders to bind stout cords around Shā′-drăch, Mē′-shăch, and Ă-bĕd′-nĕ-gō, and throw them like pieces of wood into the fire.

But Shā′-drăch, Mē′-shăch, and Ă-bĕd′-nĕ-gō were not afraid. They stood quietly while the mighty men wound the cords tightly around their bodies, and they did not cry out when the men picked them up and threw them into the furnace. But the flames leaped out of the furnace door and killed the mighty soldiers who carried them to the place of burning.

Nĕb-ū-chăd-nĕz′-zär sat in his royal chair near by, watching. He saw the flames leap out and burn the soldiers to death. He saw Shā′-drăch, Mē′-shăch, and Ă-bĕd′-nĕ-gō fall, bound hand and foot, into the fire. Then his eyes grew wide in surprize; for he saw the three men who had dared to disobey his command rise up and walk about in the fire with no cords to hinder them. And another Person, one who looked to the astonished King like a god, was walking about with them in the furnace.

At first Nĕb-ū-chăd-nĕz′-zär refused to believe his own eyes. He called to the nobles who stood near his chair and asked, "Did we not cast only three men into the fire?'' and they replied, "True, O King." "But now I see four men, unbound and walking freely about in the midst of the awful flame!'' he cried out. "They seem to have no hurt and the fourth one is like a god.''

Now Nĕb-ū-chăd-nĕz'-zär rose from his royal chair in haste and ran to the door of the furnace. He called loudly to the three men and said, "Shā'-drăch, Mē'-shăch, and Ă-bĕd'-ne-gō, ye servants of the Most High God, come forth! and come to me at once!''

The princes and nobles and rulers of the kingdom gathered round in amazement to see these three men walk out of the fire and come before Nĕb-ū-chăd-nĕz'-zär. And they saw that the fire had not harmed these Jews at all. Not even had their hair been singed by the flames, and the smell of fire was not noticed on their garments. But the stout cords that the soldiers had wrapped tightly around them before throwing them into the furnace had been burned to ashes.

Nĕb-ū-chăd-nĕz'-zär was no longer angry with Shā'-drăch, Mē'-shăch, and Ă-bĕd'-ne-gō. Now he believed they were great men, and he wished to honor them. He knew they served a great God, one who could do miracles, and he blessed the God of the Jews. He said to all the people, "Now I shall make another commandment, that no man in all my kingdom shall speak one word against the God of these brave men." And after this Nĕb-ū-chăd-nĕz'-zär set these men up in higher places in his kingdom.

STORY 5

HOW GOD HUMBLED THE PROUD HEART OF NEBUCHADNEZZAR

Daniel 4

One night while Nĕb-ū-chăd-nĕz'-zär lay asleep in his palace, God caused him to have another strange dream. This time when he awoke in the morning he remembered what the dream had been, and he wondered about its meaning. So he sent again for the wise Chăl-dē'-ănś, and told them about the dream that was troubling his mind.

The Chăl-dē'-ănś were glad because Nĕb-ū-chăd-nĕz'-zär had remembered his dream; but when they listened to it they could not tell its meaning. So the King sent them away and called for Daniel. He believed that the spirit of Daniel's God dwelt in Daniel and caused him to understand the deepest mysteries. And he called Daniel the master of all his wise men.

Daniel listened while Nĕb-ū-chăd-nĕz'-zär told the dream that was troubling him.   And God caused Daniel to understand what the dream meant.   But at first he was afraid to tell the King.   For a whole hour he sat quietly, wondering what he should do.   Then Nĕb-ū-chăd-nĕz'-zär said, "Do not be afraid, nor let the dream or its meaning trouble you." So Daniel took courage and spoke to the great ruler.

Now, the dream had been this: Nĕb-ū-chăd-nĕz'-zär had seen a tree grow up in the earth and become so great that the top of it reached to the sky.   Underneath its branches all the beasts of the field found shelter, and in its leafy boughs all the birds of the air made their nests. And the people of the earth from near and far came to eat of its fruit. Then Nĕb-ū-chăd-nĕz'-zär had seen the Lord come down from heaven and cry out: "Cut down the great tree; cut off its branches, shake off its leaves, and scatter its fruit.   Let the beasts get away from under the shadow of it, and let the dew come upon it for seven years.   But let the stump of the great tree remain with its roots in the ground until the seven years be passed.   Let this be, that all who live may know there is a God in heaven who rules over all the kingdoms of earth."

Daniel knew the dream was sent as a warning from God to the proud King.   He knew Nĕb-ū-chăd-nĕz'-zär was not willing to believe in the great God, who is over all.   But he spoke bravely and said, "This great tree which you have seen means you, for you have become a great king and you are known in every part of the land.   And the meaning of that voice which you heard crying out that the great tree should be cut down is that you shall lose your kingdom for seven years and go out from men to live among the beasts of the field.   You shall eat grass like an ox, and the dew of heaven shall be upon you.   But when you humble yourself and believe that the Most High God rules in the kingdoms of earth, giving them to whomever he pleases, then you shall return again to live among men and be restored to your kingdom."

Daniel knew that God is very merciful, and he believed that God would save the King from such severe punishment if only the King would quit his sins and do right. So he urged Nĕb-ū-chăd-nĕz'-zär to turn away from his wicked doings and begin to live differently.   Then he went back to his own house.

One year passed by, and nothing unusual happened. Perhaps Nĕb-ū-chăd-nĕz'-zär almost forgot the strange dream, at least he did not try to do as Daniel had urged him to do.   He saw about him all the splendors of his kingdom and all the beauties of his palace grounds.   He saw the famous city of Babylon, which he had helped to beautify, and his heart grew more proud and haughty.   Then one day as he walked about in his kingly palace, admiring the grandeur of his surroundings, he said, "Is not this great Babylon, which I have built for my own royal house by my own power and for my glory?" And while he spoke the words a voice called to him from heaven, saying, "O King Nĕb-ū-c̱ẖăd-nĕz′-zär, to you it is spoken: The Kingdom is taken from you!"

NEBUCHADNEZZAR IN THE FIELDS

In that very hour the great King lost his mind and became like a wild beast. And the people were afraid of him, and they drove him out of the city. There he lived in the fields and ate grass like the oxen. And his hair grew like eagle's feathers and his nails grew like claws. For seven years he roamed about in the fields, with a heart like a beast's instead of a man's. Then God allowed his mind to return again, and his heart to become like a man's heart, and Nĕb-ū-c̱ẖăd-nĕz′-zär rose up like a man and thanked God for his mercies, and praised him for his greatness.

When the people of Babylon saw that their King had returned again to their city with the mind of a well man, they welcomed him back. And they honored him as their king just as they had done before. But Nĕb-ū-chăd-nĕz'-zär did not forget the lesson that God taught him, and he no longer believed that his greatness and his glory had come by his own strength.

———•———

STORY 6
THE STRANGE HANDWRITING ON THE WALL OF THE PALACE
Daniel 5

A great feast was being held in the palace at Babylon. The king, Bĕl-shăz'-zär, had invited a thousand princes and nobles to enjoy the feast with him and his many wives. And the palace was ringing with their voices and laughter and song.

Presently, while they were drinking wine together, the King remembered the beautiful vessels of gold that Nĕb-ū-chăd-nĕz'-zär had brought from the temple of the Lord, in Jerusalem. He commanded his servants to bring the vessels into the palace, that he and his company might drink wine from them. And the vessels were brought, and the King commanded that they be filled with wine and passed among the guests. Then, as they drank from the golden vessels, they praised the gods of gold, and of silver, and of wood, and of stone.

Bĕl-shăz'-zär's heart was merry, and he felt very secure and happy in his palace-home among his guests. He joined with them in praising the gods of gold, silver, wood, and stone. Then suddenly he turned pale, and the gladness died out of his heart. A great fear swept over him, and caused his knees to tremble. For there on the wall of the palace, over near the candlestick, he saw the fingers of a man's hand writing strange words, which he could not read.

All at once everything grew quiet in the banquet-hall. And everybody became afraid, for no one could understand the strange words that the hand had written. Then the King commanded that the wise Chăl-dē'-ăns be brought in at once; for he thought they might be able to read the words and tell their meaning. He promised to give a rich reward to the one who could do this; but none of the Chăl-dē'-ăns were able to earn that reward. They could not read the writing on the wall.

News of the strange handwriting spread rapidly through the palace, and soon the old Queen Mother heard about it. She heard, too, that the wise men could not read the writing nor tell its meaning. So she came into the banquet-hall, where the King sat trembling among his

THE HANDWRITING ON THE PALACE WALL

frightened guests. And she said, "O King, there is in this city a very wise man whom you have quite forgotten. In the days of Něb-ū-chăd-něz'-zär, the king, this man was the master of all the king's wise men, for the spirit of the gods dwells in him. Now send for him, and he will tell you the meaning of this strange handwriting on the wall."

Daniel was now an old man. For a long time he had lived quietly in Babylon, for the kings who followed Něb-ū-chăd-něz'-zär had not set him up to places of honor in the kingdom. And he was almost forgotten. The Queen Mother, however, remembered how he had interpreted the dreams of Něb-ū-chăd-něz'-zär, and she knew that his wisdom was greater than any of the wisdom of the Chăl-dē'-ănś.

Běl-shăz'-zär sent in haste for Daniel, and when the old man came before him he asked, excitedly, "Are you that Daniel whom my fathers brought out of the land of the Jews?" Daniel replied that he was, and the King said, "I have heard of you, that the spirit of the gods dwells with you and enables you to understand deep mysteries. Now, if you can read the writing upon the wall and tell its meaning, I will cause you to be dressed in royal garments, and will make you the third ruler in this kingdom."

Daniel did not care for the honors of the Babylonian kingdom. He did not care for the beautiful, kingly robes, and he told the King to give those gifts to some one else. But he said, "I will read the writing, and will cause you to understand its meaning."

First Daniel reminded Běl-shăz'-zär of great punishment that God had sent upon Něb-ū-chăd-něz'-zär because of his wickedness and pride. Běl-shăz'-zär had known about this, yet he had dared to be proud and to despise the God of heaven and earth. He had dared to use the vessels that belonged in the Lord's house, in Jerusalem, for drinking wine, and he and his guests had praised the gods of gold and of silver and of wood and of stone, which cannot see nor hear. Daniel told Běl-shăz'-zär about these things, and then he said, "Because you did these things, God sent this hand to write upon the wall of your banquet-room, that you might see it and become afraid. The words that this hand has written are Mē'-nē, Mē'-nē, Tē'-kěl, Ū-phär'-sĭn, and they mean this:

"Mē'-nē; God has numbered your kingdom and finished it.

"Tē'-kěl; you are weighed in the balances and found wanting.

"Ū-phär'-sĭn; your kingdom is divided, and is given to the Medes and Persians."

Běl-shăz'-zär commanded his servants to bring a royal garment and put it on Daniel, then he fastened a gold chain about Daniel's neck and proclaimed before all the guests that Daniel was the third ruler in the

The Jews
in Captivity

THE JEWS IN CAPTIVITY

Judah, the southern kingdom, forsook God, and God permitted the Babylonians under Nebuchadnezzar to destroy the capital, Jerusalem, and carry the inhabitants away into Babylon.

King Nebuchadnezzar made an image of gold and set it up on the Plain of Dura in Babylon. At his command all the people were to fall down and worship the golden image. Three Hebrew children —Shadrach, Meshach, and Abednego—refused to bow down to the image and for punishment they were cast into a fiery furnace. But God preserved them from the flames.

When King Nebuchadnezzar refused to acknowledge the true God, for seven years he was as a wild beast, eating the grass of the field.

Darius, a king who succeeded Nebuchadnezzar, gave Daniel charge of part of the kingdom. This caused jealousy among the other rulers, who asked Darius to make a decree that all who would pray to anyone but Darius for thirty days should be cast into the den of lions. Daniel prayed to his God as formerly and was cast into the den. But God sent an angel, who closed the lions' mouths.

After the Jews had spent many years in Babylon, God sent the prophet Ezekiel to speak to them concerning the return to their own land once more.

kingdom. But that very night the kingdom of Babylon was destroyed; for the Mēdes and Persians came into the city and killed Bĕl-shăz'-zär, and placed the Mē'-dĭ-ăn king Dä-rī'-ŭs upon the throne.

DANIEL IN THE LIONS' DEN

Daniel 6

King Dä-rī'-ŭs, the new ruler, chose one hundred and twenty princes to help him govern the people of his great kingdom. Over these princes he appointed three presidents, and because he found that Daniel was a very wise old man he made Daniel the first president. So Daniel was more highly honored than any of the princes or other presidents.

A bitter feeling of jealousy began to stir in the hearts of these princes and presidents. They hated Daniel because the King had honored him so greatly. They decided to watch him carefully, and find fault with him at their first opportunity. But their careful watching only revealed to them the fact that Daniel was a very faithful man, with no faults that might displease the King.

Their careful watching revealed another fact, too; and this one was that Daniel was deeply religious. Often they saw him kneel before his open window and pray to his God. He never seemed too busy to take time to pray.

At last the men confessed among themselves that they could find no fault with Daniel. But they planned another way to rob him of his great honor. A cruel way, it was, but they were wicked men and they did not mind at all.

Dä-rī'-ŭs was surprized to see the great company of his princes assemble before him. He did not notice that Daniel was not among them. He did not guess that they were plotting against his faithful servant. So he permitted them to tell the purpose that had brought them to his palace, and they said, "King Dä-rī'-ŭs, live forever. All the presidents of the kingdom, and the princes, the governors, the counselors, and the captains have planned to establish a royal law and to make it very binding. This is the law: That whoever shall ask a request of any god or man for thirty days, except of you, O King, he shall be cast into a den of lions."

Now the truth was that all the presidents of the kingdom had not helped to plan that law, for Daniel had no part in it. But the King

THE MEN WATCHING DANIEL PRAY

did not know. And because he was a heathen king, with a proud heart,
he felt flattered to hear the law. So he readily consented to it, and he
caused it to become published among all the people.

Of course Daniel heard about the law. But three times every day
Daniel knelt, just as he had done before, and prayed by his opened window with his face toward Jerusalem, the city where God's house used
to stand. And there these men found him on his knees thanking God.

Now they were sure they should soon be rid of this good man whom
they despised. So they came to tell the King how Daniel had dared
to disobey the new law. They reminded the King that the laws he made
could not be changed, and Daniel would have to be punished for his
disobedience.

Dă-rī'-ŭs understood, when too late, why this law had been made.
He knew the presidents and princes had not desired to honor him, but
only to rid themselves of the one whom they hated. And Darius was
sorry, very sorry, that he had listened to the flattering words of these
wicked men. All day long he tried
to think of some way in which to
spare Daniel from such a cruel
fate; all day long he worked hard,
studying the laws of his country
and hoping to find something that
would release him from enforcing
such a punishment upon his faithful servant. But finally the sun
went down, and the presidents and
princes came impatiently to the
palace and told the King that his
new law must be obeyed. And Dă-
rī'-ŭs feared to try longer to save
Daniel, so he told them to bring
him out and cast him into the lions'
den.

DANIEL AMONG THE HUNGRY LIONS

The King told Daniel how sorry he was to see this dreadful punishment brought upon him. And he
said, "The God whom you serve so faithfully surely will deliver you
from the lions." Then he saw Daniel thrown into the den, and he saw
the wicked men lay the heavy stone upon the mouth of the den, making
Daniel a prisoner inside among the savage beasts. Afterwards, according to the law of his country, he put his own seal upon the great

stone, so that no one would dare to remove it without the King's command. Then, with a heavy heart, he went back to his palace.

All that night long Dă-rī'-ŭs could not sleep. He was too troubled to enjoy any kind of entertainment, for he thought constantly about his faithful servant in that terrible den. He longed for the morning light, and with the first break of dawn he rose up from his bed and ran quickly to the lions' den. Then, in a troubled, anxious voice, he cried out, ''O Daniel, servant of the living God, is your God whom you have served so faithfully able to save you from the lions?''

Then the King listened, and soon he heard an answering voice from the deep pit, saying, ''O King, live forever. My God has sent his angel, and the angel has shut the mouths of these savage beasts, and they have done me no harm at all. For God has seen that I was not guilty of any wrong-doing before him nor even before you.''

Dă-rī'-ŭs was very glad, and he called his servants to come and take Daniel up out of the den. Then he commanded that the wicked men be brought who had planned to get rid of Daniel, and he told his servants to cast them into the den of lions where Daniel had been all the long night. When they fell, screaming, into the deep pit, the lions rushed upon them and tore them in pieces, for they were not worthy to live.

Dă-rī'-ŭs wrote letters to the people of every nation, telling them about the wonderful way in which God had delivered Daniel from the lions. And he made a law that all the people in his great kingdom should fear the God of the Jews.

———————⧫———————

STORY 8

DANIEL'S ANGEL VISITOR
Daniel 8—12

Daniel had lived many years in the beautiful capital cities of the eastern kings, and he had helped these kings rule the people. But during those many years (for he was now old) he had never forgotten his childhood home in Jerusalem nor the temple of the Lord, which Nĕb-ū-chăd-nĕz'-zär and his soldiers had destroyed.

Daniel had read the letters that Jeremiah the prophet had written to the captive Jews in Babylon, and he knew Jeremiah had prophesied that the Jews might return again to their own land after seventy years. And now, when he was an old man, Daniel knew the seventy years would soon be passed, and he longed to see his people return again and rebuild the temple of the Lord in Jerusalem.

Instead of praying three times every day for himself and for his people, now Daniel sometimes prayed all day long. Sometimes he refused to eat his food because he wished to have more time to spend alone, talking with God. And he even dressed himself in sackcloth and sat in ashes when he prayed, to show God that he was very sorry for his sins and for the sins of his people.

And Daniel's earnest prayers were heard. One evening while he was praying an angel came to talk with him. This angel had come one time before, when God had caused Daniel to see a wonderful vision; but this time the angel came to comfort Daniel. He said, "O Daniel, you are a man greatly loved by the Lord, and you shall know what shall come to pass in after years." And the angel told Daniel about the coming of the Savior, Jesus Christ, who should suffer and die for the sins of the people.

Daniel, after he became a very old man, continued to do business for the King. And when Dă-rī'-ŭs died, the new King, Cyrus, took Daniel to his capital city in Persia and kept him there for a helper. And Daniel continued to pray earnestly even while he did business for the new King.

One day during the rule of King Cyrus, Daniel and several companions were by the riverside when all at once Daniel saw a heavenly visitor stand before him. The face of this heavenly visitor shone like lightning and his eyes like fire. Even his arms and his feet shone like polished brass. Daniel could not look upon him, and fell to the ground. The men who were with Daniel did not see the heavenly visitor, but they felt the earth trembling beneath their feet and they ran away in fear.

As Daniel lay on the ground like one dead, the angel came and touched him. Then Daniel rose up on his knees, and the angel spoke. And his voice sounded like a multitude of voices. At first Daniel could not answer, for he had no power of speech left in him. But the angel touched his lips and caused strength to return into his body. And Daniel talked long with his heavenly visitor. And all these things he afterwards wrote in a book.

Daniel was one of the greatest prophets, as well as a great man in the country where he lived. By his courage and trueness to God he caused several heathen kings to respect the religion of the Jews, and he lived to see the time when King Cyrus allowed the Jews to return again to Judah.

STORY 9

THE HOME-COMING OF THE JEWS

Ezra 1:1—3:7

A great company of people were gathering in the valley along the Eu-phrā'-tēs River, preparing to start on a long journey. There were old people, and young people, and even little boys and girls. These people were the Jews, and they were arranging soon to start back to the land of their fathers—Judah. For Cyrus, the new king, had sent this message to the Jews scattered everywhere throughout his kingdom: "The Lord God of heaven has given me all the kingdoms of earth; and he has charged me to build him a house at Jerusalem, which is in Judah. Now who is there among his people—the Jews—who will go up to Jerusalem and build this house for God?"

Daniel was too old to return on this long journey to Jerusalem. And perhaps the King would have been unwilling to spare this great man from his work. But there were others, many others, who were just as eager as Daniel to see the temple of the Lord rebuilt. And one of these persons was Zĕ-rŭb'-bă-bĕl, a brave young man who belonged to the family of David. He became the leader of the people who returned to Jerusalem, but he ruled as a prince under the command of King Cyrus; for the throne of David was not restored in Jerusalem again.

When the long journey began, the people moved slowly up the highway that led northward from Babylon, the same highway over which some of them had traveled seventy years before. Many of them walked, but some rode on horses, others on camels or donkeys. Now they were singing songs of joy, and they were carrying their beautiful harps back to their own land. There they would be glad and there they would play sweet music in the new house of the Lord which Cyrus had commanded them to build.

Cyrus had given them the vessels of gold and of silver which Nĕb-ū-chăd-nĕz'-zär had stolen from the temple before he set it on fire, and they were taking those vessels back to be used in the new temple. And Cyrus had commanded their neighbors and friends to give them rich gifts of gold and of silver. So they were well laden for their journey.

Not all the Jews returned to Jerusalem; for many were becoming rich in their new homes, and they did not care to go back to Judah. But they sent precious gifts to help in the building of the new temple.

And they were glad because some of their own people were returning to build up the altar of the Lord, which had been torn down.

When at last the long journey was nearing its end, the people came in sight of the crumbled walls of Jerusalem. Some of them remembered how the city looked before it had been destroyed by Něb-ū-chăd-něz'-zär, and their hearts were filled with sadness. But many of them had never seen Jerusalem, for they had been born in the land of captivity. They had heard their parents tell about the land which God had given to them long ago, and which he had allowed King Něb-ū-chăd-něz'-zär to take away from them because they had worshiped idols. And they were glad to come back and build homes in that land which Něb-ū-chăd-něz'-zär had taken away from them.

In the ruins of Jerusalem the people found the place where the temple of the Lord used to stand. They found the rock where the altar of the Lord had been built. And here the priests and the Levites cleared away the rubbish and gathered stones to build a new altar. Then they began again to offer sacrifices to God each morning and each evening, just as the law of Moses commanded them to do.

STORY 10

HOW THE NEW TEMPLE WAS BUILT IN JERUSALEM

Ezra 3: 7—6: 22; Haggai 1, 2

When Zě-rŭb'-bă-běl and his company came to Jerusalem they did not begin at once to rebuild the temple of the Lord. Winter was coming on, and first they built houses for themselves. But at the return of springtime they set to work at the great task that had brought them back to Judah.

Zě-rŭb'-bă-běl and Jěsh'-ū-ă, the high priest, hired carpenters and masons for the new building, and put to work every man among their number who was twenty years old or more. Again they sent to the Lebanon Mountains for wood to use in the building, for Cyrus the king had given them permission to do this.

When everything was ready, the workers laid the foundation of the new temple. And the priests and Levites and singers stood ready with their trumpets and musical instruments to worship the Lord. They sang together, giving praise to God. And all the people stood near by, rejoicing because the great work was so well begun. They shouted with a loud noise. But some among them had seen the temple which

Solomon had built, and when they saw the foundation of this new building they remembered how beautiful the first temple had been. Instead of shouting with joy they wept for sorrow.

There were strangers living in the country places near Jerusalem who were not Jews. When they saw the work that the Jews had commenced at Jerusalem, they asked permission to help in the building

BUILDING THE NEW TEMPLE

of the temple; they said, "We seek your God, as you do." But Zĕ-rŭb'-bă-bĕl and Jĕsh'-ū-ă, the high priest, knew these men did not worship God in the right way, and they would not accept help from them.

These strangers were Să-mâr'-ĭ-tăns, the people who came to live in Israel after the northern tribes were carried away into captivity. These were the people who had a mixed religion—a mixture of the true religion and idol-worship. When Zĕ-rŭb'-bă-bĕl and Jĕsh'-ū-ă refused to let them help build the temple they grew angry and tried to hinder the work. They sent letters back to the king of Persia, accusing the Jews of falsehoods, and they continued to do this for a long time. Finally they caused the building of the temple to come to a standstill.

Several years passed by, and the Jews were not allowed to finish the temple. So they built comfortable homes for themselves and began to work in the fields near Jerusalem.

Finally God caused the new king of Persia, another king named Dă-rī'-ŭs, to be friendly toward the Jews. But the Jews did not ask him to help them. They did not try to finish the work which they had begun on the temple. So God sent a prophet, named Hăg'-gaî, to urge them to get at work again on the temple. This prophet said that Zĕ-rŭb'-bă-bĕl had begun the new temple, and he should finish the building of it.

So Zĕ-rŭb'-bă-bĕl and Jĕsh'-ū-ă took courage and began once more on the temple-building. When they commenced work the Să-mâr'-ĭ-tăns came down to see what they were doing. They asked, "Who has given you orders to do this?" And they answered, "Cyrus, the king of Persia, commanded us to build this house of God." The Să-mâr'-ĭ-tăns did not believe their words, and they wrote a letter to King Dă-rī'-ŭs telling what the Jews had said. But when Dă-rī'-ŭs looked in the records that had been kept during the rule of Cyrus he found that Cyrus had indeed commanded the Jews to rebuild the temple. So he sent word back to the Să-mâr'-ĭ-tăns, telling them not to hinder the Jews, but rather to give them money to help hurry on the great work which Cyrus had commanded them to do. And he said that if they refused to obey his words their own houses should be torn down and they should be killed. This message caused the Să-mâr'-ĭ-tăns to become afraid, and they ceased to hinder the Jews.

When the temple was finally completed, the Jews held a great feast, and they offered many sacrifices to the Lord. They rejoiced very much because God had given them a friend in the new king of Persia, and had helped them to overcome the wicked plans of their neighbors, the Să-mâr'-ĭ-tăns.

STORY 11

THE BEAUTIFUL GIRL WHO BECAME A QUEEN

Esther 1, 2

Beauty that shines in the face alone
Not long may sit on a queenly throne;
For beauty of heart in the life must be seen
Before there can be a beautiful queen.

Esther, the Jewess, was only a little girl when both her parents died and she went to live in the home of her cousin, Môr-dĕ-cā'-ī. Her new home was in the great city of Shû'-shăn, where the King of Persia lived. Her cousin, Môr-dĕ-cā'-ī, had an office in the household of the king. He was very kind to Esther, and loved her as his own child.

After Esther grew up to young womanhood the King of Persia made a great feast in his palace. He invited all the nobles and rulers of his kingdom. Then, at the last of the feast he invited all the men of Shû'-shăn, both great and small, to come to the palace and share in his entertainment. Perhaps Môr-dĕ-cā'-ī was there, too.

Women in that country always wore veils over their faces when in the presence of men other than their own husbands, and they could not attend the same feasts with them. So the Queen, Vashti, gave a feast to the women at the same time as the King's feast to the men.

On the last day of the feast, which continued for a whole week, the King grew very reckless because he had drunk much wine. And he wished to see his beautiful wife, the Queen. He wished that all the people attending his feast might see how beautiful she was. So he sent some of his servants to bring her into his part of the royal palace, where all the guests could behold her beauty.

But Vashti, the Queen, refused to appear in the presence of all the men of Shû'-shăn. And she told the King's servants that she would not come. She believed that the King's request was unwise because it was contrary to the customs of her people.

King Ă-hăṣ-ū-ē'-rŭs was very angry when the servants returned alone and told him that Vashti would not come with them. He called his wise men and asked what should be done with Vashti, the Queen, who had dared to disobey him. And one of the wise men said, "The Queen has done wrong, not only to you, O King, but also to the princes and to all the people who dwell in your kingdom. For when this deed becomes known, the women everywhere will no longer respect their husbands as they should. Therefore let her be queen no longer, but choose another who is better than she to take her place."

This advice pleased Ă-hăs-ū-ē'-rŭs, and he refused to let Vashti come into his presence again. He refused to let her be queen any longer, and decided to choose another beautiful young woman to become queen in her stead. So he sent commands through all his kingdom that the most beautiful young women should be brought to his palace, where

ESTHER, THE BEAUTIFUL QUEEN

he might choose among them the one who would please him best. This one he would make queen instead of Vashti.

Môr-dĕ-cā'-ī knew that Esther was a beautiful young woman, and he believed she would make a beautiful queen. So he sent her to the palace with the other young women who came from different parts of the kingdom. And there she was taught the manners of the court-life, so she would know how to please the King. But Môr-dĕ-cā'-ī told her not to let the fact become known that her people were the Jews.

After living in the palace for some time, Esther was brought before the King; and she pleased him so much that he chose her at once
to become the queen instead of Vashti.

He placed the royal crown of Persia upon her head, and gave her
rooms in his palace and many servants to attend her. Then he made
a great feast for his princes and nobles, called Esther's feast, and he
published the fact that Esther had been chosen as the new queen.

Môr-dĕ-cā'-ī could no longer see the young woman whom he had
cared for as tenderly as his own daughter. But every day he passed by
the palace where she lived, and she could see him from her window. She
would send messages to him by her faithful servants, and they would
bring back the messages Môr-dĕ-cā'-ī wished her to receive. Then Môr-
dĕ-cā'-ī would return to the king's gate and sit there as a watchman.

While sitting in the gate, Môr-dĕ-cā'-ī saw two servants of the King
who whispered together about some secret matter. He watched closely
and learned that they were angry with the King and were planning
to kill him. So he sent word to the King by Queen Esther, and she
gave the warning in Môr-dĕ-cā'-ī's name. The King investigated the
matter, and found that the men were guilty, so he put them to death.
Then the warning of Môr-dĕ-cā'-ī, and how he had saved the King's life,
were written in a book. But the King forgot about Môr-dĕ-cā'-ī's kindness to him, and did not promote him in the kingdom. He did not know
that Môr-dĕ-cā'-ī, the Jew, was a relative of the beautiful young woman
who wore the royal crown.

STORY 12

WHY A PROUD MAN PLANNED TO DESTROY ALL THE JEWS

Esther 3:1—4:3

Among the princes at the royal palace in Shû'-shăn was a proud
man named Hā'-măn. He was very rich, and clever, and he knew how
to behave in the most pleasing manner whenever he appeared before
the King. So the King honored Hā'-măn above all the princes, and commanded all his servants to pay respect to this proud man.

Among the King's servants who sat in the gate of the palace was
Môr-dĕ-cā'-ī, the Jew. And whenever Hā'-măn passed through the gate
the King's servants were supposed to bow down before him, with their
faces in the dust. And they all did so except Môr-dĕ-cā'-ī. He would not
bow down before any man to give him the honor that belonged to God
only.

The King's servants were not pleased when they saw that Môr-dĕ-cā'-ī refused to bow down before the honored prince. They asked him why he dared to disobey the command of the King. And Môr-dĕ-cā'-ī told them that he was a Jew; and doubtless he told them that the Jews worshiped God only and would not reverence a man as if he were a god. Then the servants hurried to tell Hā'-măn of Môr-dĕ-cā'-ī's un-willingness to bow before him.

Hā'-măn's pride was deeply wounded when he heard that Môr-dĕ-cā'-ī, the Jew, refused to give him honor. He became very angry, and determined to punish Môr-dĕ-cā'-ī. But he thought that because he was such a great man it would look petty to punish only one Jew; he must resort to some great form of punishment. So he planned to kill all the Jews. He did not know that Esther, the beautiful queen whom the King loved, was a Jewess.

Now Hā'-măn helped to rule in the great kingdom of Persia, and he often came before the King. He thought it would be an easy matter to get the King's consent to have the Jews killed. And he planned carefully, that Ă-hăs-ū-ē'-rŭs might not know he was angry with the Jews because Môr-dĕ-cā'-ī would not bow before him. Then he came to the King and said, "O King, there is a certain people scattered throughout your countries whose laws are contrary to your laws and they refuse to obey you. They are different from other people and they are unprofitable to our kingdom, therefore if it please you, let a law be made that those people be destroyed. And I myself will pay the money to hire soldiers to kill them."

Ă-hăs-ū-ē'-rŭs did not know much about the Jews nor their strange religion. He did not know that his beautiful queen was a Jewess. And he supposed that Hā'-măn, his great prince, knew all about the people who were so unprofitable to his kingdom, so he told Hā'-măn to write let-ters to the rulers in every part of the kingdom, telling them that on a certain day they should destroy all the Jews in their part of the coun-try, every man, woman, and child.

After the letters were written, Hā'-măn gave them to postmen, who carried them to every part of the kingdom. Then he believed he had done a great deed that would bring him much honor, and he went to the palace to dine with the King. He felt that no one in all the realm of Persia was quite so important as himself, for even the King allowed him to do just as he pleased.

Soon the news of this letter reached the ears of the Jews in every part of the land. And they wondered why Ă-hăs-ū-ē'-rŭs had suddenly become so displeased with them. They had always lived peacefully among his people, and had never given him any trouble. They had worked at honest toil and many of them had become very rich. Now they were to be destroyed and their riches were to be seized by wicked men. They could not understand why this cruel law had been passed against them. And everywhere they wept with loud cries, tearing their clothes and dressing themselves in sackcloth. Many of them sat in ashes, and mourned and fasted and prayed.

Môr-dĕ-cā'-ī was among the first of the Jews to hear about the cruel law; for he lived in the city of Shû'-shăn. And he knew at once that Hā'-măn had made the law. He knew that even Esther would have to suffer death if the law were obeyed, for every Jew was to be destroyed. And his grief was very great. Tearing his garments, he wrapped himself in sackcloth and threw ashes upon his body. Then he went out into the streets and cried with a loud and bitter cry. But he did not dare to pass through the king's gate, for no one was allowed to enter the gate when dressed in sackcloth. And he could not come near the palace to send a message to the Queen. He hoped that Esther might hear about him, and send a messenger to learn why he was so deeply troubled. Then he would tell her all about the cruel law, and then perhaps she could think of some way to help them and save their lives.

STORY 13

HOW QUEEN ESTHER SAVED THE LIVES OF HER PEOPLE
Esther 4:4—10:3

Esther was happy in her beautiful palace-home. She was kind to her servants, and they liked to obey her. But she did not forget how Môr-dĕ-cā'-ī had taken her into his own home when she was a poor little orphan. And every day she watched from her window to see him pass by, and always she was eager to receive the messages that he sent. She still obeyed him just as cheerfully as when she had been a little girl in his own humble home.

But one day Môr-dĕ-cā'-ī did not pass by as usual. And Esther missed him. Perhaps she thought he might be sick. But soon her servants came to tell her that he was walking through the streets of the city, dressed in sackcloth and crying with a loud and bitter cry. "What has happened?" wondered the Queen, as she hurriedly gathered some

new clothes to send to him. How she longed to run out to comfort
him, herself! But now she was the queen, and now she could not go
about in the streets. Perhaps she wished that she were not the queen,
after all.

As she sat watching anxiously from her window, soon she saw the
servant returning with the clothes she had sent. Môr-dĕ-cā'-ī would not
take them, and Esther knew that some terrible sorrow had come into
his life. So she quickly called another servant, one of the King's servants who sometimes waited on her, and told him to learn from Môr-
dĕ-cā'-ī the cause of his intense grief.

Môr-dĕ-cā'-ī told this servant about all that had happened to him,
how Hā'-măn had planned to kill all the Jews and had even promised to
give money to the King for this cruel purpose. He gave the servant
a copy of the letter that Hā'-măn had written, and the servant brought
the letter to Esther. He told Esther, too, that Môr-dĕ-cā'-ī had commanded her to speak to the King and tell him that she was a Jew, and
that Hā'-măn had planned to kill her and all her people.

At first Esther was afraid to go to the King. She knew the law
of the palace: that any one, either a man or a woman, who should approach the throne without being called by the king would be put to
death unless the king should hold out to that person the golden scepter.
And she feared to take such a risk; for the King had not called for
her in many days, and she supposed he was attending to important
matters and did not wish to be disturbed. She sent her servant back
to Môr-dĕ-cā'-ī to tell him that she dared not go into the presence of the
King without being called by him.

Môr-dĕ-cā'-ī believed that God had permitted Esther to become
queen on purpose, so that she might at this time save the lives of her
people. So he sent word again, telling Esther that she must go, for if
she refused she would be sparing her life at that time only to lose it
later, when all the Jews in Shū'-shăn should be destroyed.

Esther still was fearful to obey the wishes of Môr-dĕ-cā'-ī; but she
longed to help her people, and she promised to try. She commanded
Môr-dĕ-cā'-ī to gather all the Jews in Shū'-shăn into one place, and there
to fast and pray for three days that God would give her favor in the
eyes of the King. She and her servants would also fast during that
time, and then if Ă-hăs-ū-ē'-rŭs had not yet called for her she would go
to him, contrary to the law of the palace, and plead for her life and
for the lives of her people.

Môr-dĕ-cā'-ī hastily called all the Jews in Shū'-shăn and told them
of Esther's words. And they fasted and prayed as she had commanded.

Then, on the third day she dressed in her most beautiful garments and went in to speak to the King.

Ă-hăs̆-ū-ē′-rŭs was surprized to see the Queen standing timidly in the court before his throne. He knew some urgent matter had brought her there, and because he loved her he held out to her the golden scepter, which was in his hand. Then she came near to his throne and touched the scepter, and he asked, "What is your request, Queen Esther? It shall be given to you though it should be the half of my kingdom."

Esther did not tell him at once about the great sorrow that clouded her life, but she requested him and his friend Hā′-măn to dine with her that day. And the King promised to come. Then she went away, and Ă-hăs̆-ū-ē′-rŭs sent word to Hā′-măn, telling him of the Queen's invitation to dinner.

Hā′-măn felt highly honored because he was the only guest invited to eat with the King and the Queen. But Ă-hăs̆-ū-ē′-rŭs guessed that Esther had some great request to make of him, so again he asked, "What is your wish, my queen?" And again Esther answer simply, "If I have found favor in your eyes, O King, my request is that you and Hā′-măn shall return tomorrow and dine with me as you have done to-day. Then I shall tell you what is my greatest wish." And the King promised that they would come.

After the banquet Hā′-măn hurried home to tell his wife and his friends about the great honor that Queen Esther had shown to him. But as he passed through the king's gate he saw Môr-dĕ-cā′-ī sitting there and refusing to bow before him as the other servants were bowing. This spoiled all of Hā′-măn's gladness of heart. How he despised that Jew! He longed to be rid of Môr-dĕ-cā′-ī's presence in the king's gate, and he told his wife and his friends how greatly Môr-dĕ-cā′-ī's presence annoyed him. He boasted loudly to them of the honors both the King and the Queen were bestowing upon him, but he complained about the contempt this humble Jew, Môr-dĕ-cā′-ī, had shown.

Hā′-măn's wife and his friends urged him to prepare a high gallows and ask permission of the King to hang Môr-dĕ-cā′-ī. Then he might enjoy fully the honors that were being shown by every one else except this much-despised Jew. Hā′-măn thought their advice sounded good, and he set to work at once to have a gallows built.

That night Ă-hăs̆-ū-ē′-rŭs, the King, could not sleep. As he tossed restlessly about on his soft pillows he commanded his servants to bring the book of records and read to him about the things that had happened since he had been the ruler of Persia. And among the other things he heard them read from the book was Môr-dĕ-cā′-ī's report of

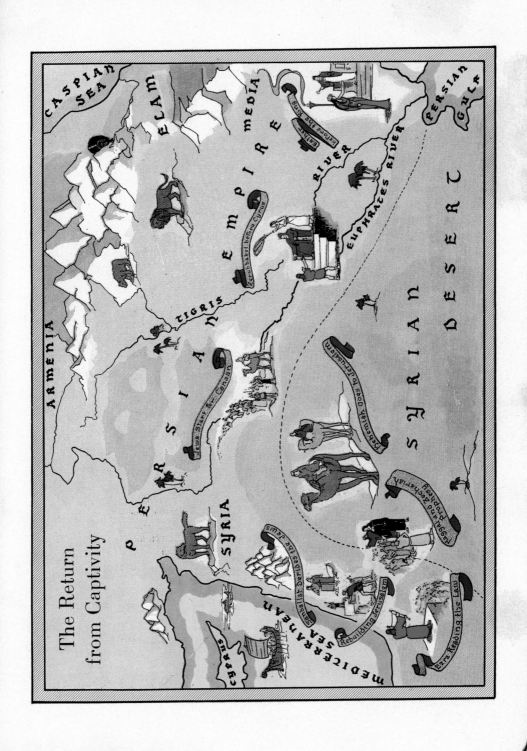

The Return from Captivity

THE RETURN FROM CAPTIVITY

Among the Jewish captives who were carried into Shushan (Persia) was a young girl by the name of Esther. Because she found favor in the sight of the king, she was made queen. When the lives of the Jews in this country were endangered, she interceded with King Ahasuerus and was able to save them.

After many years of captivity, Zerubbabel received permission from King Cyrus to lead a company of the Jews back to Jerusalem, where they began the rebuilding of the Temple.

Enemies hindered the building, and God sent the prophets Haggai and Zechariah to encourage the people to complete the Temple.

Ezra, a devout Jew of the Captivity, went up from Babylon to Jerusalem and taught the people the law of God.

Nehemiah, cupbearer to King Artaxerxes, upon hearing that the walls of Jerusalem had been broken down and the gates burned with fire, asked for permission to go up to Jerusalem and encourage his people to repair the walls. His request was granted and he went. The work of rebuilding the walls was hindered by Sanballet and a company of opposers, who made sport of their attempts. However, Nehemiah persisted and the walls were completed.

the evil plans of two servants who intended to kill the King. "Has any honor been shown to Môr-dĕ-cā'-ī for that kindness done to me?" asked Ă-hăs̆-ū-ē'-rŭs. And the servants answered, "Nothing has been done for him."

Hā'-măn rose early the next morning and went to the palace, intending to ask the King's permission to hang Môr-dĕ-cā'-ī on the gallows he had made. But just as he entered the court of the palace, Ă-hăs̆-ū-ē'-rŭs sent for him. And he came proudly, wondering what service he could perform to please his ruler. "What shall be done to the man whom the King delights to honor?" asked Ă-hăs̆-ū-ē'-rŭs of

ESTHER TOUCHES THE KING'S SCEPTER

Hā'-măn. And Hā'-măn thought quickly, "Whom would the King delight to honor more than me?" so, believing that the honor would be shown to him, he answered, "Let that man whom the King delights to honor be dressed in the King's royal garments, and let him ride upon the King's horse, with the King's crown upon his head. Let one of the most noble princes place the royal garment upon this man, and the crown upon his head, and let that prince bring him on horseback through the streets of the city and cry out before him that all may hear, 'This is done to the man whom the King delights to honor.'"

The King was pleased with Hā'-măn's answer, and he said, "You are my noble prince, so I command you to take my royal garment and my crown, and hasten to dress Môr-dĕ-cā'-ī in them. Then put him on my horse and lead him through the city, proclaiming before him the words that you have spoken. See that you do everything as you have advised should be done to the man whom I delight to honor."

Now Hā'-măn was frightened, but he dared not disobey the King's command. He took the garments, dressed Môr-dĕ-cā'-ī, the Jew, in them, and led him on horseback through the city streets, crying out, "This is done to the man whom the King delights to honor!" Then he returned with Môr-dĕ-cā'-ī to the palace, and brought back the royal garments to the King. Afterwards he ran home, covering his head in shame and sorrow, for he dared not speak to the King about the matter that had brought him to the palace at the early morning hour. And his wife and friends heard this story, and feared that greater troubles might soon befall him if the King was showing favor to the despised Jew.

Hā'-măn had forgotten about his invitation to dine again with the King and Queen. So the King sent a messenger to bring him to the palace. And then, as they sat about the table the King asked Esther the third time what her wish was, that she desired of him. And the third time he promised to grant that wish even though it should be the half of his kingdom.

Now Esther was ready to tell her story. She may have heard that very morning how highly the King honored Môr-dĕ-cā'-ī; for she spoke with courage and said, "If I have found favor in your sight, O King, and if it please you, I ask that my life and the lives of my people may be spared, for we have been sold—not to become slaves, but to be killed."

Ă-hăs-ū-ē'-rŭs was surprized to hear these words. He asked, "Who is he, and where is he, who would dare to do such a thing?" And Esther answered, "That enemy is this wicked Hā'-măn."

Now, Hā'-măn was frightened, and he did not know what to do. He had never guessed that the beautiful Queen was a Jewess. He did not know, even yet, that she had been brought up by Môr-dĕ-cā'-ī, the man whom he so much despised. Speechless he sat before them, and when he saw the King rise up in anger and leave the room, he sprang from his seat and fell before Esther, begging for mercy from her.

The King walked about in the garden, wondering what he should do to punish Hā'-măn. Then he returned and found Hā'-măn pleading for his life. But his pleading could profit him nothing, for the King's servants came in and covered his face, ready for death. Then they led him out, and one of the servants showed the King the high gallows that Hā'-măn had prepared to hang Môr-dĕ-cā'-ī. "Hang Hā'-măn on the gallows!" commanded the King, and Hā'-măn was hung on the gallows he had commanded others to build for an innocent man.

After Hā'-măn's death, the King raised Môr-dĕ-cā'-ī to a place of great honor in the kingdom, and he sent letters to every part of the land where Hā'-măn's letters had gone, telling the Jews to fight for their own lives on that day appointed when Hā'-măn had wished to put them to death. Because their enemies feared them, they did not try to kill the Jews on that day, for even the rulers of those lands helped the Jews. And the Jews celebrated the day of their great victory with a great feast, called the Feast of Pū'-rĭm. Even today the Jews keep this feast, and they always tell the story of Esther, the beautiful queen, who saved the lives of her people.

———•———

STORY 14

EZRA, THE GOOD MAN WHO TAUGHT GOD'S LAW TO THE JEWS

Ezra 7:10; Nehemiah 8.

Years passed by, and another change came in the Persian rule. A new king, named Är-tă-xĕrx'-ēs, sat on the throne in Shū'-shăn and governed the people in many lands. His kingdom included the land of Judah, where Zĕ-rŭb'-bă-bĕl had gone long before with a company of Jews to rebuild the temple of the Lord.

Now Är-tă-xĕrx'-ēs wished to know how things were going in Judah, and he planned to send a messenger to Jerusalem to learn about the people and their needs. The messenger whom he chose to send was Ezra, the priest.

Ezra was an earnest-hearted Jew, as Daniel had been. He was also called a scribe, because he wrote the words of God in books. And he longed to teach the Jews everywhere about the law of God, which had been given by Moses to the Israelites. At the King's command he assembled other Jews from Babylon and from the country places and cities near by who wished to go to Judah and help strengthen the courage of the poor Jews who lived there.

Ezra had talked much to the King about the true God, and about his great power and his willingness to care for those who love and serve him. And the King was interested. He believed that the God of the Jews must be a very powerful God indeed. He feared to displease such a great God, so he commanded that much gold and silver be given to Ezra and his companions to carry back to Jerusalem and use in the temple of the Lord.

When Ezra and his companions were ready to start on their long journey, they first spent some time fasting and praying God to bless them and protect them from the many dangers along their way. For the road over which they must travel led through dangerous places, and wild people of the desert often stopped travelers and robbed them of their possessions. Ezra knew this, and he had no soldiers of the king to go with him and protect him and his companions from the attack of robber bands. He was ashamed to ask the King for soldiers because he had told the King that God would care for those who served him. So he and his companions prayed earnestly that God would bring them through the dangers without letting any harm befall them. Then they started down the long, long road.

After about four months of travel, this company of Jews reached Judah in safety. They had lost nothing by the way, for God had heard their prayers and had cared for them. And they came with joy to the city where the temple of the Lord stood, just as Zĕ-rŭb'-bă-bĕl had built it. After resting for three days they brought their gifts of silver and gold, which the King had sent, and gave them to the priests who had charge of the temple.

Ezra soon found out that things had not been going well in Judah. The poor Jews had become much discouraged, and some of them had made friends with their heathen neighbors. They had even allowed their sons and their daughters to marry heathen people, and they were not teaching their children to keep the law as God gave it to Moses. They had never rebuilt the city of Jerusalem, and the walls lay in ruins just as Nĕb-ū-chăd-nĕz'-zär and his army had left them long years before.

When Ezra learned about the condition of the poor Jews, he was deeply troubled. He knew they had sinned again by marrying heathen women, and he saw that God could never bless them while they were not obeying his law. So he prayed earnestly that God would forgive their sins, and he called them to Jerusalem to warn them about the wrong that they had done.

The people were glad to have Ezra teach them what to do. They needed a teacher from God, like this good man, and they listened to his words. For a long time they had been without God's law, and now, when they heard his words, they quit their wrong-doing

Ezra stayed with the people for some time and taught them the words of God. He read to them from the great rolls that he had written, and they never grew tired of listening. They had no copies of God's law in their homes, for books were very few in those days and only rich people could afford them. Ezra had collected the books that Moses and Samuel and David had written, and the books of the prophets. These were the books from which he read to the Jews.

STORY 15

THE KING'S CUPBEARER AND HIS STORY

Neh. 1:1—2:18

In the palace of King Är-tă-xĕrx'-ēś was a noble young man who daily waited on the great ruler. This young man's name was Nē-hĕm-ī'-ăh, and he was a Jew. Although he was very rich, and favored more than any of the King's servants, yet Nē-hĕm-ī'-ăh was a humble-minded young man. And this is a story that he tells us about a part of his eventful life:

"In the twentieth year of King Är-tă-zĕrx'-ēś' reign I was in the palace of Shû'-shăn as cupbearer of the King when my brother Hă-nā'-nī and certain other men came from the land of Judah. I was eager to see them and to hear news from the land of my fathers, so when my duties were done I asked them about Jerusalem and about those Jews who had gone back to rebuild the temple of the Lord.

"My brother and his companions shook their heads sorrowfully, and replied that things were not going well in the city where David once ruled so gloriously as king of God's people. They told me that the walls which Nĕb-ū-chăd-nĕz'-zär and his soldiers had torn down and burned many years ago had never been repaired, and that the place looked very desolate, and unworthy of the great name that once had made it a glory in the earth. They also told me that the Jews who had returned were now poor and greatly oppressed by their enemies round about.

"When I heard these words I sat down and wept, for my heart was grieved, and I longed to see the prosperity of my people. Then there stirred within me a desire to help them, so I fasted and prayed earnestly to the God of heaven, and besought him to grant me the favor of the King. For I knew I could do nothing to help my people except the King should give his consent.

"One day while I stood by the King's table pouring wine into his goblet, I could not keep my thoughts on my work. And I could not speak so cheerfully as was my usual manner, for my heart was saddened by the great needs of my people. The King noticed my sad countenance, and he asked what had caused my sorrow of heart; for he knew I was not sick. Then I was afraid, for I thought surely he was displeased with me. But I told him that I had heard sad news from my people in Judah, and I told him about the broken walls of Jerusalem and the oppressed condition of the Jews.

NEHEMIAH BEFORE KING ARTAXERXES

"The King listened patiently, then asked what I desired of him. Before answering, I breathed a prayer to the God of heaven, and then I said, 'If it please the King, and if I have found favor in your eyes, I ask that you send me to Jerusalem to rebuild the city of my fathers.' The Queen also was sitting by, listening, and the King asked how long I should be absent from his palace. I told him how long my journey would be, and that I might not return for many days. But it pleased him to send me, and to give me letters to the rulers near Judah, telling them to help me on the way. He also gave me a letter to the man who was the keeper of his forest, telling him to permit me to get trees from the forest with which to rebuild the gates of the city walls.

"I did not start out on this long, dangerous journey alone, for the King sent captains and soldiers of his army with me, and we rode on horses, which he provided. After many days we came to the rulers of the countries near Judah, and I showed to them the letters that King Är-tă-xĕrx'-ēś had written. These rulers were not friendly with the poor Jews at Jerusalem, and they were sorry because I had come to strengthen the city. But they dared not hinder me, so I passed on and soon came to Judah.

"For three days I rested, then I rose up quietly during the night and took a few of my soldiers with me to discover the true condition of the city wall. We passed out through the entrance by the valley gate and I rode around the city. No one except my companions knew what I was doing, and none of the people of Jerusalem knew why I had come to visit them. But after my ride that night I felt prepared to talk to them about the task that I had come to accomplish. For I found the broken walls lying in heaps of ruins, and in some places my horse could not find a path.

"Then I talked to the rulers and to the priests and told them why I had come. I told them that Jerusalem was a reproach among all nations, and that God was not pleased to have his people let it remain in this broken-down condition. I told them how God had answered my prayer by causing the King to allow me to come; and when the rulers and the priests heard my words, they said, 'Let us arise and build the wall.' "

------------●------------

STORY 16

HOW THE WALLS OF JERUSALEM WERE REBUILT
Nehemiah 2:19—13:31; Malachi 1—4

News of Nē-hĕm-ī'-ăh'ś talk with the rulers and the priests spread rapidly among the Jews living in Jerusalem. And they rejoiced because God had sent this nobleman from the palace in Shū'-shăn to help them rebuild their city.

The great work began at once, and nearly everybody seemed interested. Of course there were some who stood back to find fault; but they could not crush the zeal of the busy workers. Even the women wished to help in the building, and some of the rich women hired workers to build a part of the wall.

The high priest said he would rebuild the Sheep Gate. There were several other gates to rebuild, and soon there were several other persons promising to rebuild them. So the Sheep Gate, and the Horse Gate, and the Fish Gate, and the Valley Gate, and the Water Gate, and every other gate of the broken-down wall was soon rising up in the same place where Nĕb-ū-chăd-nĕz'-zär had burned the former gates many years before.

BUILDING THE WALLS OF JERUSALEM

And some promised to repair the wall in front of their homes, while others promised to repair longer stretches. But before this work could be done, the people set to work clearing away the rubbish and gathering out the great stones. What a busy crowd of workers they were! Nē-hĕm-ī'-ăh rode around the walls on his horse and directed in the building.

When Săn-băl'-lăt and Tō-bī'-ăh, two enemies who lived near Jerusalem, heard what was taking place, they were very angry. They did not wish to see this great city rebuilt, for they feared that the Jews would no longer allow them to come into Jerusalem and oppress the people who lived there. So they planned many ways to hinder the building of the wall. First they made fun of the Jews, and pretended that the wall was not strong enough to offer protection in times of danger. They said, "If a fox should try to walk on the wall it would tumble down into ruins again."

But Nē-hĕm-ī'-ăh and his workers paid no attention to the jokes and jeers of their enemies. They kept right on with their great work, and would not stop to answer back.

Finally Săn-băl'-lăt and Tō-bī'-ăh saw they must do something else to hinder the work, so they wrote letters to Nē-hĕm-ī'-ăh, saying, "You have come to rebuild Jerusalem and set yourself up as a king over the city. Then you plan to rebel against the king of Persia." But Nē-hĕm-ī'-ăh answered, " I have not come for such a purpose," and he kept on with the building.

Now the enemies were angry, and they planned to come and fight against the men of Jerusalem, and kill them. But Nē-hĕm-ī'-ăh heard about their plan, and he armed the men with swords and spears on every part of the wall. Some worked with one hand while they held a spear in the other hand. And all the while, both day and night, guards stood about to watch for the approach of the enemy.

At last the walls were built, but the doors of the gates were not yet set up. The enemies had been afraid to come and fight, for they had heard that Nē-hĕm-ī'-ăh and his workers were armed with swords and spears, so they planned to act friendly and call Nē-hĕm-ī'-ăh away from Jerusalem, on a business trip, to one of their cities. Then perhaps they intended to kill him there. But Nē-hĕm-ī'-ăh would not go, for he said, "I am doing a great work, and I can not leave it to come down to your city."

After fifty-two days, or nearly two months, the entire wall was finished. And the people of Jerusalem were very thankful that Nē-hĕm-ī'-ăh had come to encourage them and to build up the broken wall of their ruined city. They saw he was interested in them, and soon they came to tell him about other things that troubled them. They explained why they were so poor and so discouraged.

Nē-hĕm-ī'-ăh listened to their words, and then he called the rulers and told them what the poor people had said. The rulers were ashamed because they had never tried to help these people. Now they promised Nē-hĕm-ī'-ăh that they would do better.

For twelve years Nē-hĕm-ī'-ăh stayed in Jerusalem and acted as governor of the city. Then he knew that Är-tă--xĕrx'-ēs, the King, would be expecting him back in Shû'-shăn; for he had promised to return at that time. So he appointed his brother Hă-nā'-nī and another man to rule the city while he should be absent, and then he hurried back to see the King. Är-tă-xĕrx'-ēs permitted him to return the second time to Jerusalem, and Nē-hĕm-ī'-ăh's work on this second visit was more the work of restoring the customs that God had commanded by Moses for the people to obey.

Because of the faithful efforts of men like Nē-hĕm-ī′-ăh and Ezra, the priest, the Jews began to pay more heed to the teachings of God's law. They began to act more like a separate people, uninfluenced by their heathen neighbors, and they refused to worship idols any longer. By and by other teachers rose among them, and these teachers wrote law-books, which they called "traditions." These teachings were very

EZRA TEACHING THE LAW

strict; but God was not pleased with them, for he had not commanded that they should be written and obeyed.

Măl′-ă-chī, the last of the prophets, came to speak God's word to the people while Nē-hĕm-ī′-ăh yet lived. This faithful prophet told the Jews about the coming of Jesus, the Savior, into the world, and he wrote his words in a book. The Jews kept his book with the other books that Ezra, the priest, had given to them. And Măl′-ă-chī's writings are the last words we find in the Old Testament.

WHAT HAPPENED BETWEEN THE OLD AND THE NEW TESTAMENT

Four hundred years is a long time; but more than four hundred years passed by between the stories of the Old Testament and the stories of the New Testament. And during those years many changes took place in the history of the Jews.

Although God had permitted the Jews to return from their captivity in Babylon to the homeland of their fathers, in Judah, he did not permit them to become a separate kingdom as they had been before. He did not allow another of David's descendants to rebuild a throne in Jerusalem and rule there. Now the Jews were servants of the kings of other nations, first of one country and then of another.

Once during these years the Jews freed themselves from the rule of other kings and chose one of their own nation to rule over them. But this man whom they chose was not a descendant of David. He was the son of a priest. And his sons after him ruled until the Romans came with an army and conquered the little Jewish nation. From that time the Jews became servants of the rulers of Rome.

Because the capital of the Roman government was very far from Judah, the rulers of Rome sent a general named Herod to be the king of the Jews. This king set up his throne in Jerusalem and governed the people of that country to please the Romans. And he did many things that displeased the Jews; for he was a very wicked man.

After ruling the Jews for eighteen years, King Herod found out that he had many enemies among them. He wished to make friends with them, so he planned to rebuild their temple, which was now in great need of repair. He tore down the old temple, which Zĕ-rŭb'-bă-bĕl had rebuilt, on Mount Mō-rī'-ăh, and erected in its place a very beautiful building of white marble stones. Some of these stones he covered with plates of silver and gold.

For several years Herod's workmen labored to erect the new temple, and during those years he engaged the services of over ten thousand men. This splendid structure could be seen towering above the other buildings of Jerusalem, and reflecting the dazzling glory of the morning sunlight. This new temple became the pride of the Jews, just as Solomon's temple had pleased the Israelites, their fathers, many years before. And in this new temple the priests, who were descendants of Aaron, continued to offer sacrifices to God each morning and each evening, just as Moses had commanded in the book of the law, which God gave to him on Mount Sī'-nâi.

Stories of the New Testament
In Two Parts

Hofmann

THE BOY CHRIST

PART FIRST

STORIES ABOUT JESUS

Matthew; Mark; Luke; John; Acts 1:1-15

STORY 1

AN ANGEL VISITOR IN THE TEMPLE

Luke 1:1-23

Zăch-ă-rī'-ăs, the priest, was an old man. All his lifetime he had been in the priesthood, for he was a descendant of Aaron. And he had married a woman named Elizabeth who also belonged to the family of the priests.

Zăch-ă-rī'-ăs and Elizabeth loved God and lived to please him as well as they knew how. They thought often of the promises God had given to the Jews by the old prophets who lived and died many years before their time. These promises were that some day God would send a Savior into the world, a son of David, to rule over his people forever.

Now Zăch-ă-rī'-ăs and his wife had grown old, and God had never given them any children. They had prayed many times and asked God to give them a little son or a little daughter, but their prayers had never been answered. And they had lived alone in their quiet home, thinking that God was not willing to bless them with the joy of parenthood. Still they served him faithfully; for they knew God always does what is best.

Zăch-ă-rī'-ăs did not always work in the temple. There were many priests, and these priests served in the temple by courses, just as David had planned when he arranged for the building of the first temple in Jerusalem. There were twenty-four courses of the priests, and Zăch-ă-rī'-ăs belonged to the course of Ă-bī'-ă. When his turn came to serve he left his quiet home in the hill-country of Judah and went to Jerusalem. There he did the work that fell to him by lot. And his lot was to burn incense on the golden altar, in the holy place, or the first room of the temple, where only the priests might enter. Twice each day, at the time of the morning and the evening sacrifices, Zăch-ă-rī'-ăs took his censer of burning coals from the great altar and went into the holy place alone to offer sweet perfumes upon the golden altar before God. And

383

THE ANGEL APPEARING TO ZACHARIAS

Birth and Early Life of Jesus

BIRTH AND EARLY LIFE OF JESUS

In the little village of Nazareth, an angel appeared to Mary, the intended wife of Joseph, a carpenter, and told her she was to become the mother of a Babe who should be the Savior of the world. Several months after the angel appeared to Mary there was born to Elizabeth, Mary's cousin, who lived in the hill country of Judea, a son who was named John. John was to be the forerunner of Jesus, the child who was to be born of Mary.

Just before Mary's Baby was born the king sent out a decree that all the world should be taxed. Mary and Joseph went to Bethlehem to pay their tax. It was while they were there that the Baby Jesus was born. The night of his birth angels appeared to the shepherds who were watching their flocks in the fields and told them where they would find the new-born Savior.

While Mary and Joseph were in Bethlehem, wise men from the East came searching for Jesus. They had been led to him by a star. When the king learned of the birth of Jesus he ordered that all the babies of Bethlehem under two years old should be killed. Mary and Joseph took the Christ-child to Egypt to save him. After the wicked king was dead, the holy family returned to Nazareth, where Jesus grew to be a man.

When he was twelve years old, Jesus went to Jerusalem with his parents. While there he talked with the doctors in the Temple, asking them many questions which they could not answer.

while he lingered in that room, the people who came up to the temple to worship stood in the court outside and prayed. This was called the hour of prayer.

One day while Zăch̲-ă-rī'-ăs was offering incense upon the golden altar he was surprized to see an angel standing on the right side of the altar watching him. At first Zăch̲-ă-rī'-ăs was very much afraid, for he had never seen an angel before. But the angel said, ''Do not be afraid, Zăch̲-ă-rī'-ăs, for your prayer is heard, and you wife shall have a son, whom you shall call John. This child shall bring you much joy, for he shall be great in the sight of the Lord. He shall never drink wine or strong drink, and he shall have God's Holy Spirit dwelling in him and giving him power such as Ē-lī'-jäh had, to turn the people from their sins to serve God.''

Zăch̲-ă-rī'-ăs listened, filled with wonder as to whether these words could be really true. He thought he and Elizabeth were too old to have a child, and he asked the angel to give him a sign that he might know for sure these things would happen. The angel answered, ''I am Gabriel, the angel who stands in the presence of the Lord, and I have been sent by the Lord to tell you this glad news. But you have not believed my words, because you ask for a sign. Therefore this sign shall be given to you: You shall not be able to speak another word until the child is born.'' And then the angel disappeared as suddenly as he had come.

The people stood outside waiting and wondering why Zăch̲-ă-rī'-ăs was so long in the holy place. When he came out to them he could not speak, but showed them by motions that he had seen a vision from God.

Not long afterwards Zăch̲-ă-rī'-ăs finished his course of service at the temple and returned to his home in the hill-country of Judah, as speechless as when he came out of the holy place. But he knew the time would come when his voice would return, for he believed the sign that the angel had given to him.

———·———

STORY 2

THE HEAVENLY MESSENGER IN GALILEE
Matt. 1:18-25; Luke 1: 26-56

Mary was a Jewess. She had grown to womanhood in Nazareth, a city of Galilee. And she was expecting soon to marry a good man named Joseph.

Both Mary and Joseph were descendants of King David, but they

THE ANNUNCIATION

were poor people. Joseph was a carpenter, and he worked with his tools to make a living for himself and to prepare a home for his bride.

One day God sent the angel Gabriel to Nazareth to speak to Mary, for God had chosen this young woman to become the mother of the Savior who would soon be born into the world.

Mary was surprized when she saw the angel, and she was more surprized when she heard his words. For he said, "You are highly favored and blessed among women, for the Lord is with you." Seeing that Mary did not understand his meaning, the angel told her that God was well pleased with her and he had chosen her to become the mother of Jesus, the Savior of men. He told her that Jesus, her son, would be a King, and that he would rule forever. Even yet the surprized young woman could not understand his words, so the angel told her that this wonderful child would be called the Son of God.

While Mary listened the angel told her about the promised child of Zăch-ă-rī'-ăs and Elizabeth, the old people who lived in the hill-country of Judah. And he said, "Although they are old people, nothing is too hard for God to do." Then Mary knew that God could give her this wonderful child which the angel had promised, and she said, "Be it unto me according to thy word." So the angel left her and went back to heaven.

Now, Mary knew Elizabeth, the old lady of whom the angel spoke; for Elizabeth was her cousin. And she knew how Elizabeth had longed to have a child for many years. She believed that her cousin must be very happy since God had promised to give her a child in her old age. Although the distance was great, she wished to see Elizabeth. So she decided to make her a visit.

As soon as Mary entered the home of her cousin and spoke words of greeting, God caused Elizabeth to know the secret which the angel had told this young woman in her own home. And Elizabeth rejoiced that Mary had come to visit her. She knew that Mary would some day be the mother of Jesus, the Savior of men.

The two women spent many happy days together, then Mary hurried back to her own home in Nazareth. There God's angel spoke to Joseph, the carpenter, in a dream, and told him about the wonderful secret of Jesus' birth. And Joseph was glad, for he had been longing for the time to come when the promised Savior should be born. He took Mary into his home and they waited for the angel's promise to come true.

STORY 3

HOW THE DUMB PRIEST AND HIS WIFE NAMED THEIR CHILD

Luke 1: 57-80

A time of great rejoicing had come to the quiet little home in the hill-country of Judah, for God had sent the promised child to Zăch-ă-rī'-ăs and his aged wife, Elizabeth. And all the neighbors and relatives were rejoicing with these happy parents of the baby boy.

When the child was eight days old preparations were made to give him a name, for this was the custom of the Jews. The friends and relatives said, "Let us call him Zăch-ă-rī'-ăs, after the name of his father."

But Elizabeth answered, "No, do not call him Zăch-ă-rī'-ăs, for his name is John."

"Why do you wish to call him John?" they asked in surprize. "You have no relatives who are called by that name." Then they turned to the old father, who had not spoken since the angel talked with him in the temple, and by making signs they asked him what they should call the child.

Zăch-ă-rī'-ăs understood what they wished to know, and he motioned for them to bring a writing-table. This they did. Then he wrote in plain letters, so all could read, "His name is John."

"How strange!" thought the people. And all at once Zăch-ă-rī'-ăs began to speak to them again, just as he used to speak before he had seen the angel. He praised God for giving him this wonderful baby.

News of this wonderful baby spread all through the hill-country, and people became much interested in him. They heard how the angel had appeared to Zăch-ă-rī'-ăs in the temple and promised that God would give the child, and they heard how Zăch-ă-rī'-ăs had been unable to speak from that time until after the baby was called by the name that the angel had given. They wondered much about these strange happenings, and they believed that surely the baby John would grow up into a great man.

Zăch-ă-rī'-ăs received wisdom from God and spoke words of prophecy to his neighbors and friends about his little son. He blessed the Lord. And then he said to his little boy, "You, my child, shall be called the prophet of the Highest, for you shall go before the face of the Lord to prepare his ways. You shall give knowledge of salvation to his people by the remission of their sins, through the tender mercy of our God."

THE ANGEL TALKING TO THE SHEPHERDS IN A FIELD NEAR BETHLEHEM

Many other words did Zăch-ă-rī'-ăs speak; and his words came true, for the Spirit of God caused him to speak those words. And Zăch-ă-rī'-ăs cared for his little son as long as he lived. He watched with pride the changes that came with the years in the life of his little boy. And he saw that God was blessing John and causing him to grow strong and brave.

Perhaps Zăch-ă-rī'-ăs and Elizabeth did not live to see the day when John become a very useful man for God, for he did not begin his great work until he was thirty years old. Until that time he lived quietly in the desert country, and studied the books that God's prophets had written. He also listened much to the voice of God, and learned to understand God's will.

———•———

STORY 4

THE STORY OF A WONDERFUL BABY'S BIRTH
Luke 2:1-39

Out on the streets of Nazareth the people were standing in groups, talking excitedly. News had just reached their city that the great emperor of Rome had commanded all of them to go to the town or city from which their families had come and have their names written on lists. The emperor wished to have a list of the names of all the people in his great kingdom, or empire. And no one dared to disobey his command.

Soon travelers were seen going in every direction, for the emperor's command had been read in every city in the land. Out from Nazareth a company of people started toward the south, and in that company were Joseph and Mary, for they were both of the family of David, and they were going to Bethlehem, the city of David, to have their names written upon the list at that place.

The road to the south led through the country of Să-mâr'-ĭ-ă, then over the hills of Judah into Jerusalem. From Jerusalem Joseph and Mary went farther south, till they came to Bethlehem. Some of their company had left them in other cities along the way, while others had joined them. And when they reached Bethlehem they found that it was swarming with people who belonged, as they did, to the city where David was born. From every part of the land these people had come, and they had filled the lodging-rooms till no more place could be found for the new arrivals.

The long journey from Nazareth had been very tiresome, and Mary

ARRIVAL OF THE SHEPHERDS

lónged for a place to rest. But Joseph could find no place except in the stable of the inn. And here they stayed during their first days in Bethlehem.

God had not forgotten his promise to Mary, and one night while she was in Bethlehem he gave her the child, Jesus. And Mary wrapped him in soft cloths called swaddling-clothes, and laid him in a manger where the cattle fed, because she could find no better place.

The people of Bethlehem did not know that the angels were watching over the city that night. They did not hear the angels' glad song when Jesus was born. They did not see the joy of Mary and Joseph as they bent over the wonderful child in the manger. And so it was that God's greatest gift to men came right into that neighborhood and those people did not receive it as a gift from God because they did not expect a Savior to be born of such a humble person as Mary.

But there were shepherds watching their flocks that night in a field near Bethlehem. Perhaps David, the shepherd king, had tended sheep in that same field many years before. These shepherds knew about David, and about God's promise to David that one of his descendants would be the Savior of men. And they may have been talking about God's promise when the angel of the Lord suddenly came near and a glorious light broke upon them through the darkness. Trembling with fear, they looked upon the angel and wondered why he had come to them. Then he spoke, and said: "Fear not, for I bring you good tidings of great joy, which shall be to all people. For unto you is born this day in the city of David a Savior, which is Christ the Lord. And you will find the baby wrapped in swaddling-clothes and lying in a manger."

What a wonderful message! The shepherds listened eagerly to the angel's words, and when he finished speaking they saw a multitude of angels join him and begin to sing. Such music this world had never heard, for the angels were singing one of heaven's glad songs, giving glory to God in the highest. And they also sang, "Peace on earth, good will toward men."

When the song had ended, the angels went back into heaven and the glorious light faded again into the darkness of the still night. But the shepherds never forgot the sweetness of that song nor the joy it brought to their hearts. They did not wait until daylight to hasten to Bethlehem in search of the wonderful child, but said to each other just as soon as the angels disappeared, "Let us now go to Bethlehem and see this thing which the Lord has made known to us." So they left

NAZARETH, BOYHOOD HOME OF JESUS

Here in the first light of the morning, before the business of the day has begun, are glimpsed the pink and white houses of Nazareth in their terraced gardens clinging to the slopes of a tiny Galilean upland valley. In the foreground are the flat garden lands, and in the middle distance lies the public square, which later will be thronged with traffic. Nazareth remains one of the most picturesque cities of Palestine. It is a peaceful and prosperous community. Travelers are shown the reputed site of the carpenter shop of Joseph, where Christ worked as a boy.

ADORATION OF THE SHEPHERDS

their flocks and hurried to Bethlehem, and there they found Mary and
Joseph in the stable, with the infant Savior lying in the manger as the
angel had said.

The shepherds told Mary and Joseph about their angel visitors
and about the wonderful song that the angels sang. And no doubt
they knelt before the manger and
worshiped the little babe who lay
quietly sleeping in the hay. Then
they ran into the streets of Bethlehem and told every one whom they
met about the angel's visit and
about the wonderful child who had
been born that night in a stable of
the city. And the people wondered
about the strange things that the
shepherds told.

When the baby was eight days
old, Joseph and Mary gave him a
name, and they called him by the
name the angel had chosen. That
name, Jesus, means "salvation,"
and it told to men the work that
God had sent this child to do.

THE SHEPHERDS' VISIT

There was a law among the Jews that an offering should be made
to the Lord for the first boy child born into each family. Among the
rich people this offering should be a lamb, but among the poor people
the offering of only two young pigeons would please God just as well.
When Jesus was forty days old Joseph and Mary took him to the temple at Jerusalem to give their offering to the Lord. They brought two
pigeons, for they were poor and could not bring a lamb.

An old man named Simeon was in the temple when Joseph and
Mary came to bring their offering. This old man had served God for
many years, and he longed to see the Savior whom God had promised
to send into the world. God knew about this longing in Simeon's heart,
and one day he spoke to Simeon and said, "You shall not die until you
have seen the Savior."

When Mary brought the baby Jesus to the temple, God's Spirit
caused Simeon to know this child was the promised Savior. He came
eagerly to meet Mary and took her babe in his arms. Then he said,
"Now may God let me depart in peace, for I have seen with my eyes
the salvation which he has sent."

Another faithful servant of the Lord was in the temple that day, an old lady named Anna, who spoke words of prophecy to the people. When she saw Jesus, she too gave thanks to God, and to the people who

stood in the courts of the temple she spoke about this child of promise which had been sent from God to man.

Mary never forgot the words of these dear old people concerning her wonderful child. She remembered, too, the story that the shepherds had told, about the angels' visit to them, and about their words and song. Always in the days that followed Mary thought about these

SIMEON HOLDING MARY'S BABY. JESUS

strange things and wondered how her son Jesus would finally become the King and Savior of the world.

———— • ————

STORY 5

THE WISE MEN WHO FOLLOWED A STAR

Matthew 2

In the country far to the east of Judah there lived some wise men who studied the stars. One night they discovered a new star in the sky, one that they had never seen before. And God caused them to know by this star that Christ, the promised King of the Jews, had been born.

These wise men feared God, and they wished to see the child whom he had sent to be the Savior of the world. They supposed that the Jews must be very happy because God had at last sent to them the King he had promised.

Because these wise men were rich, they planned at once to make the long journey to Judah and bring precious gifts to the new-born King. Then they would worship him as their Savior.

For many days they traveled across the sandy desert, and at last they came to the fertile country where the Jews lived. They hurried on to the city of Jerusalem; for they expected to find the wonderful child living in the most beautiful place in all the land. And surely

Jerusalem, the famous city of the Jews, would be the most beautiful place.

Herod, the man whom the emperor of Rome had set up over the land of Judah, was living in Jerusalem at that time. He was surprized when these strangers, riding on camels, came into his city and asked, "Where is the child that is born King of the Jews? We have seen his star in the far east country, and have come to worship him." Herod had heard nothing about this new-born King, and he was troubled. What could this mean? he wondered. And even the rich people in Jerusalem were puzzled, too. They had heard nothing about Jesus.

No doubt the wise men were disappointed when they found that the rulers of Jerusalem knew nothing about the birth of the Savior. Perhaps they feared that they might have been mistaken, after all. But they waited anxiously while Herod called the chief priests and the scribes and asked them where the Savior should be born.

Now the chief priests and scribes were the men who read the books that the prophets had written long ago, and they understood that Christ should be born in Bethlehem. This they told to the excited Herod, and he called the wise men and told them that they should look for the child in Bethlehem.

Herod had been troubled, because he did not want Jesus to become the king of the Jews. He thought this new-born King would take away his throne, and he wished to be king himself. But he did not let the wise men know about his troubled feelings. He called them and asked very politely when they had first seen this unusual star in the east, and they told him. Then he urged them to hurry on to Bethlehem and search diligently to find the child. "When you have found him," said Herod, "bring me word at once, that I, too, may go and worship him." And with these words he dismissed them from his presence.

The wise men mounted their camels again and took the south road, leading to Bethlehem. All day they had waited impatiently in Jerusalem, and now the shadows of night were falling over the land. But it would not be a very long ride to the birthplace of the new-born King, and, urged on by Herod's words, they hastened to find Jesus. When once outside the city gates, they saw the star, the same beautiful star that had shown so brightly in the east country, moving slowly before them, as if leading them on to the right place. Now they were sure that they had not been mistaken; and they rejoiced greatly, for they believed that God was in this manner trying to help them to find Jesus.

When they reached Bethlehem the star stood still over the place where Mary and Joseph were living. And the wise men knew they had followed the right guide, for here they found the wonderful child of whom the prophets had written. They knelt in humble worship before him, and then gave to him the rich treasures that they had brought from their homeland.

God spoke to the wise men in a dream one night while they were in Bethlehem, and warned them not to tell Herod that they had found Jesus. So they returned to their own country by another road, and Herod never saw them again. Not long afterwards an angel of the Lord spoke to Joseph in a dream and said, "Arise, and take the young child and his mother, and flee into Egypt, and stay there until I bring word to you to return again; for Herod will seek for Jesus and try to destroy him."

Joseph rose up at once, and while it was yet dark he took Mary and the baby Jesus and hurried out of Bethlehem. For many days they traveled to the southwest, until they came to the land of Egypt. There they lived until an angel came to tell them that the wicked Herod was dead.

But Herod did not die for some time after the visit of the wise men. He waited long for them to return, bringing him word from Bethlehem as he had commanded them to do. But when many days passed and they did not come, he began to suspect that they had gone home without telling him of their wonderful discovery in Bethlehem. He believed they had guessed the reason why he had been so eager to see Jesus, and now he was angry because he had missed this opportunity to find the new-born King of the Jews.

Determined to destroy this King of the prophecies, Herod commanded his soldiers to go to Bethlehem and kill every baby there from two years old and younger. Not only to Bethlehem did he send them, but to the country places round about. And when this cruel deed was done he believed that he had surely gotten rid of this child whom the wise men sought to worship.

But all the while Jesus was living in safety among the people of Egypt, and fast growing out of his babyhood years. Then the wicked Herod died, and an angel came again to speak to Joseph, telling him to return with his wife and her child to their own land.

Joseph was glad to receive this message from the angel, for he loved to live among his own people. And he started back to Bethlehem. But when he came into Judah he heard that Herod's son was now the ruler of the Jews in Judah, and he feared that this new king might be cruel like his father had been. Because of this fear Joseph journeyed on to Nazareth, in the country of Galilee, where he and Mary had lived before Jesus was born. And there he made a home for his wife and her wonderful child.

STORY 6

WHEN JESUS WAS A BOY TWELVE YEARS OLD

Luke 2: 40-52

Nazareth, the boyhood home of Jesus, was nearly seventy miles from Jerusalem. The Jews who lived in this city could not go every week to worship God at the temple, so they built a house of worship, called a synagog, in their home town. Here they attended religious services, and listened to the reading of the books written by Moses and by the prophets.

As a little boy Jesus lived in the humble home of Joseph, the carpenter, and played among the shavings that fell from Joseph's bench. He also liked to run about and play in the warm sunshine, as little children do today. But when he grew old enough to go to school his parents sent him to the synagog, where other Jewish boys were taught to read and to write.

We are sure that Jesus studied his lessons well, and that he gave careful attention to the books he read each day. These books were copies of the Psalms and of the writings of Moses, the lawgiver, and the prophets. Like other Jewish boys, he learned to repeat many of these scriptures from memory, for he never had a Bible of his own.

One spring morning after Jesus was twelve years old a company of Jews started from Nazareth to attend the Feast of the Passover, at Jerusalem. Every year since their return from Egypt, Joseph and Mary had attended this feast, and now, as usual, they were in this company. But this time they were taking with them the boy Jesus.

Other children, too, were going, and they would enjoy the long trip of nearly seventy miles much more than would their parents and grown-up friends.

As the company moved slowly along the road, other Jews from cities and villages near by joined them. And when they came to Jerusalem they met people from every part of the land. What an exciting time this must have been for the children! How wide their eyes must have opened when they saw the beautiful temple on Mount Mō-rī'-ăh, with its wide porches and immense pillars of stone! And perhaps

JESUS IN THE CARPENTER SHOP

they stayed close by their parents during the first days of the Feast, lest they should get lost in the throng of people who daily crowded the temple courts.

Jesus enjoyed this Feast as much as did his parents and grown-up friends. Although just a child, he was beginning to realize that God was his Father, and that he must work for God. So he listened to the readings of the law, and to the words of the chief priests and scribes, who taught the Jews every day. But we are sure that he acted very much like a healthy twelve-year-old boy, for his mother did not notice how deeply interested he had been in the services at the temple.

After the Feast had ended, the company started on its homeward journey. Mary did not see her young son; but since she supposed that he was among their kinsfolk and friends, she did not feel uneasy. However, when at evening he did not come, she and Joseph began to search for him. All through the company they went, asking about Jesus; but no one had seen him that day. Then they turned with anxious faces back toward Jerusalem, and for three days they searched for their missing child.

On the third day they found him, not playing with other boys in the streets, nor learning to swim in the Pool of Sī-lō'-ăm, but sitting in the temple among the wise teachers, and asking them questions, which they could hardly answer.

Mary was surprized when she found her boy in the temple among the wise men. She had looked every other place for him. She knew he was a boy, just a boy, and she was surprized to find him so deeply interested in the teachings of God. She came to him and said, "Son, why did you stay here when we were starting home? Your father and I have been anxiously seeking for you everywhere." Jesus answered, "Why did you seek for me? Did you not know that I must be about my Father's business?" He meant, "Why did you not know where to find me at once? For I must be about my heavenly Father's business." But Mary did not understand, though she wondered much about the meaning of his words.

The wise men in the temple had been much surprized to hear the wisdom of the boy Jesus. They had gathered round him to ask questions that only wise persons could answer. And Jesus answered them, every one.

But when Mary and Joseph came to the temple, Jesus left the teachers there and returned with his parents to Nazareth. He was an obedient child, and as the years passed by he grew into a noble young man. Not only did he learn how to explain the Scriptures, but he

THE BOY JESUS IN THE TEMPLE WITH THE DOCTORS

watched Joseph at his work until he, too, became a carpenter. And by his kind, thoughtful ways he won many friends. In this humble home in Nazareth, Jesus lived until he was about thirty years old.

STORY 7

THE STRANGE PREACHER IN THE WILDERNESS
Matthew 3; Mark 1: 2-11; Luke 3: 1-23; John 1: 15-34

While Jesus was growing to manhood in the city of Nazareth, in Galilee, John, the son of Zăch-ă-rī'-ăs, was growing to manhood in the desert country of Judea. John spent much of his time alone in this desert country, listening to God's voice. And when he became a man he left his lonely home in the desert and began to tell God's words to the people.

John did not go to the cities of the land to preach God's message, but stayed in the wilderness of Judea near the River Jordan. And the people came from every part of the land to hear him speak. There had been no prophet among the Jews since the days of Măl'-ă-chī, more than four hundred years before, and now everybody was eager to hear this strange preacher in the wilderness tell the words that God had spoken to him. They believed he was a prophet, sent from God, and they came in great numbers to hear his words.

And John's words were indeed wonderful. He told the people that they should turn away from their sins and begin to do right, for God's kingdom was near at hand. He said that the King for whom they had been looking would soon come among them. And those who confessed their sins he baptized in the River. For this reason they called him "John the Baptist."

All classes of people came to John to be baptized by him. Among them were even the religious rulers of the Jews—the Pharisees and the Săd'-dū-çeeś. These men were very religious, and very careful to appear righteous before others. But God, who looked into their hearts, saw that they were proud and sinful. God saw that they despised the poor unfortunate people who lived among them, and that they believed themselves to be more righteous than other men. And when they came to be baptized of John, God caused him to know that these Pharisees and Săd'-dū-çeeś were only making believe that they were good. So John said to them, "Who has warned you evil men to flee from

God's wrath? You can not be prepared to enter God's kingdom until you first turn away from your sins.''

John taught the people who came to him that they should be unselfish, and kind to the poor. He told those who were rich to share their food and their clothing with the needy. He told those who were soldiers to harm no one, and to be contented with their wages. He tried in this way to teach them that God's kingdom would be a kingdom of love and peace, and "good will toward men," just as the angels sang to the shepherds on the night of Jesus' birth.

News of the strange preacher in the wilderness spread to even the farthest corners of the land, and everywhere the people were talking about his message. They were wondering whether John was the prophet Ē-lī'-jăh come back to earth again, for John did not dress like other men. He wore only a rough garment woven of camel's hair, and tied about his waist with a skin girdle. And he ate the simple food that he found in the wilderness, dried locusts and wild honey. And he was bold, like Ē-lī'-jăh had been, and unafraid to speak the truth to even the wicked King Herod.

But when John heard about the wonderings of the people, he said, "I am the voice of one crying in the wilderness, and warning you to prepare for the coming King. After me there is coming one greater than I—so much greater that I am not worthy to unfasten his shoes. And though I baptize you with water, he shall baptize you with the Holy Spirit, sent down from heaven.''

After these things happened, one day Jesus came from Nazareth to the Jordan River, where John was preaching and baptizing the people. And Jesus asked to be baptized also. John did not believe that Jesus needed to be baptized, and he said, "You are so much greater than I that I should be baptized by you. Why do you come to me?'' But Jesus answered, "It is necessary that I should be baptized by you, because this is God's plan.'' So John took Jesus into the River and baptized him there.

When these two were coming up out of the water, suddenly the heavens opened above them and the Spirit of God, in the form of a beautiful dove, came down and sat upon Jesus' head. Then a voice from heaven said, "This is my beloved Son, in whom I am well pleased.'' And John knew by this sign who Jesus was; for God had told him that some day he would see the heavens open and the Spirit of God descend upon the coming King.

After this time John continued to preach, and sometimes Herod heard him. Although Herod was troubled because John told him about his sins, his wife was much displeased with this fearless preacher of the wilderness. She wanted her husband, Herod, to kill him; and to please her, Herod shut John up in prison.

———— • ————

STORY 8

THE TEMPTATIONS OF JESUS

Matt. 4: 1-11; Mark 1: 12, 13; Luke 4: 1-14

You remember the story about the beautiful Garden of Eden, where the first man and woman lived when the world was new. And you remember about the visit of the tempter, who came into that beautiful garden one day and persuaded Eve, the woman, to do wrong. Before that time there was no sin in the world; but after Eve listened to the tempter and obeyed his words, sin crept into her heart. And then Adam, the first man, also disobeyed God and allowed sin to creep into his heart.

Because sin found a place in the hearts of the first man and woman, sin was born in the hearts of all their children. And for this reason God sent Jesus, his dear Son, into the world, to save the people from their sins and to wash away the stains sin had made.

Satan, the tempter, knew about God's plan to save people from their sins through Jesus. And he tried to spoil God's plan just as he had done before. He tried to crowd sin into the loving heart of Jesus.

After the baptism at the Jordan River, when God's voice spoke from heaven and said, "This is my beloved Son," Jesus was led by the Spirit of God into the lonely wilderness. There he lived by himself for forty days, among the wild beasts. But God did not allow any harm to come to him.

And Satan, the tempter, found Jesus all alone in the wilderness. So he tempted him there. First in one way and then in another he tried to get Jesus to listen to his cunning plans and open his heart to let sin enter, just as Adam and Eve had done. But Jesus would not listen.

When the forty days were ended, Jesus grew very faint and hungry, for he had eaten nothing since he came into this lonely place. And Satan remembered how he had tempted Eve to eat pleasant food, and how this temptation had caused her to listen to his words. He thought he would try the same temptation on Jesus. He said, "If you really are the Son of God, command that these stones become loaves of bread." He thought Jesus would surely yield to this temptation and try to prove that he was God's Son. But Jesus answered, "Man shall not live by bread only, but by every word of God."

Although he was hungry and faint, Jesus would not use his great power to please himself. He was willing to trust his heavenly Father to care for him in that desert place, and supply his needs as he had sup-

JESUS ON THE MOUNT OF TEMPTATION

plied food for Ē-lī'-jăh. Satan soon saw that he could not cause Jesus to yield to such a temptation, so he tried another way.

Taking Jesus to the topmost part of the temple in Jerusalem, he said, "If you expect people to believe that you are really God's Son you must show some great sign. Now cast yourself down to the ground, and trust God to protect you and keep your bones from being broken; for in the Scripture he has promised that angels will bear you up and not allow any harm to befall you."

Even though Satan used Scripture words to urge Jesus to do this foolish deed, yet Jesus would not obey him. For Jesus knew that the

Scriptures had forbidden any one to tempt God in such a foolish manner and expect God's angels to help him. And again Satan saw that his plan had failed.

The third time Satan brought his greatest temptation. He took Jesus to the top of a high mountain and caused him to see all the kingdoms of the world. "These great kingdoms are mine," said the tempter, "and I can give them to any one I choose. Now I will give them to you if only you will fall down and worship me."

But Jesus knew that Satan's words were not true. He knew that Satan had told falsehoods to Eve in the beautiful Garden of Eden. Now he said, "Get away from me, you evil one! for it is written in the Scriptures that the Lord God is the only Being who should be worshiped."

Then Satan left Jesus alone; for he could find no way to crowd sin into the pure heart of the Son of God. And when he went away the angels came from heaven and supplied Jesus' needs. How they must have rejoiced because the Savior had gained such a victory over the evil one!

And Jesus was tempted in every way that people on the earth are tempted; still he did no wrong. By his temptations he was made to understand how people feel when Satan whispers to their hearts and urges them to sin, and he understands how to help those people when they call upon him in prayer.

———————•———————

STORY 9

HOW FIVE MEN BECAME ACQUAINTED WITH JESUS

John 1: 35-51

Many people who heard John preach by the riverside believed his words, and they began to look for the coming of the King from heaven. From day to day they waited, eager to hear the glad news that the King had arrived. They believed that he would set up a kingdom in Judea, like the kingdom of David had been. And they believed that the Jews would be the favored people in this great kingdom.

One day after Jesus had returned from the lonely wilderness, John the Baptist saw him walking along the road near the river. And John cried out, "Behold the Lamb of God, who bears the sin of the world!"

Two young men from Galilee were with John that day and heard him speak. These young men had been disciples, or learners, of John, for they were interested in the teachings of God. When they heard John's words concerning Jesus, the Lamb of God, they turned at once to follow this wonderful person. Perhaps they wondered why John had called him the "Lamb of God." And perhaps they wondered how he could bear the sin of the world.

Jesus knew these young men were following him, so he stopped and called to them. He asked what they wanted of him, and they an-

CHRIST AND THE FISHERMEN

swered, "Master, where do you dwell?" Then Jesus took them with him and talked with them all that day.

We do not know what Jesus told those men, but we do know that his words proved to their minds that he was the King, or Mĕs-sī'-ăh, for whom the Jews were looking. How glad they were because they had found him!

One of those young men was Andrew, who afterwards became a disciple of Jesus. Just as soon as he believed that Jesus was the promised King he remembered how eagerly his brother, Simon, was waiting to see this great person, too. So he hurried at once to find Simon and bring him to Jesus.

Both Simon and Andrew lived by the seaside in Galilee, but at this time they were numbered among the many people who daily sat listening to the words of the strange preacher in the wilderness. Never had they heard such wonderful teaching before, and they were sure that John was a prophet. But Jesus' words had convinced Andrew that he had found a new teacher who was even greater than John. So he called Simon aside from the multitude and said, "Come with me, for we have found the Měs-sī'-ăh!"

When Jesus saw the two brothers coming to his lodging-place he looked at Simon and said, "You are Simon, the son of Jona; but you shall be called Peter." Simon wondered how Jesus knew so much about him, but after he listened to Jesus' words he, too, believed that the long-looked-for King of the Jews had come. And he followed Jesus with his brother Andrew.

On the next day Jesus began his journey back to his home country in Galilee, and these men went with him. As they went they met a man named Philip, who lived in the same town as Simon and Andrew lived in. Jesus called Philip to follow him, too; and Philip obeyed. As he walked along the road with Jesus and the other followers Philip listened in wonder to the wise sayings of his new-found friend. He had longed for the coming of the Měs-sī'-ăh, and now he, too, believed that Jesus was the promised Savior and King.

Philip had a neighbor named Nă-thăn'-ă-ĕl who had often talked with him about the glorious time soon coming when the King of the Jews would appear. And now he ran to tell Nă-thăn'-ă-ĕl about Jesus. He knew how greatly Nă-thăn'-ă-ĕl longed to see the coming King, and he called to him, saying, "We have found him, of whom Moses in the law, and the prophets, did write, Jesus of Nazareth."

Nă-thăn'-ă-ĕl knew the Scriptures, and he did not believe that the King of the Jews would come from Nazareth, for the prophets had said he would be born in Bethlehem. So he said to Philip, "Can any good thing come out of Nazareth?" But Philip answered, "Come and see."

Because Philip was so eager, Nă-thăn'-ă-ĕl rose and followed him. When they came near, Jesus saw Nă-thăn'-ă-ĕl, and he said, "Behold an Israelite indeed, in whom is no guile!"

"How do you know me?" asked the astonished Jew, and Jesus answered, "Before Philip called you, when you were under the fig-tree, I saw you."

What Nă-thăn'-ă-ĕl had been doing under the fig-tree we can only guess, but he may have been kneeling there and praying that God would hasten the coming of the promised King. When he heard Jesus' answer, he was filled with wonder and surprize that Jesus could know what he had been doing and where he had been staying before Philip called him. At once he believed that only God can see all things, and can reveal them to men, so he exclaimed joyfully, "Master, you are the Son of God! you are the King of Israel!"

Jesus replied, "Do you believe just because I said I saw you under the fig-tree? You shall see greater things than these. Some day you shall see the heavens open, and the angels of God all about the Son of man."

STORY 10

THE WEDDING-FEAST WHERE JESUS SHOWED HIS POWER
John 2: 1-11

In Cana, a little town of Galilee, lived some friends of Jesus and his mother. One day these friends invited Jesus, his mother, and his followers to attend a wedding in their home. They invited many other people also, and prepared a feast for them.

Perhaps these people were poor; for they had not prepared enough wine for all the people who came to the wedding. And before the close of the feast the wine was all gone.

Mary, the mother of Jesus, saw that the wine had all been used, and she called Jesus aside to tell him about it. She knew of his wonderful power, and she believed he could surely help in a time like this. Then she told the servants who waited at the tables to do whatever Jesus might command them; for she expected him to supply the need in some wonderful manner.

In every Jewish home there were large vessels, called water-pots, which the people kept filled with water to use in washing their hands and their feet. The Jews were very careful to keep themselves clean from dust and dirt, and because they walked about everywhere with only sandals on their feet they needed often to wash. In this home where the wedding-feast was being held, six large water-pots of stone were kept for this purpose.

Jesus called the servants and told them to fill the water-pots with water. And remembering his mother's instructions to them, the servants drew water and filled the vessels to the brim. Then Jesus told

PHILIP AND NATHANAEL

IN THE VALLEY OF JEHOSHAPHAT

This winding, rock-walled, ancient roadway passes over the Brook Kidron, in the Valley of Jehoshaphat, up to the southeast corner of the frowning wall of Moriah. At left lies an old Jewish cemetery; it is said that every good Jew over the world wishes that when he dies he might be buried on this warm and sunny western slope of Olivet. In the center rises the reputed tomb of Absalom. At right is a flourishing olive orchard. This view was glimpsed not far from the Garden of Gethsemane, well down by the foot of Olivet.

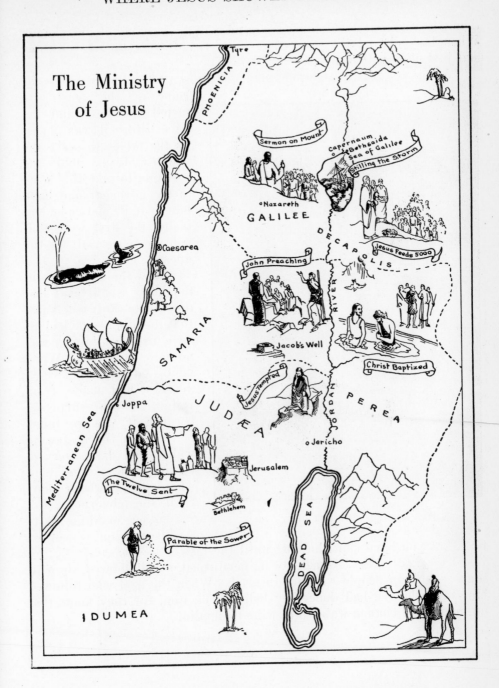

The Ministry of Jesus

them to draw out from the vessels and fill their wine-pitchers again. When they obeyed they saw that wine flowed from the vessels they had just filled with water.

At these Jewish feasts one man was chosen to be the governor, or ruler of the feast. He tasted the food and the wine before it was placed on the tables to serve the people. Jesus told the servants to take this wine to the governor and have him taste it, just as he had tasted the first wine that had been served to the guests.

JESUS MAKING WINE OUT OF WATER

Now the governor did not know what Jesus had done. He did not know that the other wine had all been used and there was no more to be had. When he tasted the wine which Jesus had made from water he was surprized because it was so much better than the first wine which had been served. Calling the young man who had just been married, the governor said, "At other wedding-feasts the best wine is served first, but you have kept the best until the last of the feast."

This was the first miracle Jesus performed, and it showed his willingness to help people who are in need. When the men who followed him saw what he had done they believed on him, for they knew that no man could change water into wine as he did.

THE GREAT TEACHER IN JERUSALEM

John 2: 13—3: 21

The time had come again for the yearly Passover Feast in Jerusalem, and from every part of the land groups of people came flocking to attend this great religious meeting.

In one of these groups were Jesus and his friends, Andrew, Simon, Philip, and Nă-thăn'-ă-ĕl. These men were also called his disciples, or learners; for they often went with him from one place to another to learn more about his wonderful teachings.

You remember that only the priests were allowed to enter the rooms of the temple, and that the people who went there to worship stood in the courts outside the rooms and prayed while the priests offered sacrifices upon the altars.

When Jesus came with his disciples and friends to attend the Feast of the Passover, he found much disorder in the court where the people were supposed to worship God. This beautiful court looked more like a market-place than like a house of prayer, for men had brought oxen and sheep and doves in there to sell as sacrifices to those who came from distant country places to worship God.

And other men, who were called money-changers, were sitting by small tables exchanging pieces of silver money, called half-shē'-kĕls, for the coins people brought from distant lands. Every Jew, we are told, who was twenty years old or older, gave one of these half-shē'-kĕls to the priests each year to buy sacrifices and to supply other needs in the temple worship. No other coins except half-shē'-kĕls could be received by the priests, so the Jews who came from other lands had to exchange their coins for half-shē'-kĕls before they could pay their dues to the priests.

Jesus was grieved to see the disorder in the temple court. He knew that worshipers could not enjoy praying in such a noisy place, where buying and selling and money-exchanging were going on around them. So he made a whip by tying small cords together, and then he drove out the oxen and sheep and the men who kept them. He even upset the tables of the money-changers, and he told them that his Father's house was a place of prayer and should not be used for a market-place.

No doubt other people had been grieved to see the disorder in the temple court at the time of the Passover feast. But none of them had ever dared to do as Jesus did at this time. None of them had courage enough to try to correct this great evil.

But not all of the Jews were pleased to see Jesus drive the money-lovers and the owners of the oxen and sheep and doves into the streets outside the temple. Some of them came to Jesus and asked him for a sign to prove that he was some great man, with authority to do such things. But Jesus knew they would not accept him even when they

JESUS TALKING TO NICODEMUS

should see a sign, so he answered, ''Destroy this temple, and in three days I will raise it.'' He spoke about himself, meaning his body, which he knew the Jews would cause to be crucified, and which he would raise up from the dead after three days. But the Jews did not understand, and they thought he meant the temple on Mount Mō-rī'-ăh, which Herod, the king, had rebuilt for them. They said, ''Many years were spent in building this temple, and you say you could rebuild it in three days!'' Then they shook their heads doubtfully and walked away, for they did not believe his words.

At this Feast, Jesus began to teach the people and to do miracles among them. And many believed in him when they heard his words and saw the great works which no other man could do.

One of those who believed in Jesus was a ruler among the Jews, a Pharisee. His name was Nĭc-ŏ-dē'-mŭs, and he was a very rich man. There were many Pharisees among the Jewish rulers, and these men were proud and unwilling to accept either John the Baptist or Jesus as being teachers sent from God. They themselves wished to be the religious leaders of the Jews and they despised humble men like John and Jesus. But Nĭc-ŏ-dē'-mŭs was not like his proud friends. He heard Jesus teach the people who had come to worship at the Feast, and he believed that surely Jesus was some great man.

While the other Pharisees were finding fault with Jesus, Nĭc-ŏ-dē'-mŭs longed to hear more of his teachings. So one night he came to the place where Jesus stayed while he was in Jerusalem, and asked to have a talk with this man from Galilee.

Jesus received Nĭc-ŏ-dē'-mŭs gladly, and talked to him about the kingdom of God. He told this ruler that no man could enter God's kingdom unless he should be born again. Nĭc-ŏ-dē'-mŭs wondered how this could be possible, so Jesus explained to him the secret of the new birth, which we call a change of heart. Never before had this wise ruler of the Jews heard such strange words, and he listened wonderingly while Jesus told about the great love of God. ''This love,'' said Jesus, ''caused God to give his only Son that whoever believes in him may not die because of sin, but have life forevermore.''

Then Jesus reminded Nĭc-ŏ-dē'-mŭs of the story of Moses in the wilderness when the people had sinned and God had sent fiery snakes into their camp. Nĭc-ŏ-dē'-mŭs remembered the story, and Jesus said, ''Just as those people who were about to die from the snake-bites found relief from their pain by looking at the brass snake that Moses put up on a pole in their camp, so the people who have sin in their hearts may find relief from sin by looking at the Son of man, who shall be raised up among them.'' Nĭc-ŏ-dē'-mŭs did not understand that Jesus was speaking about the cruel way in which he should some time be put to death to save the people from their sins. But Nĭc-ŏ-dē'-mŭs did believe more strongly than ever that Jesus was a great teacher who had come down from heaven to dwell among men.

Faith in Jesus as the Redeemer of the world gives everlasting life.

STORY 12

THE TIRED STRANGER WHO RESTED BY A WELL

John 4:1-43

Between Judea and Galilee was a little country called Să-mâr'-ĭ-ă. This country used to belong to the kingdom of Israel; but when the Israelites were carried away as captives by the king of Assyria, strangers from other lands came into that country and made their homes.

These strangers learned about the God of the Israelites, but they never worshiped God at the temple in Jerusalem. Instead, they built a temple in their country and worshiped there. They became bitter enemies of the Jews, and at the time of Jesus they were still despised by the Jews. In going to or returning from Jerusalem, the Jews of Galilee usually would not take the shorter road, through Să-mâr'-ĭ-ă, but would travel the long road, which led first to and across the Jordan River, then along the border of the land where the people lived whom they despised.

Although Jesus was a Jew he did not share the bitter feeling of the Jews toward the people of Să-mâr'-ĭ-ă, who were called Să-mâr'-ĭ-tăns. He knew they were just as precious in the eyes of God as were any other people, and he longed to teach them about the kingdom of heaven. He did not mind walking through their country on his journey back to his home in Nazareth.

Because Jesus wished to take the shorter road, through Să-mâr'-ĭ-ă, his disciples were willing to go that way too, in order to be with him. So they journeyed together as far as a little city called Sȳ'-chär.

Near the city was a wayside well, which had been dug hundreds of years before probably by Jacob, the grandson of Abraham. And in honor of him it was still called Jacob's well. When they reached this well, Jesus was tired, and sat down by it to rest from his long walk. His disciples went on to the city to buy food, leaving him there alone.

Presently a woman from Sȳ'-chär came down to the well to draw some water. She glanced at the stranger sitting there and saw that he was a Jew. Knowing that Jews paid no attention to Să-mâr'-ĭ-tăns, she passed by and hurried to lower her water-jug with the long rope that she had brought. When the jug was filled she drew it up and was ready to start back to the city, when Jesus asked for a drink.

Surprised at his request, the woman answered, "How is it that you, being a Jew, will ask a drink of me, a woman of Să-mâr'-ĭ-ă? for the Jews have no dealings with the Să-mâr'-ĭ-tăns."

Jesus replied, "If you knew who it is who asks a drink from your jug of sparkling water, you would ask of him and he would give you living water to drink."

These words aroused the interest of the woman at once. Who could this stranger be? she wondered. She knew he was not like other Jews, for they would rather suffer from thirst than ask a favor of a Să-măr′-ĭ-tăn. So she said, "Sir, this well is deep and you have no rope to draw out the water, how then could you give me living water to drink? Are you greater than Jacob, who gave us this well, and drank of it himself, and his cattle?"

"Whoever drinks of this water in Jacob's well becomes thirsty and returns again and again for more," answered Jesus, "but the living water which I give does not come from such a well. It bubbles up like a continual spring within one, and that one never grows thirsty again."

Now the woman was an eager listener. She did not know that the living water of which Jesus spoke was his free gift of salvation to all people, and she

JESUS AND THE WOMAN OF SAMARIA

said, "Sir, I want that kind of water so that I shall not need to return and refill my water-jug in this tiresome way."

Jesus saw that she was interested, so he began to talk to her about her sins. He knew she was a very sinful woman, and he told her about some wrong things that she had done. She wondered how he, a stranger, could know these things. He seemed to see her thoughts and to read them all. "You are a prophet," she exclaimed.

Although this woman was a sinner, she wondered often whether God was more pleased with the religion of the Jews than with the religion of her own people, the Să-măr′-ĭ-tăns. Now she asked Jesus whether people should worship God in Jerusalem or in the temple of the Să-măr′-ĭ-tăns.

Jesus answered that God had planned to bring salvation through the Jews, but he said the time had come when true worshipers need no longer go up to Jerusalem, for they might pray to God everywhere and worship him. "God is not found in only one place," he said; "for

God is a Spirit. And those who worship him in the right way must believe that he is a Spirit.''

Then the woman said, ''I know the Mĕ-sī'-ăh is coming from God, and when he comes he will tell us everything.''

''I am that Mĕs-sī'-ăh,'' answered Jesus, and the woman looked in joy and wonder upon him. But at that moment the disciples returned from the city bringing food to eat, so she turned away and, leaving her water-jug, ran back to tell her friends about the wonderful stranger whom she had met at the well.

The disciples wondered why Jesus would talk with a despised woman of the Să-măr'-ĭ-tăns; but they did not ask him any questions. They brought food to him, and when he refused to eat they urged him. Then he said to them, ''I have food to eat which you know nothing about.'' They asked each other, ''Has some one brought food to him while we were away?'' But Jesus knew their questionings, so he said. ''My meat is to do the will of my Father, who has sent me into the world.''

When the woman reached the city she went into the streets and told the people about Jesus, the stranger who had understood all about her life. ''He told me all the things that I ever did. Is not he the Mĕs-sī'-ăh?'' she asked. And the people decided to see this man for themselves, so they went with her to Jacob's well.

Jesus talked with the Să-măr'-ĭ-tăns about the things of God, and they invited him to stay in their city and teach them more of these wonderful truths. He spent two days in Sȳ'-chär, teaching the people. Then he went on his way to Nazareth, leaving behind him some believers among the Să-măr'-ĭ-tăns.

———◆———

STORY 13

THE STORY OF A MAN WHO HAD GREAT FAITH IN JESUS' POWER
John 4:45-54

Many people who lived in the country of Galilee were eager to see Jesus. They had heard about his first miracle at Cana, where he turned water into wine, and they had also heard about his teachings and his miracles performed in Jerusalem during the Feast of the Passover. Now when he left Sȳ'-chär and returned with his disciples to their country, the news of his coming spread rapidly from one city to another, and the Galilean people hoped he would come to their cities and perform miracles among them, too.

But one man did not wait until Jesus should come to his home city before going out to see him. This man lived in Că-pĕr′-nă-ŭm, a city that had been built on the shore of the Sea of Galilee. He was one of the rulers in that city, and he was also called a nobleman. In the eyes of the poor who lived near his home he was a great man indeed; for he did not despise them, as did many of the rulers of the Jews.

Sorrow had come into the home of this nobleman, his little son lay sick with a burning fever, and the doctors could not make him well. Hearing of Jesus, the nobleman decided to seek this wonderful prophet and beg him to come to Că-pĕr′-nă-ŭm to heal his child. So he left his home one night and hurried to Cana, where Jesus was.

When the nobleman found the place where Jesus was stopping, he called to see the wonderful prophet of Galilee. He told Jesus about his sick child lying at home at the point of death, and he asked Jesus to go with him to Că-pĕr′-nă-ŭm to heal the child. But Jesus answered, "Unless you see signs and wonders you will not believe that I am sent of God."

The nobleman was very much in earnest. He cried out, "Sir, if you do not come down at once, my little son will be dead when we reach home." Then Jesus spoke kindly to this distressed father. He said, "Return to your home without me, for your son will not die."

The nobleman believed Jesus' words and turned back to Că-pĕr′-nă-ŭm. He did not fear any longer that death would snatch his dear child away from his loving care, for Jesus had said that the child should be well again. When he came near to Că-pĕr′-nă-ŭm, his servants came to meet him with glad tidings. They said, "Your son is no longer sick."

"At what time," asked the nobleman, "did he begin to get well?" And the servants replied, "His fever left him yesterday at the seventh hour of the day." The ruler knew that Jesus had spoken to him at that very hour, and he believed surely that it was the power of this prophet that had saved the life of his child. Not only this nobleman, but all his household, too, believed in Jesus when they heard about the healing of the sick boy.

STORY 14

THE ANGRY MOB ON THE HILL-TOP OF NAZARETH

Luke 4:16-32

A sad day had come for Nazareth, the city where Jesus had lived since his babyhood years. And this sad day had come on the Sabbath.

The Jews from different parts of the city were gathering in their house of worship, the synagog. Among their number was Jesus; for he had returned from his visit in Cana. Always while he lived in Nazareth he went every Sabbath-day to the services at the synagog, where he heard God's words read from the books of the law and of the prophets.

Now, Jesus was no longer just an ordinary person among the other Jews of Nazareth, for they had heard about his teachings in other cities and they wished to hear for themselves what this son of the carpenter Joseph would say. So when the time came for the services to begin, Jesus stood up to read to the people, and the minister of the synagog brought to him the book that the prophet Isaiah had writ-

JESUS PREACHING IN THE SYNAGOG AT NAZARETH

ten long years before. Jesus found where Isaiah wrote the prophecy concerning the Mĕs-sī'-ăh, and he read Isaiah's prophecy to the people. These are some of the words he read:

"The Spirit of the Lord is upon me,
  Because he hath anointed me to preach the gospel to the poor;
  He has sent me to heal the broken-hearted,
  To preach deliverance to the captives,
  And recovering of sight to the blind,
  To set at liberty them that are bruised,
  To preach the acceptable year of the Lord."

After reading these words, Jesus closed the book, gave it back to the minister, and sat down. Then every one in the synagog looked at him, expecting to hear him speak; for the speaker in the synagog always stood up to read God's words and sat down to explain the meaning of what he had read.

Among those who listened to Jesus that day were his neighbors who had known him nearly all his lifetime. Proud men they were, unwilling that the carpenter's son should teach them new truths. They had heard of the miracles that Jesus performed in Cana and in Că-pĕr'-nă-ŭm, the city by the seashore. But they did not believe that Jesus was the promised King of the Jews. They knew he was only a poor man, and they did not respect him for being great and good.

But those proud men were surprized when they heard Jesus' words. They did not know he could speak so well; they did not know that he was the greatest teacher who had ever spoken to men. For a while they listened very carefully; then Jesus told them that Isaiah's words were fulfilled by his coming to preach the gospel to the poor and to do other wonderful things that Isaiah had promised. "How can this be true?" they asked of each other; "for is not this Joseph's son?"

Jesus knew they would not receive his words and believe them. He told them that no prophet was honored by his own people. And he reminded them of the time when Ē-lī'-jăh, the prophet, ran away from Israel to hide in the home of a poor widow who lived in a heathen land. Because this poor widow cared for God's prophet, God took care of her. He also told them about the heathen leper, Nā'-ă-măn, who was healed by God's power when he obeyed Ē-lī'-shă's words, altho many Israelites had leprosy and were never healed.

The proud men of Nazareth quickly objected to these words of Jesus, although they were true happenings among the Jews long before. They believed that Jesus was trying to show them how God cared for other people besides the Jews, and they did not like to hear such words. So they refused to listen longer to his teachings, and the service at the synagog broke up in great disorder. The leading men ran to Jesus and took hold of him roughly and drew him outside their synagog. Then a mob of angry people followed, wishing to see Jesus punished because he had spoken the truth to them.

This mob led Jesus to the top of the high hill upon which Nazareth was built, intending to throw him down upon the sharp rocks in the canon below. But the time had not yet come when Jesus should die for the sins of the people, and therefore they could not carry out their wicked intention. He simply walked quietly through the midst of the excited throng. No one seized hold of him again, and he left them and went away to live in Că-pĕr'-nă-ŭm, the city by the Sea of Galilee.

The men of Nazareth did not know what a terrible deed they had tried to do that day; they did not know that their foolish pride had caused them to drive right out of their midst the gift which God had sent from heaven to earth. And because they refused to believe in Jesus as the one of whom Isaiah had written, they never received the gift of salvation, which Jesus brought to men.

———•———

STORY 15

FOUR FISHERMEN WHO LEFT THEIR NETS TO FOLLOW JESUS
Matt. 4:18-22; Mark 1:16-34; Luke 4:33—5:11

When Jesus returned from the Feast of the Passover at Jerusalem, his disciples were with him, you remember. But after coming into Galilee Jesus went to his home in Nazareth and the disciples returned to their homes in Că-pĕr'-nă-ŭm.

After the proud men of Nazareth tried to kill Jesus, he left their city and went to live in Că-pĕr'-nă-ŭm, too. Here he taught in the synagog on the Sabbath-days, and the people of Că-pĕr'-nă-ŭm were glad to listen to his words. He did not teach them as did their usual Jewish teachers, repeating the same words again and again each time he spoke, but always his words sounded new, and just as if God were speaking to the people.

One morning Andrew and Simon were busy at work in their fishing-boats on the Sea of Galilee when they saw Jesus walking along the shore. He called to them, and they left their boats and followed him. Farther along they saw two other fishermen in a ship mending their torn nets. These men were brothers, and their names were James and John. They were partners in the fishing business with Simon and Andrew, and when they saw their partners following Jesus they ceased their work, wondering where Simon and Andrew were going. Jesus

MIRACULOUS DRAUGHT OF FISHES

called them also, and they left their ship at once in the care of their father and the servants who were helping mend the nets.

Taking these four fishermen with him, Jesus returned to the city. And on the next Sabbath-day they went with him into the synagog, where many people had come to hear his words.

Among the crowd who had gathered that day in the synagog was one man in whom Satan had put a very bad spirit. This bad spirit caused the man to cry aloud when he saw Jesus, and say, "Let us alone! What do we have to do with you, Jesus of Nazareth? I know you are the Holy One from God."

Jesus was not pleased to have a spirit of Satan speak to him like this. So he commanded the bad spirit to come out of the man. And the spirit threw the poor man on the floor before all the people, tearing him and crying with a wicked cry. But at Jesus' command the bad spirit had to leave the man; for Jesus has power over all the power of Satan, to cast out the evil spirits that come to dwell in people.

When those standing by saw what Jesus had done, they were greatly astonished. Never before had they seen any one with power to rebuke the evil spirits. They said to each other, "What thing is this? what new doctrine is this? for Jesus even dares to command evil spirits and they must obey him!"

Quickly the news of this wonderful happening in the synagog spread to every part of the city, and everybody became interested in the great teacher who had lately come to live among them. They were so glad he had come, and they wished to carry their suffering friends and loved ones to him that he might cure them of their sicknesses and diseases. So they began to plan how they might do this.

Jesus had gone with his disciples from the synagog to the home of Simon and Andrew. When they arrived they heard that Simon's mother-in-law was lying sick with fever. So they told Jesus about her, and brought him into the room where she lay suffering. Jesus came to her bedside, and taking hold of her hand he lifted her up. At that very moment the fever departed and strength came into her body again. She rose from her bed and helped to prepare food for the disciples and their wonderful teacher.

At sunset the Sabbath-day closed for the Jews and then they were free to begin their work again, for they never did any work on the Sabbath. When sunset came on this day of rest Simon and Andrew were surprized to see throngs of people coming toward their home. From every direction the people were coming, some with crippled friends leaning on their arms, and others with blind friends walking by their side. Still others were carrying cots on which lay their sick children or other relatives, and all of them were coming to ask Jesus to drive away the sicknesses and diseases and to make their friends and loved ones well again.

What a busy time followed! Jesus was glad to help these poor sufferers and to make them well. He touched them, one by one, and they were healed. He even cast out many evil spirits from the people who had come, and he would not allow those spirits to cry out like the evil spirit had done in the synagog.

Finally the last group of happy friends departed from the door-step, and Jesus lay down to sleep in Simon's house. How very tired he must have been! But after sleeping only a few hours he rose up quietly and left the city. He sought for a place where he might be all alone to talk with his heavenly Father, for often he prayed earnestly to God for strength and help to do the great work that he had to do.

When daylight broke, people began coming again to Simon's home, asking for Jesus. But Jesus was not there. Simon and his friends began to search for Jesus, and they found him at his place of prayer. They told him about the anxious seekers who had come early to find him again, and Jesus said, "I must preach the kingdom of God in other cities also, for I am sent to do this great work." So the disciples went with him to visit other cities in Galilee, and Jesus taught in the synagogs of those cities and cast out evil spirits, as he had done in Că-pĕr'-nă-ŭm. And many people believed in him.

After some time he returned again to Că-pĕr'-nă-ŭm, and his disciples went back to their work as fishermen. But Jesus continued to teach the people who came to hear his words. One day he went out to the sea-side where his disciples were at work, washing their nets. Many people saw him leave the city, and they followed. Soon a great crowd gathered on the shore, eager to hear him preach. So Jesus asked permission to sit in Simon's ship and speak to the people who stood on the shore.

When Jesus finished speaking he told Simon to row out into the deep water and lower his net to catch some fish. Simon replied, "Master, we have fished all night and have caught nothing; however, if you wish we will try again." So they rowed away from the land and let down their nets once more. This time a great many fishes quickly swam into the net and were caught. Simon and Andrew could not draw them out of the water alone, for their net began to break with the weight of the many fishes. They signaled for their partners, James and John, and the four men worked together. They had never seen so many fishes in one net before. Soon the ship was filled, and they began to put more fish in the second ship. Finally both ships began to sink with the weight of the fishes and the men.

Now, the fishermen knew that Jesus had performed a miracle by causing so many fish to be in the net. Simon fell down at Jesus' knees and cried, "Leave me, O Lord! for I am a sinful man and am not worthy of all you have given to us here." But Jesus was not ready to leave Simon. He answered, "Do not be afraid, for hereafter you shall catch men." And Simon understood from Jesus' words that he must leave his fishing business and follow the Master everywhere he went. So when the fishers made their way to the shore they forsook their ships and walked with Jesus from one city to another, helping him and learning daily more and more about the kingdom of God.

STORY 16

HOW MATTHEW THE PUBLICAN BECAME A DISCIPLE OF JESUS
Matt. 9: 9-13; Mark 2:14-17; Luke 5: 27-32

In the land where Jesus lived there was among the Jews one class of people whom all other Jews despised. This class was the publicans, or tax-gatherers, who worked for the Roman government.

The Jews hated the Roman government because they wished to be an independent nation, having a Jewish ruler over them. For this reason they were eagerly awaiting the time when the kingdom of God should come. They believed the kingdom of God would be set up in the same country as that in which David used to live and rule. And they expected to become the greatest people in all the world when that kingdom should be set up. Any Jew who was friendly with the Roman government they hated, because they thought he was not being true to his own nation.

For many years the Jews had believed God would send them a King who would deliver them from the rule of stronger nations. They did not understand when the prophets taught of Jesus' coming to earth that he would come to free them from their greatest enemy, Satan. They seemed to forget that they needed freedom from sin's bondage more than they needed freedom from the rule of the heathen kings.

But the Jews who were more friendly toward the Romans, and who worked for the Roman government, were called publicans. They took the tax money from the Jews, which the ruler at Rome demanded of them. And often they took more money than the Roman ruler called for. In this manner they stole from the people, and became very rich themselves. And the people hated them, and called them sinners.

Not all the publicans robbed the people by asking too much tax money from them. But because many of them did this, the people believed that all of them were guilty of such wrong-doing. And they called every publican a sinner.

One day while Jesus was passing along a street in the city of Că-pĕr′-nă-ŭm he saw a man named Matthew sitting at a publican's table, taking the tax money from the people. Although Matthew was a publican, whom other Jews despised, Jesus saw the heart of this man and he knew Matthew would make a good disciple. So he called this publican to follow him, and Matthew gladly left his money-table and obeyed the call.

Matthew was also called Levi, for the Jews sometimes had two names. And after he began to follow Jesus he remembered his friends of other days. He believed they, too, would be glad to see Jesus and to hear his words. So Matthew prepared a great feast or banquet and called many of his publican friends to the feast. He invited other people too, whom the proud Jews despised and called sinners, and then he brought Jesus and the other disciples to the feast.

The scribes and Pharisees also came to Matthew's house that day, though they had not been invited to the feast. They stood about in the courtyard or even in the large dining-hall, looking on and talking to each other about what they saw. This was not so rude as it seems, for this was a custom among those people and Matthew was not at all surprized when they came.

These onlookers began to find fault when they saw Jesus sitting among the publicans and sinners. They felt themselves too good to keep company with despised folk, and they were surprized that Jesus should eat with Matthew and his friends. So they called Jesus' disciples aside and asked, "How is it that your Master eats and drinks with publicans and sinners?"

Jesus heard the questioning of these fault-finders, and he said to them, "It is not well people who need to call for the services of a doctor, but people who are sick. And so I have not come to call righteous people, but I have come to call sinners to repent." He knew the scribes and Pharisees believed themselves to be too righteous to need repentance, but he knew the publicans and sinners realized that they were not

JESUS CALLING MATTHEW

pleasing God. And they would listen to Jesus' words, and humble their hearts. Many of them would gladly forsake their sins and follow Jesus to learn of him.

Matthew, the publican, became a very useful man for God. It was he who wrote the book called the "Gospel According to Matthew," in the New Testament. And in this writing he gives us more of the words that Jesus spoke than do any other of the gospel writers.

STORY 17

HOW JESUS HEALED A CRIPPLE AND A MAN WHOSE HAND WAS WITHERED

Matt. 12:1-15; Mark 2:23—3:6; Luke 6:1-12; John 5:1-18

Not far from the temple in Jerusalem was a pool called Běth-ěŝ'-dă. At certain times the water in this pool was made to bubble on the surface.

Many sick people, and cripples, and blind folk came to the pool and waited long for the water to move. And five porches were built beside the pool, where these afflicted people might rest in the shade and wait for a chance to be cured of their affliction by bathing in the troubled waters.

One Sabbath-day while Jesus was in Jerusalem he walked through the porches beside the pool. And there he saw the afflicted people who had come for healing. How many there were we do not know, but lying on a mat near the edge of a porch was one man who had not walked for nearly forty years. What a pitiful sight he was! Jesus knew how long the poor man had been crippled although no one told him. He stopped by the man and asked gently, "Would you like to be made well?"

Perhaps the cripple thought this a strange question. He answered, "Sir, I have no one to help me when the water moves, and before I can crawl down some one else steps in."

Then Jesus said, "Rise up, take your bed and walk!" The surprized man felt strength pouring into his weakened body and he sprang to his feet. Then he rolled up the mat and taking it in his arms started toward his home. How happy he felt! But he could not thank the stranger who had spoken to him, for Jesus had disappeared in the crowd.

Presently some religious Jews saw him carrying his bed. Because they believed it was sinful to carry burdens on the Sabbath-day they stopped him and asked why he was carrying his bed. He answered, ''I was lying a cripple by the pool when a stranger came to me and told me to rise up and take my bed and walk away with it.''

''Who is this stranger?'' they demanded, for they were angry to think that any one should break one of the laws they kept on the Sabbath. But the poor man did not know who Jesus was, so he could not tell.

Not long afterwards Jesus found the man in the temple, worshiping God. And Jesus told him to sin no more, lest something worse than his long affliction should come upon him. Then the man knew who Jesus was, and he ran out to tell the people that it was Jesus who had made him well.

The Jews were angry because Jesus had healed the poor man on the Sabbath-day. They did not care for the poor sufferer as much as they cared for their own pretenses to be righteous. They believed it was wrong to do even such a good work as healing the sick on the Sabbath. But Jesus told them that his Father worked on the Sabbath, and so did he. Then they were more angry than ever because he said that God was his Father. They wished to kill him.

After this time the Pharisees became enemies of Jesus. They often followed him just to find fault. One Sabbath-day while he was walking with his disciples through a field of corn, the disciples picked off some of the kernels to eat, because they were hungry. The Pharisees were near by, and seeing what the disciples had done they came to Jesus to find fault. They said, ''Your disciples are breaking the Sabbath laws, for they are gathering food to eat.''

But Jesus told the Pharisees that God was not pleased with their regard of the Sabbath law that would not allow a person to do even what is right. He reminded them of the time when David ate from the temple the bread that belonged only to the priests, and God knew David and his men were hungry so he did not punish David for this act. He told the Pharisees that the priests and the Levites work every Sabbath, when they offer the morning and the evening sacrifices. And he said, ''The Son of man is Lord even of the Sabbath-day.''

When Jesus returned to Galilee, there were Pharisees in the city where he went to teach in the synagog. And again it was on the Sabbath. Jesus knew the Pharisees were watching him. And, too, he saw a man sitting by who had a withered hand. He called the man to stand up where every one might see him, then he turned to the fault-finders and asked, "Is it lawful to do evil, or good on the Sabbath? to kill, or to make alive? If any one of you have a sheep and it fall into a pit on

JESUS HEALING THE WITHERED HAND

the Sabbath, do you not lift it out? And a man is more valuable than a sheep."

Then he turned to the man standing before him and commanded him to stretch out his withered hand. The man obeyed, and immediately the hand was healed. The Pharisees went out of the synagog in an angry mood, wishing to kill Jesus; but the man who had been healed went to his home feeling very happy.

STORY 18

THE TWELVE MEN WHO WERE CALLED APOSTLES
Matt. 10: 2-4; Mark 3:-13-19; Luke 6:12-16

Many people besides the fishermen and Philip and Nă-thăn'-ă-ĕl and Matthew, the publican, followed Jesus. His teachings were so wonder-

ful that others wished to be learners, or disciples, of him, and so they followed in his company from one place to another.

But the time came when Jesus wished to choose from among their number twelve men whom he could prepare to help in his great work. These men he wished to send out to places where he had never yet been, and have them preach to the people in those places about the kingdom of God.

Although Jesus could see the hearts of all men, yet he felt that he needed help from God to know which of his followers he should choose to be among his twelve helpers. So one night he went away quiet-ly and climbed up the slope of a mountain, where

JESUS AND THE TWELVE

no one would be near to disturb him. There he knelt down to pray, and all night he prayed to God for help and wisdom, and for strength to do his work.

When morning light returned Jesus was ready to choose his help-ers, so he left his place of prayer and joined the company of disciples who were waiting in the valley for his coming. From them he chose Simon whom he called Peter, and Andrew, the brother who first brought Simon to Jesus. Then he chose James and John, the fishermen who had been partners with Simon and Andrew at the seaside. Afterwards he chose Matthew, the publican, and Philip and Nă-thăn'-ă-ĕl, of Că-pĕr'-nă-ŭm, and Thomas, and another James, who was the son of Ăl-phæ'-ŭs, and another Simon, also called Zē-lō'-tēṡ, then Judas the brother of James, and last of all Judas Iscariot, who finally sold his Lord.

To these twelve men Jesus gave power to cure diseases and to cast out devils. He also appointed them to preach the kingdom of God. And he called them his apostles which means those who are sent out. Because he sent them out to preach to other men.

Of these twelve apostles we read the most about Simon Peter, James, John, Andrew, Matthew, Philip, and Thomas. Little mention is made of the others, except of Judas Iscariot, who near the end of Jesus' ministry became untrue and betrayed Jesus by selling him for money.

———◆———

STORY 19

THE SERMON ON THE MOUNTAIN-SIDE
Matthew 5—7; Luke 6:17-49

After Jesus had chosen his twelve apostles, who were still called disciples, he took them apart from the multitude to teach them how to do his great work. Up the side of the mountain they went together, and there Jesus sat down. His disciples stood near and he spoke to them. Other people also climbed the mountain to listen to the great sermon Jesus preached that day.

In the beginning of his sermon Jesus said: "Blessed are the poor in spirit: for theirs is the kingdom of heaven." Perhaps he had been thinking about the proud spirits of the scribes and Pharisees. He knew that proud spirits will never receive his words and learn how to enter the kingdom of God. But people who are humble and who do not believe themselves to be righteous without God's help he called poor in spirit, and he said they are blessed because to them shall be given the kingdom of God, for which all Jews were seeking.

He also said: "Blessed are they that mourn: for they shall be comforted." These words sounded strange to the listeners, for they had never thought that blessings belonged to those who are grieving because of troubles and sorrows. They did not realize how God loves to comfort the weary and sad.

"Blessed are the meek:" said Jesus next, "for they shall inherit the earth." By these words he meant that gentle people who do not lose their temper and allow thoughts of discontent to fill their minds will be happy and will enjoy the blessings God gives to all men.

Then Jesus said, "Blessed are they which do hunger and thirst after righteousness: for they shall be filled." Perhaps he was thinking again of the proud Pharisees, who believed they were righteous in themselves and therefore did not need to repent of their sins and seek the righteousness of God. Only those are blessed with God's righteousness who long for it as earnestly as they wish for food and drink to satisfy their appetites.

"Blessed are they who show mercy to others," said Jesus; "for mercy shall be shown to them. And blessed are they who have pure hearts; for they shall see God. And blessed are they who make peace among men, for they shall be called the children of God." These words the disciples understood; for they knew God will surely bless people who show mercy, and people who will not allow sin to enter their hearts, and people who bring peace where trouble is.

Then Jesus said: "Blessed are they who are persecuted for the sake of righteousness; for theirs is the kingdom of heaven." These words sounded strange; for people who are persecuted are greatly troubled, and the disciples may have wondered how the kingdom of God could belong to them when trouble was filling their lives. But afterwards they learned how people who are being persecuted for the sake of righteousness can be blessed as citizens of the kingdom of heaven. And after Jesus had been crucified and had risen from the dead, they themselves learned what it means to be persecuted for the sake of righteousness.

Jesus said that those who are so persecuted should rejoice and be very glad, because there is a great reward awaiting them in heaven. He reminded them of the persecutions that came upon the faithful prophets, and perhaps they thought of Daniel in the lions' den, and of Jeremiah in the deep dungeon.

In this wonderful sermon Jesus told the people how Christians should live. He taught them how Christians should pray, and how they should treat their enemies and their friends. He told them, too, about God's love and care for those who trust him.

At the close of his long sermon Jesus said: "Those who hear my words and do them are like the man who builds his house on a foundation of rock. When the winds blow and the rain falls fast, that foundation of rock will stand firm, and the house will not fall. But those who hear my words and do not obey them are like the man who builds his house on a foundation of sand. When the winds blow and the rain falls fast, that sandy foundation will be washed out from beneath the building, and the house will fall."

Jesus meant by these words that people who hear and obey his teachings will be saved. And when the storm of the judgment day comes they will be safe from harm. But people who hear his teachings and refuse to obey them will not be safe when the storm of the judgment-day comes upon them.

When Jesus ended his sermon, the people looked at each other in surprize. They knew his teachings were more wonderful than the teachings of Moses and of the scribes and Pharisees. They wondered who could obey such commands as these: "Love your enemies." "Pray for them who treat you wrongly." "Do good to them who hate you." But they knew that Jesus' words sounded as though they were the words of God, and by and by many of them learned that even the hardest commands could be obeyed by those who truly love the Lord.

<hr />

STORY 20

HOW JESUS HEALED A MAN WHO WAS A LEPER
Matt. 8: 1-4; Mark 1: 40-45; Luke 5: 12-16

When Jesus and his twelve disciples came down from the mountain, a great multitude of people followed them. These people had come from cities and villages in every part of Galilee, and some had come even from Jerusalem and from country places in Judea.

Near this great multitude stood one poor man who had heard of Jesus' power to work miracles. And he needed, oh, so much! to have a miracle performed in his body; for the terrible disease of leprosy had fastened on him and was eating his flesh. He was not allowed to live among his friends and relatives, for fear they might become lepers also. He was not allowed to come very close to any one who was not a leper. And what an unhappy life he lived!

When the poor leper saw Jesus and his disciples coming down the mountain-side, he thought, "I wonder if this Jesus will heal me." He decided to try him, so he ran to Jesus and knelt down on the ground at Jesus' feet, worshiping him. Then he said, "If you are willing, I know you can make me well from this terrible leprosy."

Jesus looked on the poor man kneeling before him, and great pity filled his heart. He knew how this man was dying, by inches, of the dreaded leprosy, which no doctors could cure. He knew about the unhappy days this poor man spent away from his own home and loved ones. He knew, too, how careful every one was to keep away from a leprous person for fear he might become a leper also.

Jesus was not afraid to touch the poor leper. He reached out his hand kindly and said, "I am willing; you may be healed now." And at that moment the leprosy left the poor man's body and new skin came upon his flesh.

The man sprang quickly to his feet, and the weary look had vanished from his eyes. Now he was well! How thankful he felt. No doubt the great change seemed too good to believe. But he saw how the leprosy was gone, and he knew Jesus had touched him and had sent healing power through his body.

In the law of God that Moses gave to the people, he commanded that lepers should offer sacrifices of thanksgiving to God when their leprosy was healed. So Jesus reminded the man of this command, and told him to go to the priests in Jerusalem and make an offering to God. And he asked the man to tell no one about the healing.

But soon the news of this great miracle spread over the countryside, and every one was talking about it. The poor man had been so glad that he had told his friends what Jesus had done for him. And his friends told their friends, and so the news spread far and wide. And many people left their homes and rushed into the country to see the wonderful person who by his word and by the touch of his hand could drive away the leprosy from a man whose body was full of the dreadful disease.

STORY 21

HOW A ROMAN CAPTAIN SHOWED HIS GREAT FAITH IN JESUS

Matt. 8: 5-13; Luke 7: 1-10

After healing the leper, Jesus returned with his disciples to Că-pĕr'-nă-ŭm, where he had healed so many sick people at the close of one Sabbath-day. News of his coming reached the city before he arrived, and his friends were glad to hear that he would be with them again.

Other people besides those who knew him were glad to hear of his coming. One of them was a Roman, called by the Jews a "Gentile," because he did not belong to the Jewish nation, or race. All people who are not Jews are called Gentiles, and this Gentile was captain of a band of one hundred Roman soldiers. He was called a centurion by those people; but we should call him a captain.

This captain, or centurion, was friendly toward the Jews. He treated them kindly, and was never rough to them. He even built for them a synagog, perhaps the very one in which Jesus had often taught the people on the Sabbath-days. And because of his kindness to them the Jews respected him although he was a Roman Gentile.

One day a servant of the centurion became sick. On the next day he grew worse, and soon it seemed that he could not live much longer. The centurion loved this servant and grieved because he was ill. Then news came that Jesus had returned to Că-pĕr'-nă-ŭm.

Now, the centurion had heard about the sick people whom Jesus had cured, and about the evil spirits which Jesus had driven out of people's hearts. He knew Jesus could heal his servant, but he felt too unworthy to go to Jesus and ask him to do this. He was a Roman, and he knew that Jesus was a Jew. Perhaps he thought Jesus might not be willing to listen to the request of a man who belonged to another nation. He knew about the race-pride of the Jews, and how the religious Pharisees and the scribes despised the Gentile Romans. He may have feared that Jesus would not be quite willing to heal his servant because he was a Gentile. But he loved his servant very dearly and he was willing to try some way to have Jesus come and heal him. So he called for the Jewish teachers in the synagog which he had built, and told them to go to Jesus and ask him to heal the sick man. And they gladly went.

When these Jewish teachers, or elders, came to Jesus they told him about the centurion's desire that he would come and heal the servant. They told him also about the kindness of this Roman captain, and how he had built their synagog. "He is a worthy man," they said; "for he loves our nation." And Jesus went with them.

As they were nearing the centurion's home they saw some men coming to meet them. These men were friends of the centurion, whom he had sent to tell Jesus that he need not come into the house to heal the sick man. The centurion did not feel worthy to have such a great person as Jesus enter under the roof of his house, and he felt himself too unworthy to go out to meet Jesus. So he had sent his friends to carry his message to Jesus. And this was the message: "Lord, do not trouble yourself to come into my house, for I am not worthy to receive so great a man as you are. Just speak the word, and my servant will be made well. I know you have power to command sickness to depart, just as I have power to command my soldiers to obey me."

When Jesus heard these words he was greatly pleased. He turned about and spoke to the curious people who were following, hoping to see another miracle. He said to them, "Nowhere among the Jews have I found such great faith in me as this Gentile captain has shown." Then he told the friends of the centurion that the servant would be made well.

When they returned to the house they found the servant healed. And they saw how great was the power of Jesus to heal the sick, even when he did not come near to the place where they lay.

STORY 22

WHY FOUR MEN TORE UP THE ROOF OF A CROWDED HOUSE

Matt. 9:2-8; Mark 2:1-12; Luke 5:18-26

Wherever Jesus went, crowds followed him. In the streets, or even in the homes of Că-pĕr'-nă-ŭm, many people gathered when they knew he was present. Some of these people were his friends, others were merely persons curious to hear him speak and to see him perform some miracle, while still others followed for the purpose of finding fault with him.

One day while Jesus was in Că-pĕr'-nă-ŭm so many people came to the house where he was staying that they left no room for others to enter. Among them, as usual, were his disciples and friends, the curiosity-seekers, and the fault-finders. These fault-finders were scribes and Pharisees who had come from far-off places to hear him. They had heard many reports about his wonderful teachings, and they wished to hear him for themselves. As he talked, they sat near by, watching every move he made.

Into that crowded room sick people had been brought, and Jesus healed them all. Then while he preached about the kingdom of God the listeners were surprized to hear a scrambling overhead. Presently the roof began to part, and the people saw a queer-looking object being lowered from the ceiling. Then they recognized the form of a crippled man lying on a bed.

On the roof were the four friends of this crippled man. They had tried to bring him to Jesus; but when they had carried him as far as the door they saw that it would not be possible to push with their burden through the crowd. Yet they were determined to bring this suffering man to the great Healer. The man was not able to move himself about, and day after day he had lain upon his bed because of the disease that had made him so weak and helpless.

When the crowd had refused to make way for them to pass, the four friends carried the man up on the flat roof of the house. Then they tore up the roof tiling and saw where Jesus stood. This done, they tied ropes about the bed on which the man lay, and lowered the bed very carefully into the room, before Jesus.

Of course the service was interrupted when the sick man was being lowered by the ropes from the roof. The onlookers wondered what Jesus would do. Perhaps some of them knew this sick man. They were all surprized when they heard Jesus say to him, "Son, be of good cheer, for your sins are forgiven."

The look of pain left the sick man's face and a happy smile came instead. But the astonished people were not watching him. They were looking in surprize at the one who had dared to say, "Your sins are forgiven." They knew God had power to forgive sins, but they did not know that Jesus was the Son of God. The fault-finders began to say in their hearts, "Who is this who pretends to forgive sins? None except God can do that!"

Jesus knew their thoughts, and he said, "Why do you think evil of me in your hearts? Is it easier to tell the man that his sins are forgiven, or to tell him to rise up from his bed and walk? That you may know I have power on earth to forgive sins too [then Jesus turned to the helpless man lying on the couch before him and said], Arise, take up your bed and return to your own house."

Immediately the stiffness departed from the sick man's limbs and strength came into his body. Then he arose up in the presence of all the people, rolled up the couch, or mat, upon which he had lain for many days, and lifted it up on his shoulders just as well men carried their beds in that country. The surprized people made way for him, and he walked out through their midst into the street to join his happy friends.

Great fear came upon the people in that crowded house. They glorified God, and said to each other as they hurried home, "Surely we have seen strange things today!"

STORY 23

WHEN A WIDOW'S SORROW WAS CHANGED INTO JOY
Luke 7 : 11-17

In the city of Nā'-ĭn, in Galilee, lived a woman who was a widow. She had only one child, a youth entering manhood. No doubt she often looked proudly at him and thought the time would soon come when he could provide for her needs as well as for his own. Then one day the young man fell sick.

This was a sad time for the widow, and day after day she watched at the bedside of her son, hoping to see a change for the better. Tenderly she nursed him; but in spite of all her loving care he only grew worse. Then one day he died.

Now the widow's home was broken up; for both her husband and her son were dead. How unhappy she felt! Her neighbors and friends came in to weep with her and to plan for the funeral. They wrapped long strips of linen cloth around the lifeless body and placed it on a frame, called a bier. Then they took up the bier and started with it to the burial-place outside the city gate.

Many people followed the bier and the mourners wept aloud as the procession moved slowly toward the burial-place. Outside the gate they suddenly stopped. Everybody wondered what had happened. Then they saw a great crowd coming toward them, and walking in front of the crowd was Jesus and his twelve disciples.

When Jesus saw the grief of the widow he was touched with pity for her. He knew how deep was her sorrow, and he wished to help, so he spoke kindly to her and said, "Do not weep." Then he stepped up to the bier, and the men who carried it looked at him. They were astonished when they heard him speak to the lifeless form that was lying so cold and helpless upon the frame. But at Jesus' words, "Young man, I tell you to arise!" they saw the lifeless body rise to a sitting position, and they heard the voice which death had stilled speak to them again. What a glad surprize this was! Quickly they unwrapped the long strips of linen cloth from the young man's body, and Jesus took him to his mother.

Now the cries of mourning ceased and a great silence fell over the people. They could hardly believe their own eyes. But soon they were convinced that Jesus had raised the dead young man to life again, and they began to rejoice. "A great prophet is come among us!" they

JESUS BRINGING TO LIFE THE WIDOW'S SON

exclaimed with delight. Others cried, "Surely God has visited his people!" for they believed that only the power of God could overcome death, and they believed God had come to them in the form of the man Jesus.

News of this great miracle quickly spread through the country and traveled far and wide. Even John the Baptist, shut up in the dreary prison where Herod had placed him, heard what Jesus had done. He longed to see and to know more about these things, so he asked two of his disciples who visited him at the prison if they would not go to Jesus and find out whether Jesus was really the Savior whom God had promised to send.

The men hurried to Jesus with John's question, and while they waited for an answer many afflicted people crowded close to the place where they stood and begged for healing. There were cripples, and blind folk, and lepers, and deaf people, and even some in whose bodies evil spirits were dwelling. One by one Jesus healed them, and cast out the evil spirits and sent them away. Then he turned to the inquirers who had come from John's lonely prison and said, "Go back, and tell John what you have seen; how the blind see, the lame walk, the deaf hear, the lepers are cured, the dead are raised to life, the evil spirits are cast out, and to the poor people the glad news of the kingdom is preached."

The men took this message back to John, and no doubt his heart was glad to hear about the wonderful workings of Jesus. Not long after this time Herod commanded that John should be killed, and his friends who came often to comfort him in the lonely prison took up his body and buried it. Then they came and told Jesus what Herod had done.

————— • —————

STORY 24

A PHARISEE, A SINFUL WOMAN, AND THE SAVIOR
Luke 7: 36-50

In one of the cities of Galilee where Jesus was teaching the people a Pharisee named Simon came to hear him. Like many of the other Pharisees, Simon tried to find fault with Jesus. Because he could neither see nor hear anything to criticize in Jesus, he decided to ask this teacher to take dinner at his house. There he would watch him closely, and possibly find something that would be wrong.

So Simon the Pharisee asked Jesus to come to his house one day, and Jesus went with him. Other people went, too, some who were invited and some who were not. And they all came into the dining-hall, where the food was placed on the table. Around this table the guests were given room, while the uninvited persons stood back, looking on.

Jesus and the other guests did not sit on chairs about the table, but they lay on couches with their heads near the table and their feet away from it. While they were eating, another uninvited person came into the dining-hall. This person was a woman. Looking about, she espied Jesus, and at once she hurried to kneel at his feet. Then she wept tears of sorrow for her many sins, and the tears fell upon Jesus' feet. She dried his feet with her hair, and kissed them. Afterwards she broke a beautiful box of costly perfume and anointed his feet by pouring the perfume upon them.

Simon, the Pharisee, knew this woman; for she was a great sinner. He had heard many things about her that were not good. He was surprized when he saw that Jesus allowed her to weep at his feet and to anoint them with sweet perfume. He said in his heart, "If Jesus were a prophet he would not allow this woman to come near him. He would know that she is a wretched sinner, unfit to be in his presence."

Jesus knew all about this sinful woman, and he also knew about Simon's thoughts. He looked at the proud Pharisee and said, "Simon, I have something to tell you."

Simon answered very politely, "Master, what is it?" Then Jesus told him this story:

"There was a certain rich man who had loaned money to two poor men. The first man he loaned a great sum of money, and the second man he loaned only a small amount. When the time came to repay the loan, neither of the two men could pay back the money they had borrowed. In their distress they came to the rich man, and he freely forgave them both. Which of these two men loved the rich man the more?"

"I suppose," answered Simon, "that the man whom he forgave the bigger debt loved him the more."

"You have answered rightly," said Jesus. Then he turned to the sinful woman still weeping at his feet, and said, "Simon, when I came into your home you did not treat me like an honored guest. You did not give me water to wash the dust from my feet; but this woman has washed my feet with her tears and has dried them with the hair of her head. You did not give me a kiss of welcome; but this woman has kissed my feet. You did not anoint my head with oil, as you anoint the heads of your friends who come as guests into your home; but this woman has poured costly ointment upon my feet. Wherefore I tell you that her sins, which were many, are forgiven; for she has loved much. But those love little who have little forgiven them.''

Jesus then told the woman that her sins were forgiven; that her faith had brought forgiveness, and she should go home in peace.

This woman was sorry because she had done wrong, and Jesus forgave the wrong which she had done. But Simon, the proud Pharisee, believed that he was too good to need forgiveness for sin and Jesus did not forgive him. Only those who are sorry for their sins can know the forgiveness of Jesus, the Savior.

———————◆———————

STORY 25

STORY-SERMONS BY THE SEA

Matt. 13: 1-53; Mark 4: 1-34

Helpful stories lessons teach
To the thoughtful mind;
Jesus told them, and in each
Some great truth we find.

One day Jesus went out of Că-pĕr'-nă-ŭm with his disciples and walked by the seaside. Great crowds followed along the beach; for they thought he might be going away from their city again, and they wished to go with him. They pressed so close behind that Jesus stepped into a boat at the water's edge and sat down to teach them, while they stood listening on the shore.

Jesus began to teach them by parables. These parables were short stories which he told to show them truths of the gospel. While he sat in the boat he told them four parables. The first one was about the man who went out to scatter seeds in his field. Jesus called him a sower. And here is the story:

''One day a sower went out to the field with a bag of grain and began to scatter the seeds upon the ground. The breeze caught each handful he threw while walking to and fro, and helped to scatter the grain. But some of the seeds blew upon the roadside. The birds flying overhead saw them lying uncovered on the hard ground, so they flew down and ate the seeds. Other seeds fell upon stony places, where the soil was so shallow they could take no deep root, and soon they withered after they had sprouted and begun to grow. Still other seeds fell in thorny places, and the thorns grew so fast that they choked out the good seed and it died.

"But not all the seed was wasted; for some of it fell into good ground, and there it sprouted and sent its roots down deep into the rich soil. By and by it grew up into stalks of grain that yielded many times more seeds than were first scattered on the ground."

The disciples wondered what this story might mean. They did not know why Jesus was telling stories instead of preaching sermons that the people could understand. So they came to Jesus in the boat and asked, "Why are you teaching the people with these parables?" Jesus answered, "Because I know you will seek to understand the meaning of them, for it is given to you to know the meaning of the deep truths of the kingdom of heaven. Others who hear the stories will not seek to understand the meaning of them, for they are not careful to prepare their hearts to receive the forgiveness of their sins. The prophet Isaiah spoke of them when he said, 'By hearing ye shall hear and not understand; and seeing ye shall see and not know.' Their eyes are closed, so they can not see the salvation God has sent into the world; and their ears are stopped, so they can not hear the good news of salvation and receive it into their hearts. But blessed are your eyes, for they see; and blessed are your ears, for they hear."

Then Jesus explained to the disciples the meaning of the story about the sower and his seed.

"The sower," he said, "is the one who speaks the word of God, and the different kinds of soil are the different conditions of the hearts of people who hear the word of God spoken. Those who hear the word but do not seek to understand it, are like the roadside by which the seeds fell. Just as the birds flew down and ate those seeds, so the evil one comes by and causes those people to forget the truths they have heard from God's word.

"Those who gladly hear the word of God, but do not continue to obey it, are like the stony places, where the seeds fell but could not grow because they could not take deep roots in the stony soil.

"Those who hear and receive the word of God into their hearts, but afterwards allow cares and troubles or riches and pleasures to crowd out the good truths, are like the soil where thorns sprang up and choked out the good seed.

"But those who hear and who obey the words of God are like the good ground, where some of the seeds fell and sprouted and grew into stalks that bore much grain."

Afterwards Jesus told another story to the people. This time he said: "The kingdom of heaven is like a man who sowed good seeds in his field; but while men slept an enemy came to the field and scattered bad seeds everywhere. These bad seeds are called tares. By and by the good seeds and the bad seeds both began to grow. And after they became stalks, and heads of grain appeared, the servants of the man came to him and asked, 'Did you not sow good seeds in your field? How then are these tares growing everywhere beside the stalks of wheat?' The man answered, 'An enemy has sown the tares.' Then the servants asked, 'Shall we gather out the tares?' but the master said, 'Wait until the time for harvest, lest while you pull up the tares you also pull up stalks of wheat. When all are ripened together, I will send reapers to first gather out the tares and tie them into bundles to be thrown into the fire. Then they will gather the wheat and put it into my barn.'"

The third story Jesus told was about a grain of mustard seed. He said the kingdom of heaven is like such a tiny grain, which, after it was sown quickly grew into a bush so large that even the birds could sit in the branches of it.

Then he said, "The kingdom of heaven is also like leaven, or yeast, which a woman put into her dough when she was mixing bread. The yeast soon worked through all the dough and caused it to rise light and make good bread." Perhaps the women who heard this story wondered how the kingdom of heaven could really be like yeast.

When Jesus finished all his stories he sent the people away, and afterwards he left the boat and also returned to the city. Then the disciples asked him to explain the meaning of the story about the tares. Jesus said: "The good seed are the people of God; the field is the world; and the man who sowed the good seed is the Son of man. The bad seed, or tares, are the people of the wicked one, and the enemy is Satan. The harvest is the end of the world, and the reapers are the angels. Just as the tares are gathered in bundles and thrown into the fire, so the wicked people will be separated from the good people at the end of the world. Then the good people will shine as brightly as the sun in the kingdom of God, their Father."

STORY 26

THE FLOODED SHIP THAT DID NOT SINK, AND THE WILD MAN MADE WELL

Matt. 8:23-34; Mark 4:35—5:20; Luke 8:22-40

One stormy night a little ship tossed about on the angry waters of the Sea of Galilee. Far from the shore it had sailed when the storm broke upon it, and the sailors feared they might never see land again. With all their strength they pulled the oars; but the great waves dashed the ship helplessly about, threatening every moment to destroy it.

Several of the sailors in that company had seen the rage of the sea at other times when storms swept over its surface. They knew the fearful power of such a storm. They knew how helpless they were in the grasp of this tempest. While they were wondering what

JESUS STILLING THE STORM

to do, a great wave broke over the side of the ship, flooding it with water. Now they believed that they would all be drowned.

These frightened sailors were the disciples of Jesus, and they were trying to take their master across the Sea of Galilee. Darkness had come upon them, and with the darkness of night the fearful storm broke. But Jesus, tired from his labors during the day, had lain down to rest and had fallen fast asleep. He did not know about the raging tempest, which threatened to destroy the ship and its passengers. He did not know about the fright of his disciples as they battled with the storm.

But when the great wave broke over the ship, the disciples remembered Jesus, lying asleep. They rushed to him and cried out, "Master, do you not care that we perish?" Jesus aroused from his sleep, opened his eyes, and looked into their frightened faces. Seeing their alarm he arose to his feet and asked, "Why are you so fearful? Why do you have no faith?" Then he spoke to the wind, simply telling it to be still. And at the sound of this voice the tempest ceased at once, and the dashing waves grew quiet and calm.

The disciples were surprized to see that their master had power even greater than the power of the tempest. They were surprized to know that even the wind and the waves obeyed the voice of the Son of man. And they asked each other, wonderingly, "What manner of person is Jesus, that even the sea obeys him?" They did not know that he had helped the great Father-God in the beginning of the creation, when the world was made, and the sea and the dry land were formed on the face of the earth.

After the tempest ceased, the sailors brought their ship to the land of the Găd'-ă-rēnes, on the other side of the Sea from Că-pĕr'-nă-ŭm. When they stepped onto the shore with Jesus, a man came running across the country to meet them. This man was in a pitiful state, for he was wild, living alone in the graveyard or wandering day and night through the mountains cutting himself with sharp stones and crying out in distress. Evil spirits from Satan had come to live in him, and they had made him so wild and fierce that other people were afraid of him.

Even the relatives of this wild man had long ceased trying to do anything with him. For a while they had bound him with chains; but when the evil spirits would begin to torment him he would break off the chains, tear off his clothes, and run away to the wilderness or to lonely places to cry out.

The wild man came to Jesus and fell down before him to worship. But Jesus knew that evil spirits were troubling him, and he commanded them to leave the man. The spirits talked to Jesus through the man's mouth, and begged that he would not torment them. Jesus asked, "What is your name?" and the spirits replied, "Legion, for we are many." A great host of bad spirits were dwelling in the poor man. No wonder he was in such a pitiful state.

On a mountain-side near by a herd of two thousand hogs were feeding. The Jews were forbidden by the law to eat the flesh of these animals. But the people who lived in this land on the other side of the Sea from Că-pĕr'-nă-ŭm kept many hogs for market, and they sent servants out to the fields to watch them.

The evil spirits in the wild man did not want to leave the country, though they knew Jesus would not let them stay in the poor man any longer. So they asked to enter the hogs that were feeding on the mountain-side. Jesus gave them permission to go into the hogs, and at once the great herd of two thousand ran down a steep place and fell into the Sea, where they were drowned.

The keepers of the herd were frightened, and they ran to the owners to tell what had happened. Soon a crowd of curious people came from the city not far away and saw the wild man sitting at Jesus' feet, wearing clothes and no longer acting wild and unruly. A look of peace had settled upon his face, and his right mind had come back again. Now he could speak and think and act like other men.

When the people heard what Jesus had done for the man whom they had feared so much, they were greatly surprized. But they were not pleased, because they had lost all the hogs on the mountain-side. Perhaps they had planned to sell those animals for much money. Now they did not want Jesus to stay with them any longer, for fear they might lose other things. They did not think about their sick friends, whom Jesus might heal, nor about others among them who needed to have bad spirits cast out. They were selfish people, loving their money more than they loved the people who lived about them. So Jesus saw that he was not welcome, and he turned to go away.

The man for whom he had done such a great miracle followed Jesus to the ship and begged to go with him wherever he went. How blessed it seemed to this poor man to be near the one who had freed him from the misery he had suffered!

But Jesus said, "Go back to your home, and tell your friends what great things the Lord has done for you." Gladly the man obeyed, and from city to city he went, telling people about the wonderful power of Jesus, until many who had never heard before came to know of the wonder-working teacher in Galilee.

THE LITTLE GIRL WHO DIED AND BECAME ALIVE AGAIN
Matt. 9:18—10:42; Mark 5:22-43; Luke 8:41—9:6

When Jesus and his disciples returned from the country of the Găd'-ă-rēneś they saw a crowd standing on the shore eager to welcome them back to Că-pĕr'-nă-ŭm. And again Jesus taught them and healed the sick folk they brought to him.

Presently a man came running to Jesus, looking very much distressed. He fell down at Jesus' feet and cried, ''My little daughter is lying at home ready to die; but if you will come with me and touch her, I know she shall be made well.'' This man was a ruler of the synagog in Că-pĕr'-nă-ŭm, and his name was Jā-ī'-rŭs.

No doubt Jesus knew this man, for often he had taught in the synagog. Now he started at once to go with Jā-ī'-rŭs to heal his daughter. The disciples, too, went with him. And the crowd followed, eager to see another miracle. As they went, the people pressed close to Jesus; for every one was eager to walk as near to him as possible.

In this throng was one poor woman who had been ill for twelve years. She had spent all her money in taking treatments from doctors, yet they did not cure her. Now she had no more money and still she was greatly afflicted. But she had heard of Jesus' power to heal, and this glad news brought courage to her sad heart. She decided to go to him and be made well.

How hard it was to reach him! But this woman pressed her way through the crowd till she came very near. She thought in her heart, ''I will not ask him to make me well; I will only touch the hem of his garment and I know I shall be healed.'' So she edged her way closer, until she could reach out her hand and touch Jesus' clothes. Immediately she felt the healing power go through her body, and she stepped backward into the crowd.

But Jesus knew what the woman had done. He knew about her earnest desire to be made well, and he knew about her thoughts. So he turned around and asked, ''Who touched me?''

The disciples were amazed at this question. ''Why do you ask who touched you, when the people are pressing against you from every side?'' they inquired. But Jesus answered, ''Some one has touched me, for I felt healing virtue go from my body.''

Then the woman knew that her act was known by Jesus, and she came trembling and fell down before him, telling her sad story. Jesus spoke comforting words to her, and said, "Daughter, your faith has made you well; go in peace."

Jā-ī'-rŭs stood by waiting impatiently for Jesus to start again. He was fearful that his little daughter might die before they could reach her bedside. And surely enough, a servant from his house came to meet them with the sad news that the little girl was dead. "Do not trouble the Master any longer, for it is too late," he said.

Jesus heard the message, and he saw the deep grief of Jairus. He said to the father, "Do not be afraid; only believe, and she shall yet be made well." So they journeyed on.

At the ruler's home many friends and neighbors had gathered to weep and to comfort the sorrowing mother. Jesus told them to cease their weeping, for the child was not dead, but sleeping. They did not understand that Jesus meant to say, "Death is only a sleep from which we shall all waken again." And they scoffed at his words; for they knew the little girl had no life remaining in her body.

Then Jesus sent every one out of the room except the father and mother of the little girl and three of his disciples. Simon Peter, and James, and John were the three whom he permitted to remain with him. When the others had gone out, he took the child's hand in his own and said, "Little girl, rise up!" At his command she opened her eyes and rose up to walk about the room. Jesus told her parents to give her some food to eat, and he asked them to tell no one what he had done; for already the people were thronging him, and news of this miracle would draw greater crowds than ever.

When they left the home of Jā-ī'-rŭs, two blind men followed Jesus, crying out, "O son of David, have mercy on us!" They followed him into the house where he was staying, and when they came to him there he asked, "Do you believe that I am able to open your blind eyes?" They answered quickly, "Yes, Lord." So he touched their eyes and said, "Let it be done to you just as you believe." And their eyes were opened so that they could see. Jesus asked these men to tell no one what he had done; but they went everywhere telling how Jesus had opened their blinded eyes.

Afterwards was brought to Jesus a dumb man who had an evil spirit dwelling in him. And Jesus cast out the spirit, and caused the man to be able to speak. Many onlookers were amazed at these mighty miracles of Jesus, and they said, "It was never so seen in Israel." But the fault-finding Pharisees said, "He does not cast out evil spirits by the power of God, but by the power of Satan." They were jealous of the fame that had come to Jesus, and they spoke evil of him.

So great were the crowds who pressed to hear Jesus that he saw he could not teach them all. Then he sent his twelve disciples to preach in other cities, and he gave them power to heal the sick and to cast out evil spirits, and even to raise the dead. The work was too great for him to do alone, and he had chosen these men to help him. So they went to other towns and villages, preaching the gospel and healing the sick, just as Jesus had commanded them to do.

———◆———

STORY 28

A BOY'S LUNCH-BASKET, AND A GREAT MIRACLE
Matt. 14:13-23; Mark 6:31-46; Luke 9:7-17; John 6:1-15

A boy's lunch-basket is a very small thing compared with a great miracle. But in this story we shall see how a great miracle grew out of a boy's lunch-basket. It all came about in this manner:

The disciples whom Jesus sent to preach in the towns and cities of Galilee had returned joyfully, telling their Master about their success in healing the sick and in casting out the evil spirits just as they had seen him do. And now the fame of Jesus was increasing every day, and many more people from distant parts of the country were flocking to hear him.

So urgent were the people who came to hear Jesus and to have their loved ones healed, that they pressed constantly upon him, and allowed no time for him to rest or even to eat. Then Jesus called his twelve disciples aside from the multitude and said, "Come with me to a quiet place, for we must rest a while."

Taking a ship they sailed away from the multitude to the other side of the Sea, and went into a desert place near a mountain. But they did not find much time to rest even in this lonely spot, for soon they saw a great throng of people coming toward them. The multitude had followed from the other side of the Sea. Perhaps the disciples were disappointed because the people had found them again, but Jesus looked pityingly upon the great throng, and said of them, "They are like sheep that have no shepherd. They wander about here and there hunting for their own pasture-grounds."

In this great throng were five thousand men, who had come from different parts of Galilee. Some of them had brought their wives and children along, and other women had come, too. When they had started they did not know they would have to go so very far to find Jesus, and many of them had brought nothing to eat. One boy, however, had not forgotten his lunch-basket, and in his basket he carried five little loaves of barley bread and two small fishes.

When the multitude came near, Jesus received them kindly and sat down to teach them again. He healed the sick ones whom they had brought to him, and taught them many things about the kingdom of heaven.

After a while the day wore on and evening came. Still the people lingered near, seeming to forget they could find no food or shelter in the desert place. The disciples grew impatient with them and came to ask Jesus to send them away. "They have brought no food," said the disciples, "and we can not supply food for them in this wilderness; therefore send them away that they may buy food in the towns and villages as they journey home."

But Jesus answered, "We must feed them before sending them away." Then, turning to Philip he asked, "Where shall we find bread, that all these people may eat?" Philip looked at the great multitude and shook his head. "If we should buy two hundred pennyworth of bread," he answered, "there would not be enough for each one to have a small piece."

While Jesus and the disciples were discussing what to do, the boy who had not forgotten to carry his lunch came near and heard their conversation. Then he showed his basket of food to one of the disciples, and he offered to give the food to Jesus. The disciple, who was Andrew, came and told Jesus what the boy had said. "How many loaves are there in the basket?" asked Jesus, and Andrew said, "Only five and two small fishes. But what will that be among so many people?"

Jesus replied, "Bring them to me." Then he told his disciples to bid the people sit down in groups, in some fifty and in others a hundred, and wait for their evening meal. While they waited, he took the little loaves and the fishes and blessed them and broke them into small pieces. He filled a basket for each of the twelve disciples and sent them to pass the food among the hungry people. Then the disciples returned and again he filled their empty baskets. When all the people had eaten, he sent the disciples to gather up the scraps that had been left over, and they found twelve baskets full of scraps. And every one in the great multitude had eaten enough to satisfy his hunger. The boy who had brought the lunch-basket to Jesus had all that he could eat, and he shared his little lunch with every one in the great throng because he had let Jesus bless his offering.

This unusual miracle caused much excitement among the people. They wanted Jesus to become their king instead of letting the Roman government rule them any longer. They believed that he could set them free from the rule of the Romans, whom they hated. They thought it would be wonderful to have a king rule them who could feed them by working miracles.

But Jesus would not allow the people to take him for their king. Although he was a King, yet he had not come to earth to rule an earthly kingdom. He commanded his disciples to enter their ship at once and return to the other side of the Sea. And when they left him, then he dismissed the multitude and went alone upon the mountain near by to pray.

STORY 29

THE MAN WHO WALKED ON THE WATER AND BECAME AFRAID

Matt. 14: 23-36; Mark 6: 46-56; John 6: 16-29

While Jesus was alone praying on the mountain-side, the disciples were in their ship rowing toward Că-pĕr'-nă-ŭm. And the multitude were returning homeward as they had come, walking along the northern shore of the Sea.

After nightfall a strong wind began to blow across the Sea, driving against the little ship. Row as hard as they might, the disciples could not make much progress against the wind. Higher and higher the waves dashed and rolled, and slower the vessel plowed through them. How tired the disciples were growing! Perhaps they were thinking about the time when a tempest swept over the Sea and Jesus had been with them, sleeping in the ship. Perhaps they were wishing for his presence now, to still this stormy wind that made their progress so wearisome and so slow.

Far away on the mountain Jesus had been praying for several hours. But he had not forgotten his disciples. Perhaps he had been praying for them as well as for himself. He knew how much they needed him when the strong wind began to blow against their little ship, and he started to go to them. Out across the water he walked as easily as if it had been land, and nearer and nearer he came to the tossing ship and its weary sailors. By and by he came very near, so near that they could see him through the darkness, walking past them on the rough waves.

Now the disciples were frightened; for every one had seen Jesus and they believed they had seen a spirit. They did not think he could really walk on water, for no person had ever done that. They remembered how God had parted the waters of the Red Sea for the Israelites to cross over on dry land, and how he had made a dry path across the Jordan River three times for his servants to walk upon. But never had they heard of any one walking on top of the water. This must be a spirit. And they cried out for fear of what they had seen.

Jesus stopped when he heard their cry, and turned to speak to them. He said, "Do not be afraid, for it is I." How familiar that voice sounded! Still the disciples could scarcely believe it was Jesus who spoke. Finally Simon Peter cried out, "Lord, if it is you, bid me come to

JESUS TELLING PETER TO COME

you walking on the water." And Jesus answered "Come."

With a bound Simon Peter leaped over the side of the ship and started to go to Jesus. The other disciples looked on in amazement, wondering more than ever at the great power of Jesus on both sea and land. Presently, however, they saw their fellow disciple beginning to sink in the rough waves, and they heard his voice calling frantically to Jesus to help. For Simon Peter had begun to look about at the stormy wind and waves, and just as soon as he took his eyes off Jesus he began to sink. Then Jesus reached forth his hand and caught him, saying, "O man of little faith, why did you doubt?"

When the two came to the ship, the other disciples received them joyfully, and at once the wind ceased. Again the disciples marveled at the wonderful power of their master, who could perform miracles on the sea as well as on the land. And they came to him, worshiping him and saying, "Surely you are the Son of God."

STORY 30

HOW JESUS ANSWERED A MOTHER'S PRAYER

Matt. 15: 21-29; Mark 7: 24-30

Near the land of Galilee was a small country called Phœ-nĭc'-ĭă. The people who lived in this country were Gentiles, and many of them were idol-worshipers. But because they lived so near to the home country of the Jews, many of them knew about the Jews' religion, which taught of only one great God over all.

The time had come when Jesus wished to be alone with his disciples that he might teach them deeper truths before he should die and rise again. So one day he took them for a long walk. They left Galilee and entered the neighboring country of Phœ-nĭc'-ĭā. Here they went into a house, thinking that no one would disturb them there.

But the fame of Jesus had reached those Gentile people in Phœ-nĭc'-ĭă, and they were eager to see him. Soon the news of his coming spread through the neighborhood, and Jesus saw that he could not hide himself even in a strange land.

Living in that neighborhood was one poor Gentile mother whose heart was very sad. She had a child, a little girl, who was tormented by a wicked spirit. This distressed mother had heard of the great healer in Galilee who cast out evil spirits and she longed to take her child to him. But she could not go. Then the glad news came that Jesus and twelve of his friends were visiting in a house near her home. Quickly she left her work and ran to the house where Jesus was.

When she found Jesus she began at once to tell about the sad condition of her little daughter. But the great Healer of Galilee paid no attention to her at all! He seemed not even to hear her. Then his twelve friends looked scornfully upon her because she was a Gentile woman, and urged their Master to send her away. Fearing he might do this, she fell at Jesus' feet, worshiping him and crying, ''Lord, help me!''

The loving heart of Jesus is always touched when he hears the cry of one in need. He pitied this poor woman. He knew she had faith in his power to heal her child, but he wished to test her faith. So he answered, ''I am not sent to the Gentiles, but to the lost children of Israel. And it is not fitting to take children's bread and throw it to the dogs.'' The proud Jews called the Gentiles ''dogs,'' and no doubt this Gentile woman knew how the Jews spoke of her and of her people. But she was now willing even to be called a dog if only the great Healer would answer her prayer. So she said, "I know it is true that children's bread should not be given to the dogs, yet we know that dogs eat of the crumbs that fall from the table." And she, a Gentile "dog" wanted a crumb of the Jews' healing bread for her afflicted child.

> Just a crumb of the healing bread
> With which the suffering Jews were fed,
> Just a crumb, she asked, just one—
> Would she, a Gentile, be given none?

Not long did this earnest woman need to wait for an answer from Jesus. He was greatly pleased when he heard her wise reply to his words, and he said, "O woman, great is your faith in me! And you shall receive just what you have asked. Go back to your home, for the wicked spirit is gone out from your daughter."

Gladly the woman sprang to her feet and obeyed Jesus' words, for she believed that her child was well. And when she came home she found the little girl lying on the bed, resting quietly, for the wicked spirit had gone away at Jesus' word.

------•------

STORY 31

WHAT A MULTITUDE LEARNED ABOUT JESUS
Matt. 15: 29-39; Mark 7: 31—8-10

Leaving Phœ-nĭc'-ĭă, Jesus and his twelve disciples journeyed around to the country on the eastern side of the Sea of Galilee. In this same country Jesus had healed the man in whom a legion of evil spirits had dwelt, and had sent the evil spirits into the herd of hogs that fed on the mountain-side by the Sea. And the people had run out excitedly from the cities near by, to see Jesus and ask him to leave their land. And Jesus had gone away.

But the man who had been healed by Jesus had returned home to tell his friends about the wonderful Healer of Galilee, and everywhere he went he spoke of the power of Jesus that had made him well. And the people became interested. They saw the great change that had come over the man whom they used to fear, and they felt sorry that Jesus had been sent away.

Now when Jesus returned the second time with his twelve disciples, a multitude of eager people gathered to see and to hear him.

They followed him to a dreary country place and for three days listened to his teachings, and brought their sick folk to him to be healed. And Jesus healed every one who was brought to him.

Among that number was a man who could neither hear nor speak plainly. Friends brought him to Jesus to be healed, and Jesus took him aside from the multitude, put his fingers into the man's ears, touched his tongue, then looked up to heaven and sighed, and said, "Be opened!" And immediately the man's ears were unstopped so that he was no longer deaf, and his tongue was loosed so that he could speak plainly. When the multitude saw what Jesus had done, they were astonished. And they said of him, "He has done all things well: he makes both the deaf to hear and the dumb to speak."

On the evening of the third day Jesus called his disciples aside and reminded them how long the people had been with them without food. He said, "I am sorry for them because they have nothing to eat. We can not send them away to their homes in this condition, for they are weak and may faint by the way." "How can we feed them all in this desert place?" asked the disciples. And Jesus answered, "How many loaves do you have?" They said, "Only seven, and a few little fishes."

Jesus then turned to the multitude and commanded them to sit down. When they had obeyed he took the loaves and fishes and blessed them, just as he had done when he fed the five thousand from the boy's lunch-basket. And again the loaves and the fishes increased until there was food enough for every one. More than four thousand people were fed by this miracle, and seven baskets of food remained after all had eaten their fill.

Then Jesus dismissed the multitude, and they returned to their homes with their sick folk made well. How glad they were that Jesus had come the second time to visit their country! Now they rejoiced with the man out of whom Jesus had cast the evil spirits; for they, too, had been blessed by the Healer of Galilee.

From this place Jesus went with his disciples in a ship to the country on the north side of the Sea of Galilee.

JESUS FEEDING THE FIVE THOUSAND

MAGDALA, ON THE SEA OF GALILEE

This little Moslem village of twenty huts, on the water's edge, at the southeast corner of the Plain of Genessaret, is reputed to have been the home of Mary Magdalene. It is now the only inhabited place on this plain. After Jesus fed the four thousand, "he sent away the multitude, and took ship, and came into the coasts of Magdala" (Matt. 15:39).

THE BLIND MAN OF BETHSAIDA; HOW PETER ANSWERED A GREAT QUESTION

Matt. 16: 13-28; Mark 8: 22—9: 1; Luke 9: 18-27

Near Bĕth-sā'-ĭ-dă, a town by the side of the Sea, lived a man who was blind. He had never been to Jesus, but he had heard how the eyes of blind people were opened by this wonderful man of Galilee, and he too wished to be healed. One day he heard that Jesus and twelve other men had come to Bĕth-sā'-ĭ-dă. Then his friends led him to the place where the visitors from Galilee were stopping.

Jesus did not wish to attract multitudes to himself any longer. Now he wished to have time to be alone with his disciples. So he would not heal the blind man in the place where they brought him, but took the man by the hand and led him out of town. Alone with him, he placed his hands upon the blind eyes, then asked whether the man could see.

At first the man could not see clearly. He answered, "I see men walking about, but they look like trees walking." Jesus touched his eyes again, and they were made well. Then Jesus told him to return to his home alone, and tell no one about the miracle. He did not want a crowd to gather round, for he could not stay in Bĕth-sā'-ĭ-dă to teach them.

From this place Jesus and his disciples journeyed north, to a city called Çæ-ṡă-rē'-ă Philippi, not far from Mount Hermon. On their way Jesus asked the disciples some questions. First he asked, "Who do men say that I am?" The disciples answered, "Some say you are Ē-lī'-jăh, the prophet, come back to earth; some think you are John the Baptist risen from the dead; others believe you are Jeremiah, the old prophet, or another of the old prophets who used to teach their fathers long ago."

Then Jesus asked, "But who do you men believe that I am?" And Simon Peter answered boldly, "We believe that you are Christ, the promised Mĕs-sī'-ăh and King, and the Son of the living God." Jesus told Simon Peter that God the Father had caused him to believe this, for of a truth he was the Son of the living God. But he asked the disciples to tell no one that he was the Christ, for the time had not yet come for this truth to be publicly known.

From this time Jesus began to talk to the disciples about the sorrows that would come upon them at Jerusalem when he should be taken from them and put to death by enemies among their own people. The disciples could not understand these words, for they believed Jesus would soon be their king and that they should rise to prominent places in his kingdom. They were displeased to hear him speak about dying, and rising on the third day.

Simon Peter, who often spoke for all the twelve, took Jesus aside and said, "These terrible things will never happen to you!" But Jesus looked sadly upon his disciples and answered, "You speak as Satan, the tempter; for your words are pleasing to man but not pleasing to God." How much easier it would have been for Jesus to accept a throne and earthly kingdom than to suffer and die! But never would he yield to Satan's wishes, though he must suffer the greatest agony. But Peter and the other disciples could not understand.

Afterwards Jesus called other people to him, and when they had come he began to teach them what it would mean to be one of his followers. He said, "If any one follows me, he must not try to please himself. He must be willing to bear his cross. And he must not try to save his own life; for he who saves his life shall lose it, but he who loses his life for my sake shall find it. And what is a man profited even if he should gain the whole world and lose his own soul? And what will a man give in exchange for his soul?"

These questions caused the people to wonder at his teachings. Then Jesus said, "The Son of man shall come in the glory of his Father, with his angels; and then he shall reward every man according to his works."

------- • -------

STORY 33

THE GLORIFIED MASTER ON THE MOUNTAIN-SIDE
Matt. 17:1-13; Mark 9:2-13; Luke 9:28-36

It had been a long, hard climb up the rough slope of the great mountain near Çǣ-ṡǎ-rē'-ǎ Philippi, and Simon Peter, James, and John were very tired when at last they found a resting-place far above the quiet valley. These fishermen had not been accustomed to mountain-climbing, and no doubt they would have chosen to row a boat all day rather than to take such a weary journey. But Jesus, their master, had asked them to go with him to a place of prayer, and because they loved him they had followed.

But now that they had come with him all the way up the mountain, they felt too tired to pray. So they fell asleep. And Jesus prayed alone.

While the three disciples were sleeping, a great change came over their master. His face began to shine as the brightness of the sun; his clothing, too, gleamed as white as snow. And two men from heaven came to talk with him. They were: Moses, the man who had spent forty days alone with God on Mount Sĭ'-naî when he was leading the Israelites from Egypt to Canaan; and Ē-lī'-jăh, the prophet who had heard God's voice on Mount Hôr'-ĕb, where he had gone to escape the wrath of a wicked queen. Moses had written the law of God which the Jews had as a part of their Bible; and Ē-lī'-jăh was one of the prophets through whom God had spoken to his people in other days.

While these two heavenly visitors talked with Jesus, the disciples awoke from their sleep. How surprized they were to see their master clothed in such brightness and talking with Moses and Ē-lī'-jăh! They gazed in astonishment upon the glorious scene before them. Then as Moses and Ē-lī'-jăh began to disappear from their sight Simon Peter exclaimed, "Lord, it is good for us to be here! If you are willing, let us build three tabernacles—one for you, one for Moses, and one for Ē-lī'-jăh."

But while Peter spoke, a bright cloud descended upon the disciples, and they felt afraid. Then a voice spoke from the bright cloud and said, "This is my beloved Son, in whom I am well pleased; hear him." When the disciples heard the voice they fell to the ground, trembling with fright.

After the voice spoke, the cloud lifted, and Jesus came and touched the disciples, saying, "Rise up, and do not be afraid." When they lifted their eyes they saw Jesus only; for the bright cloud had vanished, and the heavenly visitors, too, had disappeared. Now they believed that surely Jesus is the Son of God.

On the next day when they came down from the mountain Jesus told them to keep this wonderful scene for a secret among themselves until after he should rise from the dead. The disciples wondered why he should be talking about pain, and grief, and death when he the Son of God had been visited with such heavenly glory. But they were careful to tell no one about what had happened when they were alone with Jesus on the mountain.

Now the disciples asked, "Why do our teachers say that Ē-lī'-jăh must first come before the Mĕs-sī'-ăh appears?" Jesus answered, "Ē-lī'-jăh has come already, but they have not known him, and they have treated him shamefully. So also will they treat me." And the disciples knew that he was speaking of John the Baptist, whom Herod had caused to be killed in prison.

———•———

A SUFFERING CHILD, AN ANXIOUS FATHER, AND JESUS

Matt. 17:14-21; Mark 9:14-29; Luke 9:37-45

The next day after Jesus had appeared in glory on the mountain, he came with his three disciples back to the valley where he had left the nine. And he found them surrounded by a questioning throng.

As soon as Jesus came near, a man ran from the throng and fell at his feet, crying, "Lord, have mercy on my son; for he is a lunatic, and often he falls into the fire, or into the water. And I brought him to your disciples, but they could not cure him."

Jesus was grieved because he saw how little faith in him men had to heal such a pitiful case; for the child was being tormented by an evil spirit, which would throw him down and tear him until he would foam at the mouth and suffer great pain. Now Jesus said to the troubled father, "Bring your child to me." So the man hurried to bring the boy to Jesus.

When they came, the evil spirit seized the boy again and threw him violently upon the ground. There he lay in the dust, wallowing and foaming, and all the people were gazing in astonishment upon him. Jesus asked the father, "How long has your son been so afflicted?" And the father answered, "Ever since he was a small child. Often the evil spirit has tried to destroy him; but if you can do anything for us, have mercy upon us and help us!"

Jesus saw that this man lacked faith in his power to heal this son. He answered, "If you can believe, all things are possible to him who believes." Then the father cried out, weeping, "O Lord, I do believe; help me to be rid of all doubt."

So Jesus commanded the evil spirit to come out of the boy and torment him no longer. Then the spirit gave a loud cry and, tearing the child, came out, leaving him to lie still and unconscious upon the ground. The people rushed up to the place where he lay, and said, "He is dead." But Jesus stooped down, took his limp hand, and lifted him up. And the boy rose, and Jesus brought him to his father, a well child no longer to suffer the tortures of the evil spirit.

Then Jesus took his disciples away from the people, and they entered into a house alone. Here the nine asked their master, "Why was it that we could not cast out that evil spirit?'' Jesus answered, "Because you did not have faith. However, this kind goes out only when you fast and pray.'' And Jesus talked to his disciples about their need of having faith in God.

———————•———————

STORY 35

JESUS AND HIS DISCIPLES IN CAPERNAUM

Matt. 17 : 22—18 : 14; Mark 9 : 30-43; Luke 9 : 43-50

Leaving the north country near Çǣ-šǎ-rē'-ǎ Philippi, Jesus and his twelve disciples journeyed back to Cǎ-pĕr'-nǎ-ŭm. As they went Jesus talked with them again about the sufferings that would soon come upon him. He even told them that he

should be killed and that on the third day he would rise again. But they could not understand.

Soon the disciples fell to disputing among themselves which should be the greatest in the kingdom of heaven. They still believed that Jesus would set up an earthly kingdom and that they should hold positions of honor in that kingdom. But as they disputed among themselves they said nothing to Jesus about the matter, not until after they had reached Cǎ-pĕr'-nǎ-ŭm.

Now, Jesus did not wish to attract the crowds which flocked to hear him teach in other days, so he went with his disciples into a house, and few people knew about his stopping-place. But while they were in

JESUS AND THE LITTLE CHILD

Cǎ-pĕr'-nǎ-ŭm a man who collected tax money for the temple in Jerusalem saw Simon Peter and asked whether his master paid the tax, which every Jew was supposed to pay. Peter replied that Jesus did. When he returned to the house where they were staying, Jesus sent him to the seashore with a line and hook, and told him to look in the mouth of the first fish he should draw out of the water. "You will find a piece of money with which to pay your tax and mine,'' said Jesus. Peter obeyed, and found the piece of money in the fish's mouth, just as Jesus had said. With it he paid the tax to the collector, and returned again to the house where Jesus was.

When all the disciples were come together in the house, Jesus asked them what they had been disputing about on the way to Că-pĕr'-nă-ŭm. They were ashamed to tell; but Jesus knew their thoughts and he knew, too, what they had said to one another as they walked along the dusty road leading from Çæ-să-rē'-ă Philippi. So he called a little child and set him in the midst of the group. Then he took the child in his arms and said, "No one shall even be able to enter the kingdom of heaven unless he becomes like a little child. And whoever humbles himself as this little child is willing to do shall be the greatest in the kingdom of heaven."

Jesus then told the disciples to be careful not to despise little children, for their angels in heaven always look upon the face of God. And he warned them to be careful lest they cause some child to lose faith in him, for he said, "It is not the will of your Father who is in heaven that one of these little children should lose faith in me and die in sin."

One of the disciples, named John, then spoke to Jesus and told him that they had seen a man who was not a follower with them casting out evil spirits in Jesus' name. "We forbade him to cast out evil spirits any more in your name, because he would not follow with us," said John. But Jesus replied, "You should not have done so; for whoever performs a miracle in my name is helping me in my great work, although he does not walk with us."

———◆———

STORY 36

JESUS TEACHES PETER A LESSON IN FORGIVENESS
Matt. 18: 21-35

One day Simon Peter came to Jesus and asked, "Lord, how often shall I forgive my brother if he sins against me and then asks my pardon? Shall I forgive him seven times?"

Perhaps Peter did not have much patience with a man who would sin against him often and always ask to be forgiven. Perhaps he thought no person could be truly sorry for his wrong-doing if he should have to ask so many times to be forgiven.

But Jesus replied, "I do not say that you shall forgive him seven times only, but seventy times seven." How surprised Peter must have been when he heard this answer! He may have wondered whether he could ever truly forgive a man so many times as that.

Then Jesus told Peter a story about a king whose servant owed him a great amount of money. Finally the king called this servant and asked him to pay the debt. But the servant had nothing with which to pay, for he had spent all the money. Then the king said, "Because you can not pay me the money you borrowed, I shall command that you and your wife and your children be sold, and that all of your property be taken away from you. In this way I can regain some of the money you borrowed and have lost."

The servant felt very sad when he heard these words, and he fell on his face before the king crying, "O King, have patience with me and I will pay every penny I owe!" And because the king had a kind heart he felt sorry for the man. He told him to rise up and go away to his own house. He said, "I will forgive all the debt, and you need not try to pay it back."

After this servant went out from the king's presence he met a very poor man who had borrowed only a few dollars from him. He asked the man to pay it back, but the man could not. Then the servant became very angry, and seizing the poor man by the throat, he cried "Pay back what you borrowed or I shall throw you into the prison-house and keep you there until you do!" Then the poor man fell down at his feet and cried out, "Have patience with me, and I will pay every penny I owe." But the king's servant would not listen, and because the poor man had no money he threw him into the prison.

Other servants of the king were standing by and they saw how unkindly this poor man had been treated. They knew how the king had just forgiven the unkind man of a very great debt, and they felt sad because he had been unwilling to forgive the small debt of his poor neighbor. So they came to the king and told him how unmercifully the servant had treated his poor neighbor.

The king was surprised to hear that his servant whom he had treated so kindly should dare to be so unkind to another. So he quickly sent for him. Now the king, too, was angry, and when the unkind servant came in he said, "O wicked man, I forgave all your debt because you could not pay, and now should you not have been willing to forgive the small debt your poor neighbor owed? Because you have dared to be so wicked after I had pity on you, now I shall cast you into the prison-house until you pay all you owed me in the first place."

When Jesus finished the story he said to Peter, "My heavenly Father has forgiven your great debt of sin; but if you refuse from your heart to forgive the wrong-doings of those who sin against you, neither will my heavenly Father forgive your great sins against him."

STORY 37

THE UNFRIENDLY SAMARITANS; THE TEN LEPERS
Luke 9: 51-62; 17: 11-19

One day Jesus and his twelve disciples left Că-pĕr'-nă-ŭm and took the south road leading through the country of Să-mâr'-ĭ-ă. They were going to Jerusalem. On their way they came to a certain village in Să-mâr'-ĭ-ă where Jesus wished to spend the night. So he sent messengers to find a place for him and for his disciples to rest.

But the Să-măr'-ĭ-tăns in the village would not permit Jesus and his disciples to stop with them. They would not allow them to rest in their village. They knew Jesus and his disciples were Jews, and the Jews had often been unkind to their people. Now they, too, would be unkind.

Two of the disciples, James and his brother John, were very much annoyed by the unfriendly actions of these village folk. They felt that their master had been mistreated, and they wished to see the villagers punished. They remembered how Ē-lī'-jăh, the prophet, had once called fire down from heaven to destroy some wicked people, and now they came to Jesus and asked, "Will you permit us to call fire down from heaven to destroy these unkind people who have turned us away?" But Jesus answered, "Your desire is not good, for the Son of man is not come to destroy men's lives, but to save them." Then he went with his disciples to another village.

And as they went a man came to Jesus and said, "Lord, I too would follow you wherever you go." No doubt he believed as did the disciples, that Jesus would soon be the great king of the Jews for whom so many were looking, and he desired to be a friend of such a great person. But Jesus answered, "Foxes have holes in the ground for their homes, and birds of the air have nests; but the Son of man is so poor that he has not even a place of his own to lay his head."

Ten men who were lepers saw Jesus and his disciples passing by. These men had heard about Jesus, how he healed other lepers, and now they called loudly to him, for they stood far off. They cried out, "Jesus, master, have mercy on us!" And Jesus heard their cries.

Never did Jesus pass by and refuse to help one who called earnestly to him. And now he stopped and called back to the lepers, telling them to go and show themselves to the priests, as Moses had commanded every leper to do who was healed. They understood what Jesus meant, and they started at once to go to the priests for an examination. And as they went the leprosy left their bodies and they were made every bit well.

One of these lepers stopped and turned back just as soon as he saw that his leprosy had gone from him. He ran to Jesus and fell down before him, worshiping him and thanking him for the miracle he had performed. And this man was not a Jew, but a Să-măr'-ĭ-tăn. The other men, however, hurried on their way, never stopping to thank the great healer. And Jesus said to the disciples, "Were there not ten lepers who were made well? But where are the nine? There is none turned back to give thanks except this stranger who is a Să-măr'-ĭ-tăn." Then he said to the man kneeling at his feet, "Rise up and go your way, for your faith has made you well."

STORY 38

JESUS AT THE GREAT FEAST IN JERUSALEM
John 7: 2-53

Summer had passed, and the cooler days of autumn had come again. On the green hillsides around Jerusalem many booths, or huts made of the branches of trees, stood in groups, sheltering the people who had come to attend the Feast of Tabernacles, held every year at this city. And during the week of the Feast the temple was crowded with visitors from other parts of the land.

On the first day after the feast began groups of people stood together talking about the great Teacher in Galilee, whose miracles had caused much excitement in many places. They wondered whether he would come to Jerusalem and teach them there. Some of them wished he would come, for they enjoyed hearing him teach; others wished he would come because they hated him and wanted to find occasion to put him to death.

By and by Jesus came, and straight into the temple he went, to sit down there and teach the people. His enemies believed this would be a good opportunity to catch him, so they sent men to listen to his words and find some fault, that they might accuse him to the rulers.

But day after day passed by and still Jesus sat in the temple, teaching all who came to him. No one attempted to drive him away, and no one took hold of him to capture him. Many of the Jews who lived in Jerusalem knew how much their leaders hated him, and they wondered why these men did not take him now and shut him up in prison. They said, "Is this not he whom they seek to kill? But now he speaks boldly and they say nothing to him. Have they come to believe that he is the very Christ?"

But the rulers of the Jews, who were the chief priests in the temple, and the scribes, and the Pharisees, and the Săd'-dū-çêes, did not acknowledge that Jesus is the Christ. They were very jealous of him because he drew the attention of all the people who came to the Feast. They disliked his teaching because he accused them of only pretending to be righteous. And they sent officers to take him.

Even the officers were pleased to hear the teaching of this wonderful man from Galilee. They listened carefully to his words, and they believed that he was not worthy to be punished. So they returned to the rulers without him.

The chief priests and Pharisees were angry when the officers returned alone. They asked, "Why have you not brought him?" But the officers replied, "Never did a man speak like this man." And they would not harm him.

The men who sent the officers were excited. They asked, "Are you allowing this man to deceive you as he is deceiving the other people? And have any of our own number of the rulers believed on him?"

Nĭc-ŏ-dē'-mŭs, the Pharisee who had come to visit Jesus one night, sat among the angry rulers. He loved Jesus and believed in him. But he was afraid to let the other Pharisees know, for fear they would hate him, too. Now he asked timidly, "Does our law judge any man before it hears him and knows what he is doing?" His angry friends turned on him and replied, scornfully, "Are you from Galilee? Do you not know that no prophet comes from that country?" And so saying they dismissed their meeting and went to their homes.

STORY 39

HOW JESUS ANSWERED HIS ENEMIES' QUESTION
John 8

Early the next morning after the officers had failed to take Jesus, the scribes and Pharisees had planned another way to capture him. They would go themselves, and ask him a great question concerning the teaching of the law of Moses. Already they thought they knew how he would answer, and then they would have opportunity to find fault with him.

Jesus was in the temple when his enemies came, bringing with them a very wicked woman whom the law of Moses commanded should be punished by death. They went straight to Jesus and said, "Master this woman is very wicked, and Moses in the law has commanded that such a person should be stoned until she dies. But what do you say we shall do to her?"

Jesus knew they were tempting him, and at first he paid no attention to them. He stooped down and with his finger wrote on the dust of the ground. But those enemies would not be gotten rid of so easily. Now they believed they had caught him in a trap, and they kept asking until finally he raised up, and looked at them and said, "Let the man among you who is without sin cast the first stone at her." So saying, he stooped down again and continued to write with his finger in the dust.

The men were much surprized at his reply to their question. They looked at each other, then at the woman who stood trembling in their midst, and their own consciences reminded them of their sins. They were afraid to pick up stones, for fear God might cause them to fall dead because they, too, were sinners. The older men shook their heads and turned to go away. The younger men, too, felt the accusations of their own guilty consciences, and they followed the older men out of the temple.

When all the men had gone out, Jesus looked up from the ground and saw only the woman standing before him. He asked, "Woman, where are those men who accused you of this great sin? Did no one condemn you?" And she replied, "No man, Lord." Then he said, "Neither do I condemn you; go, and do not commit sin any more." So she, too, turned and went away.

Many people were now gathering in the temple, and Jesus began to teach them again. He began by saying, "I am the light of the world: the man who follows me shall not walk in darkness, but shall have the light of life." And the Pharisees who heard him began to accuse him, saying, "Your words are not true, because you speak of your own self." But Jesus answered that even though he did speak of himself, he knew that his words were true, for he knew who had sent him into the world and where he would go when he should leave the world. He said, "You can not tell these things." Then he told them that another besides himself spoke of him in the same way, and that one was his Father. So they asked, "Where is your Father?" Jesus answered, "If you knew me, you would know my Father; but you know neither me nor my Father."

All that day Jesus taught in the temple, speaking very plainly to the Jews and telling them about their sins. And the displeasure of his enemies increased more and more, until finally they thought they would listen no longer. For Jesus had said that if any one would obey his words that one should never see death. Jesus meant that that one should never die in sin and be lost. But his enemies did not understand, and they said, "Now we know you have an evil spirit, for Abraham is dead, and all the prophets are dead; and you say that any man who keeps your words will never die. Are you greater than our father Abraham, who is dead? and the prophets, too, are dead: who do you claim to be?"

Jesus replied, "I do not honor myself; but my Father, whom you call your God, he it is who honors me. You have not known my Father; but I know him. If I should say I know him not, I should be speaking a lie. I know him, and I obey his words. Your father Abraham was glad when he saw my day, but you do not behave like the children of Abraham."

Now the Jews cried out, "How could you have seen our father Abraham, for you are not yet fifty years old?" Then Jesus answered, "Before Abraham was, I am."

"I AM" was the name by which God was known, and the Jews were struck with horror when they heard Jesus call himself by that sacred name. They picked up stones to hurl at him, but Jesus hid himself among the people, then quietly passed out of the temple and walked away.

STORY 40

WHAT HAPPENED TO THE BLIND MAN WHOM JESUS HEALED

John 9

As Jesus went away from the temple, where the angry Jews were getting ready to stone him, he saw a blind man sitting by the roadside begging. This man had always been blind, for he had been born without sight. And his parents lived in Jerusalem.

The twelve disciples were with Jesus when he passed the place where the poor man sat. They knew he had been blind from his birth, and they asked Jesus whether this blindness had come upon him as a punishment for his own sin or whether it had come because of the sins of his parents. Jesus answered, "Neither this man's sins nor the sin of his parents has caused him to be without sight, but he was born blind that the works of God might be shown through him."

Then Jesus stopped. Having made a little clay he rubbed it on the blind man's eyes. Then he said to the poor man, "Go to the pool called Sī-lō'-ăm and wash." The blind man did not ask, "Why must I do this?" but he rose at once and groped his way to the pool. Here he bathed the mud from off his sightless eyes, and immediately he began to see.

Instead of returning to the roadside to beg, the happy man went home to his people, telling the good news. His neighbors and friends and even his parents were greatly surprised, because he had been born blind and they had never expected such a miracle to happen to him. Many who saw him could hardly believe he was the same man as the blind beggar whom they had known before. They said, "He is like the beggar." But the man answered, "I am the same person."

The excitement in that neighborhood grew when the people heard that Jesus had opened the blind man's eyes. They gathered round to ask, "What did Jesus do to you? How did he open your eyes?" And the man told them that Jesus first made clay, then rubbed it on his eyes, and afterward sent him to wash in the pool of Sī-lō'-ăm. "And I went and washed, and I received my sight," he said, joyfully, for he was a very happy man. "Where is this Jesus now?" they asked; but the man did not know where Jesus and his disciples had gone.

Then the neighbors brought the man who had been blind to the Pharisees, and they also questioned him. Because it was the Sabbath-

day they thought Jesus had done wrong by anointing the man's eyes
and sending him to wash in the pool. They said, ''Give God the glory,

JESUS HEALING A BLIND MAN

for we know this man Jesus is a sinner.'' Others standing by said,
''How can a man who is a sinner do such miracles?'' And the people

were divided, some thinking Jesus was a great man and others think-ing he was only deceiving those who believed in him.

The Pharisees then asked the man what he thought of Jesus, and the man replied, "I believe he is a prophet."

The enemies of Jesus were greatly stirred by this miracle. They thought perhaps the man was only pretending, after all, that he had been born blind. So they called his parents and questioned them con-cerning their son.

But the parents were afraid of these Jews. They knew of the hatred these men felt toward Jesus, and they knew the chief priests had threatened to cast them out of the synagog if they believed in him. So they said, "This man is our son, and we know he was born blind. But we do not know how his eyes received sight; he is a grown man and he can tell you for himself."

Again the excited enemies of Jesus called the man who had been blind, and asked, "What did Jesus do to you? How did he open your eyes?" The man answered, "I have told you once and you would not listen; if I tell you again will you also be his disciples?" At this they scorned him, and said, "We are Moses' disciples, for we know that God spoke to Moses, but as for this fellow we do not know where he came from.

Now the man whom Jesus had healed grew very bold, and he said. "It is strange that you do not know where Jesus came from since he opened my eyes, which were always blind! We all know that God does not hear sinners, but if any man worships him and does his will, God hears that man. Since the world began it was never heard that any man opened the eyes of one who was born blind. If Jesus was not of God he could do nothing."

These words stirred up more anger in the hearts of Jesus' enemies, and they said to the man who had been blind, "You were born a sin-ner, and do you try to teach us?" Then they cast him out of the synagog, and he could no longer worship there with his people.

Jesus soon heard what the angry priests had done, and he looked about to find the man whom they had cast out of the synagog. When he found him he asked, "Do you believe on the Son of God?" The man answered, "Who is he, Lord, that I may believe?" And Jesus said, "You have seen him with your eyes, and even now he is speaking to you." Then the man rejoiced and said, "Lord, I believe!" And he worshiped Jesus there.

STORY 41

LITTLE CHILDREN ARE BROUGHT TO JESUS;
A YOUNG MAN GOES AWAY SAD

Matt. 19:13-30; Mark 10:13-31

While Jesus was teaching the people in a country place not far from the Jordan River, some mothers brought their little children to him and asked him to bless them. Jesus loves little children, so he took them in his arms and put his hands upon their heads and prayed.

But the disciples stood by looking much displeased. They called the mothers aside and said, ''You should not trouble our master in this way, for he has more important work to do than to caress your children!'' And no doubt the mothers were grieved to hear them speak these words.

Jesus, too, was grieved with the disciples. He said, ''Do not forbid the little children to come to me, for of such is the kingdom of God. Whoever of you will not receive the kingdom of God just as a little child, can never enter into it.'' And again he took the little ones in his loving arms to caress and to bless them.

Jesus knew that little children would gladly believe him and that many times they could lead older people to believe in him, too. He knew their little hearts were tender and quick to respond to his love, while older people were more ready to doubt and to question whether or not he was the very Christ.

Then Jesus rose up and went with his disciples to another place. And as he went a young man came running to meet him. This young man was very rich, and he wore beautiful clothing. But he knelt down in the dust before Jesus and said, ''Good Master, what good thing shall I do that I may receive life in the other world?''

''Why do you call me good?'' asked Jesus, adding, ''for there is none good but God. You know the commandments—'Do not kill'; 'Do not steal'; 'Do not speak falsely'; 'Honor your father and your mother.' ''

''Yes, I know the commandments of Moses,'' answered the young man, ''and I have kept them from childhood. But I seem to lack something yet. O Master, tell me what it is!''

Jesus looked tenderly into the anxious face of the young man before him, and he loved this man. He longed to help him. But he knew the one thing that hindered this man from being contented and happy. He knew the one thing that stood between this man and the hope of

A THRESHING FLOOR OF SAMARIA

All summer long in the villages among the hills of Samaria, whole families are busy threshing and winnowing grain, harvested on the rocky acres near by. The farmer is here seen tossing forkfuls of straw, chaff, and wheat into the light wind, which carries away the refuse and allows the kernels to fall in a heap. The grain is then sifted to remove chaff and pebbles. The woman in the center with the large circular sieve has just started her work.

THE RICH YOUNG RULER

life in the other world. Just one thing; but unless that one thing should be taken away, the rich young man could never enter heaven. So he said, "You lack one thing, just one. If you would be perfectly happy, go home and sell all that you have, and give your riches to the poor people. Then you will have riches in heaven. Afterwards you may come back and be my disciple."

What a change came over the young man's face when he heard these words! His head was bent forward, and he walked very slowly away, for he was sad and deeply troubled. Jesus watched him go away, and Jesus, too, was sad. Then he turned to the disciples and said, "How hard it is for rich men to enter into the kingdom of God!" He knew this young man loved his riches more than he loved God, and that he was unwilling to sell his possessions and give his money to the poor. Because he loved his riches he could not be contented and happy, for his heart was not right in God's sight. Always he felt that something was lacking, that something clouded his hope of life in heaven. But he turned away from Jesus, choosing rather to be rich in this world than to be a disciple of the Lord. Afterwards he found out that he had made an unwise choice, for

> Riches never satisfy
> Hearts that long for God and heaven;
> Jesus can their needs supply
> When their all to him is given;
> But if they will not obey
> His commands, whate'er they be,
> Sadly then they turn away,
> Beggars through eternity.

STORY 42

SEVENTY OTHER DISCIPLES SENT OUT; THE GOOD SAMARITAN
Luke 10:1-37

Jesus knew that he had not much longer to preach, for the time was near when he must lay down his life for the sins of the people. He therefore chose seventy other men who had followed him and received his teachings, and to them he gave power to heal the sick and to cast out evil spirits. Then he sent them out, two and two, into the country east of the Jordan River, to preach in the cities and villages where he would go later on.

And just as the twelve disciples had gone, so these men went forth to heal the sick and to tell people that the kingdom of heaven was coming near to them. And when their errand was finished they hurried back to Jesus, telling him that even the evil spirits obeyed when they commanded them to depart. These seventy disciples rejoiced much because they had received power to command evil spirits to obey them; but Jesus said, "Do not rejoice in this, but rather be glad because your names are written in heaven."

Then Jesus prayed to God, the Father, and afterwards he turned to his disciples and said, "Blessed are the eyes that see the things you see; for I tell you that many prophets and kings desired to see the things which you see, but they did not see them, and to hear the things which you hear, but they did not hear them."

Then a wise Jew, called a lawyer, came to Jesus and asked a question, wishing to tempt him. He said, "Master, what shall I do to inherit life in heaven?"

Jesus knew this man had knowledge of the law of Moses, so instead of answering the question he asked the wise man another. He said, "What is written in the law of Moses? Do you not know its teachings?" The lawyer replied, "Moses wrote that we should love the Lord our God with all our heart, and with all our soul, and with all our strength, and with all our mind; and he wrote that we should love our neighbors as ourselves."

Jesus said, "You have answered right: do this and you shall have life in heaven."

But the man was not willing to turn away yet. So he asked Jesus, "Who is my neighbor?" And Jesus told him the story about the Good Să-măr'-ĭ-tăn. This is the story:

"One day a man started to travel from Jerusalem to Jericho. As he went along the lonely road he met some robbers. These men stopped him, took away his money, tore off his clothing, and beat him until he was half dead. Then they ran off, leaving him to lie by the roadside.

"Presently a priest came along the road, and he saw the poor man lying there. But he did not stop to help the stranger. He did not even speak to the poor man and ask if he might send some friends to aid him, but passed by on the other side of the road.

"After the priest had gone by a Levite came by. When he saw the poor man he also took no second look. He did not offer to help him. He hurried on his way, leaving the poor man to die.

"And no doubt the poor man would have died if a kind-hearted

Să-măr'-ĭ-tăn had not come along the road soon afterwards. When he saw the poor man he stopped his mule, climbed out of his saddle, and

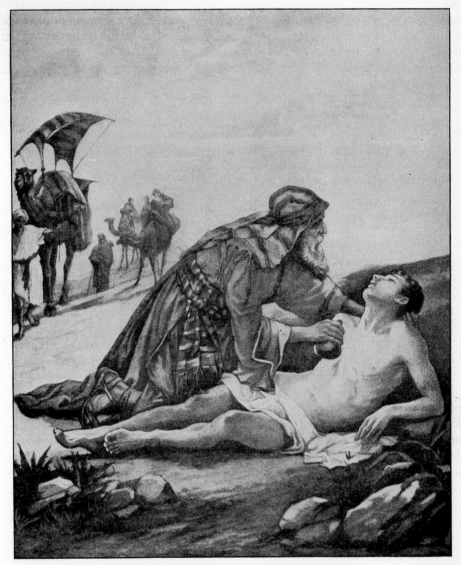

THE GOOD SAMARITAN AND THE WOUNDED MAN

bent over the stranger to speak to him. He saw that the wounded man was a Jew, and he knew the Jews were not friendly to the Să-măr'-ĭ-tănś, but he knew this Jew was in deep trouble. So he poured oil upon the wounded places and bound them up. Then he gave the wounded man a drink to revive him, and helped him to climb into the saddle on his own mule's back. He brought the wounded man to a sheltering-place called an inn, where travelers stopped overnight. Here he took care of him until the next day, and before he started on his journey again he gave money to the keeper of the inn, and said, 'Take care of this stranger until he is well, and if more money is needed I will give it when I come again.'

"Now," asked Jesus of the lawyer, "which of the three men was a neighbor to the one who was attacked by the robbers?"

"The man who treated him kindly," answered the lawyer; and Jesus said, "Go, and do as the Să-măr'-ĭ-tăn did."

STORY 43

LAZARUS, THE DEAD MAN WHOM JESUS CALLED OUT OF THE GRAVE

John 11:1-54

Lăz'-ă-rŭs was a Jew who lived with his two sisters, Martha and Mary. Their home was in the little village of Bethany, near Jerusalem, and Jesus often visited them while attending the feasts of the Jews. Always they made him feel welcome, for they loved him dearly, and they believed that he was the Christ of whom the prophets had written long ago.

One day while Jesus was in the country east of the Jordan teaching the people, a messenger came hurrying from Bethany to tell him that Lăz'-ă-rŭs was very sick. The anxious sisters had sent this message, and they believed that surely Jesus would come at once to help them. They knew of his great miracles of healing, and they longed to have him near in this hour of need. But Jesus did not go at once, for he said to his disciples, "This sickness of our friend Lăz'-ă-rŭs is for the glory of God."

And so the messenger returned without Jesus. And the disappointed sisters lingered near the bedside of their dear brother and saw him grow weaker and weaker until finally his breath left his body and he died. How grief-stricken they felt! Why had Jesus not come to them? they wondered.

Still they hoped that he might come, for he had even raised the dead to life; but the day wore on and no signs of his coming appeared.

Then at last the neighbors and friends who gathered in to help them wrapped Lăz'-ă-rŭs' body with linen cloths and carried it to the cave where he should be buried. Martha and Mary followed, weeping bitterly, and they saw Lăz'-ă-rŭs laid in the dark cave and they saw the great stone rolled over the cave's opening. Still their friend Jesus had not come.

Four days passed by, and the sorrow of the sisters grew deeper; for now they believed that even if Jesus should come he would be too late to help them. Many friends from Jerusalem were staying in their home trying to comfort them, but only one Friend could comfort and that Friend was not there.

At last, after four days had passed, news came that Jesus and his disciples were nearing the village. Martha rose quickly and ran to meet him. Falling at his feet, she cried, "If only you had been here my brother had not died!"

Jesus knew how deep was the grief in Martha's heart, and he said, "Your brother shall rise again."

"I know he shall rise in the last day, when the dead shall come forth in the great resurrection," answered Martha. "I am the resurrection, and the life," said Jesus, "he that believes in me, though he were dead yet he shall live. And those who live and believe in me shall never die. Do you believe this?" he asked.

Martha answered, "Yes, Lord, I believe you are the Christ, the Son of God, who should come into the world."

Still Martha did not understand what Jesus meant when he said he was the resurrection and the life. But she left him and hurried to call her sister, Mary; for Jesus had asked why Mary had not come, too.

When Mary heard that Jesus had called for her she left the house and hurried out to meet him, for he had not yet come into the village. She found him resting by the roadside where Martha had met him, and she, too, fell at his feet and cried, "Lord, if you had been here my brother had not died!" The Jews who had come from Jerusalem to comfort the sisters saw Mary rise up hastily and leave the house, and they supposed she was going to weep at Lăz'-ă-rŭs' grave. So they followed. And they saw her when she met Jesus, and they heard her weep when she fell at his feet. Tears flowed down their cheeks, too, and they cried aloud.

Jesus was touched with the sorrow of these sisters and their friends. He groaned when he heard them weeping, and he asked, "Where have you laid the body of Lăz'-ă-rŭs?" So they brought him to the grave. And as Jesus stood near the cave with the sisters and their sorrowing friends, he wept in sympathy with them.

The Jews who had crowded near to watch, whispered among themselves, "See how he loved Lăz'-ă-rŭs! Could not this man, who opened the eyes of one who had been born blind, have caused that Lăz'-ă-rŭs should not have died?"

While they were talking together, Jesus commanded that some one should roll away the stone from the opening of the cave. Martha exclaimed, "Lord, he has been dead four days, and by this time his body is decaying!" But Jesus answered, "Did I not tell you that if you would believe you should see the glory of God?"

So they took away the stone, and while the people stood by Jesus lifted his eyes to heaven and said, "Father, I thank thee that thou hast heard me. And I know that thou hearest me always; but because of the people who stand by I said it, that they may believe thou hast sent me." Then he looked into the door of the dark cave and cried with a loud voice, "Lăz'-ă-rŭs, come forth!"

The astonished people saw the still, white form within the cave rise up and walk out to speak with them. And Jesus told the friends to untie the linen cloths and remove the napkin, which covered his face. And Lăz'-ă-rŭs was alive once more.

After this miracle many of the Jews who had come from Jerusalem to comfort Martha and Mary believed that Jesus was the Christ. And soon the scribes and Pharisees and chief priests at Jerusalem heard what had happened at Bethany, and they were greatly excited. "What shall we do?" they asked, "for if we let him go soon all men will believe in him, and the Romans will come and take away our nation." And from that time the enemies of Jesus began to plan how they might capture him and kill him.

STORY 44

JESUS HEALS THE SICK, AND TEACHES IN A PHARISEE'S HOUSE

Luke 14:1-24

Jesus knew the plans of his enemies in Jerusalem and he did not remain long in Bethany, but took his disciples and returned again to the country near the Jordan River. While there he continued to teach, and to heal the sick who were brought to him.

One Sabbath-day a Pharisee who lived in that part of the country

asked Jesus to eat dinner at his house.   And Jesus went with him.
Other Pharisees and lawyers were present at the dinner, and, as usual,
some people were there who had not been invited.   These stood about
in the dining-hall, looking on while the guests were eating the food set
before them.

Among the onlookers was one poor man who had a disease called
dropsy.   No doubt he had come because he heard that Jesus would be
there, and he hoped Jesus would have mercy upon him and heal him.
When Jesus saw the poor man standing near by, he pitied him.   Turning to the Pharisees and lawyers, he asked, "Is it permitted in the law
to heal on the Sabbath-day?"   But the men would not answer.   Then
Jesus healed the poor man and sent him away; for he said, "No one
of you, if your ox or ass fell into a pit, would allow it to remain there
until after the Sabbath had passed, but you would pull the unfortunate
beast out at once."   And they understood that he meant to teach them
to be just as merciful toward the poor man whom he had healed of
the dropsy.

Those present at the dinner expected to hear Jesus teach, and they
were not disappointed.   He had noticed how the guests chose the best
places for themselves when they arrived, and he taught them a lesson
on humility.   He said, "When you are invited to a wedding, do not
choose for yourself the places of most honor lest a man come who is
more honorable than you.   Then you will be asked to give your place
to him, and you will feel ashamed before all the guests.   But if you
choose rather to take the lowest place, then you will be called up higher, and you will receive honor from your friends."

Then Jesus turned to the Pharisee who had invited him to the
house, and said, "When you prepare a feast, do not invite your friends
and relatives and rich neighbors; for they will reward you in the same
manner.   But if you wish to receive a reward at the time when the
righteous people are resurrected, then invite the poor and the crippled
and the blind to your feasts; for such people can not repay you, and
God will bless you for such service."

One of the guests heard the words Jesus spoke to the host, and he
said, "Blessed is he who shall eat bread in the kingdom of God."   Then
Jesus spoke a parable to them all about the kingdom of God.   He said:

"A certain man prepared a great supper and invited many guests.
When all was ready, he sent his servant to call the invited persons to
come and eat.   But every one began to make an excuse to stay away.
The first man said he had bought a piece of ground and would have to
go at once to see it, and he asked to be excused from the supper.   An-

other man said he had bought two oxen and he was going to try them out for driving, so he could not come; and another said he had gotten married, and he could not come. Everywhere the servant went the invited guests begged to be excused, and the servant returned to tell his master.

"The feast was ready and waiting, and the master was greatly disappointed to hear how his invited guests had refused to come. He became angry with them, and said they should not be allowed even to taste the supper he had prepared. Then he sent the servant out quickly to gather in the poor people from the streets, and the servant brought in the blind and the lame, and still there was room. Then the master sent the servant to the country places near by to bring in the poor people who had not been invited. And his house was filled with hungry people who enjoyed the good things he had prepared for his unfaithful friends."

STORY 45

A CROOKED WOMAN HEALED; THE PHARISEES TRY TO FRIGHTEN JESUS; PARABLES BY THE WAY

Luke 13:11—15:32

Jesus now taught in the cities and villages where the seventy had gone to preach and to heal the sick. In one city he found a crooked woman in the synagog on the Sabbath-day. This poor woman had not been able to straighten herself for eighteen years, but was stooped over in a pitiful manner. When Jesus saw her he pitied her. Calling her to him, he said, "Woman, you are set free from this infirmity, which has bound you so many years." Then he laid his hands upon her bent back and immediately she was able to stand straight again.

The woman was very happy, and she praised God because she had been made well. But the ruler of the synagog was displeased with Jesus for healing her on the Sabbath. He said, "There are six days when men ought to work; therefore let the sick come to be healed on those days, and not on the Sabbath."

But Jesus replied, "You are only pretending to be careful to please God. Do you not loose your ox and your ass and lead them to water on the Sabbath-day? And should not this poor woman, who is a daughter of Abraham, be loosed on the Sabbath-day from this infirmity with which she has been bound by Satan for eighteen years?"

The enemies of Jesus were ashamed when they heard his wise

reply, and the other people praised God with loud voices because they had seen his wonderful works.

One day some of the Pharisees came to Jesus and pretended to be friendly. They told him that Herod, the King, was seeking to take his life just as he had caused John the Baptist to be put to death. They urged Jesus to leave the country at once, and go far away, lest Herod find him and kill him. They hoped in this manner to be rid of Jesus.

But Jesus did not feel afraid of Herod. He knew that his great-est enemies were among the Jews, and among the religious rulers of the Jews. They hated him because he taught the poor people and because he told them about their sins. Now he said to these Pharisees: "Go to Herod and tell him that I cast out evil spirits and heal the sick today and tomorrow, and on the third day I shall be made perfect. For I must walk today and tomorrow and even the day following, for it can not be that a prophet shall perish outside of Jerusalem." Jesus meant that just as the Jews had killed God's prophets in other days, so they and not Herod would cause him to be put to death.

JESUS HEALING THE WOMAN

Many publicans and sinners fol-lowed Jesus, to hear his words. And the Pharisees and scribes found fault, saying, "This man receives sinners and even eats with them." Jesus knew how they were complaining about him, and he spoke to the people by parables. First he told them the parable about the Lost Sheep. Because the Jews kept many sheep he knew they would un-derstand the story. "What man of you," he asked, "having a hun-dred sheep would not leave the ninety-nine in the wilderness and seek for the one that was lost? And when he finds it he will bring it back and rejoice more over that sheep than over the ninety-nine which did not wander away. So it is in heaven when a sinner repents and for-sakes his sins; there is more rejoicing over him than over ninety-nine just persons who have no sin."

There were women in the crowd listening to Jesus' words. And Jesus saw them there, so he told a story which they might understand. "What woman," he asked, "having ten pieces of silver and losing one of them will not forget about the nine and search carefully through the house until she find the missing piece? And when she finds it she tells her neighbors and friends, and asks them to rejoice with her because she has found the piece that was lost. So also," said Jesus, "there is rejoicing in heaven when one lost sinner comes to God."

Both the men and the women were listening very carefully now, and Jesus told the parable about the unthankful son who left his father's house and went to live among strangers. This is the story:

"A certain man had two sons, and the younger son was not contented to remain at home with his father and his brother. He asked that his father divide the money which would some day be given to him and to his brother and give to him at once the part that would be his. So the father divided the money, and the younger son took his part and went away. He thought he was very rich, and he spent his money freely. He enjoyed every pleasure that he knew, and he seemed to have many friends. But after a while he spent all his money and he had nothing left. Then he grew hungry; but his friends left him and refused to help.

"In his trouble the young man offered to care for a farmer's hogs, but he could scarcely keep from starving. And no man pitied him, or gave him any decent food to eat.

"Then the young man remembered his father, and the hired servants who worked in his father's house. He knew those servants were well cared for. He decided to return to his father's house and ask to be made a servant there. So he returned to his home country to beg his father's forgiveness and to ask permission to be only a servant in the old home.

"That father loved his wandering boy, and his heart was sad when the boy left him to live among strangers. Every day he longed for the boy to come back. And when at last he saw his son coming, clothed in rags, he ran out to meet him and wept for joy. The boy began to speak; he said, 'Father, I have sinned against heaven and against you—'; but he had no opportunity to tell the father how he wished to become a servant in the old home, for the father commanded a servant to go quickly and bring the best clothes and dress the young man in them, and to prepare a feast of gladness, for the lost had been found.

"The elder son was in the field at work. When he returned to the house and saw the excitement he asked the servants what had happened. They told him that his brother had come back again. And the elder son was displeased and would not go in to see his brother.

Then his father came out and told him the glad news, but still he was displeased. 'I have served you faithfully all these years and you do not rejoice over me,' said the unhappy man, 'and now when my brother comes back from his riotous living you rejoice greatly over him.'

"Now the father understood that his elder son was jealous of his brother. He said, 'Son, you have always been with me, and all that I have is yours. Whenever you wished you could prepare a feast; but your brother has been to me like one dead, and now he is alive again. And it is right that we should be merry because he has returned to be with us again; for he was lost, but is found.' "

STORY 46

FOUR SHORT STORY-SERMONS WHICH JESUS PREACHED
Luke 16; 18:1-14

In the multitude which followed Jesus were people of many different villages. Some of his listeners were poor people, some were rich; some were educated and some were not. Jesus knew about their differences, and he wished to teach them all. He knew how well every one likes to listen to a good story, so he preached some story-sermons to the multitude. One of the story-sermons was about

AN UNFAITHFUL MAN WHO WAS A STEWARD

"A certain rich man," said Jesus, "hired a servant to take care of his goods. This servant came to live in the rich man's beautiful house and was called his steward. He was supposed to handle the master's business wisely, but he did not. And after a while the master heard that the steward was wasting his goods.

"Calling the unfaithful steward, the master told him what he had heard. And the steward hung his head in shame because he could not deny his guilt. Then the master grew angry and said, 'No longer shall you be my steward!' And he was about to dismiss the unfaithful servant.

"Now, the steward had no other home in which to live, and he wondered what he should do. He thought he could not work in the fields like a poor man, and he was too proud to beg for food from door to door. So he decided to make friends with the other servants of the rich man that they might receive him into their homes to live. And he hurried to do this very thing.

"By and by the master heard what the unfaithful steward was

doing, and he said, 'After all, that man is careful to look out for himself. He shows much wisdom in this one thing.' "

By this story Jesus wished to teach the people that they would not always have homes in this world, for some day they would have to leave their homes and go to live in another world. And just as the unfaithful steward had shown wisdom in preparing a home for himself for the time when he should no longer have a home in the rich man's house, so the people should begin to prepare for themselves a home in heaven by trying to please God.

LAZARUS AT THE RICH MAN'S GATE

Another story which Jesus told was about

A POOR RICH MAN AND A RICH BEGGAR

"There was a certain rich man who thought only of his own comfort and happiness. He wore expensive clothes, like a king's, and ate the best kind of food every day. His many servants were quick to do his bidding, and he did nothing except to live and enjoy himself.

"And there was a certain beggar man named Lăz'-ă-rŭs, who had no home or friends. He was a good man although he was a beggar, and he came to sit at the gate of the rich man to ask for crumbs which might fall from the rich man's table. Finally the poor beggar became sick and sores broke out all over his body. He could not drag himself away from the rich man's gate. As he lay there suffering, stray dogs from the street came to lick his sores. But the rich man did not try to help him at all; he let him lie there day after day in his misery.

"By and by the poor beggar died, and when he died the angels came and carried him to heaven. No longer was he a poor beggar, for now he could rest in peace and happiness with faithful Abraham and with other good people who had left this world. And the rich man died, too, and his friends buried him in a nice, new grave, and perhaps they mourned greatly because he had been taken away from them. But that was not the end of the rich man, for after death he found himself in a place of torment. Now he was poor, so poor that he could not even get a drink of water to cool his burning tongue.

"In this place of torment the poor rich man lifted up his eyes and saw, far, far away, the same Lăz'-ă-rŭs, who used to sit at his gate and beg. He remembered Lăz'-ă-rŭs, and now he saw him resting happily with Abraham in a beautiful place. The poor rich man called loudly to Abraham and cried for mercy. He knew he could not hope to rest with Abraham in that beautiful place, but he wanted Abraham to send Lăz'-ă-rŭs with just a drop of water to cool his burning tongue.

"But Abraham called back that he could send no water. He said, 'Remember that you enjoyed good things in your lifetime, while Lăz'-ă-rŭs had only poverty and suffering when he lived in the world. Now he is comforted, and you are being tormented. And I can send nothing to you because no one can pass from this place to your place of torment, neither can any one from your place come to us.'

"Now the poor rich man remembered his brothers who were yet living in the world. He did not want them to come to the place of torment, and he asked Abraham to send Lăz'-ă-rŭs back to the world to warn his brothers about that dreadful place. But Abraham said those brothers had God's law to warn them, and Lăz'-ă-rŭs need not go. Then the poor rich man pleaded that his brothers might listen if some one rose from the dead to tell them about the place of torment. But Abraham answered, 'If they will not hear the words in God's Book, neither will they listen if one should rise from the dead and speak to them.'"

Jesus knew that sometimes God does not answer prayer at once because he wishes to have people call earnestly upon him; he lets them come again and again before he gives them the things for which they ask. And Jesus wished to teach men to keep on praying when at first their prayers are not answered, so he told them this story about

A Poor Widow and an Unjust Judge

"One time there was a poor widow who had been wronged by a wicked enemy. She could not punish the enemy nor get back what he had taken from her, so she came to a judge who lived in her home city and told this judge about her troubles. The judge, too, was a wicked man, and he did not care to help the poor widow. For a while he paid no attention to her; but she kept coming and crying for him to help her. Finally he grew tired of her coming, so he said to himself, 'Though I am not a good man, yet I will punish this wicked enemy as the poor widow has asked me to do, lest she keep coming to me and troubling me from day to day.' So he punished the enemy.''

Then Jesus said, "Learn a lesson from this unjust judge. He granted the wish of the woman because she came often to him, and shall not God grant the wishes of those who call upon him day and night? For God is righteous, and he delights to do good to his people.''

In the multitude were some people who thought they were righteous, and they despised those whom they thought were not. Jesus taught them a lesson in the story-sermon about

The Pharisee and the Publican in the Temple

"Two men went up to the temple to pray. One of them was a Pharisee, and the other was a publican.

"The Pharisee stood and prayed aloud, saying, 'God, I thank thee that I am not as other men, unrighteous, unjust, unfair in business dealings, nor even as that publican standing over yonder. I fast twice each week; I give tithes of all that I possess.'

"But the publican stood in a corner by himself and would not even lift his eyes toward heaven when he prayed. He bowed his head and smote his breast, saying, 'God be merciful to me a sinner!' ''

And Jesus said, "I tell you, this publican, and not the proud Pharisee, went home to his house with God's blessing; for whoever lifts himself up in his own sight is not pleasing to God, but whoever humbles himself shall be lifted up.''

———•———

STORY 47

HAPPENINGS ON THE WAY TO JERUSALEM

Matt. 20: 17-34; Mark 10: 32-52; Luke 18: 31-43

The time had come again for the Passover Feast at Jerusalem, and Jesus knew that his life on earth would soon be ended. He took his twelve disciples aside from the crowd which followed and told them again that soon he should be given into the hands of the chief priests and the scribes, his enemies, and be condemned to die. But the disciples could not understand; for they believed surely he was the son of God and that he would become the king of the Jews.

Two of his disciples, James and John, came to him soon afterwards, bringing their mother. She knelt before Jesus and asked him to grant places of honor to her sons when he should receive his kingdom. But Jesus knew these disciples and their mother did not understand that the kingdom of heaven would not be like an earthly kingdom, and he said that places of honor would be given only by God the Father.

The other disciples felt jealous of these two, and Jesus knew about their feelings. So he called them aside again and told them that in his kingdom those who would be great must be the servants of all the others. He reminded them of how he had labored hard and long for others. and he told them that they should be willing to serve others, too.

Many other people were going to attend the feast at Jerusalem, and they walked along the roadway with Jesus and his disciples. These people had heard Jesus teach and they had seen him heal the sick. They, too, hoped that he would set up his kingdom in Jerusalem at the time of this feast.

By and by the multitude came to a city called Jericho. The road to Jerusalem led through the streets of this city, and soon the people of Jericho were much excited because Jesus was with them. News of his coming spread rapidly from one part of town to another, and many who had heard of this wonderful man came rushing to see him.

As the crowd passed along the street, a blind man named Bär-tī-mæ'-ŭs, sat by the roadside begging. He heard the sound of many footsteps and he wondered why such a crowd was passing, so he asked the reason. And some one answered, "Jesus of Nazareth is going by."

Bär-tī-mæ'-ŭs had heard about Jesus of Nazareth. He had probably heard about the man who had been born blind and who had been healed by this wonderful man from Nazareth, in Galilee. Now he wished that Jesus would have mercy on him, too, so he rose from his seat by the roadside and began to cry loudly, "Jesus, son of David, have mercy on me!"

Those who stood by were displeased to hear the blind beggar crying after Jesus in this manner. They told him to keep quiet. Perhaps they said that Jesus could not hear him; for the noise of the crowd was great. But Bär-tī-mæ'-ŭs would not be quieted. He only cried louder than ever; for he wished to have Jesus heal his blinded eyes.

Jesus knew about the poor beggar, and he knew how the men near by had urged him to keep still. Now he stopped and commanded some one to tell the blind man to come to him. So a messenger hurried to Bär-tī-mæ′-ŭs, saying, "Be of good comfort, for Jesus has heard you and now he is calling for you."

Bär-tī-mæ′-ŭs threw aside his garment and ran eagerly to the place where Jesus stood. And Jesus asked, "What do you wish me to do for you?" "Lord, give me my sight," he asked; and Jesus answered, "Go your way; your faith in me has made you well." At once the blind eyes opened, and Bär-tī-mæ′-ŭs could see as well as those who had never been blind. And he joined the crowd to follow Jesus.

STORY 48

THE LITTLE MAN WHO CLIMBED INTO A TREE TO SEE JESUS
Luke 19: 1-28

There was living in Jericho at the time a rich man named Zăc-chæ′-ŭs, and he was chief among the publicans. He had never seen Jesus, and when the news came that Jesus was passing through Jericho on his way to attend the Passover Feast in Jerusalem, Zăc-chæ′-ŭs determined that he would try to see this wonderful man. So down to the highway Zăc-chæ′-ŭs went, hurrying along with the gathering crowd; for Jesus was to pass that way.

But Zăc-chæ′-ŭs did not stop when the crowd stood still. He hurried a little farther on, and there he climbed into a sycamore-tree, which grew by the roadside. From this place he knew he could surely see Jesus when he passed by. If he had remained in the crowd he could not have seen the wonderful man from Galilee, for Zăc-chæ′-ŭs was not so tall as the other people about him.

Soon the travelers bound for Jerusalem came down the road, and the people of Jericho, who had gathered to watch them pass looked eagerly to catch a glimpse of Jesus. On the travelers went till they came to the sycamore-tree, and here Jesus and his disciples stood still. Then Jesus looked up into the tree and saw Zăc-chæ′-ŭs clinging to its branches and gazing down upon him.

"Zăc-chæ′-ŭs," said Jesus, "come down at once, for today I must stop at your house."

How surprized Zăc-chæ′-ŭs was to hear these words! He had hoped to catch at least a glimpse of Jesus; now he could take this wonderful man into his home and talk face to face with him.

With a joyful heart Zăc-chæ′-ŭs led the way to his home, to enter-

A ROMAN HIGHWAY AND AQUEDUCT

When Jesus and his disciples traveled north across the Plain of Acre, they must have passed along this road. The foundation stones of this roadway and the aqueduct beyond were placed here by the Romans two thousand years ago. Through this aqueduct still pass waters from the slopes of Mount Hermon to irrigate gardens of this historic plain. In the road the modern motor car makes way for the passing of the ancient donkey-and-camel caravan en route to Tyre.

JESUS AND ZACCHÆUS

tain Jesus and his disciples there. And as they went, others followed, some finding fault because Jesus was going to stop in the home of a publican, whom they called a sinful man. The Pharisees would not enter such a house, for they despised people they called sinners and would not be friendly with them.

Although Zăc-chæ'-ŭs was a publican his heart had been changed by the kind words of Jesus. So he stood up before Jesus and said, "Behold, Lord, I give half of my goods to the poor, and if I have in my business dealings taken more from any man than I should have taken, I give him back four times as much as I took from him."

Jesus was pleased with Zăc-chæ'-ŭs; for he knew this publican really had been changed in his heart. And he said, "To-day salvation is come to your house, for the Son of man is come to seek and to save those who are lost." He had known about this publican who longed to see him, and he had sought for Zăc-chæ'-ŭs. Now he would grant him forgiveness because Zăc-chæ'-ŭs had received him gladly, and had confessed his willingness to make his wrongs right.

JESUS CALLING TO
ZACCHAEUS

Others stood by listening, and Jesus took this time to teach them another parable, or story-sermon. He knew the people were expecting the kingdom of heaven to be set up soon like an earthly kingdom, so he told them a story to show them what the kingdom of heaven is like. He said:

"A certain nobleman went away to a far country to receive for himself a kingdom and to be made the ruler of it. Before leaving home he gave a sum of money, called a pound, to each of his ten servants and commanded them to use the money till his return.

"After some time the nobleman came back again, having received the crown and the kingdom in that far-away country. Then he called his ten servants and asked them how they had used the money he had given to them before he went away.

"The first servant came to him bringing ten pieces of money, and saying, 'I traded with the pound you gave me, and I have gained these ten pounds.' The nobleman was pleased with that servant and said to him, 'Because you have done this, I will give you the rule of ten cities in my kingdom.'

"Next came a servant who had gained five pounds by using the money the nobleman had given him. And the nobleman was pleased with him also, and said, 'To you I will give the rule of five cities in the kingdom which I have received.'

"Then came the third servant, bringing only one pound, the same one that the nobleman had given him before he went away. 'Here is your pound,' the servant said, 'I have kept it wrapped in this napkin all the while you were away for fear I might lose it. I know you are a harsh master, taking up what you do not lay down and reaping what you do not sow.' With this servant the nobleman was much displeased. He answered, 'If you know I am a harsh master, why did you not put my money into a bank that I might have it and its gains at my return?' Then he commanded those who stood by to take the one pound away from the unfaithful servant and give it to the one having ten pounds.

"The servants were surprised, and they said, 'Lord, he has ten pounds, why give him more?' But the nobleman answered, 'To every one who uses what he has, more shall be given; but those who refuse to use what is given to them shall have their own taken away.' "

After speaking this parable, Jesus, with his disciples, left Jericho and went on the way over the mountains toward Jerusalem.

———•———

STORY 49

HOW MARY SHOWED HER LOVE FOR JESUS
Matt. 26: 6-16; Mark 14: 3-11; John 12:1-11

"Simon the leper" was a friend of Jesus. He lived in the village of Bethany, not far from the home of Martha, Mary, and their brother Lăz'-ă-rŭs. But "Simon the leper" was no longer a leper, for Jesus had made him well of that disease. And once more he could live in his own home with his family, in Bethany. No wonder Simon was a friend of Jesus!

News reached the village folk of Bethany that Jesus and his disciples were coming over the road from Jericho and would soon arrive. Glad news this was to the friends who loved him so dearly, and they began to plan at once how they might give him a welcome. "Simon the leper" arranged to make a supper at his home for the tired guests, and

MARY ANOINTING JESUS

Martha, the sister of Lăz'-ă-rŭs, went to help prepare and serve the evening meal. Simon invited Lăz'-ă-rŭs to eat with the other guests at the table; for since he had risen from the grave, Lăz'-ă-rŭs was looked upon with much wonder by the people. Mary also knew about the supper.

At last the guests arrived, and they were welcomed at the home of Simon. Then the food was placed on the table and the guests were brought into the dining-hall to eat. Curious onlookers crowded in, for news of this supper had quickly spread through the village, and even as far as Jerusalem. And uninvited folk had come, not only to see Jesus, but to see Lăz'-ă-rŭs also, whom Jesus had called out of the grave after he had been dead four days.

While the guests were eating, presently Mary arrived with a box in her hand. Going directly to the couch where Jesus was reclining, she broke the box and poured its contents upon Jesus' head and feet. Now this box had contained some very rare perfume, which had cost much money, and Mary had poured it all upon the body of Jesus to show her love for him. Then she bent low and wiped the feet of Jesus with her long hair.

Just as soon as the box was broken the odor of the sweet perfume filled the room. And every one present knew this perfume had cost much money, for it was of the very best kind. At once the disciples began to whisper among themselves about what Mary had done. One of them, Judas Iscariot, who carried the money-bag for Jesus and the other disciples, became angry and said, "What a waste of money this foolish woman has made! Instead of pouring it all upon Jesus she might have given that money to buy food for the poor."

Jesus knew the thoughts and whisperings of his disciples. He saw them question Mary about her deed, and speak unkindly to her. So he spoke to them all and said, "Let this woman alone. Why do you trouble her? She has done a good work, for she has come before my death to anoint my body with sweet perfume. The poor you have with you always, but I shall not be with you much longer. And by this deed Mary has shown her love for me." And Jesus said also that wherever the gospel should be preached in the whole world this deed which Mary had done to show her love should be told in memory of her.

Perhaps Mary understood what the disciples were unable to believe—that Jesus soon must die—for she had sat at his feet and listened to his words while he visited in her home. She had heard him tell about many things, and she had believed them. And now she had poured out the costliest gift her money could buy, to anoint Jesus before he should have to lie cold in death. She had done all she could to show how great was her love.

Judas Iscariot was even more displeased when he heard Jesus' words. He was no longer a true disciple, for he had allowed Satan to plant wrong desires in his heart. And sometimes he took money from the bag to keep for himself, for he loved riches and he had hoped some day to be a rich ruler in the kingdom he expected Jesus to set up.

Now a wicked thought crept into his heart, and he planned to go as soon as possible to the enemies of Jesus in Jerusalem and promise them to give Jesus into their power if they would give him money for his work. So after the supper was ended he left Bethany and went to see the chief priests and scribes who lived in Jerusalem.

For many days the enemies of Jesus had been talking together about how they might capture Jesus. After Lăz'-ă-rŭs had been raised from the dead they were stirred more than ever, because many other people had begun to believe in Jesus, too. When Judas Iscariot came to them they were glad, and they promised to give him thirty pieces of silver money if he would bring them to Jesus when the multitude of believing friends were not near.

———•———

STORY 50

HOW JESUS RODE INTO JERUSALEM AS A KING

Matt. 21:1-11; Mark 11:1-11; Luke 19:29-40; John 12:12-19

A time of great excitement was on. People were flocking out of the city gate and hurrying along the road that led down the valley and up the slope of Mount Olivet, just outside of Jerusalem. They were rushing out to meet Jesus, of whom they had heard such great things.

Many of these people were strangers in Jerusalem. They had just come to attend the Feast of the Passover, and they had heard about the wonderful miracles Jesus performed. Others lived in Jerusalem and they had heard how Jesus raised Lăz'-ă-rŭs from the dead, so they too, were eager to see him again. As they went they took branches of palm-trees with which to wave him a welcome when they should meet him.

On the morning of that same day Jesus had sent two of his disciples to a village near Bethany to loose a colt which they should find tied. He had told them to bring this colt to him, and if the owners should question why they untied the colt they should answer, "The Lord has need of this colt today." And the disciples had gone and

JESUS ENTERING JERUSALEM

found the colt tied by the roadside, and they had told the owners the message which Jesus sent. And the owners had let them take the colt and bring it to Jesus.

Then the disciples had spread their garments on the colt's back and had set Jesus on it, while others threw their clothes along the road for Jesus to ride over. And as the crowd from Jerusalem came near to the Mount of Olives, the company which followed from Bethany began to shout, "Blessed is the King who is coming in the name of the Lord! Peace in heaven, and glory in the highest!"

The people who came out of Jerusalem met Jesus and his disciples on the slope of the Mount of Olives. They heard those who followed Jesus shout praises to him, and they too waved their palms and rejoiced, saying, "Hō-săn'-nă! Blessed is the King of Israel who comes in the name of the Lord!" Some threw their palms in the road for him to ride over, and all along the highway they stood, rejoicing greatly and praising God.

In the crowd were some Pharisees who had not come to rejoice but to find fault. When they heard the people shouting they came to Jesus and said, "Master, cause these to cease shouting." But Jesus answered, "If these should be still the stones by the roadside would immediately cry out." Jesus knew the time had come when the prophecy of Zĕch-ă-rī'-ăh should be fulfilled, for Zĕch-ă-rī'-ăh had said concerning this very time:

'Rejoice greatly, O daughter of Zion;
Shout, O daughter of Jerusalem:
Behold, your King comes unto you:
He is just, and having salvation;
Lowly, and riding upon a colt."

So the crowd passed on through the gate into the city, and Jesus rode up Mount Mō-rī'-ăh, where the temple stood. And as he went, the people before and behind cried out aloud, "Hō-săn'-nă to the Son of David." And the people in the city were stirred with the excitement. They came hurrying into the streets to ask, "What is the meaning of all this? "Who is this king you are bringing?" And the multitude answered, "This is Jesus, the prophet of Nazareth, of Galilee."

Then Jesus entered the temple and looked about upon the things there. Taking his disciples, he returned to Bethany to spend the night in the house of his friends.

THE TEACHINGS OF JESUS IN THE TEMPLE

Matt. 21:12-46; Mark 11:12—12:12; Luke 19:41—20:19

Early in the morning Jesus and his disciples started away from Bethany to go again to the temple in Jerusalem. As they went, Jesus became hungry, and seeing a fig-tree by the roadside he stopped to eat of its fruit. But there were no figs on the tree, only leaves, and Jesus turned away disappointed. As he walked away he said, "Never again shall man eat fruit from this tree."

When Jesus came to the temple he saw men in there who were buying and selling animals for sacrifice-offerings, and others who were called money-changers. Once before he had driven such men out of the temple, and now he drove them out the second time, saying, "In the Scriptures it is written, 'My house shall be called a house of prayer'; but you have made it a den of thieves." For these men demanded more money for their sacrifice-offerings than they should have asked.

The wave of excitement was still running high in the city, and every one was eager to see Jesus. The blind and the lame came to him in the temple, and he healed them there. And little children came singing, "Hō-săn'-nă to the Son of David!" No doubt they had heard the glad songs of the grown people who had come with Jesus from the Mount of Olives, and they, too, wished to praise this great man, who took little ones in his arms and blessed them.

The chief priests and scribes in the temple saw Jesus heal the blind and the lame, and they heard the children sing his praises. They were angered by these things, for they saw that every day the multitudes were becoming more excited about this Jesus. They came to him and asked, "Do you hear what these children are saying?" And Jesus replied, "Yes, I hear them. Have you never read these words in the Scriptures, 'Out of the mouths of little children thou hast perfected praise'?"

In the evening Jesus returned again with his disciples to Bethany, to be with his dear friends, and in the morning he went back to teach the eager people who gathered early to hear him. As they passed along the road by the fig-tree that he had found only leaves on, the disciples saw that the tree had withered and now stood dry and dead. They were surprized that it should have changed so soon, and they spoke about it. Then Jesus taught them a lesson from the fig-tree. He said, "Have faith in God. If you have faith to believe that God hears you when you pray you shall do greater things than I have done by my words to this fig-tree. For if you ask anything of God in prayer, and believe in your hearts that he hears you, the thing for which you ask shall be given.''

When they came to the temple many people had already gathered to hear Jesus teach. The chief priests and the scribes were there also, ready to ask him a question; for they were not willing that he should teach the people. They demanded of him, ''By what authority do you teach and work miracles? Who gave you this authority?''

Jesus knew how to answer them by asking a question of them. He said, ''Was the baptism of John from heaven or of men? Tell me this and I will answer your question.''

Now the enemies of Jesus did not know how to answer. They had not received John's baptism as of God, and they feared to tell Jesus because many people were listening, and the people all claimed that surely John was a prophet of God. If they should not own John as a prophet they feared that the people would turn bitterly against them. Yet if they should say that John's baptism was of God they knew Jesus would ask why they had not believed him. So they said, ''We can not tell whether John's baptism was from heaven or of men.'' Then Jesus answered, ''Neither will I tell you by what authority I do these things, or who gave this authority to me.''

DRIVING OUT THE MONEY CHANGERS

Again Jesus began to teach by story-sermons, called parables. He told them about a man who had two sons. This man called his elder son to him and said, ''Son, go and work today in my vineyard.'' The boy answered his father roughly, saying, ''I will not go!'' But afterwards he became sorry, and repented of his unwillingness to obey his father's command. Then he went to the vineyard and worked. To the second son the father spoke the same words of command, and this boy replied politely, ''I go, sir.'' But he did not go. ''Now,'' asked Jesus, ''which of the two boys obeyed his father?'' and the people answered, ''The first.''

Jesus said the two boys were like the two classes—the people whom the Pharisees and such called sinners, and the Pharisees and other leaders themselves. All these leaders claimed to be obedient, and yet they were not doing the things God had commanded, while the other people whom they called sinners had listened gladly to John's words and had been baptized by him.

Another story which Jesus told was about a man who planted a vineyard, and built a hedge about it, digged a winepress in it, and built a watch-tower. Then he hired some men to care for it, and went away to another country. When the time came that the fruit of the vineyard should be ripened, he sent servants to get some of the fruit and bring it back to him. But the keepers of the vineyard treated the servants roughly. The first one who came they beat, and sent him away without any fruit. The second one they threw stones at and wounded him in the head. The third one they killed. Later other servants were sent; but the wicked keepers of the vineyard treated them all shamefully.

The owner of the vineyard was very sad, and he decided at last to send his own son. "They will know he is my son," he reasoned, "and they will respect him." But when the keepers looked out from the watch-tower and saw the son coming, they said to each other, "The owner has sent his son. This vineyard will belong to him, because he is the heir, let us kill him, and take the vineyard for our own possession." So they caught him, and killed him, and threw his body outside the vineyard. "When the owner of that vineyard comes what will he do to those men?" asked Jesus. And the people answered, "He will cause them to be miserably destroyed, and he will give his vineyard into the care of better men who will give him some of its fruits."

Then Jesus looked boldly upon his enemies standing near and said, "The kingdom of God shall be taken from you, and shall be given to another nation, which will bring forth fruit." The chief priests and scribes knew he had spoken the parables against them, and they were angry. But they were afraid to seize him because they knew all the people standing round believed that Jesus was a great prophet.

———◆———

STORY 52

JESUS' LAST DAYS IN THE TEMPLE
Matt. 22: 1—24: 1; Mark 12: 13—13: 1; Luke 20: 20—21: 4;
John 12: 20-36

While Jesus was teaching in the temple he told the people by a parable that the kingdom of heaven is like a king who made a feast at the marriage of his son. The king prepared a great feast and invited guests from a city near by. When everything was ready, the guests failed to come. He sent servants to remind them of their invitation to the wedding-feast, still they would not come. They made fun of it, and went on about their own work. Some of them even treated the king's messengers cruelly and killed them.

The king heard about the conduct of those people, and he was much displeased. He called out his army and sent his soldiers to destroy them and to burn their city. Then he invited other guests to the marriage feast, and the place was filled; for every one came who was bidden this time.

Among these guests were the poor and the rich, and the good and the bad, and the king furnished each one with a garment to wear. He wished to have them appear well in his presence. When all had arrived and put on their clean garments, he came in to see them and give them a welcome to the feast.

One man was present who refused to put on the clean garment that the king had provided for him. There he stood among all the others, clothed in his dirty rags. The king saw him and said, "Friend, why did you come in here without putting on the clean garment that I had provided for you to wear?" And the man hung his head, for he had no excuse to offer. The king was displeased with him because he had disobeyed orders, so he commanded his servants to seize the man, bind him hand and foot, and take him away to a dark place where he should be punished.

The Pharisees and other enemies of Jesus knew these parables were showing the people how they, the Pharisees and the other enemies, had refused to obey God, and they determined to put a stop to his teaching. They decided to ask questions of him, and prevent him from teaching in this way. So they sent some men who pretended to be good, and told these men to ask him whether it was wrong or right to pay the tribute money, or tax money, which Cæsar, the Roman ruler, demanded of them.

The Jews disliked to pay this money, and Jesus' enemies knew that if he should say it was right for them to pay the tax then the people would no longer care to make him their king. They would no longer follow him so eagerly and listen to his words, for they hated the Roman government. But if Jesus should say it was wrong to pay this tax money, then his enemies planned to tell the Roman officers that Jesus was unwilling to obey the Roman government, and they knew Jesus would be punished.

So the men came to Jesus and said, "Master, we know you are true, and that you teach the way of God in truth without caring whether men will be pleased with your teaching or not." Thus they flattered him, thinking he would be delighted to hear such favorable things said of himself. Then they continued: "Tell us just what you think, Is it right or wrong to pay this tribute money which Cæsar demands of us Jews?" They thought Jesus would answer either yes or no. But they were mistaken.

Jesus could see the hearts of these evil men who were questioning him. He paid no attention to their flattering words, but said, "Why do you tempt me, you hypocrites? Show me the tribute money." And they brought him a penny. Jesus looked at the coin on both sides, then asked of them, "Whose image is this on the one side? and whose name is written here?" On one side of the coin was a picture of Cæsar's head, and his name was written above it. The men replied that the image and the name on the coin were both Cæsar's. "Then," said Jesus, "give to Cæsar the things that belong to him, and give to God the things that belong to God."

This answer greatly surprized the men, for they had thought they surely would catch Jesus in a.trap where he would need to say yes or no. But he had replied so wisely they could not accuse him to any man.

Others came to question Jesus, and among them was a lawyer who asked, "Which is the greatest commandment of the law?" Jesus replied that the greatest commandment of the law was, "Thou shalt love the Lord thy God with all thy heart, and with all thy soul, and with all thy mind, and with all thy strength: this is the first commandment. And the second greatest is this: Thou shalt love thy neighbor as much as thyself. No other commandments are so important as these two." The lawyer answered, "You have well spoken, for to love the Lord God in this way and to love one's neighbor as much as one's own self is surely more pleasing to God than burnt offerings and sacrifices."

Jesus was pleased with this reply of the lawyer. He saw that the lawyer understood the meaning of God's Word better than did many who pretended to be teachers of it. And he told the lawyer that he was near to the kingdom of God.

While Jesus was in the temple, some men came to Philip, one of the twelve disciples, and asked permission to see Jesus. These men were Gentiles, they were Greeks by birth, and they had come to worship the God of the Jews, so they were called proselytes. Because they were Gentiles they could not enter the part of the temple where Jesus sat teaching the people who thronged him there. They could come no farther than the outside court, called the court of the Gentiles. But they had heard much about this wonderful teacher from Galilee, and they wished to see him. Philip told Andrew, another disciple, and together they hurried to tell Jesus that strangers from Greece, a country far away, were waiting in the court of the Gentiles to catch a glimpse of him.

When Jesus heard about the inquirers from distant Greece he said to Philip and Andrew, "The hour is come that the Son of man should be glorified." He spoke to them about his coming death for the sins of the people, but the disciples could not understand his words. And because Jesus could feel pain just as we do he shrank from the thought of dying on the cross. He felt troubled because the time was drawing so near when he should die. And he said, prayerfully, "Father, save me from this hour." Then he remembered that his life-work would not be finished if he did not die for lost sinners, so he added, "Father, glorify thy name." And a voice spoke from heaven, "I have glorified it, and will glorify it again." The people standing by heard the voice but could not understand the words that were spoken. Some thought the voice sounded like thunder; others said, "An angel spoke to him." But Jesus said the voice had spoken to prove to them that God had heard him.

After teaching, Jesus had sat down near a place in the temple called the treasury. Here were money-boxes in which the people's offerings were received. And Jesus saw the rich pass by the boxes and throw in large offerings. Finally he saw a poor widow come into the treasury and stop beside a box to throw in her small offering of only two little coins. Together these coins were worth less than a penny. But Jesus told his disciples that the poor widow had given more than the rich people, for they had given out of full purses whereas she had emptied the last of her money into the box. He wished to teach them that God looks at the heart of the giver, for God saw that the poor widow gave her all because she loved him, whereas the rich people gave their offerings because it was their duty to give.

Then Jesus and his disciples left the temple, and went out to the Mount of Olives. Never again did Jesus walk in the courts of the Lord's house on Mount Mō-rī'-ăh; for soon afterwards his enemies took him and did to him all they had wished to do.

STORY 53

JESUS' TEACHING ON THE MOUNT OF OLIVES

Matt. 23:37—25:46; Mark 13; Luke 21:5-38

As Jesus left the temple for the last time, his disciples spoke to him about the beauty of the Lord's house. Like all other Jews, they took much pride in the temple where God was worshiped. And they were surprized to hear Jesus say, "The time is coming when the stones of these buildings shall be torn apart."

On the Mount of Olives, Jesus rested for a while before going on to Bethany. And his disciples gathered around him there to ask when the time should come that the beautiful temple would be destroyed. No one else was near to disturb them, and Jesus talked long and earnestly to his disciples about the things that would happen to Jerusalem, and later to the whole world. He told them that men would come who would claim to be the Christ of God, and that many would believe in them. He said that great wars would be fought among the nations of the earth, and that troubles of different kinds would come upon the people. Then he said that before the end of time the gospel of the kingdom would be preached, not only among the Jews, but to all people in every part of the world. How strange these things must have sounded to the disciples! for they had always believed that salvation belonged to the Jews only.

Then Jesus told the disciples the parable of the ten young women, called virgins. Five of these young women were wise and five were foolish. All had been invited to the marriage of a friend, and they started to meet the wedding-party. They took their lamps with them to give light, for the wedding would take place at night and only those carrying lights would be allowed to join the wedding-party.

But the wedding-party was slow in coming, and the young women grew tired waiting. So they fell asleep. At midnight a cry was made that the wedding-party was coming, and the young women aroused and began at once to trim their lamps to be ready to join the procession when it came by.

Now the five who were wise poured more oil into their lamps; for they saw the light was growing dim, and they had brought an extra supply of oil with them. But the five who were foolish had brought no more oil, and they, too, saw that their lights were growing dim. "What shall we do?" they asked each other. Then they spoke to their wise friends and said, "Please give some of your oil to us, for our lights are going out!"

The wise young women did not have enough to give to their friends in distress, so they answered, "You must go to them who sell and buy for yourselves. We do not have enough to share." And while they hurried away to buy more oil, the wedding-party came, and the five wise young women joined the party and went to the home where the marriage festivities would take place.

When all the guests had entered, the door was shut, and no other persons could enter. The foolish young women came after the door had been shut, and they knocked; but the bridegroom would not let them in. They had come too late.

By this story Jesus wished to teach his disciples to watch and be ready, for they should not know the time when he would call for them to leave this world and go to be with him. If they should not be ready when he should call, they would have no time left in which to make ready, but, like the foolish young women, they would be shut out of heaven.

Jesus told the disciples what will happen at the end of the world. He said that then the Son of man will come in his glory, bringing all the angels with him. And he will sit upon the throne of his glory. And before him all nations of the earth shall be gathered, and he will divide the good from the evil. Those who have believed in him he will place on his right, and those who have disobeyed he will place on his left, just as a shepherd in that country divided his sheep from his goats. The disciples no doubt had watched the shepherds come in from the fields and separate the sheep from the goats in their great flocks, and they understood how this separation will be.

"Then shall the Son of man be King," said Jesus; "and he will say to them on his right, 'Come, you who are blessed of my Father, and dwell in the kingdom which has been prepared for you. For I was hungry, and you fed me; I was thirsty and you gave me drink; I was a stranger, and you gave me shelter; I was shivering with cold, and you gave me clothes to keep me warm; I was sick, and you visited me; I was in prison, and you came to see me even there.' And the ones on his right will reply, 'Lord, when did we see you in need and help you thus?' And the King will answer, 'Whenever you helped one of my needy brothers, even the least of them, you helped me.'

"Then the King will turn to those on his left, and will say to them, 'Depart from me, you who are cursed, and go away into ever-lasting fire, which has been made ready for the devil and his evil spirits. For I was hungry, and you did not feed me; I was thirsty, and you gave me no water; I was a stranger, and you gave me no shelter; without clothes, and you did not give clothes to me; sick, and you did not visit me; in prison, and you did not come to me there.' And the ones on his left will reply, 'Lord, when did we see you hungry, or thirsty, or without clothes, or a stranger, or sick, or in prison, and not help you?' And he will say to them, 'Whenever you refused to help one of my brothers, even the poorest of them, you refused to help me.'

"And those on the right," said Jesus, "will go into life eternal in heaven, while those on the left shall be turned away into everlasting torment."

———•———

STORY 54

THE LAST SUPPER JESUS ATE WITH THE TWELVE

Matt. 26:17-30; Mark 14:12-26; Luke 22:3-39; John 13

Two disciples, Peter and John, were hurrying along the road from Bethany to Jerusalem. They were going on an errand for their master. The day had come when the lamb for the Passover Feast should be killed, and Jesus had chosen these two disciples to go to Jerusalem and prepare the feast that the Twelve should eat with him that evening.

After they had passed through the city gate, they looked about to find a man carrying a pitcher of water. Men seldom carried water-pitchers in the streets, for such work was usually left for women to do. But Jesus had told them they would see a man carrying a water-pitcher, and they did. Jesus also told them to follow the man to the house where he should go with his pitcher, so they followed.

At the house they met the owner, and to him they gave the message that Jesus had sent. This was the message: "Our master sent us to ask your permission for him to use your guest-room in which to eat the Passover supper with his disciples." And the owner of the house led them to a nice room up-stairs which was furnished with a table and couches on which the guests might recline while they ate. No doubt this owner knew Jesus, and was glad to give him the use of the guest-room in his home.

When evening came, Jesus and the other ten joined Peter and John and together they sat around the table in that quiet room upstairs.

168

JESUS AND HIS DISCIPLES AT THE LAST SUPPER

MORNING IN OLD JERUSALEM

The summer sun, rising in the direction of the Mountains of Moab, lights up the picturesque roofs of old Jerusalem. We view this scene from the terrace of the Austrian Hospice, where the Damascus Road and Via Dolorosa meet—pilgrim-center of Jerusalem. Arched-over, narrow, winding streets cut through the apparently solid mass of stone buildings shown in the picture.

A feeling of sadness crept into the hearts of the disciples, for their Master spoke to them so earnestly about going away soon.

It was so hard for these men to believe that Jesus would really be taken away from them. They had seen him do such wonderful things that it seemed impossible to think men could ever kill him. And soon they were talking about other matters at the supper-table. Some were wondering who would be the greatest in the kingdom that they expected Jesus to set up soon.

Jesus knew their thoughts, and he wished to teach them more about the kind of kingdom he was bringing to mankind. He rose up suddenly from the table, laid aside his outer garment, and tied a towel about his waist. Then he took a basin of water and began to wash the disciples' feet.

The disciples looked at each other in silent astonishment. They could not understand why he should be doing this humble act of service, for they had washed the dust from their feet before coming into that upper room. Finally Jesus came to Peter with his basin. But that disciple pulled his feet away, and exclaimed, "Lord, you shall never wash my feet!" "Then," answered Jesus calmly, "you shall never have a part in my kingdom." At this Peter changed his mind suddenly, and he said, "Lord, you may wash my feet, and even my hands and my head." Very desirous was this disciple of having a part in Jesus' kingdom. But by washing their feet, Jesus did not mean in this way to prepare the hearts of his disciples for his work. He said to them, "You are clean already, but not all." For he knew which one was not a true disciple.

When the strange washing was over, Jesus laid aside the towel and took up his garment again. Then he returned to his place at the table, beside John, and began to explain to his disciples what he had just done to them: "You call me Lord, and Master," said he, "and so I am. If I, your Lord and Master, have washed your feet, you ought to wash one another's feet. For I have given you an example that you should do to each other as I have done to you. The servant is not greater than his master, and if you would be good servants you will obey my words. If you know my commands, you will be happy when you obey them."

Jesus also said that one of them should give him into the hands of his enemies, who would take his life. This seemed hard to believe, but the disciples knew Jesus' words of prophecy always came true, so they were amazed. Instead of looking at each other accusingly, each man thought of himself. And each one said, "Lord, is it I?"

John, the disciple who liked to be near Jesus, was reclining next to his master at the supper. Peter motioned to John and whispered, "Ask which one will do this dreadful deed." So John asked Jesus, and Jesus replied in low tones, "The one to whom I shall give a piece of bread when I have dipped it in the dish." John watched carefully, and soon he saw Jesus give a piece of bread to Judas Iscariot.

After Judas had taken the bread that Jesus gave to him, Jesus said, "That thou doest, do quickly." Then the desire in his heart to get rid of this master became stronger, and Judas hurried out of the room into the gloom of night. None of the disciples understood what Jesus meant, but they supposed because Judas carried the money-bag that he was going to do something for their master.

Jesus then, after supper, took bread and blessed it and broke it in pieces, giving parts to each of the disciples, and saying, "Take this bread and eat it, for it is my body which is broken for you." Then he took the cup and when he had given thanks he passed it to them, saying, "Drink this, for it is my blood, which is shed for you, for I will never again drink of the fruit of the vine with you until that day when I drink it new in the kingdom of God."

They lingered a while longer in the upper room, and Jesus talked earnestly to them about the time when he should go away and leave them alone. He urged them to remember his commandment to love each other as he had loved them, and he told them that he would prepare a place for them in his Father's house.

Peter insisted that he would not leave Jesus, but would go with him wherever he went. Jesus told him that he could not go now, but that he might come later on. He also told Peter that, bold as he believed himself to be, he would prove himself a coward before daylight should return, for he would forsake Jesus and even deny that he had ever known him. Thus the Lord's Supper had been instituted. Then Jesus and his disciples sang a hymn together, and quietly left the upper room, going out of Jerusalem into a garden near by.

STORY 55

HOW AN UNTRUE DISCIPLE SOLD HIS LORD

Matt. 26:36-75; Mark 14:32-72; Luke 22:39-71; John 18:1-27

Through the deep shadows which fell from the buildings along the streets a silent figure glided along, hurrying toward the assembly-room where the enemies of Jesus were sitting together waiting. That silent figure was the evil-minded disciple, Judas Iscariot, who was hurrying on his way to sell his Lord.

Soon the footsteps of Judas fell on the floor of the hall, and his knock sounded on the door of the assembly-room. In reply to the call, "Who is there?" came the answer, "He for whom you wait," and quickly the door was thrown open and Judas entered. Now there followed a hasty conversation, some argument, and finally thirty pieces of silver were counted out and handed to Judas. Then the assembly broke up, each man hurrying to get a torch or to summon the soldiers who should go on their midnight errand.

While this was taking place, Jesus and the eleven disciples had left the room up-stairs where they had eaten the last Passover supper together, and had gone outside the city to a garden across the brook Kĭd'-rŏn. Here at the entrance of the garden Jesus had told eight of the disciples to wait, and, taking with him Peter, James, and John, he had gone into the deeper shadows of the trees to pray.

But while Jesus prayed the disciples fell asleep. They could not understand why he should seem so troubled and they did not know how to comfort him. They allowed their own sleepy feelings to overcome their love for him, and just when he longed to have them near to pray with him they slept. Three times Jesus went to waken Peter, James, and John, but not once did they offer him the comfort he sought. Then while he prayed in agony alone God sent an angel from heaven to strengthen and comfort him. For Jesus knew the sorrow that was soon to come; he knew what Judas was even then doing; and he knew his enemies would not cease to torture him till he should be hanging dead upon the cross. Not only that, for Jesus knew also that he must bear the sins of the whole world in order to become the Savior of men. And because he had a body such as we have, he dreaded to suffer the pain of such a death, and he dreaded to be left alone by those whom he loved. So he asked God to take away the suffering from him if such a thing should be possible. But he added, "Let thy will, not mine, be done"

THE GARDEN OF GETHSEMANE AS SEEN FROM JERUSALEM

When Jesus had roused the sleepy disciples the third time, he told them to arise; for it was time for them to be going on their way. And they rose up to follow him out of the garden. But as they went toward the entrance they saw a band of men coming to them carrying torches as if they were searching for some one. Jesus walked up to the men and asked, ''For whom are you seeking?'' and they replied, ''For Jesus of Nazareth.''

''I am he,'' answered Jesus. And the men fell backward. When they rose, Jesus asked them the second time whom they were seeking, and again they said, ''For Jesus of Nazareth.'' Judas, the unfaithful disciple, was with the band of men, and he stepped forward and cried, ''Hail, Master!'' and kissed Jesus on the cheek. But Jesus knew the evil thought that was in Judas' mind, and he looked sadly into the guilty face of his unfaithful disciple and asked, ''Judas, do you betray the Son of man with a kiss?''

CHRIST IN GETHSEMANE

Judas had told the band of men the sign by which they might know whom to take for their prisoner, and that sign was the kiss he had given to Jesus. Now the soldiers took hold of Jesus roughly and prepared to lead him away.

At this Peter was thoroughly aroused from his sleep. Drawing a short sword, which he carried in his belt, he struck at one of the soldiers and cut off his ear. But Jesus seemed displeased, and told Peter to put away his sword. Then he healed the soldier's ear; and Peter, unable to understand how he might now defend his master, sank back into the shadows with the other frightened disciples.

The soldiers then bound their prisoner, and the procession started toward the assembly-room where the enemies of Jesus were waiting impatiently. And far behind Peter followed, wondering what he should do, and yet fearing that the soldiers might take him, also.

First the soldiers brought Jesus to the house of a man named Annas, who was father-in-law of the high priest, Câî'-ă-phăs, and here his trial began. John, one of the disciples, gained admittance at the door, for he was acquainted with the household of the high priest. And he went in where Jesus was. But Peter stood outside, for he was a stranger, and the doorkeeper, a young girl, would not let him in.

Presently John spoke to the doorkeeper, and she allowed him to take Peter into the court-room, for the night was cold. When Peter was inside the young girl said, "Are you not also one of his disciples?" But Peter was afraid, and he said, "No, I did not know the man."

In the open court a fire was burning, and Peter went near to warm himself. Around the fire stood other men, some who were servants in the high priest's house and others who were officers.

One of the men by the fire then turned to Peter and asked, "Are you not one of this man's disciples?" Again fear crept into Peter's heart, and he replied stoutly, "No, I am not!" But a soldier standing by who had been in the garden when Jesus was taken had seen Peter use his sword, and he spoke, saying, "I saw you in the garden with him!" Peter denied fiercely, and pretended that he had never known Jesus at all.

While this had been happening to Peter, out in the high priest's courtyard, the high priest and others had been asking Jesus questions about his teachings and had been treating him shamefully. Then the enemies of Jesus led their prisoner out of the high priest's house, and as he passed by he looked sadly upon Peter. And Peter remembered how Jesus had told him that before the return of another day he would deny three times that he had ever known the Lord. Now tears filled Peter's eyes, and he turned blindly away from the fire and rushed out of the door, to weep bitterly. He saw himself no longer a true man, brave, and ready to help in the work of his master, but a coward, ashamed to own that he had once proudly followed the innocent man who now stood bound in chains and condemned to die.

THE DARKEST DAY IN ALL THE WORLD

Matt. 27: 1-54; Mark 15: 1-39; Luke 23: 1-47; John 18: 28—19: 31

After the sad, long night when Jesus was captured in the garden, morning came at last, and the news began to spread through the city streets that Jesus, the prophet from Galilee, was now a prisoner. His friends were terrified, while his enemies laughed in wicked glee. And the soldiers led him before the Roman governor, Pilate, for this governor now took the place of the King Herod who had tried to kill Jesus when he was born, in Bethlehem.

Pilate knew nothing about Jesus. He took him into his judgment-hall and talked a while with him. And he was surprized to hear the wisdom of this one whom the Jews were condemning to die. He went out to them and said, ''I find no fault in this man.'' But the Jews cried the more loudly that Jesus should be put to death, saying that he had stirred up the people throughout the country, even from Galilee.

When Pilate heard that Jesus was from Galilee, he said, ''This man belongs to the country that Herod rules.'' This Herod was a son of the wicked king who tried to take Jesus' life when he was a baby. Pilate sent Jesus to Herod at once, for Herod was in Jerusalem at that time.

Now this was the Herod who had caused John the Baptist to be put to death. He had heard much about Jesus, but he had never seen this prophet from Galilee. When the soldiers came, bringing Jesus bound with chains, Herod was glad, for he hoped that Jesus might do some miracle before him. At once he began to ask questions of Jesus, but not one question would Jesus answer. The chief priests and the scribes stood round about and said all kinds of evil things about Jesus, still he would not speak one word to defend himself.

Finally Herod grew impatient with this silent prisoner. A wicked thought came into his heart, so he began to make fun of Jesus. With his soldiers he mocked Jesus, dressing him in rich garments and pretending to honor him as a king. Then he sent him back to Pilate.

Now Pilate's wife had heard about the trial of Jesus and she was greatly troubled, for that night she had dreamed about him. She sent a message to her husband, urging him to set Jesus free, saying, ''He is a just man, not worthy of death.'' Pilate, too, wished to free Jesus; for he could find no guilt in him. He told the accusers that neither he nor Herod had been able to find him guilty of death. But the mob now cried, "If you set this man free you are not a friend of Cæsar, and Cæsar will dismiss you from being our governor." Pilate knew the Jews could accuse him to Cæsar if they were displeased with him,

PILATE WITH JESUS BEFORE THE ANGRY JEWS

and being a coward he chose rather to let an innocent man suffer than to be in danger of losing his position as governor.

As the trial went on, Judas Iscariot saw that Jesus was condemned to die. Now his guilty conscience troubled him greatly. He had hoped

JESUS CRUCIFIED

VIA DOLOROSA—TRADITIONAL WAY OF THE CROSS

This sunlit passage is reputed to be the way through the city of Jerusalem down which Jesus bore the cross on the way to Golgotha. Excavations seem to show that the city level of Christ's time lies some thirty feet below the pavement now in place. This is an unusual picture taken before the traffic of the day had started. The two children walking hand in hand are on their way to classes in the Mohammedan quarter of the city.

that Jesus would free himself in some miraculous way from the power of his enemies; but now he saw that Jesus was allowing himself to be helpless in their hands. The money that he had taken from the enemies of Jesus seemed to burn his flesh, so he hurried back to the chief priests and scribes, saying, "I have sold an innocent man! I have sinned!"

The chief priests and scribes looked scornfully upon Judas and replied, "What is that to us? You yourself must answer for your sin." And they turned away from him, refusing to take back the money they had given him for doing the dreadful act.

Neither would Judas keep the money, so he threw it upon the floor of the temple and ran down the long flight of steps, away to a lonely place, where he hung himself and died.

Before giving Jesus up to die Pilate talked to the restless mob about another prisoner whom he held—a wicked man named Bär-ăb'-băs, who as a robber had caused much trouble to the Jews. At the time of the Feast it was customary to release a prisoner, and Pilate asked whether he should release Bär-ăb'-băs, the wicked robber whom the people feared, or Jesus, the innocent man whom they hated. And with loud cries the people answered, "Set Bär-ăb'-băs free!" Then Pilate asked, "What shall I do with Jesus?" and they answered, "Crucify him! crucify him!"

JUDAS THROWING DOWN THE MONEY

So the trial came to an end, and Pilate, wishing to please the people, called some Roman soldiers and told them to lead Jesus away to be crucified. First he took water in a basin and washed his hands before the Jews, saying, "I am not guilty of the death of this innocent man." The Jews cried out, "We ourselves will bear the blame; let his blood be on our heads!"

The Roman soldiers took Jesus and put a crown of thorns upon his head. Then they put a reed in his hand, and, bowing before him, mockingly called him the king of the Jews. They also blindfolded his eyes, and spat upon him, and struck him with their hands, saying, "Tell us, prophet, who is it who struck you?" All these shameful things Jesus bore in silence for he was suffering in the place of those who deserved to suffer for their own sins. Finally the soldiers took off the purple robe and dressed him once more in his own clothes. Then they led him away outside the city to nail him on a cross. They took two other prisoners, men who had been thieves, and laid heavy crosses on the bared backs of these men, then led them away with Jesus to die.

A crowd of curious people followed the soldiers through the gate to the hillside where the crucifixion took place. Many in the crowd were enemies of Jesus, others were friends who longed to help but could not. As they went, Jesus sank down beneath the weight of the heavy cross he bore, and could not rise again. The cruel soldiers then called a stranger from the crowd and placed the cross upon his shoulder, for Jesus was too weak to carry it any farther.

On the hillside of Calvary the crowd stopped, and the soldiers began to strip their prisoners of their clothing and to fasten their hands and their feet to the crosses. Then they raised the crosses high in the air and planted them securely in the ground, leaving the prisoners to hang there till death should relieve them of their misery. Jesus prayed when they were crucifying him and said, "Father, forgive them, for they know not what they do."

The cross on which Jesus was crucified stood between the two crosses on which the thieves were hung, and a writing was nailed above the head of Jesus, which said in three languages, "This is Jesus, the King of the Jews." When the Jews read the writing they were much displeased and hurried to ask Pilate to change it, that it might read thus: "He called himself the King of the Jews." But Pilate would not change the writing, and all who passed by could read what he had written, though they were strangers in Judah.

While Jesus hung on the cross, one of the thieves began to mock him, but the other begged to be forgiven and to be remembered when Jesus came into his kingdom. He believed that Jesus was really the King from heaven, which the Jews were unwilling to receive. And Jesus saw his faith, and said to him, "Today you shall be with me in paradise." Then the thief knew that his sins were forgiven, and though he was suffering much pain a glad joy came into his heart.

While Jesus hung on the cross he saw a group of sorrowing friends standing at the edge of the crowd, and among them was his own mother. John, the disciple who loved him so much, was also there, and Jesus asked John to take care of his mother from that time.

The enemies of Jesus stood around the cross, making fun of him and telling him to come down if he were the Son of God. Even the chief priests and the scribes were there, and they said, "He said he could save others, but he can not save himself! If he is the king of Israel, let him come down, and we will believe in him, too."

About noonday the sky suddenly grew dark. For three hours the great darkness lasted, then Jesus cried with a loud voice, saying, "It is finished!" and soon he died. The Roman captain who stood near the cross, and the soldiers who were with him, saw the rocks torn apart by a terrible earthquake that came, and they were frightened. And the captain said to his soldiers, "Truly this man was the Son of God!"

———•———

STORY 57

THE WATCHERS AT THE TOMB OF JESUS

Matt. 27:55—28:1; Mark 15:42—16:5; Luke 23:50—24:1
John 19:31—20:1

The Jews who had been so gleeful when Jesus was taken prisoner and crucified still felt troubled about him. They could not put the thoughts of him out of their minds. The next day would be their Sabbath, and they did not wish to have him hanging on the cross, with the words, "This is the King of the Jews," written above his head.

However, a rich man named Joseph, who was also a ruler among the Jews, now came boldly into Pilate's judgment-hall and asked permission to take the body of Jesus and bury it. This man, although a ruler, had loved Jesus and he had taken no part in the wicked plots of his fellow rulers. He with Nĭc-ŏ-dē'-mŭs, the Pharisee, had long believed in Jesus, but for fear of the other Jews these two men had not made known their belief. Now with Pilate's permission they went to Calvary. They took Jesus' body and wrapped it in rich linen clothes with the sweet spices and perfumes that Nĭc-ŏ-dē'-mŭs the Pharisee had brought. Then they laid it in a new grave, or tomb, which had been cut out of a large rock. This grave opened into a garden, and Joseph had intended it for his own burial-place when he should die. Some of the women who had often been with Jesus when he taught the multitudes, stood by watching when Joseph and Nĭc-ŏ-dē'-mŭs laid the body of their beloved friend in the dark tomb, and they saw the men roll a heavy stone before the door.

Evening had now come and the Jews' Sabbath had commenced; for their Sabbath began at sunset on Friday evening and ended at sunset on Saturday evening. The sorrowing friends of Jesus therefore

THE DESCENT FROM THE CROSS

hastily returned to their homes to keep the Sabbath in the quiet manner that the Jews had been taught to keep it.

But the enemies of Jesus began to fear that Jesus' grave might be disturbed by his friends. They remembered that Jesus had said he would rise on the third day, and they said to each other, "His disciples may come to steal him away and then declare that he has risen. Then perhaps more people will believe in him and we shall be despised by them." So they hurried to Pilate and told him about their fears, and asked permission to place his Roman seal upon the stone in front of Jesus' grave. They also wanted Pilate to command soldiers to guard the tomb, so that no one should come by night and break the seal and take away the body. And Pilate allowed them to place his seal upon the great stone and to station soldiers to guard the grave by day and by night.

The women who had watched Joseph and Nĭc-ŏ-dē'-mŭs lay the body of Jesus away longed to show their love for Jesus, and after sunset on the next day they hurriedly prepared some sweet perfumes. Then they planned to go early the next morning to anoint the body of their dear friend, even though he had been buried.

But the eleven disciples, stricken with sorrow, hid themselves from the scornful glances of passers-by. They had forgotten the words of Jesus, that he would rise again on the third day. The cruel act of Judas, one of their own number, and the defenseless attitude of their master when in the hands of his enemies had so disappointed them that they bowed their heads in anguish and grief. Nothing seemed left for them now, when their glorious hopes of the kingdom of heaven had disappeared like a broken bubble. And they mourned and wept tears of disappointment, while a fear of the Jews' further displeasure only added to their weight of grief.

Early on the morning of the third day, before the sun had risen, a group of sorrowing women crept out of the city and sped along the highway toward the garden-tomb. As they went they wondered who would roll away the stone from the door of the grave, that they might go inside and pour their sweet perfumes upon the body of Jesus. But when they came near they saw the stone was rolled away and that the tomb was empty. Other visitors had come to the tomb even earlier than they. And the body of Jesus was not there.

WHEN JESUS, THE CRUCIFIED SAVIOR, AROSE FROM THE DEAD

Matt. 28:2-16; Mark 16:5-14; Luke 24:4-12; John 20:2-18

The hours of watching dragged slowly by to the Roman soldiers who guarded the tomb where the body of Jesus lay. No one had come even to visit the grave; and perhaps the soldiers laughed at the fears of the Jews.

The eastern sky was beginning to light up with the promise of a new day when suddenly the ground beneath the watcher's feet began to tremble. Another earthquake had come. Then the fearful watchers saw a mighty angel come down from the sky and roll the stone away from the door of the tomb and sit upon it. The face of this angel had the appearance of lightning, and the garments he wore were as white as snow. At sight of him the soldiers fell to the ground, trembling and helpless, and lay there as if they were dead. All this happened because Jesus had, in the grave, come back to life. He was risen from the dead.

When the women came to the garden they found the tomb empty, and the angel had not yet gone back to heaven. At first the women did not see the angel, and they wondered who had come and stolen the body of their Lord. Mary Măg'-dă-lēne left the others and ran quickly to tell Peter and John that the body of Jesus had been taken away from the tomb and hidden they knew not where.

After Mary had gone from them, the other women saw in the empty tomb the beautiful angel, and they were afraid and bowed themselves to the ground. But the angel said, ''Do not be afraid. Why are you seeking the living among the dead? Jesus is not here; he is risen as he said. Go quickly and tell his disciples and Peter that he is alive and will meet them in Galilee.''

The women ran from the place, filled with joy yet trembling with excitement and fear. The good news which the angel told seemed too wonderful to be true, still they believed and hurried to tell the disciples and other friends who were sorrowing.

But the disciples refused to believe the glad message. Peter and John ran to see the empty tomb for themselves, and when they came to the place they found no one, for the soldiers had risen and fled into the city to tell their strange experience to the enemies of Jesus who had stationed them to watch by the grave. John outran Peter, and coming first to the grave he looked and saw it was empty. Then Peter came, and he went into the dark room where the body of Jesus had lain. He saw there the grave-clothes that Joseph had wrapped round the body of Jesus, and he believed that surely Jesus was alive once more. John, too, entered the grave and saw the clothes lying where Jesus had left them, and he also believed.

Mary Măg'-dă-lēne had not stayed in the garden long enough to hear the message of the angel, and now she returned from the city, longing

ANGELS ON THE WAY TO JESUS' TOMB

to find the place where her crucified Lord had been taken. She did not yet know of the new hopes that were gladdening the hearts of her friends. Entering the garden again, she stood by the empty grave and wept. Then she stooped down and looked into the grave and saw two angels sitting, one at the head and another at the foot of where the body of Jesus had lain. They said to her, "Woman, why are you weeping?" and she replied, "Because they have taken away my Lord and I do not know where they have laid him." Then turning about she saw Jesus himself standing near. But tears blinded her eyes, and she did not know him. He, too, asked her why she wept, and supposing him to be the man who cared for the garden, she said, "Sir, if you have carried away my Lord, tell me where you have laid him that I may take him." Then Jesus said, "Mary!" and she knew his voice.

What glad joy filled Mary's heart when she knew that Jesus was speaking to her again. She fell at his feet and cried, "Master!" Then he told her to go at once and tell her sorrowing friends that she had

JESUS AND MARY

seen him and that he had told her to tell them he was going to ascend to their heavenly Father's home.

While these things were happening, the soldiers came into the city and told the chief priests what had taken place in the garden tomb. And the chief priests were alarmed. They quickly called the other enemies of Jesus; and they all wondered what to do. They had no thoughts of accepting Jesus even though he had truly risen from the dead. They still hoped to persuade the people that Jesus had been a false prophet, so they decided on a plan and they asked the soldiers to help them carry it out. They offered them much money if only they would promise to tell no one else that Jesus

had risen and an angel had opened the tomb. They urged the soldiers to tell the people that the disciples came and stole Jesus' body away while they were lying asleep.

The Roman soldiers cared nothing about the Jews and their religion, and they gladly took the money and went away. And when they were questioned about the disappearance of Jesus' body from the grave they said the disciples had stolen it while they slept.

———•———

STORY 59

THE STRANGER ON THE ROAD TO EMMAUS; DOUBTING THOMAS

Luke 24:13-48; John 20:19-31

The Passover Feast had ended, and some of the visitors at Jerusalem were returning to their homes. Along the roadway leading from the city of Jerusalem to the village of Ĕm-mā'-ŭs, seven miles distant,

JESUS APPEARING TO MARY AT THE TOMB

"A SEPULCHER HEWN OUT OF A ROCK"—MARK 15:46

Here is shown the "Garden Tomb" in a rocky knoll which lies just outside the present-day walls of old Jerusalem. The tomb has the general appearance of a rich man's grave, and there is much evidence to support the belief that here it was that Joseph of Arimathaea laid the body of our Lord. In front of the opening there exists today a deep groove in which could have rested a large, round stone with which ancient tombs were sealed.

RECOGNIZING JESUS

two men were walking slowly, with bowed heads. They were friends of Jesus, and they were troubled about the news that had come to the city just before they started on their journey.

As these men talked together about the trial and crucifixion of Jesus, and about the women's message that early morning, suddenly a stranger joined them and asked, "Why is it that you are so sad? What are you talking about so earnestly?" The men replied, "Can it be possible that you have not heard about the sad things that have been happening during these few days past?" And the stranger asked, "What things?"

The men began to tell this stranger about Jesus of Nazareth whom they had hoped would deliver their nation from the rule of the Romans and set up a kingdom. They told him how the chief priests and rulers had become jealous of him because he was such a mighty prophet, and how they captured him and caused him to be crucified. They told him that Jesus had died on the cross and that his body had been buried by loving friends in a nice, new tomb. "And this is the third day since these things happened," they said, "and this morning some women of our company astonished us by saying they had gone early to the tomb and had seen that his body had been taken away. But they said angels were there, and the angels said he had risen from the dead. Then some of our own number hurried to the grave and found that it was indeed empty, but they did not see the angels nor did they see our risen Lord."

The stranger listened patiently, and when they had finished he began to talk to them about the teachings of Moses' law and of the prophets concerning the promised Redeemer of Israel. He showed them by the word of God's book that Jesus, the prophet of Galilee, should suffer these very things and rise again the third day if he would really be the Redeemer for whom they were longing. And the men listened silently, wondering who this stranger could be.

Presently they came near to the village of Ĕm-mā'-ŭs, and the two men asked the stranger to stop with them until the next morning, as the day had nearly ended. So he stopped with them. And when they sat down to eat their evening meal he took bread, blessed it, and gave it to them, and they knew at once that he was Jesus, their risen Lord. But he disappeared from their sight.

Now the two men understood why the women who had seen the angels seemed so full of joy. They, too, believed in the risen Lord, and their hearts were filled with gladness. They rose up from the table and hurried back to Jerusalem to tell the disciples that they had seen the Lord.

The deep shades of night had fallen over Jerusalem when the men at last came to the house where the disciples and some of their friends were gathered together. When they entered the room they saw that a change had come over these people who had been so sad. Now every one seemed happy, and excited about something. "Jesus is indeed risen," they cried joyously, "for Peter has seen him!" Then the two men told how he had appeared to them on their way to Ĕm-mā'-ŭs, and how they had not known him until he had blessed and broken bread at their evening meal.

While they talked together suddenly Jesus himself appeared in their midst. And they were frightened, for the doors were closed when he entered and they supposed he was a spirit. But he spoke to them and said, "Why are you fearful? See my hands and my feet; touch me, and see that I am not a spirit, for a spirit does not have flesh and bones as I have." Then he asked for something to eat, and they gave him a piece of fish and some honey, which he ate before them. Great was their joy on beholding him once more in their midst, after they had seen him so cruelly tortured and killed.

But Thomas, one of the disciples, was not present when Jesus appeared. And he would not believe when the others told him that they had seen the Lord. He said, "Except I see in his hands the print of the nails and put my fingers into the nail-prints, and except I thrust my hand into the place where the spear cut his side, I will not believe."

A week passed by, and again the disciples were together in a room, the doors being closed, and this time Thomas was with them. Then Jesus appeared as suddenly as he had come before, and he said to them all, "Peace be to you!" While they were wondering at his strange coming he called Thomas and said, "Behold my hands, and put your finger into the print of the nails; and put your hand into the place where the spear cut my side. And do not doubt, but believe."

Now Thomas worshiped Jesus, saying, "My Lord, and my God!" To him Jesus said, "You believe because you have seen; but blessed are those who will believe though they do not see me."

STORY 60

JESUS' LAST MEETING WITH HIS DISCIPLES BY THE SEASHORE AND ON THE MOUNT OF OLIVES

Mark 16:15-19; Luke 24:50-53; John 21; Acts 1:1-14

Far up in Galilee, away from the reach of their enemies, a group of men and women met together on a mountain-side and waited for the appearance of their Lord. And Jesus came to them there, and talked with them again as earnestly as he had talked in other days. And they rejoiced to see him once more and worshiped him; but some doubted that he was really the same Jesus who had been nailed to the cross.

One day after this meeting some of the disciples who had been fishermen returned to the Sea of Galilee. The familiar sight of the water and fishing-boats floating about on the surface stirred within Peter's heart a desire to again go fishing. So he told his companions, and they said, "We will go with you."

All that night the men stayed in their ship, toiling with their net; but not one fish did they catch. When morning came they drew near to the shore and saw a stranger standing there beside a fire of coals. He called to them and asked whether they had any fish. They replied that they had caught none, and he bade them cast their net into the water once more, this time on the right side of the ship. They obeyed, and now the net was filled.

John, the disciple who often went with Peter and James, now whispered to his companions, "It is the Lord." And immediately Peter wrapped his fisher's coat about his body and jumped overboard to swim to shore, so eager was he to come to Jesus. The others remained in the ship and brought it to the landing. Then Jesus commanded them to bring some of the fish they had caught, and Peter drew the net from out of the water. In it they had taken one hundred and fifty-three large fishes, yet the net was not broken. Then Jesus asked the men to come and eat, for he had already prepared fish and bread on the burning coals.

After they had eaten, Jesus talked with Simon Peter, the disciple who had denied him at the time of his trial. He asked Simon three times if he loved him, and each time Simon replied, "Yes, Lord, you know that I love you." Simon believed that Jesus knew all things, and he felt sad because Jesus asked him this same question the third time. Then he remembered how only a short while ago he had denied

three times that he ever knew Jesus. Now he declared three times that
he loved him, and Jesus told him to feed his lambs and sheep.

JESUS APPEARING ON THE SHORES OF GALILEE

Simon Peter had heard Jesus speak a parable one day about the
Good Shepherd, who gave his life for his sheep. And he knew that

Jesus had called himself the Good Shepherd. Now he understood that Jesus had died for the sins of the people, and he believed that men and women were the sheep whom Jesus meant that he should feed. Not their bodies, but their souls were hungry to be fed, and Jesus wanted Peter to leave his work as a fisherman and become a preacher of the gospel. In this way he could feed the people.

Then Jesus told Peter words like these: "When you were a young man you went wherever you wished, but when you shall become an old man you shall stretch out your hands and another shall carry you where you do not wish to go." By these words he meant that when Peter should grow old he would be put to death because he loved Jesus. Then he said to Peter, "Follow me."

Simon Peter turned about and saw John standing by. At once he asked, "Lord, what shall this man do?" But Jesus said, "Never mind about John's work; see that you follow me."

Forty days passed by, and during these days Jesus often spoke with his disciples about the kingdom of God. Still they did not understand that it would not be an earthly kingdom, like the kingdom of David had been. At last the time came for their farewell-meeting.

During this time Jesus appeared to his disciples and "when they saw him, they worshiped him: but some doubted. And Jesus came and spake unto them, saying, All power is given unto me in heaven and in earth. Go ye therefore, and teach all nations, baptizing them in the name of the Father, and of the Son, and of the Holy Ghost."

While they talked earnestly together, Jesus said, "John the Baptist baptized you with water, but you shall be baptized with the Holy Spirit in a few days." And some of the disciples asked, "Will you at that time restore the kingdom of Israel?" But Jesus said, "It is not for you to know the plans of the heavenly Father; but you shall receive power from heaven when the Holy Spirit comes upon you, and this power will cause you to witness boldly to me in Jerusalem, in all the country of Judah, in Să-mâr'-ĭ-ă, and in the farthest parts of the world. But do not go away from Jerusalem until the Holy Spirit is given to you."

While Jesus talked to them they were standing together on the Mount of Olives, and suddenly the disciples saw him being caught up into heaven. They watched until he disappeared from sight in bright clouds, after which they saw him no more. But still they stood gazing upward, hoping to catch one more glimpse of their departing Lord. Then two angels came and stood beside them, clothed in beautiful garments of white. They said, "Men of Galilee, why do you stand gazing up into heaven? This same Jesus who is taken up from you into heaven will come again in the same manner as he went away.''

JESUS ASCENDING TO HEAVEN

Then they left the place and went into Jerusalem, into a room up-stairs, where they met together with other friends of Jesus to wait and pray until the promised Comforter should be given to them. No longer were they sorrowing; for now great joy filled their hearts because they knew that Jesus was really the Christ.

The Work
of the
Apostles

PART SECOND
STORIES ABOUT THE APOSTLES
The Book of Acts; The Epistles; The Book of Revelation

STORY 1
THE SOUND AS OF A RUSHING WIND, AND WHAT IT BROUGHT
Acts 1:15—2:47

In a large upper room in Jerusalem one hundred and twenty men and women were meeting daily to pray. These were disciples and friends who had been with Jesus while he lived on earth. These were the ones he had commanded to wait in Jerusalem for the promise of the Holy Spirit from heaven. And they were obeying his command.

Although Jesus had now gone up to heaven, where they could no longer see him or hear his voice, yet these people were happy. They remembered his words, that power from heaven would soon be given to them. And they were waiting to receive this wonderful power which would come with the gift of the Holy Spirit.

Ten days passed by after Jesus ascended to heaven, and another feast-day came for the Jews. This was called the Pentecost, and religious Jews from other lands had come to worship at the temple. The city was once more crowded with strangers from different parts of the world.

In the large upper room the disciples and friends of Jesus were together praying at an early hour. Suddenly there came a sound as of a rushing mighty wind. They understood the meaning of the sound from heaven, for at that very time the Holy Spirit came upon them. And they saw resting upon each other's heads what seemed to be tongue-shaped flames of fire. Now they knew the promise of the Holy Spirit had been fulfilled, and they began to praise God. No longer were they afraid lest the enemies who had caused Jesus to be put to death should hear them, for the Holy Spirit gave them boldness and courage to tell others that Jesus was really the Christ.

Soon the noise of their rejoicing was heard in the street below, and crowds gathered to learn what had happened in the upper room. In the crowds were the strangers who had come from different countries far away, where people spoke in other languages. When they came

529

to the place they were surprized to hear these happy men and women praising God in the languages of their own countrymen. The strangers looked on each other with amazement, and asked, ''What does this mean? For these who speak to us in our own language are people from

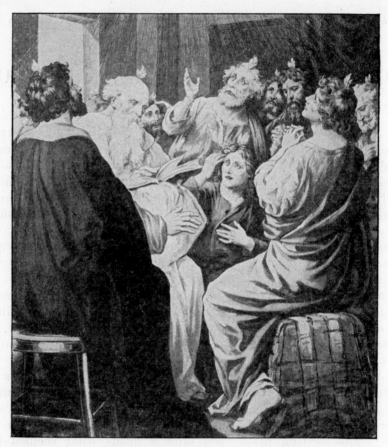

THE COMING OF THE HOLY SPIRIT

Galilee. How have they learned the language of the far-away nations where we were born?''

Others in the crowd were Jews who had lived in Jerusalem for a long time. They had been there when Jesus was crucified, and when he rose from the grave. They knew these Spirit-filled men and women were friends of Jesus. And they refused to believe in him. So they said to the strangers, ''These men who speak in your languages are drunk; pay no heed to them.''

Then Peter stood up boldly where all the crowd might see him, and said in a loud voice, "Ye men of Judah, and you who are strangers in Jerusalem, these are not drunk as you suppose. But on them God has poured out his Holy Spirit, as he promised in the prophecy of Jō'-ĕl, which reads thus in your Sacred Book: 'And it shall come to pass in the last days, says God, I will pour out my Spirit upon all people, and your sons and your daughters shall prophesy.' "

When Peter began to speak the people grew quiet and listened to his words. And he preached to them a great sermon, showing them how God had sent his Son, Jesus, into the world to be their Redeemer. But they had refused to receive him and had given him over to the Roman soldiers to be killed as a wicked person. Yet God had raised him from the dead on the third day, and had received him back to heaven. Quietly the people listened, and Peter preached on, explaining to them why the Holy Spirit had fallen upon the friends of Jesus that day. And at the end of his sermon he proved to them that God had made the Jesus whom they crucified both Lord and Christ.

Peter's words brought fear upon the people who stood listening. How guilty they felt! Now they cried out, "What shall we do?" And Peter replied, "Repent of the wrong you have done and be baptized in the name of Jesus Christ. Then God will forgive your sins and will give you the Holy Spirit as he has given us. For the promise of the Holy Spirit is given not only to us but to every one who shall believe on the Lord and be saved from sin."

Because of Peter's great sermon many people believed that Jesus is the Son of God. And on that day three thousand believers were added to the one hundred and twenty who first met to worship God in the upper room. These believers were baptized in the name of the Lord Jesus, and they, too, rejoiced greatly because they knew their sins had been forgiven.

By the power of the Holy Spirit the apostles now worked many signs and wonders in Jerusalem, and fear fell upon the people who saw and heard them. And every day more believers were added to their number, until their congregation became a great company of people.

Those who believed on Jesus sold their possessions and divided their money with those who were poor. And they met every day to praise God and worship him in the temple, and others who saw and heard them also believed. This was the beginning of the early Christian church, which is called in the Scriptures the "church of God."

STORY 2

THE CRIPPLED BEGGAR WHO RECEIVED A WONDERFUL GIFT
Acts 3:1—4:31

Just outside the gate called Beautiful which led into the temple sat a poor cripple who had never walked a step. From his babyhood he had always been a cripple, unable to move himself about. Now he was a grown man, forty years old, and every morning his friends carried him to the place where he lay just outside the Beautiful gate.

Because this poor man could not walk, he begged for a living. His friends carried him to the temple gate, where many people entered each day to pray. He believed that when these people saw him they would pity him and give him money. And they did.

One afternoon Peter and John went up to the temple to pray. As they were about to enter the Beautiful gate, the crippled beggar saw them. He called to them and asked for a gift of money, just as he had begged from every other passer-by. The two apostles stopped and turned to look on him. Seeing his pitiful condition, Peter said to the man, "Look on us!" And the cripple looked up, expecting to receive at least a small coin. But Peter said to him, "Silver and gold I do not have, but what I do have I give to you." Then with a tone of command he said: "In the name of Jesus Christ of Nazareth rise up and walk!"

With these words Peter took the surprized man by his right hand and lifted him up, and at once strength came into the feet and ankles that had always been helpless. Then the man sprang up and walked and leaped about, praising God. With Peter and John he went into the temple, and there he rejoiced aloud. The people who saw him walking and leaping for joy were amazed, because they knew he was the same beggar who had asked them for money when they entered the gate.

The happy man, wishing to express his great joy, then seized Peter and John, and while the three stood on Solomon's porch the astonished people gathered round to look on them. Seeing the people gather, Peter spoke to them and said, "Men of Israel, why do you wonder at this that has happened to the lame man? And why do you look so earnestly upon us, as though we by our own power or holiness made this man to walk?" He told them that the God of Abraham, of Isaac, and of Jacob, whom they called their forefathers, had glorified his Son Jesus, whom they had refused to believe. "Even in the presence of

Pilate, the Roman governor," said Peter, "you denied Jesus, when Pilate was determined to let him go. But you killed the Prince of life, this same Jesus whom God raised up from the dead, and of whom we are witnesses. And through faith in the name of Jesus this man who was always crippled now walks, and has perfect strength in the presence of you all."

The listening people were made sad to think they had not believed

PETER AND JOHN HEALING THE LAME MAN

in Jesus while he was with them. Peter, seeing their sorrow, said to them, "I know you did not realize what you were doing when you cried out in the mob to crucify the Lord of glory, neither did your rulers know; but God had showed by the prophets' writings how these very things would happen to his Son. And now, if you will repent of your sins, they will be blotted out. God will forgive them and you will be free from their guilt." These and more words Peter spoke earnestly to the listening crowd and many of the people believed in Jesus and were saved.

Soon the rulers of the temple, the chief priests, and other religious leaders who had caused Jesus to be put to death, heard about the healing of the lame man. And they heard Peter preaching to the wondering people who stood in the porch. For a while they listened, too, then they went away angry because Peter taught that Jesus had risen from the dead. They had paid the Roman soldiers much money to keep this marvelous thing secret and they were displeased to hear Peter and John boldly declare that God had raised up the man whom they had crucified. "This teaching must be stopped!" they cried, and in a little while they returned to take Peter and John off to prison.

On the next day these angered rulers brought their prisoners before the same wicked men who had tried Jesus, and these wicked men questioned Peter and John. First they asked, "By what power, or in what name, have you done this miracle?"

No longer was Peter afraid of these men. Now he was filled with the courage that the Holy Spirit had given him, and he stood up boldly to speak. "If you are examining us by trial because of the miracle that has happened to this man who was born crippled, I declare to you that in the name of Jesus Christ of Nazareth, whom you crucified, whom God raised from the dead, even by him does this man stand before you healed." The rulers looked on, amazed; for they saw the man who had been crippled standing with Peter and John, his face beaming with joy.

Not knowing just what to do, they dismissed the prisoners for a few moments and talked about the matter. They could not deny that a great miracle had taken place, and they marveled at the boldness of the apostles, who were unlearned men. They knew these apostles had been with Jesus, and they knew the same works Jesus did were being done by them. Although they had killed Jesus, now they saw they had not stopped his great work. Still they hoped to stop it, so they called the prisoners back and commanded them to teach no more in the name of Jesus.

But Peter and John would not promise to obey them. They answered, "Whether it will be right for us to obey you rather than God, judge for yourselves; for we can not keep from telling about the wonderful things that we have seen and heard."

The rulers threatened to punish them severely if they should catch them any more teaching in Jesus' name, and with such threats they let the men go free. And Peter and John returned to the company of believers, who were called disciples, to tell of all that had befallen them.

Instead of complaining about this persecution, the disciples knelt down to pray. They talked to God, and told him how the wicked rulers who had killed Jesus were threatening to punish them if they continued to preach about his resurrection from the dead. They did not ask God to protect them from the wrath of these wicked men, but they asked for more boldness, that they might continue to declare to all men the power of God in Christ Jesus, his Son. They asked God to help them work more miracles in the name of Jesus, even though this one had brought them into prison.

God was pleased with such a prayer. He caused the place where they were assembled to be shaken by his great power. And again the Holy Spirit came upon them, giving them more courage and boldness to preach the gospel.

STORY 3

THE STORY ABOUT TWO HYPOCRITES IN THE EARLY CHURCH
Acts 4:32—5:11

The people who now worshiped with the apostles numbered about five thousand, many times more than those one hundred and twenty who were together praying on the morning when the Holy Spirit was first given. This throng of believers met to worship God on the porch of the temple, called Solomon's porch, where Peter had preached after the lame man was healed.

In all this great number of people the selfish spirit was not shown. Some had little wealth, and others had none. Still others had plenty and enough to spare. Those who had plenty shared with those who had none, and every one's needs were supplied. Love in their hearts for their fellow men caused the rich to be kind to the poor, and to take care of them as if they were needy brothers.

Many of the rich sold their houses and their farms. Then they brought the money to the apostles to divide among the poor people who worshiped with them, that none should need to be hungry or left without shelter.

In the company of worshipers were a man and his wife whose names were Ăn-ă-nī'-ăs and Săpph-ī'-ră. These people saw the others bringing their money to the apostles and they decided to sell their property also. But they did not want to give all the money to the apostles.

Now, the tempter who came to Adam and Eve in the Garden of Eden whispered to this man and his wife. They listened, and he said:

"Sell the property if you wish, but keep back some of the money, and say that you are giving it all. Peter and the other apostles will believe that you have given all just as the others are giving their all, and they need not know you have kept back a part for yourselves." Ăn-ă-nī'-ăs and his wife thought the plan was a good one. They agreed together to tell the apostles they had brought all the money. And when the day came Ăn-ă-nī'-ăs hurried to the apostles, carrying his bag of gold.

HELPING ONE ANOTHER

Now it was wrong for them to keep back a part of the money, and then pretend to give all. God saw the desire in their hearts to deceive the apostles and appear very self-sacrificing, and he was not pleased.

Ăn-ă-nī'-ăs brought his bag of gold to the apostles and laid it down before them, saying he had sold his property and had brought the money to them. A guilty feeling stirred in his heart, but he looked at the apostles, expecting them to praise him for his self-denial. Instead

A MEDITERRANEAN SUNSET

Above the ancient harbor of Sidon, framed through the branches of the date palm, the grape, and the pomegranate, the sun is sinking into the Mediterranean. Out of this harbor, in the days of old, rode the purple-sailed cargo ships of the Phoenician merchant princes, who traded with distant countries. In the last year of Jesus' ministry, he visited the coasts of Tyre and Sidon. Here the healing of the Syrophoenician woman's daughter took place.

PETER PREACHING AT PENTECOST

of praising him, Peter looked squarely at him and said, "Ananias why has the tempter filled your heart with the thought to lie to the

THE SAD DEATH OF ANANIAS

Holy Spirit and keep back a part of the price? While the money was in your hands it belonged to you, and why have you thought to deceive us by pretending to bring all when you have really brought only a part? You are not lying to men, but to God."

When Ăn-ă-nī'-ăs heard these words he fell backward and died. And the people who were present feared greatly, because they saw what a terrible thing it is to try to deceive God. Some young men who were sitting near by rose up and took the dead man's body away to bury it.

Three hours passed by, and Săpph-ĭ'-ră, not knowing what had happened to her husband, came into the room where the apostles were staying. Peter saw her and knew she was Ăn-ă-nī'-ăs' wife. He called her to him, and she came forward, possibly expecting him to praise her for the self-sacrifice she and her husband had made.

But Peter did not look pleased. He asked, "Did you and your husband sell your property for this sum of money?" She saw the amount, and she answered, "Yes." Then Peter said, "How is it that you agreed together to tempt the Spirit of the Lord? The feet of the men who buried your husband are at the door, and they will carry you out also to your grave." Săpph-ĭ'-ră fell down before Peter when she heard these words, and died on the same spot her husband had died on. And the young men came in, picked up her body, and carried her out to bury her beside her husband.

Great fear came upon all the other people of the early church, and upon those who were not believers in Jesus. And every one was afraid to pretend to be numbered among the believers unless he really knew his sins had been forgiven.

———————•———————

STORY 4

WHEN PRISON DOORS SWUNG OPEN BY AN ANGEL'S TOUCH
Acts 5: 12-42

News of the apostles' teaching was now talked about on every street in Jerusalem, and even in the cities round about people were hearing how the mighty power of God was being shown through these fearless men. Daily more believers were being added to the church, until it numbered several more thousands.

And the great miracles performed by the apostles in the name of Jesus were also talked of everywhere. So wonderfully did the power of God to heal rest upon these men that sick folk were brought and laid in the streets where even the shadow of Peter passing by might fall upon them. And from other cities and towns sick people were brought, and people who were troubled by evil spirits; and every one was healed.

Now the wicked Jewish rulers were becoming more angry every day. They saw how the works of Jesus were steadily spreading farther and farther. They saw how the people were honoring these apostles and the Christ they taught more than they were honoring the Jewish rulers themselves. And they said, "We must do something at once to crush this new teaching out of the land." So they caught the apostles and threw them into prison, locking them securely inside. "Now," they said to each other, "we shall see what comes of their followers. Soon those crazy people will forget, and we shall be rid of this excitement."

Night came on, and the rulers went home to rest, believing they would soon see the end of this trouble. But while they slept an angel from heaven touched the iron doors of the prison and passed inside to speak to the apostles. He told them to return again to the temple and speak boldly to the people who met there. And he led them from the prison into the cool night air of the quiet street. Then he left them, and they went to their own homes to rest.

Early the next morning the high priest and his wicked counselors met together and prepared to conduct a trial. They sent officers to the prison to bring the apostles, but the officers returned alone. "We found the keepers standing before the prison doors, and the doors were tightly locked," they said; "but when we entered the room no one was there."

Now the high priest and the other rulers were perplexed. They wondered what had happened to the men whom they had shut up the night before. But while they were talking about the matter, some one came to tell them that the apostles were again in the temple, teaching the people as bravely as ever.

The rulers were afraid to seize the apostles roughly, for they knew the multitude who stood listening were friendly to these men and they thought the multitude might stone them if they knew of their wicked plans. So they sent officers to take them quietly and bring them to the council-room.

When the apostles came, the rulers looked angrily at them and asked, "Did we not strictly command you to teach no more in Jerusalem concerning this man Jesus? And now why is it that you fill all the city with your doctrine, telling the people that we are guilty of the blood of this man?"

But Peter and the other apostles stood up boldly, and said, "We ought to obey God rather than men. The God of our fathers raised up this Jesus whom you killed and hanged on a tree. And God has made of this same Jesus a Prince and a Savior, to give repentance to Israel and the forgiveness of sins. And we are witnesses of these things, and so also is the Holy Spirit whom God has given to them who obey him.''

When the rulers heard these words they were filled with fury, and they talked excitedly among themselves. They wanted to turn the apostles over to the Romans at once, or kill them some other way. Then one of their number, a more thoughtful man, stood up and asked that the apostles be dismissed from the room for a few moments. While they were outside he spoke to his fellows in words like these: ''Men of Israel, be careful how you deal with these men. Let them alone; if their work is of men it will finally come to an end of itself, but if it is of God you can not overthrow it, and if you try to do so you will be found to be fighting against God.''

Because this speaker was a very wise man, and much honored as a teacher of the law, the others listened to him and decided that it would be best to let the apostles live. But their anger against the apostles was not lessened, and they called them into the council-room once more and gave them severe beatings. Then they sent them away, commanding them to teach or speak in the name of Jesus never again.

With bleeding backs the apostles departed from the presence of the wicked rulers. But as they went they rejoiced because they were counted worthy to suffer for Jesus' sake. They knew their own sufferings were slight compared with the suffering which their master had borne for the sins of all men, and they did not expect to be treated better by these enemies than their master had been. Again they returned to the temple, and daily they continued to teach there and in the homes of the people concerning the Savior, Christ the Lord.

STORY 5

THE PREACHER WHO WAS STONED TO DEATH

Acts 6: 1—8: 2

'Gainst the cause of truth and right
Evil men will always fight,
Even killing those who dare
Gospel sermons to declare.
But God watches from on high
Those who live and those who die
For his sake; and he will bless
And reward their faithfulness.

The number of disciples, or believers in Jesus, had now reached many thousands, and among them were Jews from different parts of the world. Some were called Grecians because they lived in countries where the Greek language was used, which they also spoke, and others were called Hebrews because they used the Hebrew language and lived in Palestine.

There had been an unfriendly feeling between the Grecian Jews and the Hebrews for a long time. Now in this great company of believers in Jesus this unfriendly feeling tried to show itself. Among the poor widows it seems that the needs of the Grecian ones were being overlooked. Their Grecian friends saw this, and began to complain that they were not being cared for properly.

The apostles heard this complaint, and at once they called the multitude of believers together, and said: "It is not right that we should spend all our time looking after the needs of the poor. We must preach the gospel. There are other faithful men among you who can attend to this matter of caring for the needy ones. Choose out seven wise men who are filled with the Holy Spirit, and let them do this work, that we may have more time to pray and to preach."

This plan pleased all the people, both the Hebrews and the Grecians, so they chose seven faithful men to divide the money among those who had need. These men they brought before the apostles, who prayed and laid their hands upon them.

Stephen was the first man whom they chose for this work. Another man was named Philip. These two men were also preachers of the gospel. About the other five we hear but little.

From the first Stephen's great faith in God showed itself by the miracles he performed among the people. And he spoke boldly about Jesus to those who hated the believers, for the Holy Spirit gave him courage to do this.

In Jerusalem was a synagog where the foreign Jews met together to study the Scriptures. Here Stephen went to preach the gospel. And certain men who were leaders of the synagog argued against his teachings and tried to prove that Jesus is not the Christ. But they could not prove their argument, for God gave Stephen great wisdom to declare the truth about Jesus. When these evil-minded men saw that Stephen had spoken wisely they were angered, and at once they planned to destroy this faithful man.

Calling some friends who were not careful to speak the truth, they hired them to publish among the Jews that Stephen was teaching against the law of Moses, and was speaking evil words against the temple. As soon as the rulers and scribes heard this report they caught Stephen and dragged him into the council-room where the apostles had been tried. There they surrounded him, and questioned him about the things they heard.

Stephen was not afraid to speak bravely to these enemies of the truth and right. He talked very earnestly to them about their fathers who had lived long ago. He repeated to them the familiar story of

STEPHEN MAKING HIS DEFENSE

the Israelites, beginning with the time of Abraham. He showed them how their fathers had disobeyed God's laws and refused to listen to God's prophets, even when God had blessed them so much.

As Stephen talked, his face began to shine like an angel's. Those who stood in the council-room saw the heavenly light, but they gave no heed to it. When he told them about the sins of their fathers, the rulers grew angry. Their eyes flashed wickedly, and Stephen knew they were even then thinking how to kill him. Still he was not afraid. Looking up, he saw the heavens open and Jesus, the Savior, standing by the great white throne. God permitted him to see this wonderful glimpse of heavenly glory that he might have more courage to face his enemies. Then he said, "Behold, I see the heavens opened, and the Son of man standing on the right hand of God."

These words filled the rulers with great fury, and they rose from their seats, stopped their ears, and cried out against him. Then, like blood-thirsty animals, they rushed upon him and dragged him out of the council-room, and outside the city gate. Here those who had spoken false words against him took off their garments, threw them down at the feet of a young Pharisee named Saul, and picked up stones to hurl at Stephen.

But even here Stephen's courage did not fail. He raised his eyes toward heaven and prayed, "Lord Jesus, receive my spirit!" Then he knelt down, and while the stones struck his body he prayed, just as Jesus prayed when he hung on the cross—"Lord, lay not this sin to their charge." And after this he fell asleep in death, the first one to be killed by God's enemies in their efforts to destroy the church of God.

Some men who had known Stephen heard about his death, and they took up his mangled body and buried it tenderly. Then they mourned for him with loud and bitter cries, for they had loved this earnest young man who gave up his life to defend the gospel.

———•———

STORY 6

A MAN WHO TRIED TO BUY THE HOLY SPIRIT WITH MONEY
Acts 8: 1-25

In the city of Să-mâr'-ĭ-ă, about thirty miles north of Jerusalem, lived a man whose name was Simon. For a long time this man had made the people of Să-mâr'-ĭ-ă believe he was some great person. He would perform cunning tricks before them, which they could not understand. And they thought he had received power from God to do these things. But Simon was a very wicked man, and he had received power from Satan instead of from God.

One day a preacher came to Să-mâr'-ĭ-ă from Jerusalem. This preacher was Philip, one of the seven men whom the multitude had chosen to help care for the poor widows. No longer was he needed in Jerusalem to do this good work, for the multitude of believers were now scattered, and very few remained in Jerusalem with the apostles.

After Stephen's death the enemies of Jesus had grown bold and they had tried to destroy the new religion by troubling the believers. Some they had caught and thrown into prisons. Saul, the young Pharisee who stood by watching when Stephen was being stoned, now became one of the bitterest enemies. He went from house to house, searching for men and women who worshiped with the apostles, and when he found them he shut them up in prison. Because of these things the believers no longer met each day to worship in the temple, and many of them left Jerusalem and went to live in other cities.

The men and women who fled from Jerusalem did not run away to hide like cowards. They did not feel sad because they were believers in Christ. Everywhere they went they talked to other people about Jesus, and soon the new religion began to spread faster than ever. And so it was that Philip came to preach the gospel in Să-mâr'-ĭ-ă.

The people of Să-mâr'-ĭ-ă listened closely to Philip's preaching. They had never heard the gospel story before. Now they saw Philip work miracles among them in the name of Jesus, and they wondered at the great power God had given to him. Many of them believed in Jesus when they saw the sick and the lame healed through faith in Jesus' name. And they paid no more heed to Simon, whom they had thought to be a great man before Philip came, for now Philip was doing greater things than Simon had ever done.

Simon, too, came to hear Philip preach and to see the miracles he performed. He watched this preacher from Jerusalem heal the sick and cast out evil spirits. He saw him cause even the lame to walk. And he knew the power Philip had was greater than his own, so he joined the company of believers in Să-mâr'-ĭ-ă and was baptized with them. But all the while he had never repented of his sins and wickedness.

When the apostles in Jerusalem heard that Philip's preaching in Să-mâr'-ĭ-ă had caused many people to accept Jesus as the Savior, they sent Peter and John to visit them. And these two men came to tell them more about the power of God, for as yet none of the Să-măr'-ĭ-tăns had received the Holy Spirit. When Peter and John prayed for them and laid their hands on them, God gave the Holy Spirit to the Să-măr'-ĭ-tăn believers too.

Simon looked on with increasing wonder when he saw how Peter and John prayed and laid their hands on these people who received the Holy Spirit. He thought in his heart, "If only I had such power I might again seem to be a great man among these people. Perhaps I can persuade these visitors from Jerusalem to sell this power to me."

So he came to the apostles, saying, "I will give you money if you will sell me this power to lay my hands on whomever I please that they may receive the Holy Spirit."

But Peter looked at Simon and said, "You wicked person! May your money be lost with you if you think God's gifts can be bought. You do not have any part in this work, for your heart is not right in God's sight. Unless you repent of your sins and pray God to forgive your wicked thoughts you will be lost, for now you are bound fast with sin as with a chain."

Simon was frightened when he heard Peter's words. Even yet he did not understand, for he did not know how God could make his heart right. So he asked Peter to pray for him, that he might not be lost. But we do not know that he ever repented of his sins and turned to God.

After their visit in Să-mâr'-ĭ-ă, Peter and John returned again to Jerusalem, passing through other villages along the way and preaching the gospel to all who would listen. And all the while more believers were being added to God's church; for wherever people believed in Jesus as their Savior from sin they became members of the church of God.

———•———

STORY 7

PHILIP PREACHES TO A STRANGER ON A LONELY ROAD
Acts 8: 26-40

After Peter and John went back to Jerusalem, one day an angel spoke to Philip and told him to leave Să-mâr'-ĭ-ă too and go on an errand. Philip did not know just what the errand would be, but he rose up at once to obey the angel's command.

Along the dusty road he traveled, going south till he came to Jerusalem. Still farther south he went, not stopping to visit the apostles or any of his friends in the city. Now the road began to lead toward the desert of Gā'-ză, and few people went that way.

But Philip was not the only traveler on the road that day. Ahead of him, riding in a chariot, was a stranger who had come many, many miles to worship God at the temple in Jerusalem. This stranger was from the land of Ē-thĭ-ō'-pĭ-ă, and he was an officer of the queen of the country. He had heard about the true God and he wished to become a worshiper of that God. He had come all the long way from Ethiopia, and now he was returning again to his homeland.

God saw the desire in this man's heart to worship him in the right manner. He knew the rulers in Jerusalem would not help the man to understand the true religion, so he sent Philip on this errand to preach to the stranger. When Philip saw the chariot, God by his Spirit caused him to understand why he had been sent. So Philip ran to catch up with the chariot.

While in Jerusalem this Ē-thĭ-ō'-pĭ-ăṅ had bought a copy of the Scriptures to take with him to his own land. And as he rode along he read aloud from God's Book. When Philip came near he heard the man reading from the book of prophecy that Isaiah had written.

PHILIP TEACHING THE MAN FROM ETHIOPIA

Philip walked along beside the chariot and listened. Presently he asked, "Do you understand what you are reading?" The Ē-thĭ-ō'-pĭ-ăn looked up quickly, and seeing Philip, replied, "How can I understand when I have no one to teach me?" He then invited Philip to ride with him in the chariot and tell him the meaning of the strange words he had just read.

These are the words he read of Isaiah's prophecy:

"He was led as a sheep to the slaughter,
And as a lamb before his shearer is dumb,
So he opened not his mouth,
His story who can tell?
For his life is taken from the earth."

"About whom is the prophet writing?" asked the Ē-thĭ-ō'-pĭ-ăn, "is it of himself or some other man?" Then Philip began at that very scripture to preach to him about Jesus; for Isaiah had used those words to describe how Jesus would be treated by his enemies.

The story of Jesus was new to the Ē-thĭ-ō'-pĭ-ăn. He listened eagerly, and believed every word of this strange preacher who rode beside him in the chariot. He knew now that his long journey to Jerusalem had not been made in vain, for he was learning the very thing he had longed to understand.

As they rode along the highway they came to a place where there was water. The Ē-thĭ-ō'-pĭ-ăn thought at once of what Philip had told him about baptism, so he said, "See! here is water; why may I not be baptized?" Philip answered, "If you believe with all your heart you may be baptized just as others who believe." And the man replied, "I do believe that Jesus Christ is the Son of God."

At this he commanded the servant who drove the chariot to stop, and he stepped out with Philip and went down with him into the water. And Philip baptized him there.

When they were coming out of the water the Spirit of God caught away Philip, and the Ē-thĭ-ō'-pĭ-ăn saw him no more. But he went on his homeward journey rejoicing because he had found the true religion. Now he knew that his sins were forgiven through faith in Jesus' blood. And now he, too, could tell others about the gospel story.

After this had happened Philip came to a place called Ă-zō'-tŭs, and as he went he preached the gospel in every city along the way, until finally he came to Çæ-ṡă-rē'-ă, a city on the shore of the Mediterranean Sea.

———•———

STORY 8

THE WICKED PLAN THAT WAS SPOILED BY A VISION OF JESUS
Acts 9:1-20

Saul, the young Pharisee, was a Jew. Although his home was in another country, he had come to Jerusalem when a boy to study the Jews' religion, and now he was a very strict Pharisee. He believed in the law of Moses, and he thought the new religion of Jesus would destroy this law which God gave to Moses. Therefore he was angry with the believers in Jesus, and he wished to be rid of them all.

The chief priests and scribes were glad to have such an earnest young man as Saul take their part and defend their cause. They gave him permission to treat the disciples shamefully, hoping in this way to discourage others from accepting the new teachings. And so it was that

THE NORTH GATE OF JERUSALEM THROUGH WHICH SAUL NO DOUBT PASSED.
IT IS CALLED THE DAMASCUS GATE

Saul labored night and day working and planning how he might destroy the. church in Jerusalem. And because of his work the prison-houses were crowded with men and women who clung to their faith in Jesus, but no longer were there listening crowds standing in the temple to hear the apostles teach. Saul had indeed stopped the public worship of these people, and he thought he had done a good work.

About this time news came to Jerusalem that the religion of Jesus was spreading in other cities. Instead of destroying it, the enemies were only scattering it farther and causing it to increase faster than before. What should they do? Saul, the Pharisee, became more angry than ever. ''I will stop this crazy religion yet!'' he cried; and, rushing to the high priest, he asked permission to go as an officer to a Gentile city called Damascus and search among the Jews there for disciples of Jesus. He planned to kill them or bind them as prisoners and carry them back to Jerusalem. No doubt he hoped to visit every city and every village where the believers had gone to teach about Christ, and destroy the meetings as he had broken up the religious worship in Jerusalem.

The high priest wrote letters to the rulers of the synagogs in Damascus, telling them about Saul's purpose and commanding them to help Saul find the believers who might be in the city. These letters Saul took, and calling some friends he started at once on the long journey to Damascus. The road they traveled led north from Jerusalem and passed through numbers of villages and towns. By and by he came near to Damascus, the Gentile city where a large number of Jews had accepted the new faith.

Messengers from Jerusalem had already arrived to warn the disciples in Damascus about Saul's work. They told about his bitter hatred of believers everywhere. And they told also of his soon coming to Damascus with letters from the high priest to the rulers of the synagogs, commanding that every believer in Jesus should be punished or imprisoned. And the believers wondered what they should do, for they feared the wrath of this proud young man.

On the last day of that journey the company of riders from Jerusalem were nearing the great wall of Damascus when suddenly they stopped. A light from the sky, brighter than the shining noonday sun, had smitten them and struck them to the ground. And with the light came a voice from heaven, which only Saul understood though his companions heard the sound. This voice said, ''Saul! Saul! why are you persecuting me?'' Now Saul was greatly surprized. He had thought he was defending the true religion when he opposed the believers in

Jesus. And he cried out, "Who are you, Lord?" The voice answered, "I am Jesus of Nazareth, whom you are fighting against. It is hard for you to oppose me."

Like a flash of lightning Saul remembered how cruelly he had treated men and women who believed in this Jesus. He saw how wicked

SAUL STRUCK DOWN

he had been. Now he cried out, "What shall I do, Lord?" and Jesus answered, "Rise up and go into Damascus; there you shall be told what you must do." So Saul rose up; but he could not see which way to go, for the great light had blinded his eyes.

The men who were with Saul had also seen the light, but they were not blinded by its brightness. They, too, rose up, trembling with fright, and led him by the hand into the city. Here they took him to the house of a man whose name was Judas, and left him there.

Three days passed by, and Saul sat alone in dark blindness. He would neither eat nor drink, for his sorrow of heart was great. He saw himself a very wicked man, not a righteous person at all, though he was a famous Pharisee. Then one night God gave him a vision. In the vision he seemed to see a believer named Ăn-ă-nī′-ăs coming to put his hands on the blinded eyes that they might have sight again.

And sure enough, there was in the city of Damascus a believer named Ăn-ă-nī′-ăs. This man also had a vision from God. And in the vision he heard God's voice calling, "Ăn-ă-nī′-ăs!" He answered, "Here I am, Lord," and the voice said, "Rise up, and go to the street called Straight and ask at the house of Judas for a man called Saul, of Tarsus, the city where he was born, for this man is praying. And he has seen in a vision a man named Ăn-ă-nī′-ăs coming in and putting his hand on him, that he might receive his sight."

These tidings surprized Ăn-ă-nī′-ăs. He could hardly believe what he heard, for he knew of Saul, the great persecutor of believers everywhere. Now he exclaimed, "Lord, I have heard many things about this man, how much evil he has done to those at Jerusalem who believe in Jesus; and even here he has been given power to make prisoners of all the believers he can find." But God answered, "Go your way as I have commanded; for Saul is a chosen servant of mine to carry my name to the Gentiles and even before kings of the earth, as well as to the Jews. And I will show him how he must suffer great things for my sake."

Ăn-ă-nī'-ăs was no longer afraid to obey, for he believed the words God had spoken to him. So he rose up at once, and went out to search for Saul. And when he found the blind visitor in Judas' home he spoke to him kindly, saying, "Brother Saul, the Lord Jesus, who appeared to you on the road when you were coming to this city, has sent me that you might receive your sight, and receive the Holy Spirit." Then he placed his hands upon Saul, and what seemed to be scales fell from the blinded eyes of the stricken man.

Now Saul could see again, and he rose up to be baptized. He was eager to do the things that would please God, and no longer did he feel hatred in his heart to any one. His friends brought food to him, and when he ate of it, strength came into his body. Then he went to the synagogs, not to seize the believers in Jesus, but to worship with them. And he began at once to teach those who crowded to see him that Jesus is the Christ, whom God had sent to be the Savior of men.

STORY 9

HOW A BASKET WAS USED TO SAVE A MAN'S LIFE

Acts 9: 21-32; 22:17-21; Gal. 1:17-24

The Jews of Damascus were surprized when they found Saul in their synagogs worshiping with the disciples of Jesus. They were even more surprized to hear him preach boldly in the name of Jesus. They asked, wonderingly, "Is not this the man who imprisoned and even killed many people in Jerusalem because they believed Jesus is the Christ? We heard that he was coming to our city to persecute the believers here, and how is it that he now worships with them?"

But Saul continued to worship with the disciples, and every day he taught in the Jewish synagogs that Jesus is the Christ. Then he bade his new-found friends good-by, and went away into a country called Arabia. There he prayed much and studied the Scriptures until he understood the words of the prophets who had told about the coming Měs-sī'-ăh. Now he saw clearly that Jesus of Nazareth, whom he used to despise as a false teacher, is the very one of whom the prophets had written.

From Arabia Saul returned again to Damascus, and preached even more boldly than before. And the Jewish teachers who did not believe in Jesus were unable to prove that his teaching was wrong. When they saw that many of the Jews were beginning to accept the new religion, they became angry with Saul and planned to kill him. They set watchers by the gates of the high wall which surrounded the city, and commanded these men to kill Saul if he should try to escape through one of the gates. Then they determined to seize him before he could even try to get away.

But Saul knew about their plans, and so did his friends. These friends believed that God had much work for Saul to do before he should die, so they hid him until night darkened the city. Then they brought him to a building that stood on top of the great wall and let him down to the ground in a large basket. Once outside the city it was not difficult for him to find a place of safety.

But where should he go? Saul remembered his friends in Jerusalem—the chief priests and scribes and Pharisees. No longer would they be his

SAUL ESCAPING IN A BASKET

friends; for no doubt they had heard long ago that he had ceased to help them fight against the new religion. Three years had passed by and he had never yet brought any prisoners from Damascus as he had planned to do when he left them. No longer would they be his friends.

Then Saul thought of the ones whom he used to persecute in Jerusalem. Now he loved them and longed to worship with them. He longed to tell them how the love of Jesus had changed his wicked heart, taking away all the hatred that had made him their bitter enemy. So he came to Jerusalem and hurried to find the apostles and their unfaithful friends.

But the first meeting of Saul and the other disciples was not a happy one. The news of his conversion had never reached the ears of these people, and they were afraid that he was only pretending to be a disciple. They thought he might be planning to do more mischief to the work of God by acting friendly now. This was a sad time for Saul. He knew the disciples of Jesus had reason to be afraid of him; for they remembered how roughly he used to treat them, and even cause some of their number to be killed. He saw they did not know about the great change that had taken place in his heart and life; for now he loved them as brothers and sisters.

Then Saul found a friend in the kind-hearted man named Barnabas, who was also a believer. Barnabas listened to his story about the vision on the road to Damascus, and about the change this vision had caused in his life. And Barnabas felt sure that Saul was now a true believer in Jesus. So he brought him to the apostles, and told them to receive Saul kindly, for Jesus had spoken to him from heaven and had called him to be a follower, just as they had been called.

After this time the church in Jerusalem received Saul gladly, for they rejoiced because God had changed their enemy into a true friend. And Saul visited with Peter for fifteen days. During this time he went to the synagogs where he used to seize disciples and beat them. Now he taught there boldly in the name of Jesus. His old friends were amazed at his teaching, and soon they showed their displeasure toward him by planning to kill him as they had killed Stephen and others who believed in Jesus.

Saul knew about their ill feelings toward him; but he was willing to give his life for Jesus just as Stephen had done. God, however, had more work for Saul to do, so he appeared to him one day while he was praying in the temple, and told him to prepare to leave the city quickly, because his former friends would not believe that he had seen Jesus in a vision. God told Saul that he must be a preacher of the gospel to the people who lived in other countries, for Jesus was the Savior not only of the Jews but of the Gentiles, too.

After Saul had seen this vision the apostles heard about the plans of the Jews to kill him, so they took him away from Jerusalem and brought him to the city of Çæ-să-rē'-ă, on the sea-coast, where Philip had made his home. And from this place Saul took ship and sailed to Tarsus, the city in Asia Minor where he had been born. And after he left Jerusalem the excitement of the unfriendly Jews died out, and rest came to all the believers who had been troubled by these wicked men. During this time of rest and quiet the church continued to grow in numbers in every city and village where the gospel story had been told.

STORY 10

A SICK MAN HEALED, AND A DEAD WOMAN BROUGHT BACK TO LIFE

Acts 9: 32-43

When the disciples, or believers in Jesus, spoke of their fellow worshipers, they called them saints. For these men and women had hearts purified by faith in Jesus, and therefore they also lived holy lives, as true saints do.

The apostles at Jerusalem were pleased to hear that there were many disciples, or saints, in other cities throughout the land. Sometimes they visited them and encouraged them to serve the Lord.

One day while Peter was visiting the saints in Lỹd'-dă, a city near the Great Sea, he saw there a man named Æ-nē'-ăs who had been sick with palsy for eight years and unable to leave his cot. Peter looked with pity upon the poor man, and then he said to him, "Æ-nē'-ăs, Jesus Christ makes you well! Rise up, and make your bed."

Æ-nē'-ăs was glad to hear these words. He believed them, and when he tried to raise himself strength came into his feeble body at once and he was made perfectly well. This was the first miracle Peter performed at this place, and many people who knew Æ-nē'-ăs believed in the Lord. They met with the saints to worship God and to hear Peter preach the gospel story.

In a city called Joppa, not far from Lỹd'-dă, was another company of believers. Among them was a woman named Dorcas, who by her kind words and helpful deeds had brought gladness to many poor people. And every one who knew Dorcas loved her dearly.

While Peter was stopping with the saints in Lỹd'-dă, Dorcas fell sick. Soon her sickness became so severe that she died. Her death brought great sorrow to the hearts of her friends, for they thought they could not spare such a good woman as she had been. The saints in Joppa felt unwilling to have her taken away from them. They had heard that Peter was at Lỹd'-dă, and at once they sent for him to come quickly.

When the messengers returned from Lỹd'-dă, Peter was with them. They brought him to the house where Dorcas had died and led him to the room up-stairs where she was lying. Many of Dorcas' friends stood about him, weeping bitterly. And widowed mothers brought garments which Dorcas had made for them and for their children to show these things to Peter. They wanted him to understand how much they still needed this good woman to encourage them and help them out of their troubles.

Peter knew what Jesus would have done in a time like this. He knew Jesus was touched with the sorrow of others, and his own heart, too, was touched. He commanded every one to leave the room, and when he was alone with the dead body he prayed. Then turning toward the body he said, "Tabitha, arise!" And the woman opened her eyes. Seeing Peter, she sat up, and he gave her his hand and lifted her up. Then he called the saints and poor widows to reenter the room. How happy they were to see their dear friend alive once more!

The news of this wonderful miracle spread rapidly through Joppa, and many people became interested. When they heard the gospel preached they also believed in the Lord and were saved from their sins. And Peter stayed for a long time in this city by the Great Sea, stopping at the home of a man who was called Simon, the tanner.

STORY 11

THE GREAT SHEET LET DOWN FROM HEAVEN, AND WHAT IT TAUGHT

Acts 10:1—11:18

In the city of Çæ-să-rē'-ă, about thirty miles north of Joppa, lived a Gentile whose name was Cornelius. This man was an officer in the Roman army, having command of one hundred soldiers. He was called a centurion, but we today would call such an officer a captain.

Cornelius, although a Gentile, feared the true God and worshiped him. He also taught his household to serve God instead of idols. And because of his good example some of his soldiers forsook their idols and worshiped the God of the Jews. Cornelius had a kind heart, and he pitied the poor. Often he gave them offerings to help them when they were in distress. And every day he prayed to God as earnestly as did the religious Jews.

One afternoon while Cornelius was praying, suddenly an angel appeared in the room and called him by name. Cornelius was frightened to see the heavenly being, and he asked, "What is it, Lord?" The angel said, "Your prayers are heard in heaven, and your good works have been seen by God and are remembered by him. Now send men to Joppa and inquire at the house of Simon the tanner, who lives by the seaside, for a man named Simon Peter. This man will tell you what you ought to do.''

When the angel went away, Cornelius quickly summoned two of his household servants and one of his soldiers who also feared God. He told them about the angel's visit and command and sent them at once to Joppa on this errand. So the men started.

On the next day about noon the messengers from Cornelius were nearing Joppa. At this same time Peter had a vision from God. He

PETER'S VISION ON THE HOUSETOP

had become very hungry, and while dinner was being prepared he went up on top of the house to pray. Here in this quiet place he fell into a strange sleep. While he slept he saw coming down from the sky a great sheet caught at the four corners. This sheet was filled with all kinds of animals, both tame and wild. As it came down to the ground a voice from heaven said, ''Rise up, Peter! kill and eat.''

Peter looked into the sheet and saw that every kind of animal was in it. Now, the Jews were very careful to eat only certain meats, as the law of Moses forbade them to eat some kinds of animals. Those forbidden ones the Jews called "common" and "unclean." When Peter saw such animals in the sheet he said, "No, Lord, I can not eat, for I have never eaten anything that is common or unclean." Then the voice replied, "What God has made clean do not call common."

The sheet with its contents was lifted back to heaven and lowered the second time, and the third. Still Peter refused to touch the animals, because he was a Jew. Then the sheet disappeared out of sight, and Peter awoke. While he was wondering what this strange dream, or vision, might mean, the messengers from Cornelius stopped before the gate at Simon the tanner's house and inquired for Peter. And the Spirit of God spoke to him, saying, "Go down at once, for three men stand at the gate inquiring for you. Do not doubt, but go with them, for I have sent them." Now Peter was fully awake, and he promptly obeyed.

When he came down to the gate he said to the messengers, "I am the man for whom you inquire. What do you ask of me?" They told him about their master, Cornelius, who lived in Cæ-să-rē'-ă, and how the angel of God had commanded him to send for Peter. Then Peter invited them inside and he lodged them until the next day.

Peter took six men from Joppa, who were also believing Jews, and went with the servants of Cornelius to Çæ-să-rē'-ă. They followed the winding roadway by the seashore, and did not arrive at Cornelius' home until the fourth day after the angel had spoken to him. When they came they found a house full of people waiting to see Peter and to hear his words.

Never before had Peter been entertained in the home of a Gentile. Strict Jews refused to be on friendly terms with the Gentiles, because they knew such friendships had brought idol-worship among their people in other days. But the meaning of that vision on the housetop now became clear to Peter's mind, and he willingly stepped across the threshold of Cornelius' house to greet the Gentile family who waited so eagerly for his coming.

When Cornelius saw Peter he fell down at his feet to worship him. He thought Peter must be like a god, because the angel had told him to send for Peter to tell him how he might be saved. But Peter lifted him up, and said, "Stand on your feet; I also am a man like you." Then Cornelius led him into the crowded room where the relatives and friends of the family were waiting. All were Gentiles, but all had forsaken their idols to worship the God of the Jews. And they, too, were eager to be taught by Peter how they might serve the Lord more perfectly.

Peter looked into the faces of this company and said to them: "You know about the teaching of the Jews, how it is unlawful for one of them to be entertained by persons of any other nation. But God has showed me that I should not call any man common or unclean. Because of this I came to you as soon as I was sent for. And now I ask what has been your reason for calling me."

PETER TELLING CORNELIUS ABOUT JESUS

Cornelius told him that one afternoon while he was praying an angel suddenly appeared in the room and told him to send to Joppa for a man named Simon Peter, who was living in the home of Simon the tanner, by the side of the sea. The angel said that Peter would tell him what he should do if he wished to be accepted by God.

Peter answered, "Now I see that God accepts people of every nation who fear him and do righteous deeds." And at once he began to tell Cornelius and his friends about Jesus. He told them how Jesus had died to save people from their sins, and that whoever will believe in the name of Jesus might be saved. While he was talking, God gave the Holy Spirit to these listening Gentiles just as he had given the Holy Spirit to the believing Jews.

The six men who came with Peter were astonished when they saw how God gave the Holy Spirit to Gentiles also. They, like Peter, had always been strict Jews, and even after they believed in Jesus they supposed that salvation from sin was for the Jews only. But now they saw that God's plan of salvation was for people of every nation.

Then Peter asked, "Should we forbid these Gentiles from being baptized in the name of Jesus just as we have been, seeing that God has given them the Holy Spirit, too?" And he taught them about baptism, as Jesus had commanded; then he baptized all who believed.

After their baptism these Gentile believers urged Peter and his companions from Joppa to remain with them for a while and teach them more about Jesus. So they spent several days with Cornelius' household. Then they left Çæ-sȧ-rē'-ă and returned to Jerusalem.

News of the happening in Çæ-sȧ-rē'-ă had reached the church at Jerusalem before Peter and his companions arrived. Some of the believers were displeased to hear that Peter, always a strict Jew, had entered a Gentile home and had been entertained there. Then he told them of his strange dream, or vision, which God had given him on the housetop in Joppa one day, and about the coming of Cornelius' servants. He told also how God's Spirit had commanded him to go with these men because God had sent them. And he said that when he and his six Jewish companions came to Cornelius' house, they found a crowd of eager listeners who believed in the true God. These listeners, although Gentiles, received his words gladly, and God gave the Holy Spirit to them just as he had given the Holy Spirit to the believing Jews.

When the believers at Jerusalem heard Peter's story, they rejoiced because God's salvation was intended for people of every nation.

<hr />

STORY 12

HOW PETER'S COMING BROKE UP A MIDNIGHT PRAYER-MEETING

Acts 12

It was midnight; the streets were deserted and all was still. But even at this late hour not all the people of the city were fast asleep. A group of men and women were having prayer-meeting at the home of a widowed woman named Mary. For a long time they had been praying together, but still they continued to pray.

These people were believers in Jesus, and again they were being persecuted. Their persecutor now was the wicked king Herod Agrippa, whom the Roman government had appointed to rule the Jews. This Herod was a grandson of the Herod who killed all the little children at Bethlehem when Jesus was a baby, and a nephew of the Herod who caused the death of John the Baptist.

Wishing to please the Jews, King Herod became friendly toward the religious rulers of the people. And soon he heard about the hatred that the chief priests and scribes felt toward those who had accepted

Jesus as the Savior of men. So at once he began to trouble the believers. Seizing James, one of the apostles, he commanded his soldiers to kill this good man with a sword. And because the Jews were pleased, he decided to kill.Peter, too. So he caught Peter and shut him up in prison, intending to keep him until after the feast days, and then bring him out to have him put to death in the presence of the Jews.

The church was much distressed by the loss of James, and now when Peter was taken they felt that they could not spare him too. So they prayed daily for his release. But the days passed, and still Peter lay in the dreary prison. Finally the last day came and went but their prayers were yet unanswered. So the church met together in Mary's home to pray all night.

Peter was lying fast asleep, chained to two soldiers. Outside the prison door other soldiers stood on guard, for they knew that before another night Peter would be imprisoned there no longer. They knew about Herod's plan, but they did not know about the greater plan of God.

While Peter was sleeping, an angel from God came into the dark cell where he lay and touched him. The soldiers beside him did not see the angel, neither did they hear him speak to Peter, telling him to rise up. But Peter obeyed, and the heavy chains fell off his hands. Then the angel bade him to put on his sandals, and tie his girdle about his waist. Hardly knowing what he was doing, Peter prepared himself to leave the prison with the deliverer whom God had sent. Then the angel said, "Wrap your cloak about you," and when Peter had done so they walked out of the cell, past the guards, and on to the great iron gate which opened into the city street.

When they came to the iron gate it swung open easily to let them pass through, although it had been tightly locked. The angel led Peter through one street and then disappeared as suddenly as he had come.

Now Peter understood what had really taken place. He had moved as if in a dream; but now he was fully awakened. He decided at once to find some of his friends before leaving the city, and tell them what had happened.

To the home of the widowed Mary he went, for she had a son named John Mark who was a friend of Peter's. When he came to the door of the gate and knocked, the gate-keeper, a young girl named Rhoda, called, "Who is it?" At the sound of his answering voice she ran into the room where the people were kneeling in prayer and cried excitedly, "Peter is come! Peter is come!" So delighted was she that she forgot to open the gate and let him in.

But those who had been praying did not believe Rhoda's words. They said, "You are crazed."

Still she insisted that it was indeed Peter who had answered her call.

Then they said, "It must be his angel."

While this excitement was going on, Peter stood outside the gate and continued to knock. Soon some one ran out to see, and there was Peter, for whom they had all been praying so earnestly. Then he came into the room, and motioned for them to keep quiet while he told them how wonderfully God had answered their prayer.

Peter knew his danger was not yet over, so he bade the happy saints good-by and told them to send to James, a brother of Jesus, and to the other disciples word of his escape from prison. Then he went away to another place.

Herod, the king, was very angry when word came to him the next morning that his prisoner had escaped. He questioned the keepers, but they knew nothing about the visit of the angel. They had stood watching at their post, and the prison doors were tightly locked, but Peter was not to be found anywhere. To express his displeasure, the King ordered the keepers to be put to death.

Not long after this Herod himself died very suddenly. His death was a terrible punishment of God upon this enemy of his church. And from that time the disciples in Jerusalem were no longer persecuted so bitterly by their foes.

------&------

STORY 13

WHERE BELIEVERS IN JESUS WERE FIRST CALLED CHRISTIANS

Acts 11:19-30

With the persecution that came to the early church after the death of Stephen, men and women fled from Jerusalem to other cities and even to neighboring countries. And everywhere they went they preached about Jesus to the Jews whom they met.

Far to the north of Jerusalem, in the country of Syria, was a large city called Ăn'-tĭ-ŏch. Some of the believers went to this city and preached Jesus to the Gentiles as well as to the Jews. And many of the listeners were convinced that Jesus is the Christ, so they believed

in him as their Savior. Others, mockingly, called them "Christians,"
because they believed in Christ.

In those long-ago days news could not travel so fast as now, and
much time passed by before the church in Jerusalem heard about the
Gentile believers in this large city of Syria. When they did hear they
at once planned to send some one of their number to visit this Gentile

church and help those
who were preaching the
gospel. They chose Bar-
nabas, the kind-hearted
man who had befriended
Saul when all the other
disciples were afraid of
him. This Barnabas they
sent to visit Ăn'-tĭ-ŏch.

After many days he
came to the Syrian city
and met the believers
there. And when he saw
h o w wonderfully God
had saved that large
company of heathen Gen-

PAUL AND BARNABAS

tiles who came to believe in Jesus, he was glad. He urged them to cling
to this new faith, even though they might have to suffer persecution.
And as he preached to them, others, who came to listen to this stranger
from Jerusalem, became interested and finally trusted in Jesus as their
Savior, too.

When Barnabas saw that the Gentile church was growing into a
vast company of people, he longed to have more helpers. Then he
remembered the young man named Saul whom he had befriended at
Jerusalem. He knew that Saul was called of God to preach to the
Gentiles, and that he had gone from Jerusalem to his home city. That
city, called Tarsus, was not far from Ăn'-tĭ-ŏch, so Barnabas decided to
hunt for Saul and ask him to come to Ăn'-tĭ-ŏch to preach there to the
Gentiles.

Saul was glad to see Barnabas again, and he consented to go with
him to Ăn'-tĭ-ŏch. For a whole year they lived together in this Gentile city, preaching the gospel and encouraging those who believed in
Jesus.

Then certain men came from Jerusalem to visit this church. These
visitors were men whom God caused to understand what would happen

in the future. They told the church at Ăn'-tĭ-ŏch that a famine was coming in all the lands, when food would be scarce and many would suffer because they had nothing to eat. Not long afterwards this came to pass, and the church in Ăn'-tĭ-ŏch heard that their fellow believers in Judea were in need. They planned to send help to them. Each man gave an offering, as much as he could spare, and the whole amount was put together. Then the church chose Barnabas and Saul to carry this offering to the saints at Jerusalem.

Mary, the widowed mother of John Mark, at whose home the midnight prayer-meeting was held, was a relative of Barnabas, and these visitors from Ăn'-tĭ-ŏch were doubtless entertained in her home. When their errand was finished and they made ready to return again to Ăn'-tĭ-ŏch, they invited John Mark to go with them. And because this young man wished to work for the Lord he gladly bade his friends good-by and joined Barnabas and Saul. In later years this young man became very useful as a helper to those who preached the gospel in heathen lands. And finally he wrote the "Gospel According to Saint Mark."

———————•———————

STORY 14

THE FIRST MISSIONARIES IN THE EARLY CHURCH
Acts 13:1—14:7

The church in Ăn'-tĭ-ŏch grew in numbers until there were many who were called Christians in that city. And God caused the teachers in the church to understand that the time had come when Barnabas and Saul (who from the time of this journey was called Paul, by which name we shall hereafter know him) should begin the great work of preaching the gospel to the Gentiles, not in cities where other disciples lived, but in far-away countries where few people understood about the true God. And so it was that these two men, taking with them John Mark, the young disciple from Jerusalem, started on their first missionary journey.

The Island of Cyprus, lying in the Great Sea, was the first stopping-place of these missionaries. Here they visited two cities, called Săl'-ă-mĭs and Pā'-phŏs, and preached Christ. While they were preaching in the latter city the Roman governor who lived there sent for them. This governor, Sĕr'-gĭ-ŭs Paulus by name, desired to hear the word of God and listened carefully while the missionaries talked to him. He was almost ready to believe that Jesus is indeed the Christ, when a wicked man began to talk to him and warn him against the missionaries.

Just as the Holy Spirit gave wisdom to Peter, causing him to know when Ăn-ă-nī'-ăs and Săpph-ī'-ră were trying to deceive him, so now the Holy Spirit caused Paul to know the evil purpose of this wicked man. And with great boldness Paul spoke to him, saying, "Child of the evil one, and enemy of all righteousness, will you never cease trying to oppose the right way of the Lord? Because of your wickedness the hand of God is laid upon you now and you shall be made blind for a certain time, not seeing the light of day."

As soon as Paul had spoken the man became blind, so that he could not see which way to go, and he called for some one to lead him by the hand. When the governor, Sĕr'-ġĭ-ŭs Paulus, saw what had happened he was astonished, and at once he believed in the power of God and in the name of Jesus, his Son.

After the Roman governor believed in Christ, the missionaries went on their way, taking ship for the city of Pĕr'-gă, in the country of Asia Minor. Here John Mark left them and returned to his home in Jerusalem, while Barnabas and Paul journeyed on to another city called Ăn'-tĭ-ŏch.

In this Ăn'-tĭ-ŏch they found a Jewish synagog, so they came on the Sabbath-day to talk with the Jews who worshiped there. The rulers of the synagog, seeing they were strangers, invited them to speak, and Paul began to tell them the gospel story. When he had finished, the Jews left the synagog, and many of them were not pleased with his words. But some Gentiles had been listening, and they came to the missionaries and urged them to continue preaching the good news of salvation from sin. Some Jews also were friendly, and they, with these Gentiles, followed Barnabas and Paul, desiring to hear more about the gospel.

On the next Sabbath-day a great company of both Jews and Gentiles met to hear the missionaries tell of Jesus. But the Jewish leaders were filled with thoughts of envy when they saw how eager the Gentiles were to listen to these men and they began to speak unkindly about the missionaries, trying to turn the people away from them. Paul and Barnabas knew of their evil thoughts, and they said, "It was necessary that the word of God should have been spoken first to you; but we see that you will not believe, for you do not count yourselves fit to receive everlasting life through Jesus. Now we will turn from you and preach to the Gentiles, who are eager to hear our message. For God has commanded us to bear the light of salvation to the Gentiles, even in the farthest places in the world."

When the Gentiles heard these words they were glad, and many of them afterwards became believers in Jesus. So a church was raised up in this Ăn'-tĭ-ŏch, too, and the missionaries taught the believers more about God's words.

But the Jews were not content to let these teachers worship in peace with the Gentile believers. They stirred up a bitter feeling in the hearts of the city rulers toward Barnabas and Paul, and started persecuting them. Then they commanded them to leave the city, calling them trouble-makers and other unkind names. But the missionaries knew they were doing only what was right and pleasing to God, so they went on their way joyfully; for the Holy Spirit comforted them when they were being persecuted.

Their next stopping-place was in the city of Ī-cō'-nĭ-ŭm. Here a great company of both Jews and Gentiles believed in Jesus, and were saved. For a long time the missionaries stayed here preaching the gospel.

But there were enemies in this city also. Some Jews who did not believe talked to their Gentile neighbors and told them untruthful things about the missionaries. These false stories caused the Gentiles to dislike Barnabas and Paul, and the feeling of dislike grew until finally the enemies planned to stone the missionaries just as Stephen had been stoned at Jerusalem.

Barnabas and Paul heard about the wicked purpose of their persecutors, and they fled from the city, going to another town, called Lўs'-tră, to preach the gospel there also.

STORY 15

HOW IDOL-WORSHIPERS IN LYSTRA TREATED BARNABAS AND PAUL

Acts 14: 8-28

The people of Lўs'-tră were idol-worshipers. Never before had they heard the story of the gospel and many of them did not know about the true God of all the earth.

When Barnabas and Paul began to preach the gospel in the streets, their words sounded strange to these heathen people. They paid little heed to the preaching until after they had seen the wonderful miracle which Paul performed upon a cripple. A helpless cripple sat near by listening intently while Paul was preaching about Jesus, and when Paul noticed him he knew the poor man had faith to be healed. He looked on the man and cried with a loud voice, "Stand upon your feet!" With a leap the cripple rose to his feet and began to walk about like a well person. And the people were amazed, for they had never seen such a miracle before. Now they crowded round to look in wonder upon the missionaries, and they talked rapidly in their own language, saying, "The gods have come down to us in the form of men!" Paul and Barnabas could not understand what they were saying, for they used the speech of their own country instead of the Greek language which Paul had been using while he preached to them.

Excitement seemed to increase all the while, and presently Paul and Barnabas saw the men leading oxen to sacrifice, and bringing wreaths of flowers with which to decorate their visitors. Then the missionaries knew these heathen people had supposed they were gods come down to earth, and were preparing to offer sacrifices to them.

The Greeks worshiped two gods called Jupiter and Mĕr'-cū-ry, and the people in Lўs'-trā worshiped those gods, too. Now, they believed that Barnabas was Jupiter, and that Paul was Mĕr-cū'-rĭ-ŭs. And they called their priests from the temple of the gods to come and offer sacrifices to these men.

A feeling of horror came over Barnabas and Paul when they knew this. They rushed among the crowded throng and tore their clothes, crying out, "Sirs, why are you doing this? We also are men, like you are, and we have come to preach that you should turn away from idols to serve the living God who made the heavens, the earth, and all things. It is this living God we preach, who gives us rain from heaven, and who causes our food to grow in the fields."

At first the people would not listen to Paul and Barnabas, but finally they were persuaded to cease from their purpose. Although they understood the Greek language, they did not understand about the true God, for their minds were filled with thoughts of idol-worship. Only a few who lived in that city received the gospel gladly and were saved.

When the missionaries had been in Lўs'-trā for some time, the wicked Jews in Ī-cō'-nĭ-ŭm heard that they were preaching about Christ to the idol-worshipers in this city. So they sent men to Lўs'-trā to tell untrue things about the missionaries. Many of the people believed these false words and caught Paul and threw stones at him until he fell down as if he were dead. They seized his bleeding body and dragged it outside their city, then returned to their homes again.

But the believers stood about Paul's body, weeping. Presently they saw it move, and they knew their dear friend was not really dead. Soon Paul rose up and walked with them back to the city. On the next day he and Barnabas went away to another place, called Dĕr'-bē, and here they preached the gospel just as courageously as before Paul had been stoned.

After spending some time in Dĕr'-bē, and seeing many people turn to the Lord, the missionaries bade them good-by and started on their homeward journey. As they went they visited the same places where they had been before, and spoke encouraging words to those who believed in Jesus. And finally they came back to Ăn'-tĭ-ŏch, in Syria, the place from which they had started on this missionary journey. Here they met with the church and told how God had blessed his word as they preached to the Gentiles in far-away cities. They told about the believers in those cities who were worshiping the true God and honoring Jesus as the Son of God. And the disciples in Ăn'-tĭ-ŏch rejoiced to hear these good tidings.

STORY. 16

A PUZZLING QUESTION, AND HOW IT WAS ANSWERED
Acts 15:1-34

After Paul and Barnabas had returned from their missionary trip, some visitors came to the church at Ăn'-tĭ-ŏch from Jerusalem. These men were Jews, and they had never yet understood how Gentiles can be saved the same as Jews, without obeying the commands that Moses had given to the Israelites.

We remember that the law which God gave Moses to write in a book was intended for the Israelites, or Jews, only. The Gentiles had never kept the law, and many of them knew nothing about its teachings. This law had no power to save the people who obeyed it; the purpose of it was to separate people who worshiped God from those who worshiped idols. Without the law the Jews would have been as ignorant of the true God as were the Gentiles, while with it they could prepare themselves to receive the Mĕs-sī'-ăh, whom God had promised to send into the world, for many passages in it spoke of him.

These visitors from Jerusalem looked unkindly upon the Gentile believers and said, "Except you keep the law of Moses just as we do you can not be saved."

Paul and Barnabas had been among many Gentile Christians, and they had seen how these people received the Holy Spirit the same as did the Jews though they knew little or nothing about Moses' law. So these missionaries told the men from Jerusalem that they were mistaken, for Gentiles could be saved without keeping the law.

This question was a serious one with every person who had been a strict Jew. A vision on the housetop was necessary in order to show Peter that Gentiles might be saved as well as Jews. And there were many other strict Jews who had seen no housetop visions. These were the Jews who troubled the Gentile believers.

Finally it was decided by the church in Ăn'-tĭ-ŏch that Paul and Barnabas should go, with certain other teachers, to visit the apostles in Jerusalem and talk with them about this matter. So the company started out, and as they went they visited other churches along the way and told about the success of the first missionary journey in far-off lands. And everywhere the disciples rejoiced to hear how God had blessed the Gentiles who believed in him.

In Jerusalem the brethren from Ăn'-tĭ-ŏch were received kindly by the apostles and the other teachers in the church. And soon they told why they had come.

When their errand was made known, some of the teachers who, like Paul, had been strict Pharisees before they believed in Jesus, rose to talk. These men had not, like Paul, seen that believers in the true God and in his Son, Jesus, no longer needed to keep the law of Moses. They did not understand Jesus' teaching, that true religion shows itself in a pure life, and that people who know nothing about Moses' law can live pure and holy without keeping that law as did the Jews.

Peter listened with the other apostles and with the visitors from Ăn'-tĭ-ŏch to the speech of these Pharisees who believed in Jesus. When they had finished, others talked, and finally Peter told about his experience at Cornelius' home, in Çæ-să-rē'-ă, where many Gentiles received the gospel and were baptized. Then Barnabas and Paul told of their long journey in Gentile countries, where many turned from idol-worship to believe in the true God and in his Son, Jesus.

James, the brother of Jesus, stood up as the last speaker, and every one listened quietly for they knew he had received wisdom from God to speak to them. He urged them to cease troubling the Gentile Christians about the keeping of Moses' law. He said, however, that they might write a letter to the Gentile believers, telling them to be careful not to do certain things which they had always done while they were worshiping idols.

James's advice pleased all the assembly, and the apostles and teachers in the church at Jerusalem decided to write such a letter and send it by Paul and Barnabas to the Gentile Christians in Ăn'-tĭ-ŏch. This they did, and they also sent two of their own preachers, men named Judas and Silas, with the missionaries.

A large audience of eager-faced people greeted the company when it arrived from Jerusalem. And they listened carefully to the reading of the letter that the apostles had written and sent by these men. When they heard that they would not be demanded to live like the Jews in order to please God, they rejoiced greatly. And they continued to worship God with pure hearts, obeying the teachings of the gospel.

Judas and Silas, the men who came with Barnabas and Paul, spoke encouraging words to the believers, and urged them to cling to their faith in Jesus. Then, after certain days, Judas bade them good-by and returned again to Jerusalem. But Silas chose to remain with the church in Ăn'-tĭ-ŏch.

———•———

STORY 17

A CALL FOR HELP FROM A FAR-OFF LAND

Acts 15: 36—16: 15

One day Paul said to Barnabas, "Let us go again to visit the brethren in the Gentile countries." Barnabas was willing, so they arranged to start at once.

Now, John Mark had come to Ăn'-tĭ-ŏch again and wished to go with them on their second journey. He had started with them on their first journey but had turned back; so Paul did not care to take him this time. Barnabas, however, thought it would be well to take the young man, even tho he had turned back the first time. So he took Mark for his companion and Paul chose Silas, the preacher from Jerusalem, to go with him.

Barnabas and Mark went to the Island of Cyprus, while Paul and Silas went farther on, to the churches in Asia Minor. When they came to Lўs'-tră, the town where Paul had been stoned, they found a young man named Timothy whose father was a Gentile, though his mother was a Jew. This young man was an earnest believer in Jesus, and Paul was pleased with him.

Timothy joined Paul and Silas, going from Lўs'-tră to other cities where the gospel had been preached. And he continued with Paul for a long time, loving him as a father. Years afterwards, when Paul was shut up in prison he wrote beautiful letters to Timothy, showing how great was his love for this faithful young man.

The missionaries did not stop at every place to preach, because the time had not yet come when the people were ready to receive the gospel. The Holy Spirit caused the missionaries to understand this, and they passed on to other places.

Finally they came to Trō'-ăs, a city that was built on the seacoast where ships came from countries even farther away from Jerusalem. Those countries had never been visited by one who knew the gospel. One night while the missionaries were in Trō'-ăs, Paul had a vision. He saw in his dream a man standing on the shore of the country across the water from Trō'-ăs and calling. He was looking earnestly at **Paul**, and crying, "Come over to my country, and help us!"

Paul knew from the appearance of this man that he belonged to the country of Măç-ē-dō'-nĭ-ă. When he awoke from his dream he told his companions about the vision, and they believed, as he did, that God wanted them to cross over to Măç-ē-dō'-nĭ-ă and preach the gospel there. So they bought passage on the first ship that sailed from Trō'-ăs to Măç-ē-dō'-nĭ-ă, intending to preach the gospel to the heathen people who lived there.

Now another disciple, a doctor named Luke, joined Paul's company, and sailed with him to Măç-ē-dō'-nĭ-ă. This Luke afterwards wrote the "Gospel According to Saint Luke," and also the "Acts of the Apostles," both of which are found in the New Testament.

The first city of Macedonia which they visited was Philippi. Here they did not try to find the man whom Paul saw in his dream, calling for help. They knew the vision was meant to teach that many people were needing to know about Jesus, and they believed God had sent them to preach to all who would listen.

In this city there were only a few Jews. They had no synagog, but the missionaries found a place outside the city where people met together by the riverside on Sabbath-days to pray. So on the first Sabbath they went down to the riverside.

Only a few people were there and they were women. But Paul and his companions sat down and taught them more about the true God. Paul told them about the great gift that God had sent to men in his Son, Jesus. And while he talked, one woman, named Lydia, believed his words about Jesus and knew that her sins were forgiven. Then she was baptized in the name of Jesus. Her household also listened to the gospel and received it gladly.

Lydia, the first Christian convert in this far country, now invited

Paul and his companions to lodge in her house. She was a rich woman and she showed her gratitude to the missionaries by caring for them while they stayed in her home city.

———•———

THE PRAYER-MEETING IN PRISON, AND ITS HAPPY ENDING
Acts 16:16-40

One day a mob of angry people led two men down the streets of Philippi to the city prison. These men were wounded and bleeding from the severe beating they had just received in the public square. As they were being half dragged along by the leaders of the mob, every step caused them greater suffering. Finally they reached the prison, and the jailer, seeing the crowd, quickly unlocked the door and thrust the two wounded men inside.

These two men were Paul and Silas, the Christian missionaries to Philippi. They had done nothing wrong, but because they had done right they were being punished by the heathen people. And this is how it happened:

As Paul and Silas and their other companions walked through the streets on their way to the riverside to pray, a slave girl followed them one day, calling to every passer-by, "These men are servants of the Most High God, and they have come to show us the way of salvation!" And every day after that time she watched for the missionaries to pass that she might follow behind and cry out to others in this manner.

This slave-girl had an evil spirit dwelling in her, which caused her to know that the missionaries were true men of God. Satan and all his evil spirits know every one who loves and worships God. They know the power of God is greater than theirs, but they try to bring trouble upon the people who serve God. This slave-girl was controlled by the evil spirit, which caused her to tell people what would happen in the future. Many believed in her, and because of this they would often come to ask her questions. And always her masters would demand them to give money before she answered their questions. In this way the men who owned her for a slave became very rich.

Paul felt sorry for this poor slave-girl. One day while she was following him and his companions he turned about and said to the evil spirit that was in her, "I command you in the name of Jesus

Christ to come out of this girl.'' Immediately the evil spirit obeyed. and the girl was set free from his awful power. But no longer could she tell about future happenings; for without the evil spirit she could not do this.

The masters of the slave-girl were angered when they found out that their hopes for further gain from her fortune-telling were gone. They asked what had taken place, and when they heard what Paul had done they seized him and Silas and dragged them before the rulers of the city, saying, ''These men, being Jews, are causing great trouble in our city by teaching strange customs which we Romans can not receive.''

The people of Philippi objected to the teaching of such new religions in their city. When they heard the complaints made against Paul and Silas the rulers at once commanded that these trouble-makers should be cruelly beaten and imprisoned. And so it was that the missionaries were beaten until the blood flowed freely down their wounded bodies, and in this condition they were dragged off to prison.

Before the mob departed the leaders commanded the jailer to keep the prisoners safely, and he, supposing Paul and Silas must be dangerous men, cast them into an inner room and fastened them securely by putting their feet in stocks. Here he left them alone in the dark, ill-smelling room, to suffer from.their wounds.

But Paul and Silas were not like other prisoners. They did not complain because they were treated so cruelly. They did not murmur because they had been wrongfully punished. As the hours passed by they talked to each other about God, and about his great love. Finally they began to pray, and far into the night their voices could be heard in the outer prison, singing songs of praise to the great God who loved them so much.

The other prisoners could not sleep. They had seen these two men dragged into their prison that day. They had seen their bleeding backs and suffering faces. Now they could not understand why these prisoners could be so happy, and they listened to the songs of praise and to the prayers of Paul and Silas.

At midnight suddenly the foundations of the prison began to shake in a great earthquake, and all the tightly locked doors of the prison swung open. Even the stocks which held the feet of Paul and Silas were unfastened. The jailer heard the great noise when the earthquake shook the prison, and he sprang out of bed. Seeing the doors flung open, he supposed the prisoners had all escaped. He knew the rulers would kill him if he allowed one man to escape from the prison.

Now he believed all had gone, and quickly drew his sword to kill himself rather than have the wicked rulers torture him to death.

THE JAILER WITH PAUL AND SILAS
AFTER THE EARTHQUAKE

But Paul and Silas saw what the jailer was about to do, and Paul cried out through the darkness, "Do not harm yourself! We are all here!" Then the jailer called for a candle, and rushed into the prison. There he saw all the prisoners, with Paul and Silas among them.

Now the jailer was sure these men were not dangerous. He believed they were good men, who really taught the way of the true God, just as the slave-girl had cried. So he ran to them, tremblingly, and fell down at their feet, crying, "Sirs, what must I do to be saved?" And there in the prison Paul talked to the jailer and the others who stood by, telling them about Jesus Christ, the Savior of all men. And he said, "If you will believe on the Lord Jesus Christ, you shall be saved."

This glad news brought joy to the jailer's heart, and he believed the message of salvation. That very night he was saved, and all the others in his household also turned to God. Now they took Paul and Silas into the house and washed their wounds, and bound them with clean cloths. Then they gave these two prisoners food, and entertained them as guests instead of fearing them as dangerous men. And before it was day the jailer and his household were baptized in the name of Jesus by these Christian missionaries.

When the rulers heard what had happened at the prison that night they sent word for Paul and Silas to be set free. But Paul answered, "The rulers beat us publicly, although we were Romans and had not been condemned by the law; now they must come themselves to tell us that we may go free." These words frightened the rulers. They did not know that Paul and Silas were Romans, and the law forbade any ruler to punish a Roman in this manner. They came quickly to the jailer's house and begged Paul and Silas to leave the city.

Before going away from Philippi, the missionaries returned to Lydia's house, to speak words of comfort to the other Christians; then they bade them good-by and went to another place. Years afterward Paul wrote a letter to the church in Philippi, and that letter we have in our Bible today, called the "Epistle of Paul to the Philippians."

STORY 19

HOW THE GOSPEL WAS FIRST PREACHED IN OTHER CITIES OF MACEDONIA

Acts 17:1-15

Paul and Silas were not discouraged when they left Philippi. They rejoiced because they had been chosen by the Lord to carry the glad news of salvation to heathen people. They hurried on to other towns and cities to tell about Jesus.

In a large city called Thĕss-ă-lō-nī′-că they found a synagog of the Jews, for many Jews lived in that place. Here they went each Sabbath-day to teach the people the gospel story. And some of the Jews who listened were convinced by Paul's preaching that Jesus is really the Savior. Also many Greeks, both men and women, received the gospel gladly.

But the Jews who refused to believe in Jesus were jealous of the missionaries, because many people listened to their teaching. They decided to get rid of Paul and Silas, so they gathered a company of rough men and made great disturbance in the city. Then they called at the home of one believer, named Jā′-son, and searched his house trying to find the missionaries. But Paul and Silas were not there. Because they could not find these men they dragged Jā′-son before the rulers of the city and cried out, "These men who have turned the world upside down have come to our city, and Jā′-son has received them into his house. They are teaching things contrary to the law of the Romans, saying that another is king, even one called Jesus."

The rulers were troubled by these words, but they did not punish Jā′-son severely. However, the believers who lived in that city feared that greater troubles might happen soon if Paul and Silas remained, so they sent them away by night to another place, called Bĕ-rē′-ă.

In this second city the missionaries found another Jewish synagog, so they met with the Jews on the Sabbath-days to tell them about the Savior, who had come just as the prophets had foretold he should. These Jews listened closely to the words of Paul and Silas. They looked into the books of the prophets to see whether the missionaries had spoken truthfully. And many of them believed, for they read the words that the prophets had written long years before, concerning Jesus, the Mĕs-sī′-ăh. Many Greeks also believed, and a large congregation of believers met to hear the gospel story.

By and by the wicked Jews in Thĕss-ă-lō-nī′-că heard that Paul and Silas were preaching in Bĕ-rē′-ă. They sent at once to make trouble there. But the believers there cared for the missionaries, hiding them from the angry men who sought their lives. Then they sent Paul away at once to another city, but Silas and Timothy remained to encourage the Christians in that church.

From Bĕ-rē′-ă Paul left the country of Măc-ĕ-dō′-nĭ-ă, and went into Greece. Here he entered a large city called Athens, and waited for the coming of Silas and Timothy.

PAUL TELLS THE WISE MEN OF GREECE ABOUT THE UNKNOWN GOD
Acts 17:16—18:23

While Paul waited in Athens for his companions, Silas and Timothy, he walked about the streets and saw many idols standing here and there. He saw that the people of this city worshiped many differ-

PAUL PREACHING ON MARS HILL

ent gods. They had even built an altar to the Unknown God.

There were Jews in this city also, and Paul visited their synagog to speak to them about Christ. In the crowded streets he met some thoughtful, earnest men to whom he spoke daily about the gospel. Others gathered round, curious to hear the conversation. When they heard Paul speaking about Jesus and about the resurrection from the dead they believed he was bringing tidings to their city of a strange god from some other land.

In this city was a place called Mars Hill. Here important matters were discussed, and the wisest men of Greece met on this hill. They brought Paul here and asked him to tell about this new doctrine of which he spoke so earnestly on the streets. Then Paul rose up before all the wise men and said: "I saw an altar which you have built to the Unknown God. Of this God I wish to tell you now, for it is he who has made the world and all things in it. He is Lord of heaven and earth, and does not dwell in temples that are made by men. He

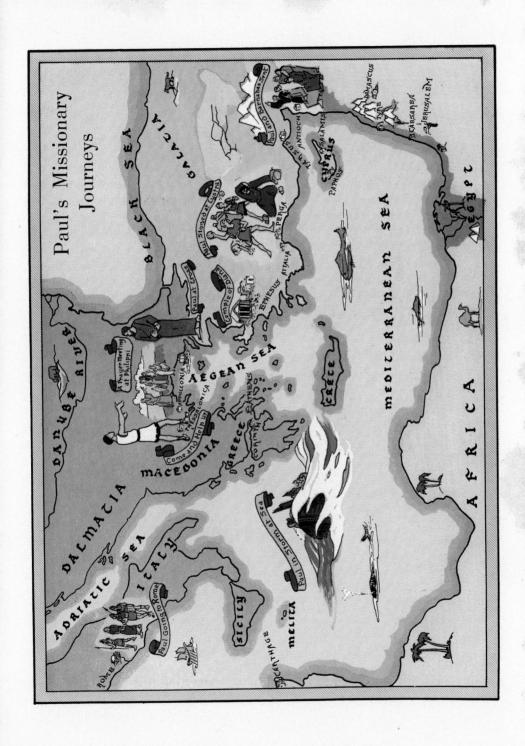

PAUL'S MISSIONARY JOURNEYS

The church at Antioch had grown until there were many preachers and teachers there. And God caused them to understand that Paul and Barnabas should preach the gospel to the Gentiles in cities where there were as yet no disciples. They laid hands on Paul and Barnabas and sent them on their first missionary journey. Among the cities visited was Lystra, where Paul was stoned.

On the second journey Paul had a vision, in which a man of Macedonia said, "Come over into Macedonia and help us." Leaving Troas, Paul went to Philippi, where they met for prayer down by the riverside. Lydia, a seller of purple, was converted in this meeting. It was on this trip, too, that Paul visited Ephesus, which was noted for its great Temple of Diana. Here Paul stayed for several years, teaching and preaching to the people.

After Paul's third missionary journey he was taken prisoner and carried to Rome for trial. The voyage to Rome was very stormy. The ship was wrecked at Melita. However, Paul was saved and was taken on to Rome, where he remained a prisoner for many years.

gives life and breath to all creatures, and has made the people of every nation. This God whom I declare to you is not far from every one of us, and he desires that people of every nation should seek to know him. They should not try to make images to represent him, for he is not like gold, or silver, or stone, fashioned as the idols your own hands have made. The time was when you did not know about this God; but now he commands you to repent of your sins, for the day will come when he will call all men into judgment.''

Paul then spoke to them about Jesus, whom God had raised from the dead to be the Savior. But when the wise men of Athens heard these words some laughed in scorn, while others shook their heads in doubt, saying, ''Come again some other day to tell us more about this strange thing.'' They did not believe that the dead shall rise again. So Paul left Mars Hill and went into the city.

Some who had listened to his sermon followed him and asked to know more about Christ. One of them who followed was a chief man of the city. He afterwards believed and was saved. A few others also turned from their idols and believed in the true God and in his Son, Jesus Christ.

From Athens, Paul went to another city of Greece, called Corinth. Here he found a man and his wife who were Jews and who, too, were strangers in the city. Because they were tent-makers by occupation, and Paul also knew how to make tents, he worked with them to earn his living, and on the Sabbath-days he preached in the synagog of the city. Among the Jews who believed his preaching were this man and his wife, Ă-quĭl'-ă and Priscilla.

Finally Silas and Timothy came from Philippi to Corinth, and Paul rejoiced to see them once more. From that time he began to speak more boldly concerning Christ, and many of the Jews opposed him. Then he left them, and turned to preach to the Gentiles.

The chief ruler of the synagog and his household believed the teachings of Paul, and many others, too, received his words with gladness. These believers were baptized in the name of Jesus. Because the Jews who worshiped in the synagog would not receive the gospel, these believers worshiped in a house near by which belonged to a believer named Justus.

One night while Paul was in Corinth, the Lord spoke to him in a dream, saying, ''Do not be afraid, but speak boldly for I am with you and no man shall hurt you here. I have many people in this city who will believe on me when they hear your words.'' After this vision Paul stayed in Corinth a long time, faithfully preaching the gospel to all who would listen. And many believers were added to the church in this city.

When Paul had been there many months, some wicked Jews who hated the believers planned to make trouble for them. They caught Paul and took him before the ruler of the city, accusing him of wrongdoing. But the ruler paid no heed to their words, and Paul was set at liberty. After this the Greeks caught one of the Jews, a ruler of a synagog, and beat him cruelly; but the Greek ruler did not help the Jew.

Paul decided to return again to Jerusalem. Taking with him Ā-quĭl'-ă and Priscilla, he sailed from Greece to Asia Minor. Here he left his friends in the city of Ĕph'-ĕ-sŭs and continued his journey to Jerusalem, to attend the Feast of the Passover. And from Jerusalem he went once more to visit the saints in Ăn'-tĭ-ŏch.

STORY 21

HOW A GREAT HEATHEN CITY RECEIVED THE GOSPEL
Acts 18 : 24—19 : 20

Ĕph'-ĕ-sŭs was a large city in Asia Minor, not far from the sea. In this city were many people who worshiped an idol, or goddess, called Diana. A great temple had been built in this city for the worship of this goddess, and many heathen people in other parts of the world had sent money to help build it. When the temple was finished it was called one of the seven wonders of the world, because of its rare beauty.

Not every one who lived in Ĕph'-ĕ-sŭs worshiped the goddess Diana. Some Jews lived there, and they had built a synagog. Here they met on Sabbath-days to study the Old Testament scriptures.

One day a man came to Ĕph'-ĕ-sŭs from Alexandria, a city of Egypt. This man, whose name was Ā-pŏl'-lŏs, was a Jew. He had heard about the preaching of John the Baptist; and believing that John was a prophet sent from God, he taught the Jews in Ĕph'-ĕ-sŭs John's words. And some of these Jews also believed, so he baptized them with the baptism of John, to show they had repented of their sins. But neither Ā-pŏl'-lŏs nor these other Jews had ever known Jesus.

Ā-quĭl'-ă and Priscilla, the friends of Paul who stopped in Ĕph'-ĕ-sŭs when he journeyed on to Jerusalem, heard Ā-pŏl'-lŏs preach. They saw how earnestly he taught the people and they believed he would become a great preacher of the gospel if only he knew all about Christ. So they invited him to their home and told him more fully about Jesus.

And Ă-pŏl'-lŏs believed their words. Then he bade his new friends good-by and sailed to Corinth, where he found the Christians who had believed through the teachings of Paul.

Shortly after Ă-pŏl'-lŏs went away from Ĕph'-ĕ-sŭs, Paul arrived on his third missionary journey to heathen lands. He met the Jews who had believed the teachings of John the Baptist, and he preached more about Christ to them. They believed Paul, and were also baptized in the name of Jesus. Afterwards Paul told them about the Holy Spirit whom God sent to believers, and when Paul laid his hands on these men and prayed, they, too, received the gift of the Holy Spirit.

For three months Paul taught in the synagog at Ĕph'-ĕ-sŭs, proving by the Scriptures that Jesus is the Christ. But many who heard him were unwilling to believe in Jesus. They spoke unkindly about Paul and about the Christ whom he preached. Then Paul took his believing friends and departed from the synagog, going to a school near by. In this school he taught every day for two years, until his teaching was known all through the city and the country around. And many believed in Jesus and were baptized.

While Paul was teaching in this city he worked special miracles in the name of Jesus. He healed many who were sick, and cast out evil spirits from many who were possessed of them. When he could not visit each needy one who wished to be healed, their friends would carry handkerchiefs or aprons from him and lay these upon the bodies of the afflicted, and the sickness and evil spirits would depart.

Many people were filled with wonder when they saw the great power of God as shown by this man. But there were seven wicked Jews who were brothers. These brothers used to cast out demons by spells and charms. They had seen Paul cast out evil spirits in Jesus' name, and not knowing the power of God that was in Paul, they supposed they could cast out evil spirits in the name of Jesus just as Paul did. So when they found a man in whom an evil spirit dwelt they said to the evil spirit, "We command you to come out, in the name of Jesus whom Paul preaches." But the evil spirit answered, "Jesus I know, and Paul I know, but who are you?" Then the spirit caused the man in whom he dwelt to leap on these wicked brothers and beat them terribly, until they fled from the house in shame.

Other people soon heard what had happened to these brothers, and they feared the great power of this mighty Jesus. They praised God by speaking respectfully and reverently of the name of Jesus. And many who believed were also afraid when they saw what had happened to these seven wicked Jews. Before Paul had preached to them they were superstitious, believing in signs and in dreams. Many had practised works of magic, trying to perform great things by these works; but now they confessed their wrong-doing and forsook those evil practices.

Books in those days were very rare and expensive. A single book would cost a sum of money that poor people could not afford. But many people in Ĕph'-ĕ-sŭs had books that taught how to work wonders by magic. When they saw the great power of God they no longer cared for these books, and they believed they should not keep them. So they brought them together in the street and built a huge bonfire with them, even though the books had cost much money. A large crowd gathered round to watch these expensive books burn to ashes. They knew the people who owned these books now believed in Jesus, and would no longer try to practise the wicked works which magic books teach.

———— • ————

STORY 22

THE UPROAR A COVETOUS MAN CAUSED IN A GREAT CITY
Acts 19:21—20:4

Not all people in Ĕph'-ĕ-sŭs believed in Jesus when they heard Paul's preaching and when they saw the miracles he performed in Jesus' name. Many still went to the great temple of Diana to worship the image of that heathen goddess, which they believed had fallen from the sky.

Those who could not go to the temple of Diana every day wished to have an image of the idol in their homes. And heathen worshipers who came from other lands wished also to carry away with them a likeness of the huge idol which stood in the beautiful temple at Ĕph'-ĕ-sŭs. Not because this idol was pretty, for Diana was not at all pleasing to look upon, but because they worshiped her they wished to have her likeness in their homes.

There were men in that city who knew how to make small idols like Diana with silver. These men were called silversmiths, and they grew rich selling idols to those who wished to buy. One of these silversmiths was named Dē-mē'-trĭ-ŭs. When he heard about the preaching of Paul and about the great miracles Paul performed in the name of Jesus, he became uneasy. Every day he listened to hear more news about this new teaching. And every day he grew more restless;

for he feared that soon all the worshipers of Diana would begin to worship Jesus.

Dē-mē′-trĭ-ŭs was not so greatly disturbed in his mind because he loved the goddess Diana—not that! But he loved the money he received from those who bought images of the goddess. He feared that

soon the people would no longer care to buy the images he made, and then he would receive no more money from them. He could not make images of Jesus to sell, for Paul taught that his God was not to be worshiped as an idol, of silver and gold, or other material.

After Dē-mē′-trĭ-ŭs heard that many people had burned their expensive magic-books because they believed in the Jesus whom Paul taught, he became much excited. Calling together his friends who also

BURNING THE BOOKS AT EPHESUS

were silversmiths, he told them about his fears. He warned them about the danger their work was in by Paul's preaching. "Not only here in our city," said Dē-mē′-trĭ-ŭs, "but in almost all Asia Minor this Paul has been turning away people from the worship of the goddess, by declaring they are no gods which are made with hands. Not only is our work in danger of falling to nothingness," he continued, "but the beautiful temple of our goddess will soon be no longer visited and admired by people from other lands."

Now all the silversmiths became excited, and they began to cry out, "Great is Diana of the Ĕph-ē'-ṣĭăns!" Through the streets they ran, crying these words, and other people followed. Soon the whole city was stirred by the excitement, and some caught two of Paul's companions, and dragged them into the theater. Paul heard what had happened, and he wished to go to the rescue of these faithful companions, but his friends refused to let him do this. They feared the people might tear him in pieces if they found him.

For two hours the excitement raged; many people did not even

A THEATER OF PAUL'S TIME

know what it was all about, and yet they joined in the cry, "Great is Diana of the Ĕph-ē'-ṣĭăns!"

Finally the clerk of the city stepped up before the people and motioned for them to be quiet. He then reproved them for their foolish conduct, and told them they were in danger of being punished for the uproar they had made. He said that Dē-mē'-trĭ-ŭs and his fellow workmen should not use this means to bring charges against Paul and his friends, for they should handle such matters according to the law of the land. Concerning Paul's two companions who had been dragged before the mob, he said, "These two men have not robbed churches, nor spoken evil of our goddess." He then dissmissed the assembly, and sent them all home.

Paul had been intending to leave Ĕph'-ĕ-sŭs even before the uproar was made, as he wished to visit the churches in Măç-ē-dō'-nĭ-ă and Greece and then return again to Jerusalem. Now he bade the Christians good-by and sailed for Măç-ē-dō'-nĭ-ă. Here he visited the saints in Philippi, where he and Silas had been treated so shamefully and imprisoned, and where God had caused an earthquake to open the prison doors and loosen their bands, setting them free. No doubt the jailer and his household were glad to see this brave preacher of Jesus Christ once more.

Passing through Thĕss-ă-lō-nī'-că and Bĕ-rē'-ă, where he had preached the gospel before, he went on to Greece. For three months he stayed with the Christians in this country, then he prepared to return for the last time to Jerusalem. Before starting he learned that his enemies, the Jews, were planning to catch him and take his life, so instead of taking ship and sailing directly to Syria he returned by the way he had come. And thus he escaped once more from the hatred of his foes.

STORY 23

THE FAITHFUL MISSIONARY AND HIS LAST FAREWELL

Acts 20:5—21:17

From Măç-ē-dō'-nĭ-ă, Paul sailed across the sea to Trō'-ăs, the city where he had seen a vision of a man of Macedonia calling for help. In this city he stayed for some days, then he made ready to start again toward Jerusalem.

On the night before leaving Trō'-ăs, Paul preached a farewell sermon to the believers who lived in that city. They met together in a large room on the third floor, and here they broke bread in memory of the special supper that Jesus ate with his disciples before he was crucified. Then Paul talked to them until midnight; for he knew he should never see them again and he had many things to say before he should go away forever.

While Paul was talking, a young man named Ĕu'-tỹ-chŭs sat in an open window listening. After some time he grew sleepy and began to nod. Then he fell into a deep sleep and sank down on the window-sill. Losing his balance soon afterwards, he dropped from the window to the ground below. Friends rushed down the stairs and found that the fall had killed him. Then Paul went down to them and saw them weeping. He fell on the lifeless body, embraced it, and said to those who stood near, "Do not be troubled, for his life is yet in him."

After this had happened Paul returned to the company of believers upstairs and took food with them. He then continued his talk until break of day, when he bade them farewell and departed. They brought

EPHESIANS BIDDING PAUL GOOD-BY

again into the assembly the young man who had fallen from the window. And the believers rejoiced to see him alive.

Paul's next farewell-meeting was with the men who had come from Ĕph'-ĕ-sŭs to the seacoast to meet him. These men were the ones who had taken the leadership in the church at Ĕph'-ĕ-sŭs when Paul left them. They were men whom he loved, and whom he counted faithful. They were called the "elders" of the church.

Paul talked earnestly to these Ĕph-ē'-sĭăn brethren, reminding them of his work among them, and of his desire to teach them the whole word of God. He told them that now he was journeying toward Jerusalem and that they should never see his face again. He said he did not know what would befall him in that city, only the Holy Spirit was warning him of danger ahead. But he said, "None of these things make me afraid; for I do not count my life dear to myself. I am determined to finish with joy the work I have received of the Lord Jesus, to tell the gospel story to all men."

Paul reminded them also of his work among them, how he had coveted no man's riches but had worked with his own hands to earn money for his food and clothes while he preached the gospel in their city. And he urged them to remember the words Jesus had spoken, that it is more blessed to give than to receive.

When Paul had finished speaking he knelt down with the men and prayed earnestly to God, then he bade them good-by. These men wept aloud, and embraced their beloved teacher who would never more return to them. Then they went with him to the ship, on which he and his companions sailed away toward the homeland of the Jews.

At the seacoast town of Tyre the ship stopped several days, and here Paul and his companions met some more Christians and worshiped with them. When the time came for the ship to leave port again, the Christians went with Paul to the seaside, and they knelt down on the shore to pray. Even the children of these Christian fathers and mothers went with Paul and his friends to the ship. The Holy Spirit had caused these Christians to understand that troubles would befall Paul in Jerusalem, and they urged him not to continue his journey; but he believed it would please God for him to go on.

While Paul and his fellow travelers were visiting the church in Çǣ-sǎ-rē'-ǎ, an old man named Ăg'-ǎ-bǔs came from Jerusalem. This old man was a prophet, for God caused him to know things that were to happen after a while. When he saw Paul he took off Paul's girdle and tied it about his own hands and feet. Then he said, "So shall the wicked Jews at Jerusalem do to the man who owns this girdle, binding him and giving him over to the Gentiles."

Paul's friends were greatly troubled when they heard this. They gathered round him, weeping, and pleaded with him to stay away from Jerusalem. But he answered, "Why do you weep and break my heart? I am ready, not only to be bound at Jerusalem, but also to die there for the name of the Lord Jesus." When they saw they could not prevent him from going, they said, "The will of God be done."

Not many days afterwards Paul and his companions went over the mountains to the great city of the Jews. Other Christians from

Çæ-să-rē'-ă joined their company, and when they came to Jerusalem the elders in the church there welcomed them with joy.

TYRE, WHERE PAUL MET WITH BRETHREN

STORY 24

HOW THE PROPHET'S WORDS CAME TRUE

Acts 21:18—23:10

Years had passed since the wicked Herod had tried to kill Peter, and during those years the church in Jerusalem had grown into a multitude. Some of the enemies who had killed Jesus were yet alive, and they hated the Christians. But they had ceased persecuting them as bitterly as in the first days of the early church.

Paul had met with multitudes of believers in the churches of other lands. But these in Jerusalem were all Jews, and many of them looked with displeasure upon the people of other nations. They had not yet learned how God's love reaches out to all men. And because they had heard much about Paul's missionary labors among the Gentiles they felt unwilling to approve of his work.

The leaders in the church at Jerusalem understood how God had chosen Paul to be a missionary to the Gentiles. They rejoiced to know that even the Gentiles might be saved by faith in Jesus. But they understood also the feelings of many who worshiped in their services, so they warned Paul about these Jewish believers. They said, "These men have heard that you do not keep the law of Moses, but that you teach the Gentiles to forsake the law." And they urged Paul to show these believers that he did not despise Moses' teachings, as they supposed.

To please these men Paul visited the temple and performed the ceremony of cleansing, according to Moses' law. Almost a week passed by, then one day while he was in the temple some Jews from Asia Minor came to worship there. Seeing Paul, they recognized him at once, for he had taught in their synagog concerning Christ. And they had not accepted his teaching. They hated him because he taught that Gentiles as well as Jews might become the people of God. They became excited when they saw him worshiping in the Jewish temple, and they cried out against him.

Soon the old enemies of Jesus heard about the excitement, and they rushed in to seize Paul. A crowd quickly gathered, and they pulled Paul out of the temple and shut the doors. Not waiting to drag him outside the city, they began beating him at once, and would have killed him had not the Roman captain arrived with soldiers to investigate the trouble.

Supposing Paul must be a desperate fellow, the captain commanded that he should be bound with two heavy chains. Then he asked what Paul had done. But some cried one thing and some another, and he could not hear in the noise of the angry mob what offenses Paul was guilty of committing. So he led Paul away to the castle where prisoners were kept.

The mob followed, crying, "Away with him!" And the soldiers, fearing the people would tear Paul in pieces, picked him up and carried him on their shoulders to the castle stairs. As they went Paul

PAUL BEING BOUND

asked to speak to the captain. At this, the Roman captain was surprized, for he did not know Paul could speak his language. He gave Paul permission to speak to the mob when they reached the stairs.

Then, standing on the stairs above the heads of the excited followers, Paul beckoned to them with his hand, and they grew quiet. He began at once to talk to them in the Hebrew language, which the Romans could not understand. This language the Jews loved, and they

listened attentively to him while he told them about his early life and training. He reminded them of his student-life in their city, where he became a Pharisee. He reminded them also of his former hatred toward the believers in Jesus, and of his bitter persecutions against them. Many who stood in the crowd below had not forgotten the Saul who tried to break up the early church in Jerusalem.

Paul then told about his journey to Damascus, where he intended to persecute the Christians. He told about the vision that came to him on the way, and about the voice that spoke to him from heaven. He even told how he had been baptized in the name of Jesus, and how when he had come to Jerusalem to worship God showed him in a vision in the temple that he must go to Gentile countries and there preach the gospel.

But when Paul began speaking about preaching to the Gentiles, then no longer would the people listen to his speech. Their hatred of Gentiles stirred their hearts to cry out once more against Paul, and now they even cast off their cloaks and threw dust into the air, shouting aloud, "Away with such a fellow from the earth! He is not fit to live!"

The Roman captain and his soldiers did not understand what Paul had spoken to the angry people, and they supposed he must be a dangerous fellow. They therefore brought him into the castle and determined to learn the nature of his crime. Bringing out cruel instruments of torture, they began to bind Paul. But Paul knew the law of the Romans, that it did not permit a Roman citizen to be punished in this manner, so he spoke to a soldier who stood near by and told him he was a Roman. This soldier hurried away to tell the chief captain, who came quickly and asked, "Tell me, are you a Roman?" Paul answered, "I am."

This frightened the men who were preparing to torture Paul. Even the chief captain was frightened, for he had given the command that Paul should be bound and punished.

Still the Romans were puzzled about their prisoner. They could not understand what terrible thing he had done. On the next day they called the chief rulers of the Jews to assemble together, and brought Paul before them. While Paul spoke the chief captain saw that even these Jewish rulers were not agreed what to do with him. Some wished to set him free, while others insisted on putting him to death. Then the captain sent his soldiers to take Paul away from their midst, fearing they might kill him.

STORY 25

HOW A YOUNG MAN SAVED HIS UNCLE'S LIFE
Acts 23:11—24:27

Paul now understood why he had been so often warned of danger in Jerusalem. He knew his life was not safe among his own people, the Jews. No doubt he felt sad, because he loved the Jews and longed to have them catch a glimpse of the great love of God, which reaches down to all men.

On Paul's second night in the castle, while he was sleeping the Lord appeared to him and said, "Be of good courage, Paul; for just as you have spoken boldly for me in Jerusalem, you shall speak boldly for me in Rome." This encouraged Paul greatly, for he had long desired to visit Rome, the capital city of the Roman Empire, and preach the gospel there also.

The enemies of Paul were not content to have him imprisoned; they desired to kill him. Forty of them met together and purposed to eat nothing until they had killed him. Then they hurried to tell the chief priests and other Jewish rulers about their purpose. "You can help us," they said, "by asking the chief captain to send Paul down tomorrow so that the rulers may hear his case again. And while the soldiers are bringing him from the castle, we will rush upon them, seize Paul, and kill him."

Paul's nephew heard about this wicked plan and he hurried at once to the castle to tell his uncle what the Jews were planning to do. Paul quickly called a centurion, a captain of one hundred men, and asked him to take his nephew to the chief captain. "The lad has something important to tell him," said Paul, so the centurion brought the young man to see the chief captain at once.

The chief captain felt interested in Paul because he knew this prisoner was a Roman Jew. He knew also that the Jews in Jerusalem despised Paul for no just reason; and when he heard the young man tell about the plot of the Jews against Paul's life, he said, "Do not let any one know you have told this to me." With these words he sent the young man away.

Calling two centurions to him at once, the chief captain told them to prepare to take Paul that night to Çæ-sä-rē'-ä. And to make sure of Paul's safety, he commanded them to take two hundred soldiers with them, and seventy men on horseback, and two hundred spearmen. Paul, too, should be given a horse to ride on.

Then the captain wrote a letter to the Roman governor Felix, who lived in Çæ-sä-rē'-ä, explaining why he was sending this prisoner from Jerusalem to him.

At nine o'clock that night the sound of horses' hoofs clattered on the pavement before the castle door. Then Paul was brought out and placed on one of the horses, and the small army began to move rapidly down the dark street. None of the Jews knew about the errand of this company of soldiers, and they did not guess until too late what might be happening to the man whom they wished to kill.

On the next afternoon Paul was brought safely to the Roman governor, Felix, and the chief captain's letter was also delivered. This is what Lўs'-ĭ-ăs, the chief captain, had written concerning Paul: "This man, who is a Roman, was taken by the Jews and would have been killed by them had I not come with my army and rescued him. When I sought to know the reason why they accused him I brought him before the council of the Jews; but I found that they had no charge worthy of death or even of imprisonment to bring against him. Then it was told me how they were plotting to take his life, therefore I have sent him to you. And I have given commandment to his accusers that they come before you to his trial.''

Felix, the Governor, asked Paul to what Roman province, or country, he belonged, and he learned that Paul's home was in Tarsus of Çĭ-lĭç'-ĭ-ă. Then he placed him in the palace which used to belong to Herod, to wait there until his trial.

The enemies of Paul were greatly displeased when they saw how Lŷs'-ĭ-ăs, the chief captain, had spoiled their plan. They arranged at once to go down to Çæ-ṡă-rē'-ă to speak to Felix, accusing Paul before him. So the high priest, Ăn-ă-nī'-ăs, and the Jewish elders and a lawyer named Tĕr-tŭl'-lŭs hurried to Çæ-ṡă-rē'-ă on this mission.

Felix brought Paul before this council. Tĕr-tŭl'-lŭs rose to speak. He said many things about Paul that were not true. He called Paul a pestilent fellow, a trouble-maker among the Jews in every country where he went. Tĕr-tŭl'-lŭs also accused Paul of being the leader of a new religion, which he called the sect of the Nazarenes (by this he referred to the church of God).

When this lawyer had finished making his complaints against Paul, the Governor motioned for Paul to rise and defend himself. Then Paul said, ''These men can not prove anything this lawyer has spoken against me. Only twelve days ago I went up to Jerusalem to worship God; and they did not find me stirring up the people, but they seized me when I was alone in the temple. Those men who accused me then should have come now with their charges, if they have anything against me, for after the manner which they condemn so I worship the God of my fathers, believing all things that are written in the law of Moses and in the books of the prophets. And I have always tried to keep my heart free from wrong toward my God and toward all men.''

Felix then spoke. He said he would wait until Lŷs'-ĭ-ăs, the chief captain, should also come from Jerusalem, and with those words he dismissed the council. He then gave Paul to a centurion, saying, ''Let this man have his liberty, and do not forbid any of his friends from coming to visit him in the palace.''

Several days later Felix called for Paul again. This time Felix' wife, Drû-sĭl'-lă, who was a Jewess, was with him, and wished to hear this prisoner tell about the gospel of Christ. Paul talked earnestly to these two, and while he talked Felix trembled because of his great sins. He knew he was guilty before God, and he became afraid. But he did not wish to humble his proud heart, so he sent Paul away, saying, ''Some other day I will call again for you.''

Two years passed by, and during this time Paul was kept in Çæ-ṡă-rē'-ă as a prisoner. He was given many privileges, and often Felix called for him, hoping that Paul's friends might notice the interest he took in Paul and offer him money to set Paul free. He knew Paul did not deserve to be kept a prisoner, still he refused to let him go. After the two years had passed Felix was taken away and a new governor was sent to Çæ-ṡă-rē'-ă. And wishing to please the Jews before leaving their country, Felix left Paul in prison.

———•———

STORY 26

A KING LISTENS TO PAUL'S STORY

Acts 25, 26

After Felix went to Rome a new governor was sent to take his place. This new governor was called Festus.

Now, Festus was also a Roman as was Felix. He was unacquainted with the Jews and knew little about their customs, religion, and such things. He went to visit Jerusalem three days after he arrived in Çæ-ṡă-rē'-ă; for there he could learn more about the people he had come to govern, as Jerusalem was the Jews' chief city.

Several days later, after Festus had returned to Çæ-ṡă-rē'-ă, he called for Paul, who had been in prison all this time, more than two years. And men who had come from Jerusalem stood up to speak false things against Paul. But none of those things could they prove. The Jews still wished to have Paul taken to Jerusalem, hiding their reason. As Festus wished to please the Jewish people he said to Paul, "Are you willing to go up to Jerusalem and be judged there before me, concerning these things of which the Jews accuse you?"

Paul replied, "Against the Jews I have done nothing to offend their law. If I have done anything worthy of death, I refuse not to die. I appeal to Cæsar." Festus knew that every Roman citizen had a right to ask this privilege, of appearing before the great ruler of all the Roman Empire, Cæsar, so he answered, "You have asked to be sent to Cæsar, at Rome, and your request shall be granted."

About this time some distinguished visitors came to Çæ-ṡă-rē'-ă to see the new Governor. They were Agrippa, the governor of the country east of the Jordan River, and Bĕr-nī'-çē, his sister. This Agrippa was sometimes called a king. During their visit Festus told them about Paul. He told how the Jews had accused this prisoner of some offense concerning their religious law, which he could not understand.

He said also that in his trial before the Jews, Paul had spoken earnestly about one named Jesus, who he said had risen from the grave.

On the next day Agrippa and Bĕr-nī'-çē entered the judgment-hall with Festus. Then Festus gave command and Paul was brought.

Festus rose to introduce this prisoner to the King. He said, "Be-

PAUL SPEAKING BEFORE AGRIPPA

fore you stands this man whom the multitude of Jews in Jerusalem have declared is not fit to live any longer. But when I found that he had done nothing deserving of death, and when he had expressed his wish to be taken before Cæsar, in Rome, I determined to send him there to be judged. Now, however, I have no charge to make against him, therefore I have brought him before you people and especially before you, King Agrippa, that you may hear him and know for what purpose he is being held in bonds."

Agrippa now spoke, and said to Paul, "You are permitted to tell your own story before us."

Paul rose up, stretched out his hand on which hung the heavy chain, and said:

"I am glad, O King, that I may speak for myself today before you, and tell why I am accused by the Jews. I know that you understand the customs and questions which are among the Jews, and you will understand my words.

"From my youth the Jews know my life, for I was brought up in their city. And if they would, they could testify that I lived among the strictest of the Pharisees, keeping the law of Moses as carefully as any of them tried to do. And now I am accused by them because I believe the promise which God made to our fathers, concerning Jesus Christ, whom God raised from the dead.

"The time was when I, too, thought I ought to persecute those who believe in Jesus of Nazareth. And this I did, shutting in prison many of the saints who lived in Jerusalem. I even received authority from the high priest to persecute the saints who lived in distant cities. I was on my way to Damascus to persecute the Christians there when I saw a vision from God. It was at midday, O King, when suddenly I saw on the road a light from heaven, more dazzling than the noonday sun, and the brightness of it frightened me and my companions. We fell to the ground, then a voice spoke to me in the Hebrew language, saying, 'Saul! Saul! why are you persecuting me?' I cried, 'Who are you, Lord?' and the voice replied, 'I am Jesus, whom you are persecuting.' That voice commanded me to stand on my feet while I received Jesus' orders. And that voice told me I should tell of Jesus not only to the Jews, but to the Gentiles as well.

"Because I have obeyed the command I received in that heavenly vision, O King, I am now being persecuted by the Jews who will not believe in Jesus. Again and again they have sought to kill me, but God has thus far delivered me from their plots, and he has given me strength to tell to all who come to me that Jesus is indeed the Christ of whom Moses and the prophets wrote."

Festus beheld the earnestness of this chained speaker and he decided that Paul must be crazy. Not wishing to listen longer to speech he could not understand, he cried out, "Paul, you are not in your right mind. Too much learning has made you crazy!"

But Paul answered calmly, "I am not crazy, most noble Festus, but am speaking words of truth and soberness. King Agrippa knows these things of which I speak, therefore I talk freely to him." Then, turning to Agrippa, Paul said, "King Agrippa, do you believe the prophets? I know that you believe."

Agrippa answered, "Almost you persuade me to be a Christian." And Paul replied, "I would to God that not only you but all who hear me today were such as I am except for this chain."

But the King was not ready to humble his proud heart and become a Christian. He rose up at once and went aside with Ber-ni'-çē and Festus and others to discuss Paul's case. He said to Festus, "This man has done nothing worthy of death or even of imprisonment. If he had not asked to be sent to Cæsar he might be set free at once." But now it was too late to change the arrangement, and Festus could not set Paul at liberty.

———•———

STORY 27

THE STORY OF A SHIPWRECK
Acts 27

A ship was leaving port at Çæ-så-rē'-å, and among the passengers on board was Paul, the prisoner. As the shore faded away in the distance, Paul saw his last glimpse of the land that is dear to the heart of every Jew, for never again would he return to this country.

Paul was not the only prisoner on board that vessel. Before leaving Çæ-så-rē'-å he and several others had been given into the keeping of a Roman centurion whose name was Julius. Festus had commanded this centurion and his soldiers to bring the prisoners safely to Rome and deliver them to Cæsar.

No doubt the Christians who lived in Çæ-så-rē'-å gathered at the seashore to watch their beloved friend sail away toward far-off Rome. And no doubt they wept when they realized that Paul would not return to them again.

But Paul was not the only Christian among the passengers. Two of his friends, Luke, the doctor, and Ar-ĭs-tär'-chŭs, who had been with Paul on his third missionary journey, were also going to Rome with him. So they all boarded the vessel and sailed away to Italy.

The next day after leaving port at Çæ-så-rē'-å the ship stopped at Sī'-dŏn, a seacoast town of Phœ-nĭc'-iå, which is north of the homeland of the Jews. In this city Paul had some friends, and by this time he had won the respect of the Roman officer, who kindly allowed him to go ashore with Luke and Ar-ĭs-tär'-chŭs and a soldier. There they visited for a short time with the Christians who lived in Sī'-dŏn, and then returned to the ship.

Their next stopping-place was at Mȳ'-rå, a city on the southern coast of Asia Minor. Here the centurion found another ship ready to sail for Italy, and because their first vessel would not take them all the way he and his soldiers transferred their prisoners to this ship. Luke and Ăr-ĭs-tär'-c͟hŭs also boarded this vessel, that they might continue their journey with Paul.

From Mȳ'-ră the ship left the shore and pushed out once again into the great Mediterranean Sea. But it made little progress, for the winds blew against it. Finally, after sailing many days, the passengers were gladdened to see the Island of Crete. Here they stopped in a harbor called the Fair Havens.

After resting for some time the captain of the vessel thought about putting out to sea once more. But Paul protested, saying, "This voyage will bring much trouble upon us, for sailing at this time of the year is very dangerous." He urged them to remain in that port for the winter. But the centurion believed they could reach another port not far away. And because the port at the Fair Havens was not a desirable place, the captain and many of the passengers were eager to go farther before they should stop for the winter. On the first fair day the ship glided out of the harbor and entered the broad sea.

But they had not gone far when suddenly a tempestuous wind swept down upon them. They could not turn back, neither could they sail on to the port for which they were bound. All they could do was to toss about on the angry waves, not knowing how soon the ship might be torn to pieces.

Now, when all too late, the captain and the centurion saw that Paul had spoken wisely when he urged them to remain in the harbor at the Fair Havens. At once they set about trying to save the ship. They threw out everything that might be spared to lighten the weight of the vessel, and waited anxiously for the storm to pass. But the storm raged on. Day after day passed by and still the sky frowned down upon them with dark clouds and cold rains, and night after night came and went without one bit of light from the moon or stars.

One morning Paul, the prisoner, stood up on the deck and shouted to the sailors and passengers, trying to make his voice heard above the roar of the storm. They listened, and heard him say, "Sirs, if you had believed me when I warned you at Crete you would not have suffered the harm of this storm. But now be of good cheer, for there shall be no loss of life among us, only of the ship. This I know because an angel of God, to whom I belong, and whom I serve, stood by me last night and said, 'Fear not, Paul; you must be brought before Cæsar. And lo, the lives of all these who sail with you God has given to you.' Therefore I urge you to be of good cheer, for we shall all be saved alive, although we shall be cast upon an island and the ship lost.''

While the sailors had been struggling against the storm, Paul had been praying, and God had sent an angel to cheer him with this mes-

CAST ASHORE ON THE ISLAND OF MELITA

sage. For Paul longed to see Rome, even though he must be taken there with chains on his hands.

But the storm did not cease when Paul spoke to the men, and still they feared they might all be drowned in the sea. When two weeks had passed by, one night the sailors found they were nearing some land. They had no way of telling where they were, for they had drifted on the waves for many days, and they could not see the moon and stars. They could not tell whether they were nearing a rocky coast or a sandy beach, and not wishing to drift any nearer they threw the anchors overboard and waited anxiously for the morning light.

The sailors knew the dangerous condition of the ship. They saw how helpless it was before the storm. They doubted whether they could bring it to shore. So now they planned to escape, leaving the passengers and the prisoners on board the sinking vessel. They prepared to lower a boat, as if to cast more anchors into the sea. But Paul knew what they were planning to do, and he said to the centurion, "Unless these sailors stay in the ship, we can not be saved."

Now the Roman officer believed Paul's words, so he hastily cut the ropes that held the boat, allowing it to drift away into the darkness.

When daylight was coming on Paul urged those on board to take food. For many days they had not eaten a proper meal, being too worried to feel their hunger. Now they were weak, and Paul knew their bodies needed food to strengthen them. He reminded them of the angel's words, that not one hair of their heads should perish; and when he had spoken thus he took bread and gave thanks to God before them all. Then he ate of it, and the others took courage and also ate. After all had eaten, they threw overboard the wheat their ship was carrying to Italy. And everything else that added weight to the ship and might be spared they threw into the sea.

Now the daylight shone clearly enough for them to see the land near by. The sailors did not recognize it; but they saw a place where there was a sandy shore, and lifting the anchors, they tried to steer the ship into this place. As they went the swirling waters caught the ship in a narrow place, where it struck a hidden rock and stuck tight. Then the rear of the ship was broken by the violent sea.

The soldiers on board knew they must give their own lives if their prisoners should escape, and not wishing to do that, they urged the centurion to allow them to kill all the prisoners at once. But because the centurion loved Paul, he refused to let them do this. He commanded every one who could swim to jump overboard and swim to land, and those who could not swim he commanded to take broken pieces of the ship and float upon them toward the shore.

No time was lost, and every one, wishing to save his life, struggled through the water toward the sandy beach. And not one of all the two hundred and seventy-six on board the sinking vessel was drowned.

———•———

STORY 28

HOW A CHAINED PRISONER BROUGHT JOY TO ISLANDERS

Acts 28:1-10

On the wooded shore of the island where Paul's ship was stranded stood a group of excited men anxiously watching those who were escaping from the wrecked vessel near by. These men were natives of the island, and they felt sorry for the strangers who had suffered shipwreck. They hurried out to meet them and to help them reach the land. Then they built a fire, for it was still raining, and it was cold.

Around this fire the drenched strangers gathered eagerly, for the sea had chilled them through. They were glad for the kindness these natives showed. And they learned from them the name of the island where they had landed. This island, called Měl'-ĭ-tă, was south of Italy.

As the strangers from the wrecked vessel stood warming round the fire, the natives saw that many of them were soldiers and prisoners. But they treated every one kindly. Paul wished to be helpful, so he gathered a bundle of sticks to keep the fire burning. As he laid them on the fire the heat from the flames aroused to action a very poisonous snake which was hidden among the sticks. At once the snake sprang at Paul, seizing his hand with its deadly fangs.

The natives knew Paul was a prisoner. When they saw the snake hanging from his hand they whispered to each other, "This must be a very wicked man, whom the gods will not allow to live even though he has escaped from the stormy sea." But while they waited, expecting to see Paul's arm swell with poison and then to see him drop over dead, they were surprized; for Paul shook off the snake, and no harm came to him. They looked in wonder, and then said, "This must be a god instead of a man, whom a deadly snake can not destroy."

Not far from this place lived a man named Publius, who was the ruler of the Island. He, too, received the shipwrecked strangers kindly, and after Paul had not been harmed by the bite of the poisonous snake he invited Paul and his friends into his home. For three days he entertained them there.

The father of Publius was lying very ill with fever and a disease which often causes death. When Paul heard of this he visited the man, and he prayed for him and healed him.

The news of this healing quickly spread over the Island, and others who were suffering from diseases came to Paul, asking to be healed. In this way many people became interested in the prisoner who had escaped from the sea, and were happy because of him.

And so it was that Paul published the good news of Jesus wherever he went, even though he was bound by a heavy chain. And everywhere he went those who received the good news were made happy. Now the islanders as well as those who had been with Paul on the ship saw that God's power was with this good man, and they respected him.

For three months Paul and his companions stayed on this island;

then when the spring days returned they took another ship and continued their journey to Rome.

THE LAST OF PAUL'S JOURNEY, AND HIS LIFE IN ROME

Acts 28:11-31; Philemon; Colossians; 2 Timothy

When the spring days returned the Roman centurion, Julius, placed his soldiers and prisoners on board a vessel that had lain all winter in a harbor of the Island. This vessel was bound for Italy and would take its passengers to the end of their journey by sea. The remaining distance to Rome they would travel by land.

Paul's two friends, Luke and Ăr-ĭs-tär'-chŭs, continued the journey with him from the Island. When the ship was ready to leave the harbor, the kind-hearted natives brought gifts of necessary things to these Christian men who had taught them about the Lord. In this way they tried to show how glad they were that these men had come to them.

A city called Pū-tē'-ŏ-lĭ, in Italy, was the last stopping-place of the ship. Here all the passengers landed, and those going to Rome made ready to start on the last stretch of their journey.

In this city some Christians were living, and they were glad to see Paul and his friends. The Roman centurion allowed Paul to remain with these Christians for one week.

The journey from Pū-tē'-ŏ-lĭ to Rome was made on foot, over a well-built highway. As Paul trudged along the road his heart felt sad. Perhaps he feared that he might not have many opportunities to preach the gospel because he was a prisoner. Perhaps he thought that only a few people would be willing to listen to the words of a strange preacher who was bound with a heavy chain.

But there were some Christians living in Rome also. Paul had never met these Christians, although he had written a long letter to them before he had been captured by the Jews. In that letter he had told them of his desire to visit Rome and to preach the gospel there also.

When these Roman Christians heard of Paul's coming, they were very glad. Some of them started down the highway to meet him. Even though he was a prisoner they were happy to welcome such a good man to their city. And when they met the company of dusty travelers from Puteoli, they eagerly inquired for Paul.

The coming of these Christians encouraged Paul very much. The sad feelings now left him and he thanked God for bringing him thus far on his long journey to Rome. He knew that he should have true friends in this strange city, friends who would not be ashamed of him even though he wore a chain.

Julius, the centurion, gave his prisoners into the keeping of the captain of the guard in Rome. No doubt he told this captain about Paul, the prisoner who did not deserve to wear a chain, for the captain looked kindly upon Paul and did not cast him into the dreary prison but allowed him to live in a hired house. He could not take off the heavy chain Paul wore, for he did not have authority to do that. And always a soldier stayed with Paul to guard him as a prisoner.

PAUL PREACHING IN ROME

For two years he lived in his hired house, with first one and then another soldier with him, and these men learned from him the story of Jesus.

Not only was Paul allowed to preach the gospel to the soldiers, but any one who wished might come to see him. When he had been in Rome only three days he sent for the chief Jews who lived in that city. They came to him, and he told them how the Jews in Jerusalem had ac-

cused him of wrong-doing and had caused him to be bound with that
chain. He explained why they had become displeased with him. These
Jews in Rome had heard nothing about Paul. They had received no
letters from their friends in Jerusalem, accusing him of wrong-doing.
But now they asked him to speak to them about the new religion that
had so greatly displeased their people in the homeland. And Paul
gladly consented to do this.

On the day which they had appointed many Jews who lived in
Rome came to Paul's lodging to hear him tell the gospel story. For a
long time they had heard about the Christians, but never had they
heard the teachings of the new religion. And always they heard unkind remarks about those who believed in Jesus.

Paul took the books of Scripture, which they knew and loved—
the writings of Moses and of the prophets—and he explained how Jesus came to earth, suffered, died on the cross for the sins of men, and
rose from the dead, all in fulfilment of the Scriptures, which spoke
of his coming.

While Paul talked, the Jews listened carefully. Some of them believed his words, and they were very glad to hear that God's promised
gift to men had really come. But many others shook their heads and
said, "We do not believe this teaching."

When Paul saw that many would not believe he said, "It is just as
the Holy Spirit spoke by the prophet Isaiah, saying, 'The heart of this
people has grown hard, and their ears will not hear my words.' But
the Gentiles," said Paul, "will hear and believe the salvation which
God has sent to all men."

As a prisoner in Rome, Paul taught many people about Jesus. He
also wrote letters to the Christians who lived in other cities where he
had preached. Some of these letters we have today in our Bibles.
They are called epistles.

One day while in Rome, Paul chanced to meet with a runaway
slave, named Ō-nĕs'-ĭ-mŭs. This runaway belonged to a man who lived
in Cŏ-lŏs'-sē, in Asia Minor, and who was a Christian and a friend of
Paul's. Many people in those days owned slaves, just as farmers now
own horses and cattle and sheep. They bought and sold these slaves,
men, women, and children, just as people buy animals today. But
Ō-nĕs'-ĭ-mŭs had run away from his master, and had come all the long
distance to Rome.

Paul talked kindly to this runaway, and finally he helped Onesimus to find God. How happy this poor slave became when he knew
the joy which salvation brings! He longed to stay with Paul and to

learn more about Jesus. He liked to do acts of kindness for this chained prisoner who had done so much for him. But Ō-nĕs'-ĭ-mŭs knew he belonged to Phī-lē'-mon, who lived in Cŏ-lŏs'-sē, and from whom he had run away, so he decided to return again to his master.

Paul loved this slave who had become a Christian. He knew how cruelly the law treated runaway slaves when they were captured; but he believed that Phī-lē'-mon would not treat Ō-nĕs'-ĭ-mŭs so unkindly. He wrote a letter to Phī-lē'-mon and sent it by Ō-nĕs'-ĭ-mŭs. In this let-

THE RUINS OF ROME'S ANCIENT FORUM, WHERE JUSTICE
WAS ADMINISTERED

ter he told Phī-lē'-mon about the helpful deeds this slave had done for him since they had met in Rome. He urged Phī-lē'-mon to welcome Ō-nĕs'-ĭ-mŭs as a brother, not as a wicked runaway, for God had saved him from his sins and now he, too, was a Christian. This letter to Phī-lē'-mon we have in our Bibles. Ō-nĕs'-ĭ-mŭs also delivered the letter Paul wrote to the church at Cŏ-lŏs'-sē, and that letter we have.

The Acts of the Apostles does not tell us any more about Paul, nor about the other apostles. But history tells us that Paul was finally killed by the wicked Nero, who was ruler of Rome. Not long before Paul was killed he wrote a letter to Timothy, the young man whom he loved as his own son. In this letter he said that soon he must die. He did not seem discouraged, but rejoiced because he had worked faith-

fully for God. And he said, ''I am now ready to be offered.'' He told
Timothy that a crown of righteousness was waiting for him in heaven,
and not only for him but for every one who loves the Lord and desires
to see him. This beautiful letter is also in our Bibles, and the words
Paul wrote to Timothy encourage every Christian who reads them.

———————•———————

STORY 30

THINGS WE LEARN FROM THE EPISTLES
The Epistles

Not all the letters, or epistles, that we find in the New Testament
were written by Paul. Two were written by Peter, three by John, the
beloved disciple of Jesus, one by James, and one by Jude.

In these epistles we learn about the teachings of the preachers in
the early church. We learn how they depended on God to help them
teach rightly. And we learn that their letters were intended to be
read, not only by those to whom they were written, but by all who hear
the word of God even today.

Many parts of the gospel which are not explained in the stories
of Jesus are told clearly in these letters. Here we learn that all people are sinners who have been born into the world since Adam and
Eve sinned against God. We learn that every one deserves to be punished for his sins, but because God loves sinners he planned a way to
save them from punishment. He gave his only Son, Jesus, to be punished in their stead, that every guilty sinner might go free from
punishment.

But we learn also that not every sinner will be saved from punishment. Only those who believe that Jesus died for their sins will
be saved. Those who refuse to believe in Jesus will die in their sins.
For it is by believing in Jesus that his blood washes away the stains
which sin has made on the souls of men and women. And those who
do not believe can not have the stains of their sins washed away.

Another thing these epistles, or letters, teach us is how Christians
live. We learn in them that Christians are honest, good to the poor,
willing to suffer for Jesus' sake, kind to those who treat them wrongly,
always ready to forgive their enemies, and that they love one another,
and try to lead others to Christ. We learn that Christians are a happy
people; for God gives them joy that sinners know nothing about. This

joy comes into their hearts when they believe that Jesus washes away their sins with his blood. Sinners do not believe this, and they can not understand the Christian's joy. Always they feel guilty before God and afraid to die.

We learn in these epistles that some day Jesus is coming again. When he comes he will take with him all those who believe in him, and they shall dwell with him forever. In that day all who are lying in their graves asleep in death will waken, for a great trumpet will blow which will be heard in every part of the world. And those who died believing in Jesus will rise to meet him in the clouds of the sky. Those who did not believe in Jesus will cry out in fear when they rise from their graves. They will try to hide from the Lord, but nowhere shall they find a place.

These epistles tell us that no one shall know when the last day will come, for it will come like a thief comes in the night. Just as Jesus warned his disciples to watch and be ready, so the epistles tell us to look for the coming of the Lord.

Although many years have passed since these letters were written, we know their words are true. They tell us about things that are happening now. They say that men in the last days will not believe Jesus is coming again, and that they will scoff at those who try to please God. And we find many people in the world today who do not believe in Jesus, and who make fun of the true religion. Such people do not believe that God will destroy this world with fire, just as the people who lived before the great flood did not believe Noah's words when he warned them about the rain that would come on the earth. But God sent the rain, and God will send the fire, which will destroy this world and everything in it. No wicked person will be able to hide from God, for every hiding-place will be burned up.

The epistles also tell us much about God the Father, and God the Son, and God the Holy Spirit. These three are not three different Gods, but they are all one God. We can not understand how this is true, yet it is true. If we worship God the Father we must believe in God the Son and also in God the Holy Spirit. It is God the Holy Spirit who causes the sinner to feel that he should quit his wrong-doing and ask Jesus to forgive his sins. It is God the Holy Spirit who comes into the Christian's heart to dwell. And when we pray, whether we call on the name of the Father or on the name of his Son or on the name of the Holy Spirit, we are praying to the same God, and the same God will hear and answer our prayers.

STORY 31

WHAT GOD'S FAITHFUL SERVANT SAW WHILE HE WAS ON A LONELY ISLAND

The Book of Revelation

On a lonely island far from his friends and his homeland sat an old man. This old man was a Jew. In his younger days he had been a fisherman, and his home had been near the Sea of Galilee. But one morning he had left his fishing-net to follow a dear friend, and always from that time he had tried to please this friend. The time came not long afterwards when this friend went away, to heaven; but never again did the young man return to his humble toil by the seaside. Hereafter he became a preacher of the gospel, for his friend was Jesus. he was one of the twelve apostles of Jesus.

This old man was John. He was now on the lonely island because a wicked ruler had sent him there as a prisoner. But John was not unhappy, although he was often lonely. He knew the time would soon come when death would take him out of this world of trouble. Then he could go to be with Jesus, his beloved master and Lord. How he longed for that time to come!

One day while John was on the island he sat thinking about God. He remembered how the Christians always met together to worship on that day, which they called the Lord's day. While he thought about these things, presently he heard behind him a voice like a trumpet-blast, speaking. This voice said, "I am Alpha and Omega, the first and the last: what you see write in a book and send to the seven churches which are in Asia."

John turned about to see who was standing behind him and speaking with such a mighty voice. And when he had turned he saw seven golden candlesticks and among them one standing who looked like Jesus. But never before, not even on the mountain-side when Jesus talked with Moses and Ē-lī'-jăh, had John seen his master look like this. Now he was dressed in a long garment which reached his feet. About his chest was a girdle of gold, and in his right hand were seven stars. The face of Jesus shone like the noonday sun, his eyes like a flame of fire, and his feet shone like polished brass. When he spoke his voice sounded like the rushing of a mighty torrent of water.

John fell down at the feet of Jesus as if he were dead. Then he felt a touch, and looking up he saw Jesus bending over him and saying,

"Do not be afraid; I am the same one who was crucified, and who died, but now I am alive forevermore. Write the things that you see and hear and the things which shall be hereafter."

Jesus then told John that the seven stars he saw were the seven ministers who preached to the seven churches in Asia. The seven golden candlesticks which he saw were the seven churches, and to these seven churches John should write letters. And Jesus told John what he should write in each letter. One of these letters he intended for the church at Ĕph'-ĕ-sŭs, where Paul had preached the gospel during his missionary labors.

John faithfully wrote these letters; and they were kept safely, and finally copied in other books. Today we have each one of them written in the Book of Revelation, which is the last book of our Bible.

After John had written these letters he had a vision of the throne of God in heaven. He saw a door open in heaven and he heard the voice like a trumpet calling him to come up and enter the door. When he had entered he saw the great throne of God and around this throne sat twenty-four old men dressed in white and wearing crowns of gold. Other heavenly beings were round about, and all were worshiping the one who sat on the throne.

While John was looking on this wonderful sight he noticed in the hands of God a sealed book. And a strong angel cried out with a mighty voice, "Who is able to break the seals and to open the book?" Then a search began in heaven, but no one was found who was worthy to take the book, break the seven seals, and open it to see what was written inside. John wept when he saw that no one could do this. He longed to know what was written in the book of God. While he wept one of the old men who sat near the throne spoke to him and said, "Do not weep, for, see, the Lion of the tribe of Judah has been able to take the book and open it." John looked quickly and saw one who looked like a lamb. He knew it was Jesus, who had been killed like the lambs at Passover, and whom John the Baptist had called the Lamb of God. This one came to the throne and took the book.

The heavenly beings who stood around the throne now rejoiced greatly, and fell down to worship before the Lamb who had taken the book right from the right hand of God. They sang a new song, praising this one who took the book because he had given his own life to redeem them from sin and make them pure, that they might enter heaven.

When the Lamb of God opened the book, John saw the strange things that were in it. These things he wrote down, that others might read them and know what he had seen.

Afterwards John saw a new heaven and a new earth, for the old earth on which he lived seemed to pass away out of sight. Then, in the clouds he saw the great city of God coming down to dwell in the new earth. And he heard a great voice out of heaven, saying, "Behold, God's house is with men and he shall dwell with them. They shall be his people and he himself shall be their God. And God shall wipe away all tears from the eyes of his people. Never again shall they weep for sorrow, never again shall they cry for pain, because sorrow, pain, and death shall be taken away from them."

And John saw the beautiful city of God, far more beautiful than anything he had ever seen on earth. And he saw there is no need of the sun to shine as light for the people of God, because God himself is their light. No shadows of night ever darken that beautiful place, for night does not come in heaven.

John saw that people from every nation of earth dwelt in that city, people whose sins had been forgiven because they believed in Jesus. He saw that nothing unclean or impure entered that city, and only those were admitted whose names were written in heaven's book.

Through the city John saw a pure river of crystal water flowing, and along the banks of that river he saw the tree of life, on which fruit was always ripe. And the leaves of the tree were for the healing of the nations.

When John saw all these things he fell down to worship at the feet of the angel who showed them to him. But the angel picked him up and said, "Do not worship me, for I am just a servant. Worship God. And blessed are they who obey his commands, for they shall be able to enter the gates of the beautiful city, and to eat of the fruit that grows on the tree of life by the banks of the river."

Jesus then said to John, "I have sent my angel to tell you these things in the churches. And whoever wishes may come and drink of the water of life freely, for the invitation is to all men. But only those who hear and obey the words of God may share the blessings of the heavenly city. Any one who tries to add more words to the book of God shall be punished, and any one who tries to take away any part from that book shall have his own part taken away from the book of life, and from the holy city."

Then Jesus said, "Surely I come quickly." And John, the aged prisoner, replied, "Even so, come, Lord Jesus." And all those who love God and whose hearts have been made pure by the blood of Jesus feel, just as John did, the desire for the coming of the Lord.

Questions on the Stories

BY ELSIE E. EGERMEIER

These questions were purposely made simple; yet they are clear and comprehensive. They are suited to those of junior age and above. They follow the outline of the stories as told in the Bible Story Book, and a person who is able to answer them will have knowledge of the contents of the book.

Sunday-school teachers and junior and young people's leaders will find them invaluable. But especially will they be appreciated by parents, who after reading or telling the stories in the home will find these questions good to help organize the child's knowledge of Bible facts and impress the thoughts presented in the stories.

The Publishers.

QUESTIONS ON THE STORIES

STORIES OF THE OLD TESTAMENT

Part First—Stories of the Patriarchs

Story 1—How the World Was Made—Page 23
1. Who made the world in which we live?
2. How many days did God work when he created the world and everything in it?
3. What did God think about everything which he had made?
4. What did God give to man that the other living creatures did not have?
5. How did God spend the seventh day of the creation week?

Story 2—The Story of the First Earth-Home—Page 24
1. In what garden did God make the first earth-home?
2. Who lived in this beautiful home?
3. Why did God plant a test-tree in this garden?
4. In the form of which creature did the tempter come to the first woman?
5. Why were Adam and Eve afraid to meet God after they had eaten fruit from the test-tree?
6. Tell what happened to this man and woman after they had disobeyed God.

Story 3—The Story of the First Children—Page 27
1. Who was the first child born into the world?
2. What kind of work did this boy do when he grew to manhood?
3. Who was the second child born into the world?
4. What kind of work did this second child do when he became a man?
5. What kind of offerings did these brothers bring to God?
6. With whose offering was God pleased?
7. Which of these boys killed his brother?

Story 4—The First Great Ship and Why It Was Built—Page 31
1. Who was the oldest man that ever lived?
2. Why did God plan to destroy the people in the world?
3. How did Noah and his three sons please God?
4. Tell how God spared their lives because they pleased him.

Story 5—The Tower of Babel, and Why It Was Never Finished—Page 35
1. On what mountain did the ark lodge when the waters of the flood went down?
2. Why did the people plan to build for themselves a city and a great tower?
3. What did God think about their work when he looked upon it?
4. What strange thing did God cause to happen to the people about that time?
5. Why did many of the people move away to other lands and leave the great tower unfinished?

PART FIRST—STORIES OF THE PATRIARCHS

Story 6—A Man Who Heard and Obeyed God's Call—Page 36

1. Why did the people of Chăl-dē'-ă call the name of their great city Ur?
2. How was Abram, the son of Tē'-räh, different from his neighbors and friends?
3. Why did Abram decide to leave the land of Chaldea?
4. Who started on the long journey with Abram?
5. At what place did Abram's aged father die?
6. What land did God promise to give to Abram and to his children?

Story 7—How Abram Ended a Quarrel—Page 39

1. Who was Lot?
2. About what did the servants of Abram and of Lot quarrel?
3. Tell how Abram showed his unselfish disposition.
4. To whom had God promised all the land of Canaan?

Story 8—How Lot's Choice Brought Trouble—Page 40

1. Into what city did Lot with his family move?
2. What did God think about the people of Sodom?
3. Tell about the trouble which befell the people of the city.
4. How did Abram again show kindness to his nephew, Lot?
5. Why did not Abram accept a reward from the king of Sodom?

Story 9—Things That Happened Inside and Outside Abram's Tent-Home— Page 43

1. What reward for faithfulness did God promise to Abram?
2. Why did the servant-girl, Hā'-gär, try to run away from her mistress, Sâr'-ā-ī?
3. Who found her lying down to rest beside a fountain in the wilderness?
4. What did the angel of the Lord tell Hā'gär to do?
5. What name did Abraham give to Hā'-gär's infant son?
6. Who changed the names of Abram and of his wife?
7. What did their new names mean?

Story 10—Strange Visitors at Abraham's Tent-Home—Page 44

1. How did Abraham show kindness to the strange visitors who came to his tent-home?
2. Whom did Abraham discover those visitors to be?
3. To what place were they going?
4. Why did Abraham plead with the Lord to spare Sodom?
5. For how many righteous persons living in Sodom did the Lord finally promise Abraham that he would spare the city?

Story 11—What Happened to Sodom—Page 46

1. Who entertained the angel-visitors at Sodom?
2. Why did the angels smite with blindness the men who came rushing to Lot's house to see them?
3. Whom did Lot take with him when he fled from the city?
4. Tell what happened to Lot's wife.
5. Where did Lot and his daughters afterwards make their home?

4

Story 12—The Little Boy Who Became a Great Hunter—Page 48

1. What did Abraham name the infant son whom God had given to him and Sarah?
2. Why did Sarah ask Abraham to send Ĭsh'-mā-ĕl and his mother away from their home?
3. Who found Ĭsh'-mā-ĕl and his mother when they were lost in the great wilderness?
4. Where did Ĭsh'-mā-ĕl and his mother afterwards make their home?
5. What kind of man did Ĭsh'-mā-ĕl become when he grew up?

Story 13—How Abraham Gave Isaac Back to God—Page 50

1. Why did God ask Abraham to give Isaac back to him as an offering?
2. How did Abraham feel about God's strange request?
3. Whom did Abraham take with him on his journey to the place God had appointed?
4. Who carried the wood up the mountain-side to place on the altar of sacrifice?
5. What question did Isaac ask his father as they climbed the mountain together?
6. Tell how God provided an animal for the offering in Isaac's stead.

Story 14—How Abraham Found a Wife for Isaac—Page 52

1. Why was Abraham unwilling for Isaac to marry a daughter of his Canaanite neighbors?
2. To what place did he send his faithful servant to find a wife for Isaac?
3. Tell how God answered this servant's prayer at the well.
4. Why were Rebecca's father and brother willing to let her go back with Abraham's servant to become the wife of Isaac?

Story 15—What Two Boys Thought About Their Father's Blessing—Page 56

1. What were the names of Isaac's two sons?
2. Why was the elder brother a queer-looking lad?
3. What was the birthright?
4. How did Esau show that he did not value his birthright very much?
5. Why did the mother wish that Jacob instead of Esau should receive their father's blessing?
6. Why could Isaac not tell Jacob from Esau when he came to seek the coveted blessing?
7. How did Esau afterwards show his sorrow for having sold his birthright?

Story 16—Jacob's Lonely Journey and His Wonderful Dream—Page 59

1. Why did Jacob feel afraid to remain at home after he had received his father's blessing?
2. Who sent him back to his mother's home country?
3. Why was this done?
4. Tell how God cheered Jacob one night while he slept with a stone for a pillow.
5. Whom did Jacob meet at a well near the city of Hâr'ăn?

Story 17—How Jacob Was Deceived by Laban—Page 62

1. How did Jacob's uncle show that he was glad to see him?
2. What did Jacob ask for as wages when he worked for his uncle?
3. How was Jacob cheated by his uncle?
4. Whom did Jacob take with him when he started on his homeward journey?
5. Who warned Laban not to harm Jacob?

Story 18—Why Jacob's Name Was Changed to Israel—Page 64

1. Why did Jacob fear to return to Canaan?
2. With whom did Jacob wrestle all night?
3. What new name did the angel give Jacob?
4. What did the new name mean?
5. Tell about the meeting of the two brothers, Jacob and Esau.
6. What sad thing happened before Jacob and his family reached their old home?
7. Who helped Jacob bury his aged father, Isaac?

Story 19—How Jacob's Favorite Son Became a Slave—Page 67

1. How many sons did Jacob have?
2. Which of these sons was his favorite?
3. What kind of a lad was Joseph?
4. Why did the elder brothers hate him?
5. What did their hatred finally cause them to do?

Story 20—Joseph a Prisoner in Egypt—Page 71

1. To what country was Joseph taken by the Ishmaelites?
2 To whom did they sell him?
3. Why did the Egyptian officer cast Joseph into the king's prison?
4. Who showed kindness to Joseph in the prison?
5. Tell what Joseph did for two of the prisoners.

Story 21—Joseph a Ruler in Egypt—Page 73

1. Why did Pharaoh send to the prison for Joseph?
2. What did Joseph tell Pharaoh at the palace?
3. Tell what the King's dreams meant.
4. What honor did Pharaoh then bestow upon Joseph?
5. How did Joseph show his wisdom as a ruler?
6. When the years of famine came, what did Joseph do with the grain which he had stored away?

Story 22—How Joseph's Dreams Came True—Page 76

1. Why did Joseph's ten brothers come down to Egypt?
2. Of what was Joseph reminded when his brothers bowed before him?
3. Why did he not tell them at once who he was?
4. What did Joseph learn about his brothers' conduct that pleased him?
5. Which of the ten brothers did he keep in Egypt?

Story 23—Joseph Makes Himself Known to His Brothers—Page 79

1. Why was Jacob unwilling to send Benjamin to Egypt?
2. Why was Jacob finally persuaded to let him go?
3. How did Joseph receive his brothers when they returned the second time?
4. Why did Joseph instruct the steward to put his silver cup in Benjamin's sack?
5. How did the ten brothers show their care for Benjamin's safety?
6. Which of the brothers offered himself to become a lifetime slave in Benjamin's stead?
7. Tell how Joseph made himself known to his brothers.

Story 24—Joseph's Father and Brothers Come to Live in Egypt—Page 84

1. How did Jacob receive the tidings that Joseph was still alive?
2. Who spoke to Jacob one night in a vision, telling him not to be afraid to go to Egypt?
3. In what part of the land of Egypt did Joseph place his brethren?
4. In what land did Jacob die, and where was he buried?
5. What were the names of Joseph's two sons?
6. How did Joseph show his brothers that he had fully forgiven them?

Story 25—The Story of Job—Page 89

1. What kind of a man was Job?
2. Who accused Job before God?
3. How did God permit Satan to trouble Job?
4. What kind of afflictions did Satan then bring upon him?
5. How did Job's three friends act when they visited him?
6. How did the Lord comfort Job at the end of his severe trial?

Part Second—Stories About Moses

Story 1—How the Child Moses Came to Live in the King's Palace—Page 93

1. By what name were the descendants of Abraham, Isaac, and Jacob called?
2. How did the new Pharaoh treat them, after they had become a strong nation in Egypt?
3. Why did Pharaoh command that all the boy babies should be thrown into the River Nile?
4. Why was Moses' mother not afraid to disobey the king's command?
5. What did she do with her baby when she could no longer hide him?
6. What did the princess decide to do when she found the baby Moses?
7. Whom did she hire to be his nurse?

Story 2—Why Moses Lived in the Wilderness—Page 96

1. How do we know that Moses did not forget his own people when he lived in the king's palace-home?
2. What unwise thing did Moses do when he tried to help one of his people?
3. Why did Moses flee from Pharaoh's presence?
4. What kind of work did Moses do when he lived in the land of Mĭd′-ĭ-ăn?
5. How many years did Moses spend in that country?

Story 3—How God Spoke to Moses From a Burning Bush—Page 98

1. Where was Moses when God spoke to him from a burning bush?
2. What did God first tell Moses to do?
3. Where did God now wish to send Moses?
4. Why did Moses at first feel unwilling to go?
5. What signs did God give to Moses by which Moses could prove to his people that God was with him?
6. Whom did God finally send to go with Moses and to speak for him?

Story 4—Moses and Aaron Talk With a Stubborn King—Page 101

1. Why was Pharaoh unwilling to let the Israelites leave his country?
2. Why did the Israelites accuse Moses and Aaron of bringing greater trouble upon them?
3. Who comforted Moses when he felt unhappy because Pharaoh would not listen to his request?
4. Tell about the miracle which Moses and Aaron performed when they met Pharaoh on the river bank.

Story 5—Pharaoh Sees God's Mighty Signs and Miracles—Page 105

1. Tell how the plague of frogs affected Pharaoh.
2. What did the Egyptian magicians tell Pharaoh when the plague of lice and fleas came upon the land?
3. In what way was the plague of flies different from the other plagues which God had sent?
4. Tell about the terrible hail-storm, and how it frightened Pharaoh.

8

5. Why did the Egyptians plead with their stubborn ruler to let the Israelites go?
6. After which plague did Pharaoh send Moses away with a threat to kill him if he ever returned?

Story 6—When the Death-Angel Visited Pharaoh's Palace—Page 108

1. Tell about the first Passover supper.
2. Why had the Egyptian people grown friendly toward the Israelites?
3. What did the Israelites take with them when they left the land of Gō'-shĕn?
4. By what signs did the Israelites know that God was leading them when they started on their journey?
5. Whose coffin did the Israelites carry away with them when they left Egypt?

Story 7—How God Showed His Power at the Red Sea—Page 112

1. How many did the Israelites number when they first came into Gō'-shĕn?
2. How many large companies did they form when they left Gō'-shĕn?
3. Along the shore of what sea did they plan to make their first camp?
4. Why were the Israelites frightened when they knew that Pharaoh's army was following them?
5. Whom did they blame for bringing this trouble upon them?
6. Tell how God answered Moses' prayer for deliverance.

Story 8—What Happened in the Wilderness of Shur—Page 116

1. In what way was the Wilderness of Shur unlike the land of Gō'-shĕn?
2. How were the Israelites disappointed when they camped at Mâr'-ăh?
3. Tell how God healed the bitter spring-water at the camp.
4. What did God, at this place, promise the Israelites if they would obey him?
5. Where did the Israelites pitch camp the second time in the Wilderness of Shur?

Story 9—How God Fed the Hungry People in the Wilderness—Page 117

1. By what sign did God cause the people to know when he wished them to break camp and start forward on their journey?
2. In what way did the Israelites behave like fretful children?
3. Tell how God supplied meat and bread for the people in the Wilderness of Sin.
4. On how many days each week could the people gather the bread from heaven?
5. What happened to those who disobeyed Moses in failing to gather on the sixth morning enough for two days' supply?

Story 10—How God Showed His Power at Rephidim—Page 120

1. What fault did the Israelites find with their camping place at Rĕph'-ĭ-dĭm?
2. Tell how God supplied them with plenty of water.
3. With what wild people did the Israelites have a battle at Rĕph'-ĭ-dĭm?
4. What brave young man did Moses choose to lead the army of Israel against their enemy?
5. Who were Moses' visitors at this camp?

PART SECOND—STORIES ABOUT MOSES

Story 11—The Voice From a Smoking Mountain—Page 121

1. From what mountain did God speak to the Israelites?
2. Why had God commanded that none of the people should touch the mountain?
3. Why were the people afraid when they heard God's voice?
4. What do we call the words which God spoke in a voice of thunder to the people?
5. On what kind of tablets did God afterwards write those words?
6. How many days did Moses spend up on the mountain with God?
7. Whom did Moses command the people to obey during his absence?

Story 12—The Story of a Golden Calf—Page 124

1. Why did Aaron make a golden calf?
2. Whose example were the Israelites following when they worshiped this god of gold?
3. Who told Moses about Israel's great sin?
4. What did God plan to do with the people because they had so quickly forgotten him?
5. How did Moses show his love for Israel?
6. Why did Moses break the two tablets of stone on which God had written the Ten Commandments?
7. Tell how the Israelites were punished for their sin.

Story 13—How God Planned to Live Among His People—Page 127

1. Why did Moses cover his face with a veil whenever he talked to the people about God's words?
2. How did the people feel when they learned that God wished to dwell in their camp?
3. In which part of the camp did God tell Moses to set up the tabernacle?
4. From which of the twelve tribes did God choose men to care for the tabernacle?

Story 14—The Tabernacle, Where the Israelites Worshiped God—Page 129

1. What was the uncovered space surrounding the tabernacle called?
2. Of what was the "altar of burnt offering" built?
3. Into how many rooms was the tabernacle divided?
4. What was the first room called?
5. What was the second room called?
6. In what room were the two stone tablets containing the words of the Ten Commandments kept?

Story 15—How the People Worshiped God at the Tabernacle—Page 131

1. Whom did God choose to be high priest?
2. What work did God give to Aaron's sons?
3. Who lighted the first fire on the altar of burnt offering?
4. How many sacrifices for sin did the priests offer daily on the great altar?

5. What sad thing happened to two of Aaron's sons not long after the tabernacle worship had begun?
6. What great lesson did Aaron and his other sons learn from this experience?

Story 16—The Israelites' Journey From Sinai to the Border of Canaan—Page 133
1. At which place did the Israelites keep the second Passover supper?
2. Why did God send a fire into the camp at Tăb'-ĕ-räh?
3. When the people cried for meat what did God then do?
4. Why did God permit Moses' sister, Miriam, to become afflicted with leprosy?
5. Tell how Moses showed his forgiveness.

Story 17—How Ten Men Spoiled God's Plan—Page 135
1. Why did the Israelites wish to send spies into Canaan?
2. How many spies did God tell Moses to send?
3. What kind of report did ten of the spies bring back to camp?
4. Who were the two faithful spies?
5. Why did the people plan to kill Caleb and Joshua with stones?
6. How did God protect them?
7. What punishment did God send upon the people because they had refused to enter Canaan?

Story 18—Why God Caused the Earth to Swallow Some Israelites—Page 139
1. Whom did Kôr'-ăh and his friends envy?
2. In what terrible manner were they punished?
3. How did the Israelites displease God on the following day?
4. Tell how God began to punish them, and how Aaron stepped between them and death.
5. How did God use a blossoming rod to prove to the Israelites his choice of a high priest?

Story 19—Things That Happened to the Israelites During the Forty Years They Lived in the Wilderness—Page 142
1. At which place did Miriam, the sister of Moses and Aaron, die?
2. Tell what happened when the wells dried up at this same camp.
3. How did Moses and Aaron displease God, and because of this what did God say should happen to both of them?
4. Why did not Moses lead the Israelites through the land of Ē'-dom?
5. On what mountain did Aaron die?
6. Who then became the high priest?

Story 20—Why the Brass Serpent Hung on a Pole in the Israelites' Camp—Page 144
1. Why did God permit fiery serpents to enter the camp of Israel?
2. What happened to those who were bitten by the serpents?
3. Why did Moses make a serpent of brass and hang it on a pole?
4. In what way does the serpent of brass which Moses made remind us of our Savior, Jesus?

PART SECOND—STORIES ABOUT MOSES

Story 21—How God Helped the Israelites When They Trusted in Him—Page 145

1. Tell about the well which the chief men of the tribes dug in the wilderness.
2. What kind of people were the Amorites?
3. What happened to Sihon, king of the Amorites, and to the Amorites' country?
4. Who told Moses not to be afraid of Og, the king of Bā'-shăn, nor afraid of his army?
5. Near what river did the Israelites pitch their camp after taking possession of the countries of these kings?
6. How many years had passed since the Israelites approached the borders of the land of Canaan for the first time?

Story 22—What Happened to a Wise Man Who Tried to Disobey God—Page 146

1. Why did the king of Moab send for Bā'-laām?
2. Who warned Bā'-laām in the night not to help the king?
3. Why did Bā'-laām desire to return with them when the king sent messengers the second time?
4. Tell how the beast on which Bā'-laām rode saved his life.
5. What warning did the angel give Bā'-laām?

Story 23—How Balaam Tried to Please the King—Page 149

1. Why would Bā'-laām speak only words of blessing about the Israelites?
2. How many times did Balak, king of Moab, try to get Bā'-laām to speak against Israel?
3. Why was Bā'-laām sorry when he could not please the king?
4. How did Bā'-laām finally help the Moabites?
5. How did God punish the people of Israel when they became friendly with the Moabites?
6. What finally happened to Bā'-laām?

Story 24—The Last Journey of Moses—Page 150

1. Whom did God choose to take Moses' place as leader of the Israelites?
2. Why did the men of Reuben's tribe and the men of Gad's tribe wish to possess the land east of the river Jordan?
3. Who wrote the fifth book in the Old Testament, and what is that book called?
4. From what mountain did Moses look across the river, and far over into the land of Canaan?
5. Who buried Moses when he died?
6. How do we know that Moses was indeed a great man?

Part Third—Stories About Joshua and the Judges of Israel

Story 1—How a Woman Spoiled the Plan of a Wicked King—Page 153

1. How many spies did Joshua send across the river to Jericho?
2. In whose house did the spies hide when the king sent for them?
3. How did they escape from the city?
4. How did they promise to repay Rahab for her kindness to them?
5. By what sign were the men of Israel to know where to find Rahab and her family, that they might spare their lives?

Story 2—How the Israelites Crossed Over a Dangerous River—Page 155

1. Why were the Israelites not afraid to prepare to cross the Jordan although its waters were dangerously swift and deep?
2. What wonderful thing happened when the priests who carried the ark stepped into the edge of the stream?
3. Why did one man from each of the twelve tribes pick up a large stone from the bed of the river and carry it across to the Canaan shore?
4. At what place did the Israelites pitch their first camp in Canaan?
5. Why did God cease to send bread from heaven to the people after this time?

Story 3—What Happened to the Stone Walls of Jericho—Page 157

1. Whom did Joshua meet when he went out to view the city of Jericho?
2. How many days did the Israelites march around the city wall before it fell down?
3. How many times did they march around the city on the last day?
4. What did they do after they had marched around the city for the last time?
5. What caused the great walls to tumble?
6. Whom did the Israelites save alive?
7. What did God command the people to do with the treasures which they took from the ruined city?

Story 4—The Story About a Buried Sin—Page 161

1. Why could Ā'-chăn not enjoy the great victory at Jericho as much as did his neighbors and friends?
2. Who only probably knew of the buried stolen goods beneath Ā'-chăn's tent floor?
3. Why were the Israelites defeated in their first attack against Ā'-ī?
4. How was Ā'-chăn punished?
5. Tell about the Israelites' second attack against Ā'-ī.

Story 5—The Altar Where God's Law Was Written Upon Stone—Page 163

1. Why did Joshua lead all the Israelites to the bowl-shaped valley which lay between Mount Ē'băl and Mount Gĕ-rī'-zĭm?
2. Who, many years before, had built an altar and worshiped God at that place?

13

3. Who read in the hearing of all the people from the book in which Moses had written the laws of God?
4. What did the people mean when they said, "Amen!" to the reading of the law?
5. Where were these words afterwards written, that every one passing through the valley might read them?

Story 6—The People Who Fooled Joshua—Page 164

1. Why did the people of Gibeon wish to become friendly with the Israelites?
2. Tell of their clever plan to deceive Joshua.
3. How did the men of Israel feel when they found out that they had been fooled?
4. In what way were the Gibeonites punished because they had spoken falsely to Joshua?

Story 7—Why Joshua Spoke to the Sun and to the Moon—Page 165

1. Why did the five kings of Canaan make war against the Gibeonites?
2. Who helped the Gibeonites to gain a great victory?
3. Why were not Joshua and his soldiers afraid to meet these kings in battle?
4. Tell why Joshua commanded the sun and the moon to stand still.
5. What effect did the news of this great victory have upon the other inhabitants of Canaan?
6. How many kings of Canaan did Joshua and his army destroy?

Story 8—How the Land of Canaan Became the Land of Israel—Page 167

1. Into how many parts was the land of Canaan divided among the tribes of Israel?
2. What was each tribe to do with the Canaanites who lived in its part of the country?
3. What request did faithful old Caleb make of Joshua?
4. Why was not Caleb afraid to fight against the giants of Canaan?
5. To what place in Canaan was the tabernacle moved from Gĭl'-găl, and why?
6. How many times each year did God want the people to meet at the tabernacle to worship him?

Story 9—How God Planned to Use Some Cities in the Land of Israel—Page 169

1. What special work had God given to the Levites?
2. How many cities did God give them to live in?
3. Why were these cities scattered all through the twelve tribes?
4. For what purpose were the "cities of refuge"?
5. How many cities of refuge were there among the Israelites?

Story 10—The Story of the Altar Beside the Jordan River—Page 170

1. How many tribes had their homes on the east side of the river Jordan?
2. Whom did Joshua send with the men from these tribes when they returned to their homes after the conquest of Canaan?

3. Why did these men build an altar on the bank of the River?
4. Where had God commanded the Israelites to offer all their sacrifices?
5. Why did the men on the west side of the River feel angry when they heard about the new altar?
6. Whom did they send to learn why the new altar had been built?
7. Where was Joseph's coffin finally buried?

Story 11—Joshua's Last Meeting With the Israelites—Page 173

1. Why did Joshua send for all the tribes to meet him at Shē'-chĕm?
2. How old was Joshua when he talked with the Israelites for the last time?
3. What good promise did the people make when Joshua talked to them?
4. Why did Joshua set up a great stone under an oak-tree at Shē'-chĕm?
5. Who became high priest after Ĕl-ē-ā'-zär died?

Story 12—How God Helped the Israelites Out of Their Troubles—Page 174

1. What trouble came upon the Israelites because they failed to drive all the heathen nations out of Canaan?
2. Why did the angel's words bring sadness to the Israelites?
3. What great work did Ŏth'-nĭ-ĕl do for Israel?
4. For how many years did Ŏth'-nĭ-ĕl rule Israel as judge?
5. Why did God permit the king of Moab to defeat the Israelites in battle and rule over them?

Story 13—The Left-Handed Man Who Judged Israel—Page 176

1. Why were the Israelites unhappy when the king of Moab ruled over them?
2. Where did they go to offer sacrifices when they asked God's forgiveness?
3. Whom did God send as a deliverer to help them out of their troubles?
4. For how many years did the Israelites then enjoy rest from their enemies?
5. Who was the third judge of Israel?
6. Tell how he killed six hundred Philistines.

Story 14—Two Brave Women Who Helped the Israelites Out of Trouble—Page 178

1. Why did the people of Israel show great respect to Dĕb'-ŏ-räh, the prophetess?
2. For whom did Dĕb'-ŏ-räh send, to lead the Israelites to battle against Sĭs'-ĕ-rä's army?
3. Why did Bâr'-ăk refuse to go unless Dĕb'-ŏ-räh should accompany him?
4. Tell how God destroyed Sĭs'-ĕ-rä's army.
5. By whom was Sĭs'-ĕ-rä killed?

Story 15—How a Brave Man Tore Down an Altar of Baal—Page 180

1. What kind of people were the Mĭd'-ĭ-ä-nītes, and how did they trouble Israel?
2. Why did Gideon try to hide from the Mĭd'-ĭ-ä-nītes when he threshed out his grain?
3. Whom did God send to tell Gideon that he had been chosen to deliver Israel?
4. Tell how Gideon destroyed the heathen god which his relatives and neighbors had worshiped.

5. By what two signs did God prove to Gideon that he had been chosen to drive the Mĭd′-ĭ-ă-nītes out of the land?

Story 16—How the Midianites Were Surprized at Midnight—Page 184
1. Why did God plan that Gideon's army should be very small?
2. How many men left the camp before the battle because they were afraid?
3. How many remained after the last test to go to battle with Gideon?
4. Why did Gideon steal into the enemy's camp one night, and what did he hear that encouraged him?
5. Into how many companies did Gideon divide his men?
6. What did he tell them to carry in their hands?
7. Describe the midnight attack, and the results.
8. Why did Gideon refuse to be king over the Israelites?

Story 17—The Man Who Made Himself King Over Israel—Page 186
1. After Gideon died, how did his son, Ă-bĭm′-ĕ-lĕch, prove himself unfit to rule Israel?
2. Why did Ă-bĭm′-ĕ-lĕch kill his brothers?
3. Where was Ă-bĭm′-ĕ-lĕch crowned king?
4. Who spoke a parable about the trees making for themselves a king?
5. How long did Ă-bĭm′-ĕ-lĕch rule Israel?
6. Tell how Ă-bĭm′-ĕ-lĕch finally met his death?

Story 18—How a Girl Suffered for Her Father's Rash Promise—Page 188
1. Why did Jĕph′-thăh go away to live in the land called Tŏb?
2. Who heard about his brave deeds, and sent for him to help them?
3. What rash promise did Jĕph′-thăh make to God?
4. Who first met him when he returned home from battle victorious?
5. For how many years did Jĕph′-thăh judge Israel?

Story 19—The Story of a Strong Man Who Judged Israel—Page 191
1. What kind of person was a Nazarite?
2. In what way did Samson differ from other men when he grew to manhood?
3. Among which nation did Samson insist on making friends?
4. Why did Samson set fire to the Philistines' corn-fields?
5. How did he do this?
6. With what small weapon did Samson kill his enemies who had come to capture him?
7. How did Samson show his great strength to the men of Gā′-ză?

Story 20—How Samson Came to His Death—Page 194
1. Whom did the Philistines ask to help them discover the secret of Samson's great strength?
2. Why did Samson finally tell Dĕ-lī′-lăh the truth?
3. How was Samson captured by his enemies?
4. In what cruel manner was Samson treated by them?
5. Tell how he finally met his death.

PART THIRD—ABOUT JOSHUA AND THE JUDGES OF ISRAEL

Story 21—The Young Woman Who Forsook Idols to Serve God—Page 198

1. From whom did Ruth, the Moabitess, learn about the true God?
2. Why did Nā'-ō-mī and Ruth leave the land of Moab?
3. In which city of Israel did they make their home?
4. What rich man of that city showed much kindness to Ruth?
5. Tell how God blessed Ruth later on with a good husband and a happy home.

Story 22—The Little Boy Whose Mother Lent Him to the Lord—Page 202

1. For what did Hannah ask God one day while she prayed at Shī'-lōh?
2. What did Hannah call her little baby boy?
3. Why did Hannah take little Samuel to the Lord's house at Shī'-lōh one day and leave him there?
4. With what old man did Samuel then make his home?
5. Tell how God spoke to Samuel one night.

Story 23—The Story of the Stolen Ark—Page 205

1. Why did the men of Israel take the ark of God out to battle?
2. Why did God not protect them at this time when the ark was in their midst?
3. What happened to the ark of God?
4. How had Ē'-lī felt about it when his sons took the ark of God away from the tabernacle?
5. What did Ē'-lī do when he heard that the ark of God had been captured by the Philistines?

Story 24—How the Ark of God Troubled Dagon and His Worshipers—Page 207

1. In what place did the Philistines first set up the stolen ark?
2. What happened to the god, Dā'-gŏn, when the ark stood in his temple?
3. How did the people of the city suffer after they had stolen the ark?
4. Why did the Philistines finally become afraid of the ark?
5. Tell how they sent it back to Israel.
6. What happened to the men of Bĕth-shē'-mĕsh who looked inside the ark?

Story 25—How Samuel Judged the Israelites—Page 209

1. What happened to the tabernacle at Shī'-lōh after the ark of God was taken from it?
2. Where did Samuel then make his home?
3. What did Samuel tell the people of Israel to do if they wished to be delivered from the rule of the Philistines?
4. Tell what happened at Mĭz'-pēh when the Israelites met there with Samuel to ask God's forgiveness.
5. Who helped Samuel to judge the Israelites when he grew old?
6. Why did the people finally desire a king to rule over them?

Part Fourth—Stories About the Three Kings of United Israel

Story 1—The Tall Man Whom God Chose to Become Israel's First King—Page 213

1. To which of the twelve tribes did Israel's first king belong?
2. Relate the circumstances that brought about Samuel's meeting with Saul.
3. Why did Samuel treat Saul with such great respect at the feast?
4. By whom was Saul anointed to become Israel's first king?
5. Why did Samuel call the men of Israel to meet him at Mĭz'-pēh?
6. Where was Saul when Samuel wished to bring him before the people?

Story 2—How the Eyes of Some of Saul's People Were Saved—Page 216

1. In what cruel manner did the Ammonite king intend to treat the people of Jā'-bĕsh?
2. How did the men of Gĭb'-ĕ-ăh show their sympathy when they heard about the distress of the Jā'-bĕsh-ītes?
3. How did Saul show his kingly authority when he heard the news?
4. At what place did Saul and his army sacrifice to the Lord after their victory over the Ammonites?
5. Tell about the thunder and rain-storm at Shī'-lōh.

Story 3—King Saul and His People in Trouble—Page 218

1. How did Jonathan, Saul's son, prove himself to be a brave leader?
2. With which people were the Israelites now at war?
3. What had the Philistines done to frighten the Israelites and to weaken their army?
4. Who sent for Saul to meet him at Gĭl'-găl?
5. How did Saul act unwisely at this time?
6. In what way did God afterwards punish Saul for this sin?

Story 4—How the Faith of a Brave Young Prince Brought a Great Victory—Page 220

1. In whom did Jonathan trust when he went with his armor-bearer to the Philistine's camp?
2. How did God show that he was pleased with Jonathan?
3. What did the Philistines begin to do when the earthquake shook their camp?
4. What rash command did Saul give that day?
5. Who disobeyed the command?
6. Why did he act thus?
7. How was Jonathan's life spared?

Story 5—How Sin Robbed Saul of His Kingdom—Page 222

1. Whom did King Saul appoint as captain of his army?
2. Why did God send King Saul to destroy the Ă-măl'-ĕk-ītes?
3. What part of God's command did the king disobey?
4. Who told Samuel that Saul had disobeyed God?

5. Whom did King Saul try to blame for his disobedience?
6. Why, after this time, did Samuel never again visit King Saul?

Story 6—Why God Sent Samuel to Bethlehem—Page 224

1. Why was Samuel at first afraid to go to Bethlehem at God's command?
2. What old man with his sons did Samuel invite to the feast at Bethlehem?
3. Which of Jesse's eight sons did he not bring to the feast with him?
4. What work was David doing when the messenger found him in the fields near Bethlehem?
5. What did God tell Samuel to do when David came into his presence?

Story 7—Why Jesse Sent David to Visit King Saul—Page 227

1. Why did David not become king at once after Samuel had anointed him?
2. What terrible thing happened to King Saul after he refused to obey God's words?
3. Why did King Saul send for David to come to his palace-home?
4. In what way did David help the troubled King?

Story 8—How David Killed the Giant, Goliath—Page 228

1. To what nation did the giant, Gō-lī'-ăth, belong?
2. What request did Gō-lī'-ăth make of the army of Israel?
3. On what two occasions had God given wonderful strength to David, the shepherd lad?
4. Why did David leave the sheep and visit the camp of Israel?
5. How did David show his courage and his faith in God when he heard the giant defy the army of Israel?
6. Tell how David met the giant and killed him.
7. How did the death of their champion affect the Philistines?

Story 9—How Saul Became David's Enemy—Page 234

1. With what brave young Prince did David form a lifetime friendship after he had slain the giant, Gō-lī'-ăth?
2. Why would King Saul not permit David to return to his father's home after David had killed the giant?
3. What prompted King Saul to become jealous of David?
4. How did Saul try, on two occasions, to kill David?
5. Why did King Saul give his daughter to become David's wife?

Story 10—How Jonathan and Michal Saved David's Life—Page 236

1. How did Prince Jonathan prove himself to be David's friend?
2. How did David's wife help him to escape from the king's guard?
3. To whom did David go when he ran away from King Saul?
4. What happened to the messengers, and to King Saul, too, when they came to Samuel's home seeking for David?

PART FOURTH—ABOUT THE THREE KINGS OF UNITED ISRAEL

Story 11—Why a Little Boy Picked Up Arrows for a Prince—Page 238
1. Whom did Prince Jonathan take with him into the fields one day?
2. What did the Prince ask the boy to do for him?
3. Who was hiding behind a great rock in the field?
4. What sad news did Prince Jonathan bring to David?
5. What promise did David make to the Prince before they parted?

Story 12—Things That Happened While David Had No Home—Page 240
1. Why did David visit the tabernacle and talk with the high priest?
2. Who saw David talking with the high priest?
3. Why did David afterwards go to the land of the Philistines?
4. In what wilderness did David hide in a cave?
5. Who came to live with him there?
6. Tell how three of David's soldiers risked their lives to please him.

Story 13—How a Wicked Servant Obeyed a Wicked King—Page 242
1. Why did King Saul send for Ă-hĭm'-ĕ-lĕch, the high priest?
2. How did Ă-hĭm'-ĕ-lĕch's reply to the King's question cost him his life?
3. Why would not King Saul's soldiers obey his command to kill all the priests?
4. Who finally consented to do the wicked deed?
5. From whom did David hear about the sad news?

Story 14—How David Spared Saul's Life—Page 244
1. How did David show his kingly spirit at Kē-ī'-lăh?
2. Who warned David to leave the city lest King Saul kill him there?
3. Where did David and Prince Jonathan have their farewell visit?
4. Why would David not permit his soldiers to kill King Saul when Saul lay asleep in the cave?
5. Tell about David's visit to King Saul's camp one night.
6. To what land did David and his soldiers finally go to live until they heard of King Saul's death?

Story 15—The Unhappy Ending of Saul's Life—Page 248
1. Why did King Saul decide to visit the witch at Endor?
2. Whom did the witch say would kill her if she talked with the dead?
3. What message did King Saul receive from the mantled spirit that the witch called up?
4. What noble Prince was killed the following day on the battle-field?
5. How did King Saul come to his death?

Story 16—What Happened to David's Home at Ziklag—Page 250
1. Why did David and his soldiers not engage in battle with the Philistines?
2. What happened to the city where David and his soldiers had made their home?
3. How did David show kindness to an Egyptian whom they found in the wilderness?
4. Who brought tidings to David about the death of King Saul and Prince Jonathan?
5. How did David act when he heard that his enemy, King Saul, was dead?

20

Story 17—When the Shepherd Boy Became the King of Israel—Page 252
1. Where did David make his home when he returned to the land of Israel after Saul's death?
2. Over which one of the twelve tribes did David reign as king at Hē'-brŏn?
3. Why did the chief men of the other tribes finally send word to David that they wished him to be their king?
4. In what city did David set up his kingdom?
5. Why did David and his army wait under the mulberry-trees before going out to battle against the Philistines?
6. How did David and the Israelites first attempt to move the ark of God?
7. Tell how the ark was finally brought to the new tabernacle in Jerusalem.

Story 18—What Happened to a Little Lame Prince When He Grew Up—Page 254
1. Whose son was the little lame Prince?
2. How did he become crippled in his feet?
3. Why did King David send for him after he had grown to manhood?
4. What kindness did King David show to Mĕ-phĭb'-ŏ-shĕth for Jonathan's sake?

Story 19—David's Sin and His Punishment—Page 255
1. Whom did God send to speak to King David about his great sin?
2. What punishment did God say would fall upon the king because of his wrong-doing?
3. How did King David show that he was sorry because he had sinned against God?
4. What happened to the little Prince whom King David loved so dearly?
5. Why were the servants at first afraid to tell King David when the child had died?
6. Which of David's sons did God choose to become the third king of Israel?

Story 20—The Wicked Prince Who Tried to Steal His Father's Kingdom—Page 257
1. What kind of a prince was young Ăb'-să-lǫm?
2. How did he succeed in stealing the hearts of the people away from his father, David?
3. What excuse did he make when he asked permission of the King to go to Hē'-brŏn?
4. Why did King David and his faithful servants leave Jerusalem when they heard what had taken place at Hē'-brŏn?
5. How did King David's friend, Hū'-shâi, hinder Ăb'-să-lǫm from sending soldiers to capture his father, David, at once?

Story 21—How the Wicked Prince Was Hung in the Boughs of a Great Oak Tree—Page 259
1. Why did Ăb'-să-lǫm go out with his soldiers to capture King David?
2. Into how many companies did David divide his servants before sending them out to battle?
3. In what woods did the battle take place?
4. How did Ăb'-să-lǫm meet his death?
5. What did King David do when he heard how the battle had ended?

PART FOURTH—ABOUT THE THREE KINGS OF UNITED ISRAEL

Story 22—Why the Death-Angel Visited Jerusalem—Page 261

1. Why was God displeased to have King David count the number of soldiers in Israel?
2. Whom did God send to tell King David that he had done wrong?
3. Why did David choose the three days' pestilence instead of one of the two other evils?
4. What effect did the standing of the death-angel over Jerusalem with a drawn sword, have on David?
5. Why did the king build an altar on the top of Mount Mō-rī'-ăh?

Story 23—Why Solomon Rode Upon the King's Mule—Page 263

1. Who tried to take the throne when King David became too old to rule over Israel?
2. Why was the prophet, Nathan, displeased when he heard about Prince Ăd-ō-nī'-jăh's plans?
3. How did King David cause the people to know whom he had chosen to take his throne?
4. Why was Prince Ăd-ō-nī'-jăh frightened when he heard that his young brother, Solomon, had been anointed king?
5. How did Solomon show kindness to his elder brother?

Story 24—How God Spoke in a Dream to Solomon—Page 265

1. What kind of man was young Solomon?
2. How did God speak to him at Gibeon?
3. For what did Solomon ask God?
4. How may we know today that Solomon was indeed a wise man?
5. Who came from a far country to visit Solomon and to hear of his great wisdom?

Story 25—The Temple of the Lord, Which Solomon Built on Mount Moriah—Page 268

1. Why was God unwilling for King David to build the temple?
2. Where did King Solomon get wood to use for the temple building?
3. How many years did the builders work before the great temple was finished?
4. Whom did King Solomon call to attend the first religious service at the temple?
5. By what sign did the people know that God was pleased with the temple which Solomon had built?

Story 26—The Last Days of King Solomon—Page 270

1. Who led King Solomon into idolatry?
2. Why did the people of Israel become restless and dissatisfied with King Solomon's rule?
3. Who was Jĕr-ŏ-bō'-ăm?
4. Tell about the meeting of Ā-hī'-jăh, the prophet, with Jĕr-ŏ-bō'-ăm, in a field just outside Jerusalem.
5. Why did Jĕr-ŏ-bō'-ăm run away from the land of Israel to live in Egypt?

Part Fifth—Stories About the Divided Kingdom

Story 1—The Foolish Young Prince Who Lost His Father's Kingdom—Page 273

1. Who was next chosen to sit on David's throne after King Solomon died?
2. Why had Prince Rē-hō-bō'-ăm not learned to worship God?
3. Whom did the people of Israel call back from Egypt before they were ready to crown their new king?
4. To whose advice did Prince Rē-hō-bō'-ăm listen?
5. What was the result?
6. Which one of the twelve tribes crowned Rē-hō-bō'-ăm to be their king?

Story 2—The Story About Two Golden Calves—Page 275

1. Whom did the ten tribes choose for their ruler?
2. At what city was the new kingdom set up?
3. Why did King Jĕr-ŏ-bō'-ăm plan to change the religious worship of his people?
4. At what two places did he set up new altars?
5. What form of idolatry did he introduce to his people?
6. Tell what happened when the prophet of God reproved King Jĕr-ŏ-bō'-ăm for his great sin.

Story 3—Why a Prophet Was Killed by a Lion—Page 278

1. Why did the prophet refuse to accept the king's invitation to stay a while in Bethel and rest from his journey?
2. Who tempted the prophet to disobey God?
3. How was the prophet punished for his disobedience?
4. How did the old man who had tempted the prophet act when he heard that a lion had killed a stranger near the city?
5. Where was the disobedient prophet buried?

Story 4—What the Blind Prophet Told the Queen of Israel—Page 280

1. Why were the king and queen of Israel distressed about their little son, Ā-bī'-jăh?
2. To whom did King Jĕr-ŏ-bō'-ăm wish to speak about his child?
3. Why did the queen disguise herself like a poor woman when she went to visit the prophet?
4. In what dreadful way was the king punished for displeasing God?

Story 5—The Story of a King Who Tried to Destroy Idol-Worship—Page 281

1. In what way was King Ā'-să different from his father and his grandfather?
2. Why did King Ā'-să refuse to permit his grandmother to be queen of Judah?
3. How did God help King Ā'-să when a strong army came to war against his people?
4. What mistake did King Ā'-să make when he tried to hinder the plans of King Bā-ăsh'-ă?
5. From what kind of affliction did King Ā'-să suffer before he died?

23

PART FIFTH—STORIES ABOUT THE DIVIDED KINGDOM

Story 6—Why Birds Fed a Prophet by the Brook Near Jordan—Page 283

1. Why did things grow worse in the land of Israel when Ahab became King?
2. What kind of person was Ahab's wife, Queen Jĕz'-ĕ-bĕl?
3. On what errand did God send the prophet, Ē-lī'-jäh, to speak to King Ahab?
4. Why did Ē-lī'-jäh seek a hiding place by the Brook Chē'-rĭth?
5. Tell how God cared for his prophet while he lived by the Brook.
6. Where did God send Ē-lī'-jäh when the waters of the Brook dried up?
7. How did the poor widow show that she believed in Ē-lī'-jäh's God?
8. Tell how Ē-lī'-jäh afterwards rewarded her for her kindness to him.

Story 7—How God Showed His Great Power on Mount Carmel—Page 287

1. For about how many years did the famine last in the land of Israel and countries that were near by?
2. Why did King Ahab search everywhere for the missing prophet?
3. To whom did Ē-lī'-jäh first appear when he returned to the land of Israel?
4. Why was Ē-lī'-jäh not afraid to meet the angry king?
5. For what purpose did Ē-lī'-jäh wish to meet the prophets of Bā'-ăl?
6. How did Ē-lī'-jäh prove to all the people that the Lord is God?

Story 8—The Little Cloud That Brought a Great Rain—Page 291

1. What happened to the priests of Bā'-ăl after God sent fire to burn up Ē-lī'-jäh's sacrifice?
2. What was Ē-lī'-jäh doing while King Ahab and the people feasted on top of the mountain?
3. How many times did Ē-lī'-jäh ask God to send rain?
4. What message did Ē-lī'-jäh send to King Ahab when he heard that a little cloud was rising in the sky?
5. To what city did Ē-lī'-jäh then go?
6. How did King Ahab's account of the day's happenings to Queen Jĕz'-ĕ-bĕl spoil Ē-lī'-jäh's good feelings?

Story 9—What an Angel Found Under a Juniper-Tree in the Wilderness—Page 292

1. Where did the angel of God find Ē-lī'-jäh?
2. Why was the prophet feeling so unhappy?
3. How many times did the angel try to comfort Ē-lī'-jäh?
4. For how many days did Ē-lī'-jäh live on the strength he received from eating the angel's food?
5. Who talked with Ē-lī'-jäh when he hid in the cave on the mountain-side?
6. Tell how God comforted the unhappy prophet.
7. Whom did Ē-lī'-jäh anoint to become the next great prophet in Israel?

Story 10—Ahab and the Beggar-King—Page 295

1. Who helped King Ahab's soldiers to drive the Syrian army out of the land of Israel?
2. Why did the Syrians plan to fight in the valley when they came the next year to trouble Israel?

3. What happened to the city in which many of the Syrian soldiers had run to hide?
4. Why did King Ahab spare the life of the Syrian king?
5. How did God's prophet reprove King Ahab for letting his enemy return home safely?

Story 11—How a King's Pout Cost a Man's Life—Page 297
1. Why did Naboth not wish to sell his vineyard to King Ahab?
2. How did the king act when he found he could not have Naboth's vineyard?
3. In what cruel manner did Queen Jĕz'-ĕ-bĕl secure the vineyard for her husband?
4. Whom did God send to speak to King Ahab after he had taken possession of the coveted land?
5. Why could not King Ahab ever enjoy his new possession?

Story 12—When Fire Fell from the Sky and Burned Up Some Wicked Men—Page 300
1. How did wicked King Ā-hǎ-zī'-ǎh become injured?
2. To whom did he send messengers to inquire whether he should ever recover?
3. What message did God send to him?
4. How did King Ā-hǎ-zī'-ǎh feel toward Ē-lī'-jǎh for sending a message to him from the true God?
5. What happened to two of the companies which the king sent to capture Ē-lī'-jǎh?
6. Why was not the third company destroyed in the same manner?

Story 13—The Story of a Great Whirlwind—Page 302
1. Who accompanied Ē-lī'-jǎh on his last journey to visit the schools of the young prophets?
2. Why would not Ē-lī'-shǎ leave Ē-lī'-jǎh?
3. In what miraculous way did God provide a crossing at the River Jordan for his two prophets?
4. What last request did Ē-lī'-shǎ make of his master?
5. By what sign did Ē-lī'-shǎ know that God had granted his request?
6. How was Ē-lī'-jǎh taken to heaven?
7. How did the young prophets know that the spirit of Ē-lī'-jǎh rested on Ē-lī'-shǎ when they saw him return alone?

Story 14—Why Two Hungry Bears Killed Some Children from Bethel—Page 304
1. How did God heal the waters at Jericho?
2. Why did the children of Bethel mock Ē-lī'-shǎ, the prophet?
3. When Ē-lī'-shǎ asked God to punish them, what happened?
4. Whom did Ē-lī'-shǎ wish to visit at Bethel?

Story 15—Elisha's Miracle That Saved Two Boys from Becoming Slaves—Page 306
1. To whom did the poor widow tell her troubles?
2. What did the prophet advise her to do?
3. Who helped her to obey the prophet's words?

25

4. Why did the widow not empty her own pot of oil?
5. How did she pay off the debt which her husband had owed the rich man?

Story 16—The Story About a Little Boy Who Died and Became Alive Again—Page 308

1. Who entertained Ē-lī'-shǎ and his servant whenever they passed through Shû'-nĕm?
2. How did God reward the Shû'nǎm-mīte woman and her husband for their kindness to his prophet?
3. What great sorrow came to this woman one day?
4. Why did she at once seek for Ē-lī'-shǎ?
5. Tell how God answered Ē-lī'-shǎ's prayer.

Story 17—Elisha's Kindness to the Poor—Page 311

1. How did Ē-lī'-shǎ take the poison from the food which the people were eating?
2. Tell about the miracle of the twenty barley loaves and some ears of new corn in the husks.
3. On what occasion did God cause iron to swim?
4. Why was Ē-lī'-shǎ so dearly loved by his friends?

Story 18—How a Little Slave-Girl Helped a Heathen Man to Find the True God—Page 312

1. How did the little Israelite girl come to live in Syria?
2. To whose home was she taken as a slave?
3. With what terrible disease was Nā'-ǎ-mǎn afflicted?
4. Who told Nā'-ǎ-mǎn that Israel's prophet could cure leprosy?
5. Why was Israel's king alarmed when Nā'-ǎ-mǎn came to him with a letter from the King of Syria?
6. How did Ē-lī'-shǎ's message to Nā'-ǎ-mǎn offend him at first?
7. Tell what happened when Nā'-ǎ-mǎn decided to do as Ē-lī'-shǎ had bidden.
8. Why was Gĕ-hā'-zī, Ē-lī'-shǎ's servant, afterwards smitten with leprosy?

Story 19—A Little Boy Who Became King, and How He Ruled in Judah—Page 317

1. How old was Prince Jō'-ǎsh when he was crowned king of Judah?
2. From whom had he been hidden since he was a baby?
3. Why had this been done?
4. What happened to the wicked queen, Ăth-ǎ-lī'-ǎh after Jō'-ǎsh was crowned king?
5. Why did Jō'-ǎsh in his last days do many things which displeased God?

Story 20—How Elisha Led His Enemies Into a Trap—Page 319

1. How did Jĕ-hôr'-ǎm learn about the plans of the Syrian king?
2. Why was Ē-lī'-shǎ's servant alarmed when he saw the Syrian army approaching their home?
3. What wonderful sight did the servant behold after Ē-lī'-shǎ asked God to open his eyes?
4. How did God enable Ē-lī'-shǎ to lead the entire Syrian army into the capital city of Israel?
5. What kindness did the prophet command King Jĕ-hôr'-ǎm to show to his captives?

PART FIFTH—STORIES ABOUT THE DIVIDED KINGDOM

Story 21—Where Four Lepers Found Food for a Starving City—Page 321
1. Why were the people of Să-mâr′-ĭ-ă starving for food?
2. Who did King Jĕ-hôr′-ăm say was to blame for the famine in the city?
3. What strange words did Ē-lĭ′-shă tell the King when the King came to kill the prophet?
4. What frightened the Syrian army away from the city?
5. Who first discovered that the enemy had gone?
6. Tell how Ē-lĭ′-shă′ŝ strange words to the King came true.

Story 22—The Prophet Who Tried to Run Away from God—Page 323
1. Why did God wish to send a prophet to Nĭn′-ĕ-vēh?
2. Whom did God choose to go on this errand?
3. Why did Jonah try to run away from God?
4. How was Jonah's life spared?
5. What did the people of Nĭn′-ĕ-vēh do when they heard Jonah's words?
6. Why did God spare the city from destruction?
7. How did God use a gourd-vine to teach his prophet a lesson?

Story 23—The Sad Ending of the Kingdom of Israel—Page 327
1. Why did God permit the kingdom of Israel to be destroyed?
2. Who came to live in the land of Israel after the Israelites were carried away into captivity?
3. Why were the strange, new people afraid of the God of the land of Israel?
4. Whom did the King of Assyria send to teach the new people about the true God?
5. What kind of religion did the people of the land then have?

Story 24—The Good King Hezekiah—Page 329
1. How did King Hĕz-ē-kĭ′-ăh restore the worship of the true God in Judah?
2. Why was King Hĕz-ē-kĭ′-ăh frightened when he heard the message which the Assyrian king had sent?
3. How did the prophet, Isaiah, comfort King Hĕz-ē-kĭ′-ăh?
4. Why did the Assyrian king hurry back to his own country without troubling Judah any more?
5. Tell how God added fifteen years to King Hĕz-ē-kĭ′-ăh′ŝ life.

Story 25—The Story About a Forgotten Book—Page 332
1. Why had the book of Moses been forgotten?
2. Who found the book hidden beneath some rubbish in the temple?
3. What did King Jō-sī′-ăh do when he heard the words read from the book of Moses?
4. How may we know that Jō-sī′-ăh was a good king?
5. Why did the prophet of God weep when King Jō-sī′-ăh died?

Story 26—The Weeping Prophet, and His Great Work—Page 334
1. Why were the princes of Judah alarmed when they heard the words of God which Jeremiah's friend had written?
2. How did the words of God affect the wicked king?
3. Why was Jeremiah thrown into a dungeon beneath the prison?
4. How was Jeremiah afterwards taken out of this dungeon?
5. Who brought an army against Jerusalem and destroyed the city?
6. Why was Jeremiah called the "weeping prophet"?

Part Sixth—Stories About the Jews

Story 1—How the People of Judah Lived in a Strange Land—Page 339
1. By what name were the Israelites called when they were taken captive to Babylon?
2. How did their new ruler treat them in the land of captivity?
3. By what faithful prophet did God still send messages to the people?
4. Why would not the Jews worship the idols of their heathen neighbors?

Story 2—Four Brave Boys Who Stood Before a Great King—Page 340
1. Why were Daniel and his three friends unwilling to eat food from the King's table?
2. What request did Daniel make of the King's officer who brought food to the young princes?
3. What favorable change did the officer observe in Daniel and his friends at the end of the ten days' trial?
4. For how many years did these four young men study the language and the wisdom of the Chăl-dē'-ăns?
5. What did the King's examination of these young princes reveal?

Story 3—How Daniel Became a Great Man in Babylon—Page 342
1. What strange request did King Nĕb-ū-chăd-nĕz'-zär make of his wise men?
2. Why did he threaten to kill every one of them?
3. Who entreated the angry King to spare the lives of the wise men?
4. How did God reveal to Daniel the King's dream and its meaning?
5. What honor did King Nĕb-ū-chăd-nĕz'-zär bestow upon Daniel after he had told the dream and its interpretation?
6. Why did the King give honorable offices to Daniel's three friends also?

Story 4—What the King Saw in the Fiery Furnace—Page 345
1. Why did King Nĕb-ū-chăd-nĕz'-zär command all the princes, rulers, and officers in his kingdom to come to the plain of Dū'-rä?
2. Why had the King prepared a fiery furnace?
3. Why did Shā'-drăch, Mē'-shăch, and Ā-bĕd'-nĕ-gō refuse a second opportunity to bow down before the image?
4. What happened to the mighty men who threw these three brave rulers into the furnace?
5. What strange sight did King Nĕb-ū-chăd-nĕz'-zär see in the fiery furnace?
6. Why had not these brave rulers been injured by the fire?
7. What did King Nĕb-ū-chăd-nĕz'-zär now think about the God of these three men?

Story 5—How God Humbled the Proud Heart of Nebuchadnezzar—Page 347
1. Why was Daniel at first afraid to tell King Nĕb-ū-chăd-nĕz'-zär the meaning of the King's second strange dream?

28

2. Tell how God caused the dream to come true.
3. How did Něb-ū-chăd-něz'-zär show his change of mind after God had permitted his mind to return, and his heart to become like a man's heart?

Story 6—The Strange Handwriting on the Wall of the Palace—Page 350

1. How did Běl-shăz'-zär dishonor the vessels of gold which his grandfather,
King Něb-ū-chăd-něz'-zär, had taken from the temple in Jerusalem?
2. Why, during the feast, did the gladness suddenly die out of King Běl-
shăz'-zär's heart?
3. Whom did the old Queen Mother tell Běl-shăz'-zär to send for, when the
Chăl-dē'-ăn wise men could not read the strange handwriting on the
wall?
4. What did brave old Daniel tell the King that the strange writing meant?
5. How did the King honor Daniel for his wisdom?
6. What happened to the kingdom of Babylon that same night?

Story 7—Daniel in the Lions' Den—Page 354

1. What honorable position did King Dă-rī'-ŭs give to Daniel?
2. Why did the princes and presidents hate Daniel?
3. What scheme did those wicked men devise in order to get rid of Daniel?
4. Why did King Dă-rī'-ŭs consent to make such a new law?
5. How did the King feel when he heard that Daniel had broken the new law?
6. How long was Daniel kept in the lions' den?
7. Tell how God cared for him there.

Story 8—Daniel's Angel Visitor—Page 356

1. For what did Daniel pray very earnestly when he became an old man
2. Whom did God send to comfort Daniel?
3. Tell about Daniel's heavenly visitor at the riverside.
4. How did Daniel rank among the prophets?

Story 9—The Home-Coming of the Jews—Page 358

1. What King permitted the Jews to return again to Judah and rebuild the
temple?
2. Who became leader of the company of returning Jews?
3. What treasures did they carry with them on their long journey?
4. Why did not all the Jews return again to their own country?
5. What did the priests and the Levites do as soon as they had located the
ruins of the temple?

Story 10—How the New Temple Was Built in Jerusalem—Page 359

1. How did the people celebrate the occasion, when the foundation of the new
temple was laid?
2. Why were not Zĕ-rŭb'-bă-bĕl and Jĕsh'-ū-ă, the high priest, willing to let the
Să-mâr'-ĭ-tăns assist in building the new temple?
3. Who encouraged the Jews to begin the second time on the building?
4. What caused the Să-mâr'-ĭ-tăns to cease trying to hinder the Jews?

Story 11—The Beautiful Girl Who Became a Queen—Page 362
1. In whose home did Esther, the Jewess, grow up to womanhood?
2. Why did King Ā-hǎs-ū-ē'-rŭs wish to choose a new queen?
3. Who sent Esther to the King's palace with the other beautiful maidens?
4. What did the King do when Esther was brought before him?
5. Tell how Môr-dĕ-cā'-ī saved the King's life.

Story 12—Why a Proud Man Planned to Destroy All the Jews—Page 364
1. Why did Hā'-mǎn become displeased with Môr-dĕ-cā'-ī?
2. How did Hā'-mǎn finally plan to get revenge on Môr-dĕ-cā'-ī because he had refused to bow before him?
3. Why did the King consent to Hā'-mǎn's wicked plan?
4. Why did not Môr-dĕ-cā'-ī dare to come near the palace to send a message to Queen Esther?

Story 13—How Queen Esther Saved the Lives of Her People—Page 366
1. From whom did Queen Esther learn about the wicked plot of Hā'-mǎn's?
2. Why was Esther at first afraid to speak to the King, as Môr-dĕ-cā'-ī urged her to do?
3. On what conditions did she finally consent to appeal to the King?
4. Why did Hā'-mǎn feel honored when Queen Esther invited him to attend her banquet?
5. Who urged Hā'-mǎn to erect a gallows from which to hang Môr-dĕ-cā'-ī?
6. What humiliating ordeal did the King command Hā'-mǎn to pass through?
7. Who was hanged on the gallows which Hā'-mǎn had built for Môr-dĕ-cā'-ī?
8. How were the Jews delivered from their enemies?

Story 14—Ezra, the Good Man Who Taught God's Law to the Jews—Page 371
1. Why was Ezra, the priest, called a scribe?
2. For what purpose did the King of Persia send Ezra to Judah?
3. Why was Ezra ashamed to ask the King for soldiers to protect his company from robber-bands along the way to Judah?
4. Whom did they ask to take care of them?
5. How did Ezra show his interest in the true service of God when he reached Jerusalem?

Story 15—The King's Cupbearer and His Story—Page 373
1. Who brought messages to Nē-hĕm-ī'-ǎh from the land of Judah?
2. Why did Nē-hĕm-ī'-ǎh weep when he heard how things were faring at Jerusalem?
3. Why was Nē-hĕm-ī'-ǎh afraid when the King asked the reason for his sorrow?
4. What kindness did the King show to Nē-hĕm-ī'-ǎh?
5. Tell about Nē-hĕm-ī'-ǎh's midnight ride around Jerusalem, and his resolve.

Story 16—How the Walls of Jerusalem Were Rebuilt—Page 375
1. Who tried to hinder the rebuilding of Jerusalem's wall?
2. Why did Nē-hĕm-ī'-ǎh and his workmen carry swords and spears while they worked on the wall?
3. For how many years did Nē-hĕm-ī'-ǎh act as governor of Jerusalem?
4. How many times did Nē-hĕm-ī'-ǎh visit Jerusalem?
5. Who was the last prophet that God sent to speak to the Jews during Old Testament times?

STORIES OF THE NEW TESTAMENT

Part First—Stories About Jesus

Story 1—An Angel Visitor in the Temple—Page 383

1. Why had Zăch-ă-rī'-ăs left his home in the hill-country of Judah and gone to Jerusalem?
2. What work was Zăch-ă-rī'-ăs doing when he had an angel visitor in the temple?
3. What were the people who stood in the court outside doing?
4. What wonderful news did the angel bring to Zăch-ă-rī'-ăs?
5. Why was Zăch-ă-rī'-ăs stricken dumb?

Story 2—The Heavenly Messenger in Galilee—Page 385

1. To what young woman in Nazareth did God send the angel Gabriel?
2. Why had God chosen Mary to become the mother of Jesus?
3. About what other promised child did the angel tell Mary?
4. Why was Elizabeth glad when Mary came to visit her?
5. Who told Joseph, the carpenter, about the secret of Jesus' birth?

Story 3—How the Dumb Priest and His Wife Named Their Child—Page 388

1. What did Zăch-ă-rī'-ăs and Elizabeth prepare to do when their child was eight days old?
2. By what name did the relatives and friends wish to call the child?
3. Why did both his parents wish to call him John?
4. What happened to Zacharias after the baby had been given a name?
5. How old was John before he began the great work which God had given him to do?

Story 4—The Story of a Wonderful Baby's Birth—Page 390

1. Why did Joseph and Mary journey to Bethlehem?
2. Where did they find lodging when they came into that city?
3. Why did the angels watch over Bethlehem one night while Mary and Joseph were there?
4. Who heard the glorious song the angels sang?
5. Where did the shepherds go after they had heard the angel?
6. What is the meaning of the name "Jesus"?
7. Why did Joseph and Mary take Jesus to the temple when he was forty days old?
8. How did the aged Simeon, and the prophetess, Anna, know that the baby Jesus was the Savior of men?

31

Story 5—The Wise Men Who Followed a Star—Page 394

1. What wonderful meaning did the new star in the heavens have to the wise men in the east country?
2. Why did these wise men decide to journey to Judah?
3. From whom, in Jerusalem, did the wise men inquire about the new-born King of the Jews?
4. What request did King Herod make of the wise men when he sent them away to Bethlehem?
5. How did God help the wise men to find the baby Jesus?
6. Why did the men not return to Jerusalem and tell King Herod that they had found the new-born King?
7. Who warned Joseph to take Mary and the baby Jesus away to the land of Egypt?
8. What wicked deed did King Herod do because he was jealous of the baby Jesus?
9. Why did Joseph afterwards take Mary and Jesus to their home town of Nazareth?

Story 6—When Jesus Was a Boy Twelve Years Old—Page 397

1. Why did Joseph and Mary take Jesus on this journey to the temple?
2. How did Jesus disappoint Joseph and Mary?
3. For how many days did they search before they found Jesus?
4. What was Jesus doing when they found him?
5. Why did he return with Joseph and Mary to their home in Nazareth?

Story 7—The Strange Preacher in the Wilderness—Page 401

1. Why was the wilderness preacher called John the Baptist?
2. Of what great prophet did John remind the people?
3. Why did Jesus ask John to Baptize him?
4. By what sign did John know that Jesus was God's promised Savior?
5. Who influenced King Herod to shut John up in prison?

Story 8—The Temptations of Jesus—Page 403

1. Who found Jesus alone in the wilderness?
2. How long had Jesus been without food?
3. Why would not Jesus turn stones into bread?
4. Why did Satan want Jesus to cast himself down from the pinnacle of the Temple?
5. What did Satan promise to give to Jesus if he would fall down and worship him?
6. Who came from heaven to supply his need of food and strength after Satan's temptations had failed to defeat Jesus?

Story 9—How Five Men Became Acquainted With Jesus—Page 405
1. What did John say of Jesus when he saw him walking by?
2. Why did two of John's disciples follow Jesus that day?
3. Who brought Simon to Jesus?
4. What new name did Jesus give to him?
5. Why did Philip become a follower of Jesus?
6. Whom did Philip then bring to Jesus?

Story 10—The Wedding-Feast Where Jesus Showed His Power—Page 408
1. Where did Jesus perform his first miracle?
2. Why were the servants careful to do just as Jesus had bidden them?
3. What did the governor of the feast say concerning the wine which Jesus had made from water?

Story 11—The Great Teacher in Jerusalem—Page 411
1. What did Jesus do when he beheld the disorder in the temple court?
2. What did Jesus say that his Father's house should be used for?
3. Who among the proud Pharisees sought to become acquainted with Jesus?
4. What did Nĭc-ŏ-dē'-mŭs think concerning Jesus after he had visited with him?

Story 12—The Tired Stranger Who Rested by a Well—Page 414
1. Why did Jesus stop by the wayside well at Sȳ'-chär?
2. Who came to draw water from the well while Jesus sat near by?
3. Why was the woman of Să-mâr'-ĭ-ă surprized when Jesus asked her for drink?
4. Why did the woman believe that Jesus was a prophet?
5. Who did Jesus tell the woman that he was?
6. How long did Jesus remain at Sȳ'-chär, teaching the people?

Story 13—The Story of a Man Who Had Great Faith in Jesus' Power—Page 416
1. Why did the nobleman from Că-pĕr'-nă-ŭm wish to see Jesus?
2. Where did he go to find Jesus?
3. Why did Jesus not return with the nobleman?
4. What happened to the sick child while the father was talking with Jesus?
5. What effect did this miracle have upon the members of that home where the sick child was healed?

Story 14—The Angry Mob on the Hill-Top of Nazareth—Page 418
1. How had Jesus spent every Sabbath while he had lived in Nazareth?
2. Why did the people of Nazareth become displeased with Jesus' teaching?
3. What did they attempt to do with him?
4. In what city did Jesus afterwards make his home?

Story 15—Four Fishermen Who Left Their Nets to Follow Jesus—Page 420
1. Why did the four fishermen quit their boats and follow Jesus?
2. Who were these four men?
3. How did Jesus help the demon-possessed man in the synagog of Că-pĕr'-nă-ŭm?

33

4. What did Jesus do for Simon's mother-in-law who lay sick with fever?
5. Tell how Jesus helped his friends who had fished all night and caught nothing.

Story 16—How Matthew the Publican Became a Disciple of Jesus—Page 424
1. Why were the publicans called "sinners"?
2. What work was Matthew doing when Jesus called him to be a disciple?
3. Why did Matthew prepare a great feast at his house?
4. Who came to this feast to find fault with Jesus?
5. What part of the Bible did Matthew, the publican, write?

Story 17—How Jesus Healed a Cripple and a Man Whose Hand Was Withered—Page 427
1. Why did many afflicted people gather at the pool called Bĕth-ĕs'-dă?
2. How long had the poor man been crippled to whom Jesus talked?
3. What did Jesus tell this man to do?
4. Why did the Jews find fault with the man when he obeyed Jesus?
5. What did Jesus tell the poor man when he found him in the temple?
6. What miracle did Jesus perform on the Sabbath in a synagog of Galilee?

Story 18—The Twelve Men Who Were Called Apostles—Page 430
1. Why did Jesus choose twelve men to be his disciples?
2. How did Jesus get new strength on the night before he chose his twelve helpers?
3. Which of these twelve men proved unworthy of Jesus' confidence?
4. What did Jesus give to these twelve men before he sent them out to work for him?
5. Give the names of the twelve disciples.

Story 19—The Sermon on the Mountain-Side—Page 431
1. To what place did Jesus take his twelve apostles to teach them his doctrine?
2. Whom did Jesus say were blessed?
3. Why was Jesus' sermon on the mountain-side more wonderful than the teachings of Moses?
4. Who did Jesus say those who hear his words and obey them are like?

Story 20—How Jesus Healed a Man Who Was a Leper—Page 433
1. Why were leprous persons not permitted to come near to other people?
2. What did the poor leper tell Jesus as this leper knelt in the dust of the roadside?
3. Why was Jesus not afraid to touch the leper?
4. What did Jesus tell the man to do after he was healed?
5. Why did the man tell others what Jesus had done for him?

Story 21—How a Roman Captain Showed His Great Faith in Jesus—Page 435
1. What kindness had the Roman captain shown toward the Jews?
2. Why was he glad when he heard that Jesus had returned to Că-pĕr'-nă-ŭm?
3. Whom did he send to speak to Jesus about coming to heal his servant?
4. What message did the friends of the Roman captain take to Jesus before he came to the house where the servant lay ill?
5. With what words did Jesus praise the Roman captain?

Story 22—Why Four men Tore Up the Roof of a Crowded House—Page 436

1. What strange thing happened while Jesus was teaching in a house in Că-pĕr'-nă-ŭm one day?
2. Why had the four men brought their crippled friend to Jesus in this queer way?
3. How did Jesus encourage the poor man's faith?
4. What did Jesus say to the cripple lying on the mat when He had read the thoughts of his fault-finders?
5. What caused the people in that crowded house to glorify God on that day?

Story 23—When a Widow's Sorrow Was Changed into Joy—Page 438

1. Who stopped the funeral procession outside the city of Nā'-ĭn?
2. How did Jesus show his great power there?
3. Why did John the Baptist send two friends to speak to Jesus?
4. What was the sad end of John the Baptist?

Story 24—A Pharisee, a Sinful Woman, and the Savior—Page 441

1. Why did Simon, the Pharisee, ask Jesus to dine at his home?
2. Who washed Jesus' feet with tears that day?
3. What did the proud Pharisee think of Jesus when he permitted the woman to touch his feet?
4. How did Jesus rebuke Simon for his wrong thoughts?
5. How did he show his pity to the sinful woman?

Story 25—Story Sermons by the Sea—Page 442

1. What is a parable?
2. Who asked Jesus why he spoke in parables to the people?
3. To whom did Jesus explain the meaning of his parables?
4. Tell the parable of the sower.
5. Why are those who hear and obey God's words like the good ground of this parable?

Story 26—The Flooded Ship That Did Not Sink, and the Wild Man Made Well—Page 445

1. Why did the disciples of Jesus become so frightened one night on the Sea of Galilee?
2. What did they ask Jesus when they roused him from sleep?
3. How did Jesus show his great power that night?
4. Who met them when the ship came to land at the other side of the Sea?
5. What request did the evil spirits make of Jesus?
6. What happened to the hogs when the evil spirits entered into them?
7. How did the people of that country treat Jesus?
8. What did Jesus tell the man to do after he had made him well?

Story 27—The Little Girl Who Died and Became Alive Again—Page 448

1. Why did Jā-ī'-rŭs ask Jesus to come to his house?
2. Who pressed through the crowd that followed Jesus to touch the hem of his garment?
3. Why did Jesus ask, "Who touched me?"
4. What happened to the daughter of Jā-ī'-rŭs before Jesus reached her bedside?
5. How did Jesus change sorrow into joy in Jā-ī'-rŭs' home?
6. How did Jesus help the two blind men who cried after him?
7. How did Jesus help the demon-possessed man who could not cry for mercy because he was dumb?

Story 28—A Boy's Lunch-Basket, and a Great Miracle—Page 450

1. Why did the people follow Jesus into the desert place?
2. Of what did that throng of eager people remind Jesus?
3. Who in that company had brought a lunch with him?
4. Which of the disciples brought the boy with the lunch to Jesus?
5. Tell about the great miracle.
6. Why would Jesus not allow the people to take him for their king?

Story 29—The Man Who Walked on the Water and Became Afraid—Page 452

1. Where was Jesus when the disciples were rowing against the wind-blown waves?
2. How did Jesus come to them across the water?
3. Why were the disciples frightened when they saw Jesus?
4. What strange request did Simon Peter make of Jesus?
5. Why did Simon Peter begin to sink into the Sea?
6. What happened after Jesus brought Simon safely into the ship?

Story 30—How Jesus Answered a Mother's Prayer—Page 454

1. Why did Jesus take his disciples into the land of Phœ-nĭç'-ĭä?
2. Who came with her sorrow to ask Jesus for help?
3. How did Jesus treat this Gentile woman at first?
4. What did the disciples urge him to do with her?
5. How did the woman show her great faith in Jesus' power?
6. What happened to the afflicted daughter in her home?

Story 31—What a Multitude Learned About Jesus—Page 455

1. How did the people of Găd'-ä-rä receive Jesus when he came the second time to visit their country?
2. For how many days did they stay with him in the desert without food?
3. Why did Jesus tell his disciples to feed the people before sending them away?
4. How many loaves did Jesus have with which to feed this throng?
5. How many people were fed from the few loaves and little fishes?

Story 32—The Blind Man of Bethsaida; How Peter Answered a Great Question—Page 457

1. Why did Jesus lead the blind man out of town before he healed him?
2. How many times did Jesus touch the man's eyes before he saw clearly?
3. What great question did Jesus ask his disciples one day?
4. How did Simon Peter answer that question?
5. Why did Jesus soon afterwards need to rebuke Simon Peter?

Story 33—The Glorified Master on the Mountain-Side—Page 458

1. Which of the twelve disciples did Jesus take with him up on the mountain?
2. What did these disciples do while Jesus prayed?
3. Who came to visit with Jesus while the disciples slept?
4. What wonderful sight met their gaze when the disciples awakened?
5. What did Simon Peter wish to do when he saw the heavenly visitors with Jesus?
6. Whom did the voice from the cloud bid the disciples to heed?
7. For how long a time did Jesus wish the disciples to keep this wonderful scene as a secret?

Story 34—A Suffering Child, an Anxious Father, and Jesus—Page 460

1. How had the nine disciples failed when Jesus was not with them?
2. Who came running to meet Jesus when he came down from the mountain with the three disciples?
3. Why had the nine disciples failed to heal the afflicted boy?
4. Tell how Jesus made him well.

Story 35—Jesus and His Disciples in Capernaum—Page 461

1. Where did Jesus send Peter to find money with which to pay their tax?
2. What lesson did Jesus seek to teach his disciples with a little child?
3. Whom did Jesus say would be greatest in the kingdom of heaven?
4. What did Jesus teach his disciples about the Father's will concerning little children?

Story 36—Jesus Teaches Peter a Lesson on Forgiveness—Page 462

1. What question did Peter ask Jesus about forgiveness?
2. How many times did Jesus say that Peter should forgive his brother who might sin against him and then ask to be forgiven?
3. How may God be likened to the king in the story which Jesus told Peter?
4. Why is it necessary that we forgive those who wrong us and ask forgiveness?

Story 37—The Unfriendly Samaritans; the Ten Lepers—Page 464

1. Why did two of Jesus' disciples wish to call fire down from heaven to destroy a Să-măr'-ĭ-tăn village?
2. What reply did Jesus give when they asked his permission to do this?
3. What did the ten lepers ask of Jesus?
4. Why did Jesus send them to the priests?

5. What happened as they hurried on their way to obey Jesus?
6. How many returned first to thank Jesus for what he had done?
7. To what people did the thankful man belong?

Story 38—Jesus at the Great Feast in Jerusalem—Page 465

1. What great feast was held each autumn in Jerusalem?
2. What did Jesus do when he came to the feast?
3. Why did the·officers whom his enemies had sent refuse to capture Jesus?
4. How was Nĭc-ŏ-dē'-mŭs unlike the. other Pharisees?

Story 39—How Jesus Answered His Enemies' Question—Page 467

1. Whom did Jesus' enemies bring to him for condemnation one day?
2. Why did Jesus stoop down and write in the dust with his finger?
3. What did Jesus finally tell them to do?
4. Why were the. men afraid to pick up stones and throw them at the woman?
5. What did Jesus tell the woman when all the men had gone away?
6. Why were the Jews struck with terror when they heard Jesus call himself by the sacred name, "I AM"?
7. How did Jesus escape from being stoned by them?

Story 40—What Happened to the Blind Man Whom Jesus Healed—Page 469

1. How long had the blind beggar been without his sight?
2. Why did Jesus send him to the pool of Sī-lō'-ăm?
3. Who brought the man who had been blind to the Pharisees?
4. Why did the Pharisees call the parents of the man who had been blind?
5. What did they do with the man when he spoke in defense of Jesus?
6. How did Jesus afterwards encourage the poor man?

Story 41—Little Children are Brought to Jesus; a Young Man Goes Away Sad—Page 472

1. Why were the disciples displeased with some women one day?
2. How do we know that Jesus loves children?
3. What great question did a rich young man ask of Jesus?
4. How many of Moses' commands had the young man kept?
5. What did Jesus tell him to do if he wished to please God?
6. Why did the young man turn away from Jesus with a sad heart?

Story 42—Seventy Other Disciples Sent Out; the Good Samaritan—Page 473

1. Why did Jesus send out seventy other disciples?
2. How did the lawyer try to tempt Jesus?
3. Why did Jesus tell him the story about the good Să-măr'-ĭ-tăn?
4. Whose example did Jesus tell the lawyer to follow in his treatment of his fellow men?

Story 43—Lazarus, the Dead Man Whom Jesus Called Out of the Grave—Page 476

1. Who sent a messenger from Bethany to Jesus one day?
2. Why did Jesus not go at once to help his dear friends?
3. How many days had Lăz'-ă-rŭs lain in the grave before Jesus came to Bethany?
4. Why had many Jews from Jerusalem come to the grave with Martha and Mary?
5. What effect did this greatest miracle of Jesus have upon the people who witnessed its performance?
6. Why did the enemies of Jesus at Jerusalem become greatly excited when they heard about the miracle?

Story 44—Jesus Heals the Sick, and Teaches in a Pharisee's House—Page 478

1. Whom did Jesus heal one Sabbath when he dined at a Pharisee's house?
2. How did Jesus teach the guests a lesson on humility?
3. What lesson did Jesus teach the guests in his parable about the Kingdom of God?

Story 45—A Crooked Woman Healed; the Pharisees Try to Frighten Jesus; Parables by the Way—Page 480

1. Why was the ruler of the synagog displeased when Jesus healed the crooked woman?
2. By whom had this poor woman been bound with affliction for eighteen years?
3. How did the Jews try to frighten Jesus about King Herod?
4. With what beautiful story did Jesus teach God's love to the sinner who comes repenting?

Story 46—Four Short Story-Sermons Which Jesus Preached—Page 483

1. How did the unfaithful steward in Jesus' story show wisdom?
2. Why did the rich man who failed to help the beggar, Lăz'-ă-rŭs, afterwards wish that Lăz'-ă-rŭs might help him?
3. Why did the wicked judge help the poor widow?
4. With which of the two men, the Pharisee or the publican, was God pleased?

Story 47—Happenings on the Way to Jerusalem—Page 486

1. What request did the mother of James and John make of Jesus?
2. When Jesus came to Jericho, who wished to see him but could not because of being blind?
3. What effect did it have on the blind beggar when some who heard him crying after Jesus told him to keep quiet?
4. Why did Jesus send for Bär-tĭ-mæ'-ŭs?
5. How did Bär-tĭ-mæ'-ŭs please Jesus?

PART FIRST—STORIES ABOUT JESUS

Story 48—The Little Man Who Climbed into a Tree to See Jesus—Page 488

1. Why did Zăc-chǣ'-ŭs climb into a tree when he heard that Jesus was passing that way?
2. Who called him to come down from the tree?
3. How may we know that Zăc-chǣ'-ŭs was pleased to have Jesus visit his home?
4. What great blessing did Jesus bring to that home?
5. Tell the story of the nobleman who went away from home to receive a kingdom.

Story 49—How Mary Showed Her Love for Jesus—Page 490

1. When Jesus came from Jericho to Bethany, who made a supper for him?
2. What interesting man from Bethany sat among the invited guests at this supper?
3. Who helped prepare and serve the evening meal?
4. Why did many curious onlookers crowd into the dining-hall that evening?
5. How did Mary show her great love for Jesus at this supper?
6. Who found fault with Mary?
7. On what wicked errand did Judas Iscariot go when supper had ended?

Story 50—How Jesus Rode into Jerusalem as a King—Page 493

1. Why did Jesus have to borrow a colt on which to ride into Jerusalem?
2. Whom did he send to borrow the colt?
3. How did the disciples and friends of Jesus show their pleasure as he rode towards the city?
4. Who found fault when the people shouted praises to God?

Story 51—The Teachings of Jesus in the Temple—Page 496

1. What did Jesus say when he found no fruit on the fig-tree by the roadside?
2. How did the children in the temple displease the chief priests and scribes?
3. What great change did the disciples observe in the fig-tree as they returned to Bethany that same evening?
4. Why would not Jesus' enemies tell him what they thought about John's baptism?
5. Why, in the story which Jesus told, did the owner send his son to bring fruit from his vineyard?
6. Why were the chief priests and scribes angry when they heard this parable?

Story 52—Jesus' Last Days in the Temple—Page 499

1. Why did Jesus ask his enemies to show him the tribute money?
2. From what country had the Gentile strangers come, who asked to see Jesus?
3. Why was Jesus troubled at this time?
4. How did God encourage him?
5. What did Jesus say about the poor widow's offering which she threw into the temple treasury?

40

Story 53—Jesus' Teaching on the Mount of Olives—Page 502

1. What did the disciples ask Jesus about the beautiful temple?
2. What were some things which Jesus said would happen before the end of time should come?
3. Tell the parable of the Ten Virgins.
4. What did Jesus wish to teach his disciples from this parable?
5. To whom did Jesus liken the sheep and the goats in his parable of the End of the World?

Story 54—The Last Supper Jesus Ate With the Twelve—Page 504

1. On what errand to Jerusalem did Peter send Peter and John?
2. By what sign were they to find their way to the guest-room where Jesus wished to eat the Passover with his disciples?
3. What strange example of humility did Jesus set before his disciples in that guest-room?
4. By what sign did Jesus tell John which of the twelve should betray him?
5. What did Jesus do with bread and wine after supper had ended?

Story 55—How an Untrue Disciple Sold His Lord—Page 507

1. For how many pieces of money did Judas Iscariot sell his Lord?
2. Where had Jesus and the eleven disciples gone from the guest-room?
3. Which of the eleven did Jesus take with him into the garden?
4. Whom did God send to comfort and strengthen Jesus while the disciples slept?
5. How did Judas, the unfaithful disciple, betray Jesus?
6. How did Peter try to defend Jesus?
7. Why did Peter afterwards deny that he was a disciple of Jesus?

Story 56—The Darkest Day in All the World—Page 511

1. Before what Roman ruler was Jesus led as a prisoner?
2. Why did Pilate send Jesus to King Herod?
3. Who urged Pilate to set Jesus free?
4. What did Judas Iscariot do when he saw that Jesus was condemned to die?
5. Whom did the Jews ask to have released instead of Jesus?
6. With what did the Roman soldiers crown Jesus?
7. Where was Jesus crucified?
8. What writing did Pilate cause to be nailed on the cross above the head of Jesus?
9. What did the Roman captain who saw Jesus die say of him?

Story 57—The Watchers at the Tomb of Jesus—Page 515

1. Who asked permission of Pilate to take the body of Jesus from the cross?
2. Where was the body of Jesus buried?
3. Why did Pilate place his Roman seal upon the stone at the tomb?
4. Why did Pilate station Roman soldiers about the tomb?
5. Who came to visit the tomb at early dawn the first day of the week?

Story 58—When Jesus, the Crucified Savior, Arose from the Dead—Page 518

1. Why did the Roman soldiers fall to the ground helpless near the tomb of Jesus?
2. Who ran to tell Peter and John that the body of Jesus had been stolen?
3. What message did the other women hasten to bring to the disciples?
4. Why did Mary Măg'-dă-lēne return the second time to weep at Jesus' grave?
5. To whom did Jesus first appear after he had arisen from the dead?
6. What plan did the chief priests make when they heard from the soldiers what had taken place at the garden-tomb?

Story 59—The Stranger on the Road to Emmaus; Doubting Thomas—Page 520

1. About what were the two friends of Jesus talking when they walked towards Ĕm-mā'-ŭs?
2. How did these two men finally recognize Jesus?
3. Why did they hasten back to Jerusalem?
4. To which one of the eleven disciples had Jesus appeared that same day?
5. Why were these disciples frightened when Jesus suddenly stood in their midst?
6. How was doubting Thomas convinced that Jesus had truly risen from the dead?

Story 60—Jesus' Last Meeting with His Disciples by the Seashore and on the Mount of Olives—Page 524

1. What was the last miracle of Jesus by the Sea of Galilee?
2. What question did Jesus ask Simon Peter three times?
3. Whom did Jesus say he would send to the disciples after he should go away?
4. Where did Jesus have his farewell talk with his disciples?
5. Why were the disciples filled with joy when they returned to Jerusalem from the Mount of Olives?

Part Second—Stories About the Apostles

Story 1—The Sound as of a Rushing Wind, and What It Brought—Page 529

1. For what purpose did the one hundred and twenty men and women meet daily in the upper room?
2. What strange thing happened on the morning of the tenth day?
3. Why were there many strangers in Jerusalem on that day?
4. What wrong charge did some unfriendly Jews make against the Spirit-filled men and women?
5. Why was Peter no longer afraid to speak boldly for Jesus?
6. How many people, after listening to Peter's sermon, became believers in Jesus that day?

Story 2—The Crippled Beggar Who Received a Wonderful Gift—Page 532

1. Why was the crippled man carried to the temple gate every day?
2. How long had he been crippled?
3. From which of the disciples did he beg money?
4. In whose name did Peter command the cripple to rise up and walk?
5. What effect did this great miracle produce upon the people who had met to worship at the temple?
6. Why were Peter and John put in prison?
7. How did the threat of the rulers against Peter and John affect the disciples?

Story 3—The Story About Two Hypocrites in the Early Church—Page 535

1. How did the people in the first company of believers show their unselfishness?
2. Why did Ăn-ă-nī'-ăs and Săpph-ī'-ră sell their property?
3. What did Peter say when Ăn-ă-nī'-ăs brought his bag of gold to the Apostles?
4. How was Ăn-ă-nī'-ăs punished because he lied to God?
5. What happened to his wife, Săpph-ī'-ră?

Story 4—When Prison Doors Swung Open by an Angel's Touch—Page 538

1. What effect did the shadow of Peter have when it fell upon the sick folk who lay in the streets?
2. How did the Jewish rulers try again to crush out the teaching of Jesus?
3. Who set the imprisoned disciples at liberty?
4. Why did the disciples return to the temple to teach about Jesus?
5. How did the rulers mistreat the disciples?
6. Why did the disciples rejoice when they were mistreated?

Story 5—The Preacher Who Was Stoned to Death—Page 540

1. What task was assigned to the seven Spirit-filled men?
2. Where did Stephen go to preach the gospel?
3. Who became angered with him there?
4. In what cruel manner was he put to death?
5. How did Stephen show his great courage and love when wicked men were destroying him?

Story 6—A Man Who Tried to Buy the Holy Spirit With Money—Page 543

1. To what city did Philip go to preach the gospel?
2. From whom had Simon received power to perform cunning tricks?
3. What effect did Philip's preaching have upon the people of Să-mâr'-ĭ-ă?
4. How did Simon regard the teachings and miracles of Philip?
5. Why did Peter and John visit the Să-măr'-ĭ-tăn believers?
6. What did Simon try to buy with money?
7. How did Peter answer Simon?
8. What, then, did Simon ask Peter to do for him?

Story 7—Philip Preaches to a Stranger on a Lonely Road—Page 545

1. Who sent Philip on an errand from Să-mâr'-ĭ-ă?
2. To what desert country did Philip go?
3. Whom did he overtake on the road?
4. What questions did Philip ask the eunuch when he heard him reading from the Scriptures?
5. How did Philip help the eunuch?

Story 8—The Wicked Plan That Was Spoiled by a Vision of Jesus—Page 547

1. Why was Saul, the young Pharisee, angry with the believers in Jesus?
2. How did he mistreat them in Jerusalem?
3. What did he plan to do when he should reach Damascus?
4. Who spoke to Saul in a vision by the roadside?
5. Why did Ăn-ă-nī'-ăs bravely go to lay hands on Saul that he might receive his sight?
6. What did Saul then do in the synagogs of Damascus?

Story 9—How a Basket Was Used to Save a Man's Life—Page 551

1. How did Saul's enemies in Damascus plan to capture him?
2. Why did his friends lower him in a basket from a high wall to the ground outside the city?
3. Where did Saul go when he escaped from Damascus?
4. Why were the believers in Jerusalem afraid of him?
5. Who befriended Saul?
6. Why did Saul soon afterwards leave Jerusalem and return to his childhood home?

PART SECOND—STORIES ABOUT THE APOSTLES

Story 10—A Sick Man Healed, and a Dead Woman Brought Back to Life—Page 554

1. Why were the believers in Jesus called "saints"?
2. What miracle did Peter perform while he was visiting the saints at Lȳd'dă?
3. Why did the saints at Joppa send for Peter to come at once?
4. Who spoke to Peter about the good work which Dorcas had done?
5. How did Peter bring gladness again to the weeping friends of Dorcas?

Story 11—The Great Sheet Let Down from Heaven, and What It Taught Page 555

1. Why was Cornelius unlike other Gentile officers?
2. Who appeared suddenly to him one afternoon while he was praying?
3. What did the angel tell him to do?
4. What remarkable vision did God give to Peter?
5. Why was Peter willing to go to Çæ-ṣā-rē'-ă with the messengers whom Cornelius had sent?
6. How did God show his power in Cornelius' household?
7. Why was Peter at first criticized because he had visited the home of a Gentile?

Story 12—How Peter's Coming Broke Up a Midnight Prayer-Meeting —Page 559

1. Why had King Herod begun to persecute the believers at Jerusalem?
2. What had he done with Peter?
3. How was Peter guarded in the prison?
4. Who aroused Peter from slumber the night before King Herod intended to kill him?
5. To whose home did Peter go after the angel departed from him?
6. What were the saints doing at Mary's home when Peter arrived?
7. Why would they not at first permit him to enter?
8. How did King Herod show his displeasure when the next day he found that Peter was gone from the prison?

Story 13—Where Believers in Jesus Were First Called Christians—Page 561

1. By whom were the believers in Jesus first called "Christians"?
2. Whom did the church at Jerusalem send to visit the Gentile church at An'-tĭ-ŏch?
3. Why did Barnabas seek for Saul?
4. On what errand did Barnabas and Saul go to Jerusalem?
5. What young man did they bring back with them when they returned to An'-tĭ-ŏch?

Story 14—The First Missionaries in the Early Church—Page 563

1. Who were the first missionaries sent out in the early church?
2. Why did Paul cause blindness to come upon a certain man in the Island of Cyprus?
3. What effect did this manifestation of God's power have upon the governor of the island?
4. How were the missionaries treated in the Gentile cities which they visited?

Story 15—How Idol-Worshipers in Lystra Treated Barnabas and Paul—Page 565

1. Why did Paul command the cripple at Lȳs'-trȧ to stand upon his feet?
2. Who did the people of Lȳs'-trȧ believe Paul and Barnabas to be after they had seen this miracle?
3. How did they decide to honor these miracle workers?
4. What did Paul and Barnabas do when they saw the intentions of the people?
5. How did these people soon afterwards treat Paul?

Story 16—A Puzzling Question, and How It Was Answered—Page 567

1. Why did the visitors from Jerusalem look unkindly upon the Gentile Christians at Ăn'-tĭ-ŏch?
2. Whom did the church at Ăn'-tĭ-ŏch decide to send to Jerusalem to settle this question?
3. Why did Peter, Paul, and Barnabas believe that Gentiles could be saved without obeying the law of Moses?
4. Who returned with Paul and Barnabas from Jerusalem to Ăn'-tĭ-ŏch?
5. Which of the two visitors decided to remain with the church at Ăn'-tĭ-ŏch?

Story 17—A Call for Help from a Far-Off Land—Page 569

1. Whom did Paul take with him on his second missionary journey?
2. What young man from Lȳs'-trȧ decided to travel with Paul and Silas?
3. Why did Paul and his companions plan to visit Măç-ē-dō'-nĭ-ȧ?
4. Who joined Paul's company at Trō'-ăs?
5. Where did the missionaries first preach the gospel in Philippi?
6. Who was the first Christian convert in that far-off country?

Story 18—The Prayer-Meeting in Prison and Its Happy Ending—Page 571

1. Why were Paul and Silas cast into the Philippian jail?
2. How did the jailer make sure that these prisoners would not escape?
3. Tell how Paul and Silas glorified God in the prison.
4. Why did God send the great earthquake?
5. Who prevented the jailer from taking his own life?
6. What great question did the jailer ask of Paul and Silas?
7. After his conversion how did the jailer then treat these two men?

Story 19—How the Gospel Was First Preached in Other Cities of Macedonia—Page 574

1. To whom did Paul and Silas preach about Jesus in Thĕss-ȧ-lō-nī'-cȧ?
2. Who became jealous of the missionaries at this place?
3. Why did the friends of Paul and Silas send them away by night to another city?
4. How did the Jews of Bĕ-rē'-ȧ receive the words of the missionaries?

Story 20—Paul Tells the Wise Men of Greece About the Unknown God—Page 576

1. What strange altar did Paul find on the streets of Athens?
2. Why did the wise men of Athens bring Paul to Mars Hill?
3. In what kind of work did Paul engage while he waited at Corinth for Silas and Timothy?

4. How did God encourage Paul in a dream one night?
5. Whom did Paul take with him when he sailed away from Greece?

Story 21—How a Great Heathen City Received the Gospel—Page 578

1. To whom did Ä-quĭl'-ă and Priscilla talk about Jesus, the Christ?
2. For how many years did Paul teach daily in a school in Eph'-ĕ-sŭs?
3. How were special miracles performed in the name of Jesus in this city?
4. What happened to the seven brothers who tried to cast out an evil spirit in the name of Jesus?
5. What did the Ĕph-ē'-s̄ian Christians do with the books of magic?

Story 22—The Uproar a Covetous Man Caused in a Great City—Page 580

1. What heathen goddess did the Ĕph-ē'-s̄ĭăn̄s worship?
2. Why did Dē-mē'-trĭ-ŭs, the silversmith, feel uneasy about the teachings of Paul?
3. How did he cause a great uproar in the city?
4. For how long did the excitement last?
5. Who quieted the people?

Story 23—The Faithful Missionary and His Last Farewell—Page 583

1. What happened during Paul's farewell visit with the saints at Trō'-ăs?
2. Where did Paul have a farewell meeting with the elders from Ĕph-ē'-sŭs?
3. What part did the children have in Paul's farewell meeting with the saints at Tyre?
4. How did Ăg'-ă-bŭs, the old prophet from Jerusalem, trouble the minds of Paul's friends?

Story 24—How the Prophet's Words Came True—Page 587

1. Why did Paul visit the temple and perform the ceremony of cleansing, according to Moses' law?
2. Who seized Paul in the temple?
3. How did they treat him?
4. By whom was Paul rescued from these angry men?
5. Why did Paul's speech on the castle-stairs excite the Jewish listeners?
6. Why did the Roman captain become frightened when he learned that Paul too, was a Roman?

Story 25—How a Young Man Saved His Uncle's Life—Page 589

1. Who visited Paul the second night while Paul lay sleeping in the castle prison?
2. What foolish thing did a band of forty Jews purpose?
3. Who warned Paul about the plan of these wicked men?
4. How did the Roman captain save Paul's life from attack by these men?
5. Why did Felix, the Roman governor, tremble when he heard Paul tell about the gospel of Christ?
6. How long did Felix keep Paul imprisoned at Çæ̆-s̆ă-rē'-ă?

Story 26—A King Listens to Paul's Story—Page 592

1. Why did Paul ask the new governor, Festus, to send him to Rome instead of to Jerusalem?
2. Who came from east of the River Jordan to visit Festus?
3. Why did Festus bring Paul before King Agrippa?
4. How did Agrippa receive Paul's words?
5. Why did the king think that Paul deserved to be set at liberty?

Story 27—The Story of a Shipwreck—Page 595

1. Who accompanied Paul on his last journey away from Palestine?
2. Why did Paul wish to remain at Fair Havens for the winter?
3. What was the result of the centurion's unwillingness to heed Paul's warning?
4. How did God encourage Paul during the storm?
5. Why did the sailors plan to escape from the ship?
6. What did the soldiers wish to do to all the prisoners?
7. For whose sake did the centurion refuse to grant their request?

Story 28—How a Chained Prisoner Brought Joy to Islanders—Page 598

1. How did the islanders receive the shipwrecked passengers?
2. What caused them to think that Paul must be a god?
3. What kindness did the ruler of the island show to Paul and his friends?
4. How did Paul repay him for this kindness?
5. Tell how Paul brought joy to the islanders.

Story 29—The Last of Paul's Journey, and His Life in Rome—Page 600

1. How was Paul cheered on the last stretch of his journey to Rome?
2. What special privilege did the captain grant Paul when Paul lived in Rome?
3. How long did Paul live in his hired house in Rome?
4. To whom did Paul preach while he lived in Rome?
5. Tell about the runaway slave whom Paul found in Rome.
6. To whom did Paul write a farewell letter before he was killed?
7. Name some parts of the New Testament which were written by Paul.

Story 30—Things We Learn from the Epistles—Page 604

1. Why will not every sinner be saved from the punishment of sin?
2. Why do not Christians need to feel guilty before God and afraid to die?
3. Why will no wicked person be able to hide from God in the last day?
4. What have we learned about God the Father, God the Son, and God the Holy Spirit?

Story 31—What God's Faithful Servant Saw When He Was on a Lonely Island—Page 606

1. Why was John left all alone on the island?
2. Who spoke to John one day in a voice like a trumpet-blast?
3. To whom did Jesus tell John to send the letters which John was to write in a book?
4. What wonderful city did John behold that day?
5. Who may become citizens of that wonderful city?

HOW WE GOT OUR BIBLE

Our Bible is printed in English. But the Bible was not always printed or written in English. Away back in Old Testament times men wrote on rolls of a kind of writing-paper made from a plant they called papyrus. They also wrote on parchment made from the skins of animals. Jesus used one of these rolls in preaching at Nazareth (see page 418). Probably all the Old Testament was first written on such rolls. We do not have the rolls on which the Bible was first written.

In the time of Ezra the Scribe (see page 371) a large company of men working with Ezra called the Great Synagog collected the books that Moses and Samuel and David and perhaps other men had written, and the books of the prophets. A few more books were added later and this made the Old Testament as we have it. These books were then in Hebrew, but about the third century before Christ they were translated down in Egypt into Greek. We call this version the Septuagint, or LXX.

Jesus never wrote anything, but his disciples did. The four gospel writers who record his life and works and the rest of the New Testament authors wrote in the Greek language, not, however, the Greek that is now spoken and used in the country of Greece. We do not have these original writings, which like the Old Testament writings, were more than likely all made on papyrus or parchment. We do, however, have a great many (over four thousand) old Greek manuscripts that are copies of these originals. Editors of the Greek text classify and examine these manuscripts to find out what the correct reading should be. Some of these manuscripts are very old. There is one in the library at Rome called the Vatican that was written on antelope skin in the fourth century. Another in the library at Leningrad, Russia, (the Sinaitic) was found on Mount Sinai by the great scholar Tischendorf, when it was just about to be burned up as rubbish. It is almost as old as the Vatican manuscript.

John Wycliff was the first man to translate the Bible into English. He completed it about the year 1380. But William Tyndale translated it from the original Greek in the years 1525-1530. Our King James, or Authorized Version, was translated in 1611 by a committee appointed by King James for that work. They did the best they could, but there were many of the ancient parchment and papyrus manuscripts that we have now which they did not have. In 1885 another committee of great scholars presented to the world the Revised Version of the Scriptures, which was followed in 1901 by the American Standard Revised Version.

THE BOOKS OF THE BIBLE

There are thirty-nine books in the Old Testament and ·twenty-seven in the New Testament, making a total of sixty-six books. There are five divisions of the Old Testament books—law, history, poetry, major prophets, and minor prophets. In the history and minor prophets division there are twelve books each. In the other divisions there are five books each.

The New Testament also contains five divisions, viz., biography, history, Pauline epistles, general epistles, and prophecy. There are four books of biography—Matthew, Mark, Luke, and John, called gospels; one book of history, the Acts; fourteen Pauline epistles; and seven general epistles. There is only one book of prophecy—the book of Revelation.

OLD TESTAMENT BOOKS

Books of the Law

The books of the law are Genesis, Exodus, Leviticus, Numbers, and Deuteronomy. All of these books were written by Moses over fifteen hundred years before Christ.

Genesis.—This first book of Moses tells of the beginning of things. It gives the story of the creation of the world and of man, tells how man fell, and gives God's original promise of a Savior who would redeem man. It also tells us of the great flood and the beginning of the history of the Jews, ending at the death of Joseph.

Exodus.—Is named from the "exodus" or going out of the Hebrews from Egypt. It tells us about the bondage of Israel in Egypt, the ten plagues, the wandering of the children of Israel in the wilderness, the giving of the law on Mount Sinai. In it are found the Ten Commandments.

Leviticus.—Contains religious laws that Israel was to observe. The tribe of Levi, after which the book is named, was to be responsible to see that these laws were carried out.

Numbers.—So named because it tells us of the numbering of the children of Israel. It gives us the history of the thirty-eight years' wandering after Israel left Sinai. It also contains some of the laws to govern Israel, and directions for dividing the land of Canaan.

Deuteronomy.—The name of this book means "The Second Law." Moses repeated much of the law in this book and plead with the Israelites to keep it. In the last chapter there is an occount of Moses' death on Mount Nebo, which was added to the book by some one other than Moses.

THE BOOKS OF THE BIBLE

Historical Books of the Old Testament

The historical books of the Old Testament are Joshua, Judges, Ruth, First Samuel, Second Samuel, First Kings, Second Kings, First Chronicles, Second Chronicles, Ezra, Nehemiah, and Esther.

Joshua.—Tells about the choosing of Joshua as leader, and the entrance of the Israelites into the Promised Land; also about the conquest and division of Canaan among the twelve tribes. In the latter part we find related the farewell, death, and burial of Joshua. Part of it was written by Joshua.

Judges.—In this book we learn of troublous times in Israel. It covers a period of over three hundred years, during which time Israel rebelled and was conquered by other nations at different times. Then God raised up "judges" to deliver them. Some of these judges were Jephtha, Deborah, Gideon, Samson, and Samuel. The book was possibly written by Samuel.

Ruth.—This is a beautiful story of a family that went to Moab during the time of the Judges. It tells us of Ruth and Boaz who were ancestors of Jesus. It contains only four short chapters, and we do not know who was its writer, perhaps Samuel.

The Two Books of Samuel.—These books were named after Samuel, the great prophet-judge of Israel. First Samuel is a history of the judgeship of Samuel and the reign of Saul; Second Samuel of the reign of David. Some scholars think the prophet Nathan may have written them.

First and Second Kings.—These books continue the history of the united kingdom of Israel and carry us step by step down to the time of the divided kingdoms of Juda and Israel. They tell of the reign of Solomon and the division made at the death of Solomon by King Rehoboam. The works of the prophets Elijah and Elisha are also given here. The writer is unknown, more than likely a prophet who lived after the year 597 B.C.

Books of Chronicles.—Contain the history of Juda only during the time of the divided kingdom. They contain many important family records of Juda. Probably Ezra compiled them.

Ezra.—Was written mainly by him. He takes up the history of the Jews beginning with the return and continuing for a period of nearly eighty years. The rebuilding of the temple in Jerusalem and the religious reformation that took place after the return are of special interest.

Nehemiah.—Was originally called the Second Book of Ezra. Most of it was written by Nehemiah, who was a great Jewish historian and statesman.

51

THE BOOKS OF THE BIBLE

Esther.—Probably written by Mordecai. Ahasuerus of this book was probably the great Persian king, Xerxes II., This book shows the providential care of God for his people.

Poetical Books of the Old Testament

The poetical books of the Old Testament are Job, Psalms, Proverbs, Ecclesiastes, and Song of Solomon.

Job.—Some think Job is the most ancient book in the world. It describes the sufferings of Job and his faithfulness through those sufferings. Its author and date of writing are not known. Its lesson is the attitude one should take when undergoing trial and test.

Psalms.—There are really five books contained in this one book. This collection was the Hebrew hymnal. Many of the songs are Messianic, i.e., they predict the life, character, and sufferings of the Savior. Many men composed them, but David wrote most of them.

Proverbs.—This is a book of wisdom. It contains a collection of wise sayings compiled from many sources, but mostly written by Solomon.

Ecclesiastes.—Many think it was written by Solomon. Its name means "the preacher." The chief lesson of this book is, "Fear God, and keep his commandments: for this is the whole duty of man."

Song of Solomon.—Many think that this book is an allegory setting forth love between Christ and the church. It has been attributed to Solomon.

Major Prophets

The books of the major prophets are Isaiah, Jeremiah, Lamentations, Ezekiel, and Daniel.

Isaiah.—Takes its name from its author, who was the greatest of the Hebrew prophets. It was written about 700 B.C. Its Messianic prophecies are clear, especially the fifty-third chapter. Some have called the book "Isaiah's Gospel," because it is so full of Christ and evangelical truth.

Jeremiah.—The book is named after the great prophet who wrote it. He prophesied before and during the siege of Jerusalem and the captivity of Juda. During Zedekiah's reign, because of his prophecy, he was arrested, and cast into prison where he continued until the time Jerusalem was captured. Some of the prophecy in this book was given in Egypt to which country Jeremiah went after the captivity. His prophecy, like that of Isaiah's, contains many Messianic predictions.

Lamentations.—Is a sort of funeral dirge. The weeping prophet, Jeremiah, here bewails the sins of his people, much as Christ wept over the coming destruction of Jerusalem. The Book is remarkable for its poetic beauty and novel construction.

Ezekiel.—This prophet wrote during the captivity. This Book is also rich in its prophecy concerning the Messianic kingdom. The last part contains a vision of a restored temple, which evidently refers to the glory of the Lord's kingdom.

Daniel.—Written by the prophet Daniel, a captive from Jerusalem to Babylon. In it is the Story of Daniel in the lions' den, also other interesting events that occurred during the time of the captivity. Some of the book is apocalyptic, i.e., written in the style of the Book of Revelation in the New Testament.

Minor Prophets

The minor prophets are Hosea, Joel, Amos, Obadiah, Jonah, Micah, Nahum, Habakkuk, Zephaniah, Haggai, Zechariah, and Malachi. These books were each written by the prophet whose name it bears.

Hosea.—Prophesied in the kingdom of Israel during the reign of five kings. It rebukes the Jews for their gross wickedness, and is a plea for them to return to Jehovah from their backsliding. These backslidings are represented as a wife's treachery in being untrue to her husband.

Joel.—The author lived before the fall of Samaria. He uses the punishment by a plague of locusts and a severe drought as symbols of conquering foes sent to punish Juda.

Amos.—Written to Israel. In this book deliverance is promised to Israel if they will turn away from their sin. He probably lived about 800 B.C.

Obadiah.—The shortest of the prophetical books. It contains only one chapter, and is directed against the country of Edom, the people of which country were descended from Esau—foes to the descendants of Jacob.

Jonah.—The son of Ammittai. He was sent to prophesy against Nineveh. His experiences are here related. The Book shows the spread of the knowledge of God among nations other than Jews.

Micah.—Altho written mostly to Juda, the author also includes the Northern Kingdom. He lived to see the fall of Samaria in 722 B.C. A very clear prophecy in Micah foretells the birth of Jesus in Bethlehem.

Nahum.—This prophecy is a companion book to Jonah. It is directed against Nineveh, the capital of Assyria and enemy of Israel. Little is known concerning Nahum, its author.

Habakkuk.—This prophet lived during the reign of Jehoiakim, and prophesied in the kingdom of Juda about 608—597 B. C. The prayer in the last chapter of this book is noted as one of the sublimest strains in prophecy.

Zephaniah.—A prophet who prophesied during the reign of King Josiah of Judah before the reformation by that king. He foretells judgment not only on Jerusalem and Juda, but on the surrounding nations. His description of the day of wrath is graphic.

Haggai.—A companion prophet with Zechariah. He along with Zechariah urged the returned captives to rebuild the ruined temple.

Zechariah.—Second of the prophets of the restoration, describes the destruction of the foes of Jerusalem and the revealing of the Messiah. He ranks the moral law above the ceremonial.

Malachi.—The last of the Old Testament prophets. His message closes the Old Testament. He prophesied in the days of Nehemiah, foretelling the coming of both John the Baptist and Christ.

NEW TESTAMENT
Biography

The books of biography, or gospels, are Matthew, Mark, Luke, and John, written by the authors whose names they bear.

Matthew.—This Gospel was written particularly for the Jews, hence the book abounds in statements of fulfilled Old Testament prophecies. It shows Jesus as the Messiah and King predicted by those prophets.

Mark.—Was written particularly to the Romans. It is noted for its powerful, yet concise style. It sets forth the mighty character of the Son of God.

Luke.—Written particularly for the Greeks. Luke was a physician of Gentile birth who accompanied Paul on a part of one of his missionary journeys. Its language characterizes it as the most beautiful of the Gospels.

John.—The Gospel of the divine Son of God. It was written later than the other Gospels, probably about A.D. 95. Especially does John prove the divinity of Christ. The first part of the Messiah's public ministry is given only in this Gospel.

Historical

The only historical book in the New Testament is that of the Acts of the Apostles.

Acts.—Gives the history of the church during the generation after Christ's ascension. It sets forth the coming of the Holy Spirit and his workings in the church through Peter and Paul and the other apostles. Also the conversion and missionary journeys of the apostle Paul are related. Luke is its author.

Pauline Epistles

The Pauline Epistles are Romans, First Corinthians, Second Corinthians, Galatians, Ephesians, Philippians, Colossians, First Thessalonians, Second Thessalonians, First Timothy, Second Timothy, Titus, Philemon, and Hebrews.

Romans.—The keynote of this book is "justification by faith." It was written to the Roman brethren about the year A.D. 57. Its main outline is— God's law condemns all sinners, but his love manifested through Christ offers to all justification through faith in Christ's name.

First and Second Corinthians.—These books were written to the church in Corinth, principally to correct certain abuses that had entered into the congregation there. Many great doctrines and truths of the church are set forth in these Epistles.

Galatians.—Was written to the Christians of Galatia, in Asia Minor. Here Paul points out that they should not be in bondage to the old law, but should take advantage of their freedom through the gospel. Certain Jewish teachers were trying to turn these churches away from the faith.

Ephesians.—Ephesus was a city of Ionia in the province of Asia. It was famous for its great temple of Diana. In his Epistle to this church, written about A.D. 62, from Rome, Paul describes the ideal church and the work of its members.

Philippians.—Also written at Rome during Paul's imprisonment, in A.D. 62. It describes the self-denial of Christ in taking upon himself the form of a servant, and calls upon the Christians at Philippi likewise to deny themselves for his sake. Paul thanks the Philippians for their expressions of regard for him.

Colossians.—Written A.D. 62 to the Christians at Colossa, Asia Minor. They had made inquiry as to Paul's health and welfare. He warns this church against heresy and tells them how to be complete in Christ.

First and Second Thessalonians.—Possibly the earliest of Paul's Epistles. They both treat of the second coming of Christ, with an apostasy preceding it. Paul commends the Thessalonians for turning to God from idols.

First and Second Timothy.—These books were written to Paul's son in the faith, a young minister, Timothy. They exhort him in pastoral wisdom. Second Timothy was evidently written not long before Paul's martyrdom.

Titus.—This is also a pastoral epistle, laying special stress upon the life that God approves as worthy of those in his service.

Philemon.—Written to a person of that name whose servant, Onesimus, had run away. The purpose of the letter was to reconcile the master with the slave. It is a beautiful example of Christian courtesy and brotherly kindness.

Hebrews.—Possibly written by Paul, but not certainly known. It was particularly addressed to the Jews and contains many types foreshadowed in the Mosaic system. Christ is lifted up as the great High Priest of his people. The writer particularly points out the danger of falling away to Judaism of Jewish Christians.

General Epistles

The General Epistles are James, First Peter, Second Peter, First John, Second John, Third John, Jude, and Revelation.

James.—Probably written about A.D. 61. Much practical wisdom is recorded in this book. It is the **works** side of the gospel. The keynote is, "Faith without works is dead." Holy living is enjoined.

First and Second Peter.—The author represents the Christian as a pilgrim to another country, hence points out that he must conduct himself as a citizen of that country to which he is going. His style is peculiarly vigorous. The books are full of exhortations to purity in life.

First, Second, and Third John.—These are the works of "the beloved disciple" who wrote the Fourth Gospel. He continually says, "We know." He argues strongly against sin in the life and points out that the Christian should conduct himself before the world as a son of the Father.

Jude.—A warning against those who have apostatized. He warns believers to keep themselves from stumbling.

Prophecy

The one prophetic book of the New Testament is the Revelation of John.

Revelation.—This book is also called the Apocalypse. It was written by the apostle John on the isle of Patmos about the year A.D. 95. Its purpose was to encourage the early church to consider their heavenly reward amidst the troubles and persecutions that were to come. Most of it is symbolic in character.

INTERESTING FACTS ABOUT THE BIBLE

The Bible contains:

    66 books (39 in the Old Testament; 27 in the New Testament).

    1,189 chapters (929 in the Old Testament; 260 in the New Testament).

    31,175 verses (23,216 in the Old Testament; 7,959 in the New Testament).

    773,692 words (592,439 in the Old Testament; 181,253 in the New Testament).

3,567,180 letters (2,728,800 in the Old Testament; 838,380 in the New Testament).

    The middle verse is the 8th verse of the 118th Psalm.

    The longest verse is the 9th verse of the 8th chapter of Esther.

    The shortest verse is the 35th verse of the 11th chapter of John.

    The longest chapter is the 119th Psalm.

    The shortest and middle chapter is the 117th Psalm.

    The longest name is in the 8th chapter of Isaiah—Mahersalalhashbaz.

    The word "and" occurs 46,227 times; 35,543 times in the Old Testament and 10,684 times in the New Testament.

    The word "Lord" occurs 8,000 times.

    Isaiah 37 and II Kings 19 are alike.

    The 21st verse of the 7th chapter of Ezra contains all the letters of the alphabet except "j."

    The name of God is not mentioned in the Book of Esther.

Old Testament

    The middle book is Proverbs.

    The middle chapter is Job 29.

    The middle verses are II Chron. 20:17, 18.

    The shortest verse is I Chron. 1:25.

New Testament

    The middle book is II Thessalonians.

    The middle chapters are Romans 13 and 14.

    The middle verse is Acts 17:17.

    The shortest verse is John 11:35.

GREAT PRAYERS OF THE BIBLE
OLD TESTAMENT PRAYERS

Offered by	Subject	Where Recorded
Abraham	For God to spare Sodom	Gen. 18
Eliezer	For success in seeking a wife for Isaac	Gen. 24
Jacob	For a successful life	Gen. 28
Jacob	For deliverance from Esau	Gen. 32
Moses	For forgiveness of Israel's idolatry	Exod. 32
		Deut. 9
Moses	For God's presence	Exod. 33
Moses	For help to lead Israel	Num. 11
Moses	For cure of Miriam's leprosy	Num. 12
Moses	For forgiveness of Israel's murmuring	Num. 14
Moses	For a successor	Num. 27
Moses	For entrance to Canaan	Deut. 3
Joshua	Reason of defeat at Ai	Josh. 7
Manoah	For guidance in training his child	Judg. 13
Samson	For vengeance on Philistines	Judg. 16
Hannah	For a son	I Sam. 1
David	For blessing on his house	II Sam. 7
David	For God's mercy on Israel, whom he had numbered	II Sam. 24
Solomon	For wisdom to govern Israel	I Kings 3
Solomon	Dedication of the Temple	I Kings 8
Elijah	For restoration of widow's son	I Kings 17
Elijah	For divine proof of truth of his mission	I Kings 18
Elijah	For death	I Kings 19
Elisha	For his servant's eyes to be opened	II Kings 6
Elisha	For blindness upon the enemy	II Kings 6
Hezekiah	For protection against Sennacherib	II Kings 19
Hezekiah	For recovery from illness	II Kings 20
Jabez	For God's protection from evil	I Chron. 4
David	For blessing on Solomon	I Chron. 29
Asa	For victory over Ethiopians	II Chron. 14
Jehoshaphat	For protection against invading armies	II Chron. 20
Hezekiah	For unprepared at Passover	II Chron. 30
Ezra	For blessing on the people	Ezra 9
Nehemiah	For the Jews of his day	Neh. 1
Nehemiah	For protection against Sanballat	Neh. 4
Levites	For pardon of nation's sins	Neh. 9

Offered by	Subject	Where Recorded
David	For pardon of his heinous sin	Psa. 51
Agur	For moderate earthly blessings	Prov. 30
Jeremiah	For removal of famine	Jer. 14
Jeremiah	For comfort in his trials	Jer. 15
Ezekiel	For mercy upon the people	Ezek. 9
Daniel	For pardon of sins and restoration of Jerusalem	Dan. 9
Jonah	For deliverance from the fish	Jonah 2
	For death	Jonah 4
Habakkuk	For revival of God's work	Hab. 3

NEW TESTAMENT PRAYERS

Offered by	Subject	Where Recorded
Christ	Daily Needs	Matt. 6
Christ	Praise for revelation of God's truth	Matt. 11
Christ	In Gethsemane	Matt. 26
Christ	When God hid his face from him	Matt. 27
Pharisee	Self-righteous boasting	Luke 18
Publican	For mercy	Luke 18
Christ	For his murderers	Luke 23
Dying Thief	For remembrance in glory	Luke 23
Christ	Thanksgiving that his Father heard him	John 11
Christ	For his Father's aid	John 12
Christ	For himself, and his disciples through all ages	John 17
Apostles	On choosing Judas' successor	Acts 1
Christians	For help in persecution	Acts 4
Stephen	For entrance to heaven, and pardon of his murderers	Acts 7

OUR LORD'S PARABLES

Parables	Matt.	Mark	Luke	Principal Point
I. Recorded in One Gospel Only				
The Tares	13:24			Good and bad grow together.
The Hid Treasure	13:44			True value of God's kingdom.
The Goodly Pearl	13:45			Looking for and finding salvation.
The Draw-net	13:47			Not all who say they are Christians are true Christians.
The Householder	13:52			Watch for the Lord's coming.
The Unmerciful Servant	18:23			We must forgive.
The Laborers in the Vineyard.	20:1			The Lord rewards all his workers as he sees fit.
The Two Sons	21:28			Those who do what is right are better in God's sight than those who just say they will do right.
The Marriage of the King's Son	22:2			We should have on the robe of right-eousness.
The Ten Virgins	25:1			Be ready for the Lord's coming.
The Talents	25:14			Use the things the Lord has given you to use for him.
The Sheep and the Goats	25:31			Be whole-hearted in Christian service.
The Seed Growing Secretly		4:26		The gradual growth of God's kingdom.

OUR LORD'S PARABLES

Parables	Matt.	Mark	Luke	Principal Point
The Two Debtors			7:41	He whom the Lord forgives much will love him much.
The Good Samaritan			10:30	All who need help are our neighbors and we should help them.
The Importunate Friend			11:5	Do not stop praying.
The Rich Fool			12:16	Do not love earthly things so much we do not love God.
Servants Watching			12:35	Expect the Lord to come.
The Wise Steward			12:42	Be found serving the Lord faithfully when he comes.
The Barren Fig-Tree			13:6	The Lord gives us time to repent.
The Great Supper			14:16	God calls everybody to come into his kingdom.
Tower; King Going to War			14:28	It pays to count the cost of entering the kingdom of God.
The Piece of Money			15:8	Joy over those who are saved.
The Prodigal Son			15:11	The Father's love to a returning sinner.
The Unjust Steward			16:1	Be faithful in taking care of what the Lord has left with you.
The Rich Man and Lazarus			16:19	Rewards after death.
Unprofitable Servants			17:7	We must not think our own good works are sufficient.

OUR LORD'S PARABLES

Parables	Matt.	Mark	Luke	Principal Point
The Unjust Judge			18:2	Pray until you get the answer.
The Pharisee and Publican			18:10	Be humble and trust in God rather than in your own good works.
The Pounds			19:12	The workers rewarded, the lazy punished.
II Recorded in Two Gospels				
House on Rock and House on The Sand	7:24		6:47	Not only hear the Lord's words, but obey them.
The Leaven	13:33		13:20	The spread of Christianity throughout the world.
The Lost Sheep	18:12		15:4	The Lord does not want to see one person lost.
III Recorded in Three Gospels				
Candle Under the Bushel	5:15	4:21	11:33 8:16	Let people see your good works.
New Cloth on Old Garment	9:16	2:21	5:36	Get rid of old things that keep you from using new truth.
New Wine in Old Bottles	9:17	2:22	5:37	A new spirit to do God's will is not possible in the unsaved.
The Sower	13:3	4:3	8:5	How men hear and obey God's word.
The Mustard-seed	13:31	4:30	13:18	Great growth of God's kingdom.
The Wicked Husbandmen	21:33	12:1	20:9	Rejection of Christ by the Jews.
The Fig-tree and All the Trees	24:32	13:28	21:29	Signs of the Lord's second coming.